38402

.3 Weiss, Frederick T.
436d   1916-

Determination of
organic compounds:
methods and
procedures

DATE			

CHEMICAL ANALYSIS

Vol. 1. **The Analytical Chemistry of Industrial Poisons, Hazards, and Solvents.** *Second Edition.* By Morris B. Jacobs

Vol. 2. **Chromatographic Adsorption Analysis.** By Harold H. Strain (*out of print*)

Vol. 3. **Colorimetric Determination of Traces of Metals.** *Third Edition.* By E. B. Sandell

Vol. 4. **Organic Reagents Used in Gravimetric and Volumetric Analysis.** By John F. Flagg (*out of print*)

Vol. 5. **Aquametry: Application of the Karl Fischer Reagent to Quantitative Analyses Involving Water.** By John Mitchell, Jr. and Donald Milton Smith (*temporarily out of print*)

Vol. 6. **Analysis of Insecticides and Acaricides.** By Francis A. Gunther and Roger C. Blinn (*out of print*)

Vol. 7. **Chemical Analysis of Industrial Solvents.** By Morris B. Jacobs and Leopold Scheflan

Vol. 8. **Colorimetric Determination of Nonmetals.** Edited by David F. Boltz

Vol. 9. **Analytical Chemistry of Titanium Metals and Compounds.** By Maurice Codell

Vol. 10. **The Chemical Analysis of Air Pollutants.** By Morris B. Jacobs

Vol. 11. **X-Ray Spectrochemical Analysis.** By L. S. Birks

Vol. 12. **Systematic Analysis of Surface-Active Agents.** By Milton J. Rosen and Henry A. Goldsmith

Vol. 13. **Alternating Current Polarography and Tensammetry.** By B. Breyer and H. H. Bauer

Vol. 14. **Flame Photometry.** By R. Herrmann and J. Alkemade

Vol. 15. **The Titration of Organic Compounds** (*in two parts*). By M. R. F. Ashworth

Vol. 16. **Complexation in Analytical Chemistry: A Guide for the Critical Selection of Analytical Methods Based on Complexation Reactions.** By Anders Ringbom

Vol. 17. **Electron Probe Microanalysis.** By L. S. Birks

Vol. 18. **Organic Complexing Reagents: Structure, Behavior, and Application to Inorganic Analysis.** By D. D. Perrin

Vol. 19. **Thermal Methods of Analysis.** By Wesley Wm. Wendlandt

Vol. 20. **Amperometric Titrations.** By John T. Stock

Vol. 21. **Reflectance Spectroscopy.** By Wesley Wm. Wendlandt and Harry G. Hecht

Vol. 22. **The Analytical Toxicology of Industrial Inorganic Poisons.** By the late Morris B. Jacobs

Vol. 23. **The Formation and Properties of Precipitates.** By Alan G. Walton

Vol. 24. **Kinetics in Analytical Chemistry.** By Harry B. Mark, Jr. and Garry A. Rechnitz

Vol. 25. **Atomic Absorption Spectroscopy.** By Walter Slavin

Vol. 26. **Characterization of Organometallic Compounds** (*in two parts*). Edited by Minoru Tsutsui

Vol. 27. **Rock and Mineral Analysis.** By John A. Maxwell

Vol. 28. **The Analytical Chemistry of Nitrogen and Its Compounds** (*in two parts*). Edited by C. A. Streuli and Philip R. Averell

Vol. 29. **The Analytical Chemistry of Sulfur and Its Compounds** (*in two parts*). By J. H. Karchmer

Vol. 30. **Ultramicro Elemental Analysis.** By Günther Tölg

Vol. 31. **Photometric Organic Analysis** (*in two parts*). By Eugene Sawicki

Vol. 32. **Determination of Organic Compounds: Methods and Procedures.** By Frederick T. Weiss

Vol. 33. **Masking and Demasking of Chemical Reactions.** By D. D. Perrin

CHEMICAL ANALYSIS

A SERIES OF MONOGRAPHS ON
ANALYTICAL CHEMISTRY AND ITS APPLICATIONS

Editors

P. J. ELVING · I. M. KOLTHOFF

VOLUME 32

WILEY-INTERSCIENCE

a Division of John Wiley & Sons, New York · London · Sydney · Toronto

Determination of Organic Compounds: Methods and Procedures

FREDERICK T. WEISS

Shell Development Company
Emeryville, California

WILEY-INTERSCIENCE

a Division of John Wiley & Sons, New York · London · Sydney · Toronto

Library of Congress Catalog Card Number: 76-114010

ISBN 0-471-92705-8

Printed in the United States of America

10 9 8 7 6 5 4 3 2 1

PREFACE

Although there is certainly no deficiency of books on the analysis of organic materials, they have generally been written from the standpoint of a specialty, usually setting forth in detail the techniques and accomplishments of that specialty without regard to the application or utilization of other techniques. Since there seemed to be no currently available text that compares the many methods for the analysis of organic compounds, I have striven to put together such a volume. My aim has been, first, to present detailed methods for many of the principal determinations and, second, to give specific data obtained by these methods to indicate accurately their comparative scopes, applications, and limitations. The analyst, faced as he is with an ever-increasing literature, should have available to him a volume of methods in which critical comparisons based on extensive data have been made to allow him to make precise decisions on the design of his determinations. Within the limitations of time and scope, I have endeavored to collect information that will provide guidance for the necessary judgments without involving any but a minimum of theory. My goal in all the writing has been to be of service to the busy analyst, and it is my hope that this book will be useful at the laboratory bench.

Over the last thirty years there have been three major areas of activity in the development of methods for the analysis of organic compounds: (1) functional analysis with chemical reagents, (2) spectroscopic measurements, and (3) separation techniques, among which gas chromatography is now paramount. Each of these areas in turn has generated its own subspecialties. The knowledge of the proper place for each type of analytical equipment or technique and of their interrelationships is generally obtained only by long experience and often by a costly process of comparisons. The attempt has been made in this book to provide some guidance in the utility and choice of methods and techniques in the important types of determination commonly encountered in the analysis of organic compounds.

This volume contains a description of the functional analysis of organic compounds by chemical, spectroscopic, and chromatographic techniques. The recommended methods, given in full detail, are in most cases of wide and general applicability and allow the determination of many of the compounds in a functional series. Laboratory data are given on the application of these methods to pure organic compounds and commercial materials. Critical evaluations, with tabulated results, are included to enable the analyst to choose methods and conditions and to understand their limitations and sensitivities. In addition to describing the determination of the common

v

functional groups, it has been possible to discuss the analysis of a number of organic materials in detail, including hydrocarbons, organic solvents, heterocyclic materials, surface-active agents, and industrial chemicals, to pick a few examples. Since many of the methods recommended for the determination of functional groups can be applied to polymers, coverage is made, whenever possible, of the analysis of resins and polymers.

A glance at the table of contents will indicate the organization of information. The heart of the text is the series of chapters in which the determination of the organic functional compounds is described. In each of these the methods have been derived from consideration of chemical, spectroscopic, and chromatographic techniques. The recommended methods are set out in detail, except that the sections describing the preparation of the common analytical reagents and some frequently used equipment are given separately in Part Three. Examples of the application of the methods to a series of important types of materials are given in Part Two to illustrate the way in which the techniques can be employed in practical systems of some complexity. The use of chromatography is so basic to the analysis of organic materials that a review of the principal chromatographic methods is included in Part Three to make it possible for the analyst to choose appropriate techniques and conditions.

Several important areas of organic analysis are not discussed. The determination of the elements or physical properties, including molecular weight, is not covered. These measurements are, of course, fundamental in importance but occupy too large an area to be included in one book. In the discussion of functional analysis no effort has been made to provide a complete bibliography of the literature or the historical or theoretical background of the methods, since it is my opinion that this is better done in the many monographs already available to which references are made.

A great deal of the information has been taken from published work of my colleagues and myself. This bias I trust will not offend but was indulged in because I felt that personal knowledge of the validity and limitations of the methods was of great importance. The work described and much of the data provided, unless otherwise indicated, were obtained in the laboratories of the Shell Development Company. It is my responsibility and my pleasure to acknowledge the assistance of my associates, principally from the Analytical Department of the Shell Development Company, Emeryville, California, and the generosity of Shell's management for approval to publish. In particular I should like to express my appreciation to A. E. O'Donnell, G. A. Stenmark, R. N. McCoy, and E. D. Peters for information and advice on functional organic analysis; to D. H. Morman and G. A. Harlow for acid–base reactions and titrations in nonaqueous media; to E. M. Fredericks, H. S. Knight, M. A. Muhs, and F. M. Nelsen for gas chromatography; to

H. Siegel for ion-exchange separations; to J. Boor, Jr., M. Dimbat, and F. T. Eggertsen for advice on polymer analysis; to A. G. Polgar for hydrocarbon analysis; to D. B. Bruss for information on organic electrochemistry; and to J. M. Gordon, J. L. Jungnickel, R. W. Kearney, and P. A. Wadsworth, Jr., for information on organic spectroscopy. On the subject of chromatography it was my good fortune to have the valuable comments of E. R. Adlard of the Shell Thornton Research Center, who was on temporary assignment at Emeryville. Mrs. Dee Murray was always competent and conscientious in putting the manuscript carefully into its final typed form.

Emeryville, California   F. T. WEISS
April, 1970

CONTENTS

Part One   Determination of Organic Compounds

CHAPTER

1	Determination of Saturated Hydrocarbons	3
2	Determination of Aromatic Hydrocarbons	19
3	Determination of Olefinic Unsaturation	29
4	Determination of Acetylenes	57
5	Determination of Acids	63
6	Determination of Carbonyl Compounds	84
7	Determination of Esters	116
8	Determination of the Hydroxyl Group	124
9	Determination of Polyhydroxy Alcohols	165
10	Determination of Phenols	174
11	Determination of Ethers	187
12	Determination of the Alpha-Epoxide Group	200
13	Determination of Organic Peroxides	218
14	Determination of Organic Bases	235
15	Determination of Nonbasic Nitrogen Compounds	259
16	Determination of Sulfur Compounds	278

Part Two   Analysis of Materials

17	Application of Analytical Methods to Polymers	303
18	Trace Analysis	317
19	Analysis of Surface-Active Materials	335
20	Analysis of Petroleum and its Products	355

ix

Part Three Laboratory Methodology and Practice

CHAPTER

21	Chromatography	369
22	Determination of Water	417
23	Preparation of the Common Reagents	423
24	Analytical Equipment	439
25	Safety in the Laboratory	444

Author Index 447

Subject Index 461

Determination of Organic Compounds: Methods and Procedures

PART ONE

Determination of Organic Compounds

DETERMINATION OF SATURATED HYDROCARBONS

Saturated hydrocarbons do not contain functional groups and consequently the saturates behave as inert substances in chemical methods of analysis. The electronic spectra of the saturates is weak and therefore ultraviolet absorption is not important for their determination. The vibrational and rotational infrared spectra and proton magnetic resonance spectra are significant for this class of hydrocarbons and can provide some structural information. However, the two most important tools for the determination and characterization of the saturates are gas chromatography and mass spectroscopy. Gas chromatography alone is useful for identification of specific compounds through C_8, but it is with the combined use of these two techniques that a really powerful and detailed compositional or type analysis can be made of gasoline, kerosine, and heavier materials.

The complexity of many practical samples, such as the saturates fraction from gasoline, stems from the large number of isomers possible in this series, especially above C_9. In the paraffin series the number of isomers calculated to exist by Henze and Blair (1) is listed in Table 1.1, from which it can be seen that very large numbers can be expected at even moderate carbon numbers. The number of possible C_{20} paraffin isomers is calculated to be over 300,000 and for the C_{25} isomers the number is of the order of 30,000,000. Thus a completely detailed analysis cannot be made of wide-range mixtures of hydrocarbons of appreciable molecular weight.

DETERMINATION OF SATURATES BY GAS CHROMATOGRAPHY

The use of gas chromatography for the analysis of complex hydrocarbon samples has been widely described. Golay (2) showed some years ago that high resolution could be obtained using capillary columns and a hydrogen flame detector. Polgár, Holst, and Groennings (3) successfully separated complex mixtures of alkanes and cycloalkanes up to C_8 on silicone-coated glass capillary columns. Schwartz and Brasseaux (4) used a mixture of fluorocarbons and hydrocarbon oils to coat a stainless steel capillary for the

Table 1.1.   Number of Possible Isomers for the Paraffinic
Hydrocarbons[a]

Paraffin carbon number	Number of isomers
1 (methane)	1
2	1
3	1
4	2
5	3
6	5
7	9
8	18
9	35
10	75
11	159
12	355
13	802
14	1858
15	4347

[a] From Henze and Blair (1).

highly effective separation of saturated hydrocarbon mixtures. They prepared a 39-component blend of the composition given in Table 1.2. This was completely separated into individual components when analyzed on a capillary column coated with a mixture of hexadecane and Kel-F 10157, as is shown in Figure 1.1. The application of this chromatographic separation to that portion of a crude oil distilling below 114°C allowed for the detailed analysis of Figure 1.2, where the peaks are identified by retention times. Sanders and Maynard (5) described the application of a capillary column method for the determination of the individual C_3–C_{12} hydrocarbons in full-range motor gasolines. The analysis, using a 200-ft squalane column programmed for both temperature and inlet pressure, resolved some 240 peaks in application to a typical gasoline. As many as 180 peaks were identified, representing over 98% of the gasoline sample. For assistance in the identification of some of the peaks, a time-of-flight mass spectrometer (Bendix Model 14–101) was coupled to the gas chromatograph, which allowed effective identification of a component on as little as 10^{-8} g eluted from the column.

USE OF INFRARED AND NUCLEAR MAGNETIC RESONANCE SPECTROSCOPY FOR THE DETERMINATION OF SATURATES

Although the saturates do not contain groups reactive to organic reagents, functional analysis in a broader sense still does apply to these molecules.

Table 1.2.   Hydrocarbons in the 39-Component Blend Listed in Order of Elution on Hexadecane + Hexadecene + Fluorocarbon Capillary Column[a]

Compound	Symbol	Boiling point, °C
Isopentane	$1C_5$	27.9
Normal pentane	NC_5	36.1
2,2-Dimethylbutane	22 DMB	49.7
Cyclopentane	CP	49.3
2,3-Dimethylbutane	23 DMB	58.0
2-Methylpentane	2 MP	60.3
3-Methylpentane	3 MP	63.3
Normal hexane	NC_6	68.7
Methylcyclopentane	MCP	71.8
2,2-Dimethylpentane	22 DMP	79.2
Benzene	Benzene	80.1
2,4-Dimethylpentane	24 DMP	80.5
2,2,3-Trimethylbutane	223 TMB	80.9
Cyclohexane	CH	80.7
3,3-Dimethylpentane	33 DMP	86.1
1,1-Dimethylcyclopentane	11 DMCP	87.9
2-Methylhexane	2 MH	90.1
2,3-Dimethylpentane	23 DMP	89.8
1,cis-3-Dimethylcyclopentane	$1C_3$ DMCP	90.8
3-Methylhexane	3 MH	91.9
1,trans-3-Dimethylcyclopentane	$1T_3$ DMCP	91.7
1,trans-2-Dimethylcyclopentane	$1T_2$ DMCP	91.9
3-Ethylpentane	3 EP	93.5
2,2,4-Trimethylpentane	224 TMP	99.2
Normal heptane	NC_7	98.4
1,cis-2-Dimethylcyclopentane	$1C_2$ DMCP	99.5
Methylcyclohexane	MCH	100.9
1,1,3-Trimethylcyclopentane	113 TMCP	104.9
2,2-Dimethylhexane	22 DMH	106.8
Ethylcyclopentane	ECP	103.5
2,5-Dimethylhexane	25 DMH	109.1
2,4-Dimethylhexane	24 DMH	109.4
2,2,3-Trimethylpentane	223 TMP	109.8
1,trans-2,cis-4-Trimethylcyclopentane	$1T_2C_4$ TMCP	109.3
Toluene	Toluene	110.6
1,trans-2,cis-3-Trimethylcyclopentane	$1T_2C_3$ TMCP	110.2
3,3-Dimethylhexane	33 DMH	112.0
2,3,4-Trimethylpentane	234 TMP	113.5
1,1,2-Trimethylcyclopentane	112 TMCP	113.7

[a] From Schwartz and Brasseaux (4). Copyright 1963 by the American Chemical Society. Reprinted by permission of the copyright owner.

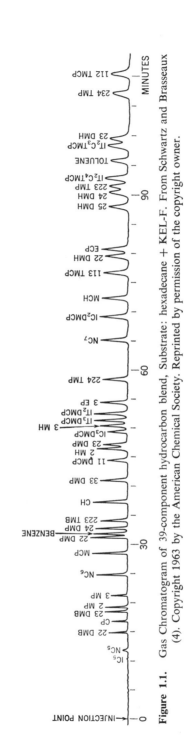

Figure 1.1. Gas Chromatogram of 39-component hydrocarbon blend, Substrate: hexadecane + KEL-F. From Schwartz and Brasseaux (4). Copyright 1963 by the American Chemical Society. Reprinted by permission of the copyright owner.

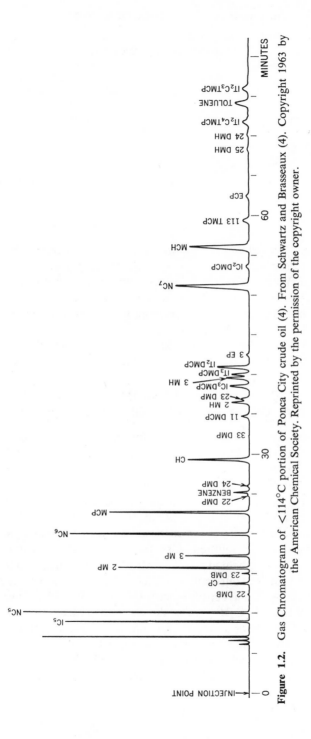

Figure 1.2. Gas Chromatogram of <114°C portion of Ponca City crude oil (4). From Schwartz and Brasseaux (4). Copyright 1963 by the American Chemical Society. Reprinted by the permission of the copyright owner.

Table 1.3. Absorption Regions of Saturated Hydrocarbons in the Infrared and in Nuclear Magnetic Resonance Spectroscopy

		Infrared	NMR	
Group		absorption maxima, μ	Chemical shift, ppm	Coupling constant, Hz
—CH$_3$	Methyl	7.1–7.3	0.8–1.0	5–7
—CH$_2$—	Methylene			
H —C— |	Methine	6.8–6.9	1.1–1.4	5–7

For instance, infrared and proton magnetic resonance can each be somewhat useful in determining the types and amounts of component groups, as shown in Table 1.3. With a 60-MHz instrument, the methyl group is fairly distinguished from the methylene and methine. The latter two are overlapping at 60MHz but are separated at very high fields. In the infrared the methyl group can be distinguished in the region of 7.1–7.3 μ and various types of methyl substituents can sometimes be separated. The methylene and methine absorb together in the region 6.8–6.9 μ and cannot be distinguished.

USE OF MASS SPECTROMETRY FOR THE DETERMINATION OF SATURATES

The mass spectrometer is a powerful instrument for classification of mixtures into component types, as well as for the identification of individual compounds in less complex substances. That mass spectrometric analysis can be applied to kerosines and heavier fractions of petroleum has been demonstrated by the work of O'Neal and Wier (6), who developed the technique and overcame the experimental difficulties of working with heavier materials. An interesting example of this measurement, showing the application of a high resolution mass spectrometer for the group analysis of very complex, unfractionated petroleum distillates, was published by Gallegos, Green, Lindeman, LeTourneau, and Teeter (7). The usual means of classifying hydrocarbons in mass spectrometry is by number of hydrogen atoms in the empirical formula C_nH_{2n+z}. For the saturated hydrocarbons z will be $+2$ for the paraffins, 0 for monocycloparaffins, -2 for dicycloparaffins, etc. Olefins also have a z number of 0 and will interfere unless removed prior to analysis, such as by hydrogenation. It is preferable to use parent peaks for identification and determination. Fragment peaks which are likewise 2 mass units apart for each ring structure can also be used for this measurement but with reduced accuracy. Polycyclic aromatic structures may produce a series of nominal masses that fall on the saturates of one carbon number less. This can be overcome in the high resolution mass spectrometer in that actual mass measurements can be made to the third place. For instance, the actual mass for a naphthalene is 0.0938 units less than for the corresponding paraffin of equal nominal mass. Using these measurements it was possible (7) to obtain values for the content of paraffins, monocycloparaffins, dicycloparaffins, and so on, in a series of petroleum fractions, as well as to distinguish the types of aromatics and heterocyclic compounds present. Some of the published data are given in Table 1.4. The lack of a sufficient number of known, pure materials

Table 1.4. High Resolution Mass Spectrometer Group-Type Results[a]

| | Petroleum Distillates, Liquid volume, % | | | | | |
| | Arabian | | | California | | |
	500–650°F	650–800°F	800–950°F	500–650°F	650–800°F	800–950°F
Saturates						
Paraffins	38	21	15	2	2	3
Monocycloparaffins	7	7	7	18	9	5
Dicycloparaffins	5	4	7	15	9	8
Tricycloparaffins	3	2	5	11	8	14
Tetracycloparaffins	3	3	3	6	10	15
Pentacycloparaffins	2	4	3	4	4	6
Hexacycloparaffins	0	0	5	0	4	5
Total	58	41	45	56	46	56
Aromatics						
Alkylbenzenes	13	8	10	7	7	3
Benzocycloparaffins	4	2	4	9	7	4
Benzodicycloparaffins	3	2	2	10	5	4
Naphthalenes	4	0.6	0.7	5	2	2
Acenaphthenes	1	1	1	6	5	4
Fluorenes	1	4	0.4	5	6	4
Phenanthrenes	2	10	6	0	12	7
Pyrenes	0	5	11	0	6	9
Chrysenes	0	2	3	0	0	3
Total	28	35	38	42	50	40
Sulfur compounds						
Benzothiophenes	9	5	7	2.4	2	2
Dibenzothiophenes	5	19	6	0.1	2	1
Naphthobenzothiophenes	0	0	4	0	0	0.7
Total	14	24	17	2	4	4

[a] From Gallegos, Green, Lindeman, LeTourneau, and Teeter (7). Copyright 1967 by the American Chemical Society. Reprinted by permission of the copyright owner.

in these boiling ranges makes it difficult to be certain of the quantitative accuracy of the assignments, although they should be useful for comparative purposes.

DETERMINATION OF NORMAL PARAFFINS

A specific reagent for isolation of n-paraffins is the molecular sieve. Molecular sieves are silicate minerals of several compositions whose crystal lattices, when the mineral is dried, have pores of distinctive and tunnel-like structures, generally several angstroms in diameter. Zeolites occur naturally but the most useful sieves are of synthetic origin, as discussed in Chapter 21. Barrer and his coworkers (8, 9) showed many years ago that n-paraffins were absorbed in the tunnel structures of some natural zeolites and that n-paraffins could be quantitatively separated from branched-chain paraffins, naphthenes, and aromatics. Use of synthetic molecular sieves for the quantitative separation of n-paraffins has been reported by a number of investigators, including Nelson, Grimes, and Heinrich (10) and Breck, Eversole, Milton, Reed, and Thomas (11). Since molecular sieves have such a distinctive selectivity for allowing n-paraffins to enter and remain in the channels of the sieve while rejecting branched paraffins, naphthenes, or aromatics, a number of gas chromatographic techniques have been developed around this property of the molecular sieve. Methods involving a subtractive technique have been published by Brenner and Coates (12) and by Whitham (13). Eggertsen and Groennings (14) and, later, Blytas and Peterson (15) utilized a method in which the n-paraffins were released from the molecular sieve by heating to temperatures as high as 550°C. The n-paraffins are condensed at the inlet of a gas chromatographic column held at 0°C and subsequently analyzed by temperature programming. Blytas and Peterson point out that this technique is applicable to n-paraffins as high boiling as eicosane ($C_{20}H_{42}$).

It was shown by Brunnock (16, 17) that destruction of the sieve lattice by acid treatment allows the liberation of the n-paraffins trapped within the cavities. The liberated n-paraffins can then be analyzed by gas chromatography. Mortimer and Luke (18) and Knight (19) have published simple micro techniques based on the recovery of n-paraffins after destruction of the sieve. This method is so useful and simple that it has been included in this chapter (Molecular Sieve–Gas Chromatographic method). The detailed procedure is taken from the publication of Knight (19) and some data obtained on a blend of known n-paraffins with a carbon number range of C_{10} to C_{14} are shown in Table 1.5, from which it can be seen that the repeatability is good. Although the published method was successfully applied to kerosine-range paraffins, it can also be used for higher molecular weight materials by increasing the time and temperature of contact with the molecular sieve.

Table 1.5. Analysis of a Known Paraffin Blend by the Molecular Sieve–Gas Chromatographic Method[a]

	n-Paraffin carbon number				
	10	11	12	13	14
Known, wt %	20.1	18.6	19.9	19.6	20.7
Found on successive analysis, wt %	20.6	17.5	20.0	20.0	20.6
	20.6	18.2	20.6	20.2	20.8
	19.7	18.0	20.3	20.2	21.8
	20.7	18.3	20.0	19.9	21.1

[a] Data from Knight (19).

For instance, for petroleum fractions that contain n-paraffins as large as $C_{25}H_{52}$, good results can be obtained if the material is contacted with the molecular sieve for 1 hr at 150–160°C in the first stage of the analysis. Marquart, Dellow, and Freitas (20) showed that n-paraffins in heavy gas oils could be determined by formation of the urea adduct to isolate the n-paraffins followed by their gas chromatographic determination. By their technique, they were able to obtain meaningful analyses for fractions that contained n-paraffins in the C_{30}–C_{32} range. The usefulness of this method is such that it is included in this chapter as a recommended method (Urea Adduction–Gas Chromatographic method). A typical gas chromatogram for the adducted n-paraffins from a heavy gas oil is shown in Figure 1.3 and the corresponding carbon number distribution is indicated in Figure 1.4. Figure 1.4 also shows the results obtained on the same material by a mass spectrometric technique of Stevenson and Polgár (21) that involves a urea adduction step prior to examination of the n-paraffins by a high resolution mass spectrometer.

DETERMINATION OF NORMAL PARAFFINS

MOLECULAR SIEVE–GAS CHROMATOGRAPHIC METHOD

Apparatus

A temperature-programmed gas chromatograph with hydrogen flame detector, having a 2-ft × ⅛-in. thin-walled stainless steel column packed with 5% SE-30 on Chromosorb W. It should be programmed from 60 to 160°C in 5 min. Helium is to be used as carrier gas at 30–50 ml/min.

Atmospheric oven, operating at 110–120°C.

Glass vials, 1-dram.

Plastic vials, 2-dram.

Stirring rods, polyethylene.

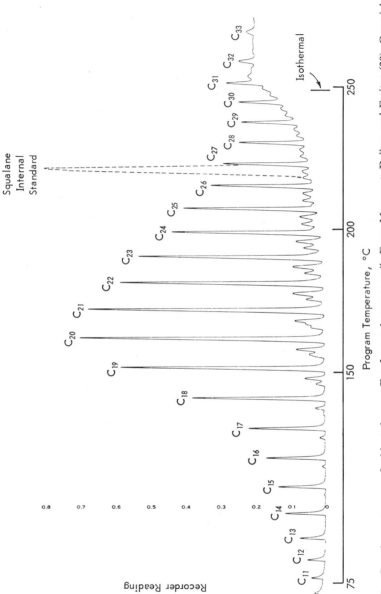

Figure 1.3. Gas chromatogram of adducted *n*-paraffins from a heavy gas oil. From Marquart, Dellow and Freitas (20). Copyright 1968 by the American Chemical Society. Reprinted by permission of the copyright owner.

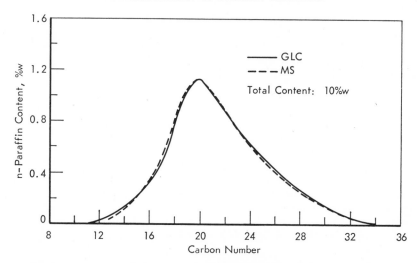

Figure 1.4. *n*-Paraffins in heavy gas oil as determined by gas chromatography and mass spectroscopy. From Marquart, Dellow and Freitas (20). Copyright 1968 by the American Chemical Society. Reprinted by permission of the copyright owner.

Reagents

Hydrofluoric acid, 16% aqueous, prepared by diluting commercial CP hydrofluoric acid with twice its volume of distilled water. Hydrofluoric acid is hazardous and must be handled with care.

Molecular sieves, 5A, 80–100 mesh. Before using, activate in a stream of dry N_2 for 2 hr at 250–300°C.

Procedure

To about 1 ml of sample add accurately 2–5% of a normal paraffin not present in the sample originally; nonane and hexadecane have been employed. The added paraffin serves as a marker for the GC analysis. In a 1-dram glass vial place 0.4 g of freshly activated molecular sieve, add 25 μl of the sample with marker, cap the vial, and shake it to mix the contents thoroughly. Place the vial in the oven at 110–120°C and shake to mix the contents after 5 and 15 min, tightening the cap if necessary.

After $\frac{1}{2}$ hr cool the vial and transfer the sieve to a glass tube made from a small medicine dropper with a cotton wool plug in the tip and wash the sieve with isooctane to remove unsorbed material. Draw air through the dropper to evaporate most of the solvent and transfer the free-flowing sieve to a plastic vial. Add 1 ml of isooctane and then 1 ml of water, and fill the vial about half full with dilute HF solution. Leave the vial uncapped. After the first rapid gas evolution ceases, fill the vial to about 1 cm from the top with the HF solution and let it stand until the sieve structure has disappeared. Occasional stirring hastens the process. Cap the vial and cool it in cold water or allow it to cool to room temperature. Then shake it vigorously to extract the released normals into the isooctane layer. If the vial is not cool it may leak, and in any case rubber gloves should be worn.

Analyze 2 μl of the isooctane layer by gas chromatography. Whatever conditions are used should be confirmed with known blends of normal paraffins in isooctane that approximate the extracts in composition.

DETERMINATION OF NORMAL PARAFFINS IN HEAVY FRACTIONS

UREA ADDUCTION–GAS CHROMATOGRAPHIC METHOD

Apparatus

A temperature-programmed gas chromatograph with hydrogen flame detector, having a 9-ft × ⅛-in. thin-wall, stainless steel column packed with 2 wt% Carbowax 1000 on Chromosorb W. It should be programmed typically from 75°C to 250°C at a rate of 6°C/min. Helium is to be used as carrier gas at a rate of 50–60 ml/min.

Reagents

Urea, reagent grade.
Squalane, 98% pure, Eastman Kodak.
n-Decane, pure grade, Phillips Petroleum.
n-Paraffins, up to C_{32}, of high purity.
Methanol, reagent grade.
Methyl ethyl ketone, 99.5%, Shell Chemical.

Procedure

Accurately weigh enough oil into a 2-ounce bottle to give about 0.3 g of *n*-paraffins. Add 8 g of urea and 25 ml of methanol to the oil. Shake the mixture for approximately 30 min at 55–60°C. Continue shaking for 1 hr while allowing to cool to about 25°C.

Separate the adduct crystals from the oil by filtration through number 5, 50, or 51 Whatman filter paper in a Buchner funnel at room temperature. Be certain the paper is properly sealed by prewetting with methyl ethyl ketone (MEK) saturated with urea at room temperature. Wash the adduct four times with 20-ml portions of the urea-saturated MEK per wash, mixing thoroughly to a slurry each time. Scrape the washed adduct into a 1-ounce bottle. Wash any residual adduct from the paper with water. Fill the bottle to the shoulder with water and make certain that all solid adduct has dissolved. Add about 2 ml of *n*-decane to dissolve the solid wax. Weigh an internal standard into the layer of *n*-decane solution of decomposed adduct. Squalane is recommended as a convenient internal standard, although it often does not resolve well from the $n\text{-}C_{27}$ peak. To minimize the interference from $n\text{-}C_{27}$, use sufficient squalane so that it is the predominant peak in the spectrum. Generally 0.1–0.3 g is sufficient. The contribution from $n\text{-}C_{27}$ may be established by linear interpolation of the $n\text{-}C_{26}$ and $n\text{-}C_{28}$ peak areas and subtracted from the squalane if necessary. Contributions from adductable non-normals are small and can be neglected.

A sample of the marked hydrocarbon solution is injected into the chromatograph in amounts varying from 0.5 to 1.5 μl. The smaller portions give slightly better resolution, but for oils that are fairly low in n-paraffin content (10 wt%) larger samples are often necessary to get sufficiently large peak areas. Temperature programming from 75 to 250°C at 6°C/min gives good resolution of n-C$_{12}$ through n-C$_{36}$ with a reasonable running time of about 30 min. Baseline drift for the chromatogram is generally negligible below about 200°C. Above 200°C, the baseline rises gradually because of column bleed but does not interfere with the resolution of peaks.

Small peaks evolving between the regularly spaced normal-paraffin peaks are presumed to be monomethyl branched paraffins that form adducts along with the normals. These resolve from the major peaks and are not included in the count of n-paraffins.

DETERMINATION OF ISOPARAFFINS

The lower isoparaffins can be determined by gas chromatography or by the combination of gas chromatography and mass spectroscopy discussed elsewhere. Since aromatics can be removed readily by silica gel and n-paraffins by molecular sieves, these adsorption techniques are often applied to fractions prior to the analytical step, to simplify the actual determination. A particularly interesting application is for the determination of isoprenoid hydrocarbons in straight-run distillates. Certain of these materials are present in surprising concentrations, as individual compounds, in crude oil. A thorough survey of this fascinating analytical topic, together with a description of the separation techniques and the methods employed, is given by Bendoraitis, Brown, and Hepner (22). They initiated their study with a sample of an East Texas straight-run gas oil which was first freed of aromatics by silica gel adsorption. Fractionation into a number of distillation cuts was carried out at reduced pressure, and the normal paraffins were subsequently removed by percolation through molecular sieves. At this point, 0.1–0.5 ml of the fractions were separated on preparative scale ($\frac{1}{2}$ in. $\times$ 25 ft) gas chromatographic columns. The fractions obtained from the preparative columns were reprocessed through a second gas chromatographic column and the effluents trapped for investigation by infrared, mass, and nuclear magnetic resonance spectroscopy. Seven individual isoprenoid alkanes were isolated from crude oil, of which pristane (2,6,10,14-tetramethylpentadecane) is the most abundant. The content of this individual compound corresponds to 0.5% of the total crude. The suggestion was made that a likely precursor of pristane is the phytol portion of the chlorophyll molecule. Similar examinations (23–26) of the hydrocarbons found in certain shales have shown the presence of pristane and phytane as well as certain other isoprenoids in these sedimentary rocks, indicating the biogenesis of petroleum.

DETERMINATION OF NAPHTHENES

Generally the first step required in the determination of naphthenes is the isolation of the saturates fraction, which can be done either by acid absorption or by chromatography over silica gel as described in Chapter 20. The saturates fraction of petroleum products will then consist of a mixture of n-paraffins, C_5-ring naphthenes, C_6-naphthenes, and, if of high molecular weight, polycyclic naphthenes. For the lower boiling fractions, gas chromatography, especially with a capillary column, will allow the identification of individual saturated components. Brunnock and Luke (27) reported that Type 13X molecular sieve offers the possibility, when used in gas–solid chromatography, of allowing the separation of saturated hydrocarbons into hydrocarbon types within each carbon number in distillates boiling as high as 185°C. For materials of higher boiling points, extensive work has been done in two principal directions to obtain a type analysis for naphthenes. One has been to attempt to develop an optimum catalyst system to convert cyclohexane derivatives into the corresponding aromatics, which can then be more readily determined. The other principal avenue has been to take a closer look at the application of mass spectrometry. Of these two, the latter has shown more promise and, when coupled with effective gas chromatography, mass spectrometry can be quite useful in many cases.

The use of catalytic dehydrogenation for conversion of cyclohexanes to aromatics has a long history and is important both for laboratory preparations (28, 29) and in the production of Platformate for automotive gasolines. The analytical use of the dehydrogenation reaction as a means of determining C_6-ring naphthenes has been explored by a number of investigators. Rampton (30) used a platinum-on-charcoal catalyst operated at 325°C and found the results useful for comparison with a refining process using essentially the same reaction but on a much greater scale. The substituted cyclohexanes gave 99–100% conversions except that geminal derivatives did not react, as would be expected. Paraffins and C_5-ring hydrocarbons were converted to aromatics to an extent generally less than 1%, although in several cases the conversion of some cyclopentanes ran to 2–3% and higher conversions have been observed by others. For instance, Rowan (31) found that ethyl and n-propyl cyclopentanes could yield approximately 8% of aromatics at 299°C and gave even higher conversions at somewhat more elevated temperatures over a Pt–Al$_2$O$_3$–halogen catalyst. Rowan concluded that there is a great difference in reactivity between C_5- and C_6-ring naphthenes and this difference can be used to distinguish between them. With the catalyst employed, he

$$H_2C \overset{\overset{\displaystyle H_2}{\displaystyle C}}{\underset{\underset{\displaystyle H_2}{\displaystyle C}}{\bigvee}} \overset{CH_2}{\underset{CH_2}{}} \xrightarrow{\text{catalyst}} \bigcirc$$

$$H_2C \overset{\overset{\displaystyle H_2}{\displaystyle C}}{\underset{\underset{\displaystyle H_2}{\displaystyle C}}{\bigvee}} \overset{\overset{R}{\displaystyle C}}{\underset{CH_2 \, R}{}} \xrightarrow{\times} \text{No Reaction}$$

recommended 300°C as the optimum temperature and the use of excess hydrogen to suppress dehydrogenation of the C_5 rings. Topchiev and his co-workers (32) used a platinum–iron catalyst at a temperature of 300–305°C for dehydrogenation of cyclohexane homologs. Since the introduction of gas chromatography, the dehydrogenation reaction has been employed to assist in the identification of components separated by the chromatographic column (31, 33, 34). The limitations of the dehydrogenation method in regard to nonreactivity of geminally substituted cyclohexanes and the partial reaction of some cyclopentanes have prevented it from becoming generally valuable.

The mass spectrometric method for the determination of naphthenes is, in most cases, the most suitable technique, especially with the higher boiling and the more complex samples, as discussed earlier in this chapter. A number of examples have been described (7, 35) of the applications of the mass spectrometric technique to complex petroleum fractions.

REFERENCES

1. H. R. Henze and C. M. Blair, *J. Am. Chem. Soc.*, **53**, 3077 (1931).
2. M. J. E. Golay, "Gas Chromatography," in V. J. Coates, H. J. Noebels, and I. S. Fayerson, Eds., Academic, New York, 1958, pp. 1–11.
3. A. G. Polgár, J. J. Holst, and S. Groennings, *Anal. Chem.*, **34**, 1226 (1962).
4. R. D. Schwartz and D. J. Brasseaux, *ibid.*, **35**, 1374 (1963).
5. W. N. Sanders and J. B. Maynard, *ibid.*, **40**, 527 (1968).
6. M. J. O'Neal, Jr., and T. P. Wier, Jr., *ibid.*, **23**, 830 (1951).
7. E. J. Gallegos, J. W. Green, L. P. Lindeman, R. L. LeTourneau, and R. M. Teeter, *ibid.*, **39**, 1833 (1967).

8. R. M. Barrer and L. Belchetz, *J. Soc. Chem. Ind.*, **64**, 131 (1945).
9. R. M. Barrer and D. A. Ibbitson, *Trans. Faraday Soc.*, **40**, 195 (1944).
10. K. H. Nelson, M. D. Grimes, and B. J. Heinrich, *Anal. Chem.*, **29**, 1026 (1957).
11. D. W. Breck, W. G. Eversole, R. M. Milton, T. B. Reed, and T. L. Thomas, *J. Am. Chem. Soc.*, **78**, 5963 (1956).
12. N. Brenner and V. J. Coates, *Nature*, **181**, 1401 (1958).
13. B. Whitham, *ibid.*, **182**, 391 (1958).
14. F. T. Eggertsen and S. Groennings, *Anal. Chem.*, **33**, 1147 (1961).
15. G. C. Blytas and D. L. Peterson, *ibid.*, **39**, 1434 (1967).
16. J. V. Brunnock, *Nature*, **212**, 385 (1966).
17. J. V. Brunnock, *Anal. Chem.*, **38**, 1648 (1966).
18. J. V. Mortimer and L. A. Luke, *Anal. Chim. Acta*, **38**, 119 (1967).
19. H. S. Knight, *Anal. Chem.*, **39**, 1452 (1967).
20. J. R. Marquart, G. B. Dellow, and E. R. Freitas, *ibid.*, **40**, 1633 (1968).
21. D. P. Stevenson and A. G. Polgár, NASA Contractor Report CR 519 (July, 1966).
22. J. G. Bendoraitis, B. L. Brown, and L. S. Hepner, *Proc. Sixth World Petroleum Congr.*, *1963*, Section V, p. 13.
23. W. G. Meinschein, E. S. Barghoorn, and J. W. Schopf, *Science*, **145**, 262 (1964).
24. G. Eglinton, P. M. Scott, T. Belsky, A. L. Burlingame, and M. Calvin, *ibid.*, **145**, 263 (1964).
25. T. Belsky, R. B. Johns, E. D. McCarthy, A. L. Burlingame, W. Richter, and M. Calvin, *Nature*, **206**, 446 (1965).
26. K. E. H. Göhring, P. A. Schenck, and E. D. Engelhardt, *ibid.*, **215**, 503 (1967).
27. J. V. Brunnock and L. A. Luke, *Anal. Chem.*, **40**, 2158 (1968).
28. N. D. Zelinsky, *Ber.*, **44**, 3121 (1911).
29. N. D. Zelinsky and M. B. Turowa-Pollak, *ibid.*, **58**, 1298 (1925).
30. H. C. Rampton, *Anal. Chem.*, **21**, 1377 (1949).
31. R. Rowan, Jr., *ibid.*, **33**, 658 (1961).
32. A. V. Topchiev, I. A. Musayev, E. K. Iskhakova, A. N. Kislinsky, and G. D. Halpern, *Proc. Fifth World Petroleum Congr.*, *1959*, Section V, p. 191.
33. M. Beroza and R. Sarmiento, *Anal. Chem.*, **36**, 1744 (1964).
34. W. J. Hines and D. E. Smith, *ibid.*, **36**, 2250 (1964).
35. D. P. Stevenson and P. A. Wadsworth, in *Standard Methods of Chemical Analysis*, F. J. Welcher, Ed., Van Nostrand, Princeton, N.J., 1966, pp. 1518–1527.

DETERMINATION OF AROMATIC HYDROCARBONS

The monocyclic aromatic hydrocarbons have a relatively low order of chemical reactivity, which increases in the multicyclic aromatics in such a way that benzene is essentially nonreactive in the bromination methods, α-methylnaphthalene reacts to some 1%, whereas anthracene reacts to 85–130%, calculated on the basis of one molecule of Br_2 per aromatic molecule. The chemical methods of analysis are not suitable for determination of the common aromatic hydrocarbons because, generally, rather severe reaction conditions are required for alteration of the molecular structures. Of the spectroscopic methods, the use of ultraviolet absorption is important because the aromatics have unique and strong absorption in this region. Chromatographic methods are particularly useful because the aromatics generally adsorb strongly and reversibly in many systems, allowing them to be isolated as types (e.g., monoaromatics, polyaromatics) or as specific compounds. The ability of aromatic compounds to engage in charge-transfer reactions with electron acceptors is important in some of the chromatographic methods in which typical electron acceptors are chloranil, tetracyanoethylene, and the polynitro compounds. The more condensed aromatics will form the tighter complexes (1), which provides a means for increased sensitivity in chromatographic separations.

DETERMINATION OF AROMATIC HYDROCARBONS BY ULTRAVIOLET ABSORPTION SPECTROSCOPY

The ultraviolet absorption spectra of aromatic hydrocarbons exhibit many regular features that can be used both for the qualitative identification of aromatic types and for their quantitative determination (2–4). Monoaromatic hydrocarbons, defined as hydrocarbon derivatives of benzene containing no other unsaturated group, show an ultraviolet absorption band in the region 2500–2800 Å with a peak intensity having a molar absorptivity of 100–1500 liters/mole-cm. A second and much more intense absorption band is in the range 1950–2100 Å with peak intensities as high as 50,000 liters/mole-cm. The general appearance of the absorption bands of monoaromatics

19

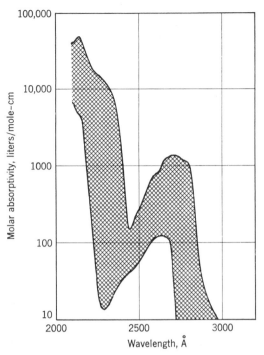

Figure 2.1. General spectral region of monoaromatic hydrocarbon absorption. Data from Stevenson and McConnell (5). Copyright 1958 by Pergamon Press. Reprinted by permission of the copyright owner.

can be judged from Figure 2.1, in which the shaded region was constructed by drawing on a single graph the absorption spectra of many pure monoaromatics. These data are from the work of Stevenson and McConnell (5), who point out the significance of the observation that at wavelengths ≥ 3000 Å the molar absorptivities of pure monoaromatics are less than 10 liters/mole-cm. This was shown by them to be an important criterion of purity since more highly condensed aromatics, such as naphthalene and benzothiophenes, have such relatively strong absorption in the region of 3000 Å that absorptivity measurements at 3000 Å are sufficient to allow the detection of as little as 0.01 % of these materials in a monoaromatic concentrate. Marketos (6) has shown that benzene can be determined readily in aqueous solutions in micromolar concentrations by ultraviolet absorption spectroscopy.

The ultraviolet absorption spectra of the polynuclear condensed aromatics tend to show considerable complexity with a number of maxima. Table 2.1 lists the principal absorption bands of some of the more common polynuclear aromatic hydrocarbons. Very high levels of molar absorptivities are

Table 2.1.   Principal Absorption Bands of Some Polynuclear Aromatics in the Ultraviolet Region between 2000 and 4000 Å[a]

Compound	Maxima, Å	Molar absorptivity[b]	Maxima, Å	Molar absorptivity[b]	Maxima, Å	Molar absorptivity[b]
Naphthalene[c]	2205	1.2×10^5	2750	5.4×10^3	3110	2.5×10^2
Anthracene[c]	2520	2.3×10^5	3560	8.5×10^3	3750	8.6×10^3
1,2-Benzanthracene[d]	2760	7.4×10^4	2875	9.0×10^4	3410	7.1×10^3
Chrysene[d]	2680	1.3×10^5	3200	1.2×10^4	3610	6.9×10^2

[a] Data from American Petroleum Institute Research Project 44.
[b] Liters per mole-cm.
[c] Solvent is isooctane.
[d] Solvent is ethanol.

common even in the higher wavelength regions of the ultraviolet where mono-aromatic hydrocarbons do not absorb appreciably. Consequently the ultraviolet region makes a sensitive area for the determination of the condensed aromatics. A practical ultraviolet method for the determination of naphthalene hydrocarbons in aviation fuels has been issued by the Americal Society for Testing and Materials (6a).

DETERMINATION OF POLYNUCLEAR AROMATIC HYDROCARBONS BY FLUORESCENCE MEASUREMENTS

Visible, fluorescent spectra of solutions of the aromatic hydrocarbons have been found useful for their qualitative identification and semiquantitative determination. VanDuuren has reviewed (7) the field and has used the technique for determination of aromatic hydrocarbons in cigarette tar (8). In typical measurements the sample is dissolved in spectroscopically pure cyclohexane (9) or hexane (10) and irradiated with a narrow-wavelength light band obtained either by a filter or by a monochromator. The fluorescence spectra are then recorded in the usual way.

ANALYSIS OF AROMATIC HYDROCARBONS BY NUCLEAR MAGNETIC RESONANCE

Nuclear magnetic resonance (NMR) has been used effectively to determine individual aromatic hydrocarbons in concentrates derived from petroleum (11) as well as for the characterization of petroleum fractions containing many components (12). The value of NMR analysis is that the ring protons fall far downfield from the alkyl substituents so that examination of the spectra permits an extensive degree of interpretation of the alkyl groups, not only in regard to the total number of protons, but their distribution as methyl, methine, or methylene and also their proximity to and position on the ring.

SEPARATION OF AROMATIC HYDROCARBONS BY ADSORPTION CHROMATOGRAPHY

The use of adsorption chromatography over silica gel to separate lower boiling hydrocarbon mixtures into saturates, olefins, and aromatics is described in Chapter 20. This technique has extensive use not only for the direct analysis of gasolines as in the FIA method but for the separation of aromatic concentrates to allow their further identification by more specific analytical methods. Modification of the FIA method described in Chapter 20, is quite useful for the determination of trace concentrations of aromatics (13, 14). Mair and Mayer (11) employed silica gel to separate the dinuclear aromatics (C_{12}–C_{14}) from a petroleum light gas oil fraction preparatory to the detailed analysis of the aromatics by spectroscopic techniques. Lijinsky (15) used a mixture of magnesium oxide and Celite to separate polycyclic aromatics added to petroleum waxes. Magnesia has a high adsorption affinity for polynuclear aromatics but not for benzene and consequently benzene could be used to elute the wax. However, the polynuclear aromatics adsorbed so strongly that the most expeditious recovery was by solution of the magnesia in aqueous acid and partition of the aromatics into a mixed solvent. In subsequent work, Lijinsky and his coworkers (16) utilized silica gel as the adsorbent and found that the solvent system dimethylformamide–isooctane was effective in resolving mixtures of polycyclic aromatic hydrocarbons. Thorough studies carried out by Sawicki (17) and his coworkers, concerning the characterization of polynuclear aromatic hydrocarbons as airborne pollutants, involved the initial separation of the accumulated polynuclear aromatics by chromatography. In experiments with an alumina column (18), successive volumes of pentane containing added diethyl ether (0, 3, 6, 9, and 12%) eluted hydrocarbons in the following order: saturates, olefins, monoaromatics, naphthalenes, anthracenes, pyrenes, benzofluorenes, chrysenes, benzopyrenes, and coronenes. Chromatographic variables, such as the water content of the alumina, would cause a difference in the retention volumes of the hydrocarbon types, although the relative order was unchanged.

ANALYSIS OF AROMATIC HYDROCARBONS BY GAS CHROMATOGRAPHY

As in the analysis of saturated hydrocarbons, gas–liquid chromatography provides the strongest analytical tool and was used for this purpose early in the history of gas chromatography. Many publications have described practical operating conditions for the high resolution separation of alkylbenzene mixtures. Carnes (19) recommended a capillary column coated with Dow-Corning 550 silicone fluid for the separation of linear alkyl benzenes with chains between C_9 and C_{14}. The isomers obtained from the positions of the phenyl group were resolved except for the 6- and 7-phenyl isomers. Walker and Ahlberg (20) found that the polar substrate m-bis(m-phenoxyphenoxy)-benzene made an effective capillary column coating for the detailed resolution of aromatic hydrocarbons in the C_6–C_{11} range. Clemons, Leach, and Altshuller (21) obtained good results with 1,2,3-tris(2-cyanoethoxy)propane as a stationary phase in the separation of a wide range of aromatics. The high selectivity for aromatics shown by the cyanoethoxy derivatives is such that saturated and olefinic compounds are eluted far ahead of the aromatics. It is possible to develop systems in which C_{12} and C_{13} saturates are eluted prior to toluene. The tetrachlorophthalate esters, which form charge-transfer complexes with aromatic hydrocarbons, can be used as liquid phases for both packed (22, 23) and capillary columns (24, 25). Nitro compounds likewise form charge-transfer complexes and it has been shown (26) that 2,4,6-trinitrophenetole has good aromatic selectivity when used as a substrate. On this column benzene emerges between n-undecane and n-dodecane.

An organo clay complex, Bentone 34, provides an interesting substrate for the separation of the lower aromatics with a high order of resolution (27). When the Bentone 34 was modified with an equal amount of diisodecylphthalate (28) and supported on Chromosorb, Celite, or firebrick, good resolution of the individual xylenes, ethylbenzene, and toluene were found. Silicone oil (29) can also be used as a modifier although it has been pointed out that each batch of Bentone seems to have a different behavior (30), and it was found necessary to reoptimize the modifier concentration with new batches of Bentone. Naphthalene and its homologs can be well resolved on a 300-ft long capillary column coated with Dow Corning 550 phenyl silicone oil (31) and determined using a flame ionization detector. More highly condensed polynuclear aromatics in concentrates obtained by preliminary adsorption chromatography have been determined with a packed column using an ionization detector (32). A particularly interesting technique for the determination of traces of polynuclear aromatics was reported by Dawson (33), who utilized the high degree of selectivity shown by the electron-capture detector for polynuclear aromatics. Results obtained by Dawson are shown in Figure 2.2, which is the chromatogram obtained using a flame ionization detector and an electron-capture detector in parallel. The white oil had been treated with 50 ppm of each of the polynuclear aromatics labeled. The separation was made on a packed, silicone oil-treated column. Since the flame detector responds in a relatively uniform fashion to hydrocarbons, no differentiation is possible from the white oil components. The high electronic absorption coefficients of some polynuclear hydrocarbons, shown in Table 2.2, was first observed by Lovelock, Zlatkis, and Becker (34).

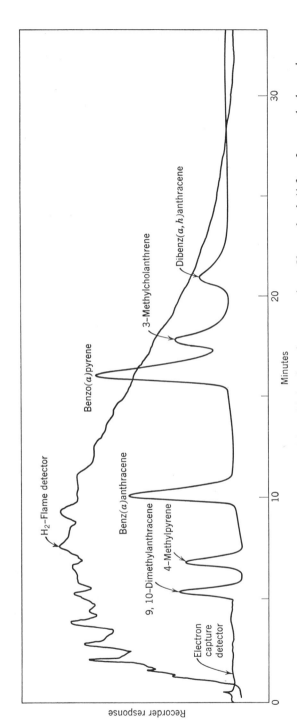

Figure 2.2. Gas Chromatograms of white oil containing added polynuclear aromatics at 50 ppm level. (4 ft × 3 mm o.d. glass column, 0.5% SE-30 on nonacid-washed 30- to 60-mesh Chromosorb W; flow rate, 20 ml N$_2$/min; no dilution gas; 1.0 μl sample. Column temp. programmed from 130 to 260°C at 4°C/min; 33 V on electron capture detector, 300 V on hydrogen flame detector.) From Dawson (33), copyright 1964 by the American Chemical Society. Reprinted by permission of the copyright owner.

Table 2.2. Electron Absorption Coefficients of Some Hydrocarbons in the Electron-Capture Detector[a]

Hydrocarbon	Relative absorption coefficient[b]
Azulene	340
Cyclooctatetraene	210
Monomethylbenzanthracenes	16–80
Benzanthracene	29
Anthracene	12
Pyrene	6.0
Naphthacene	1.7
Chlorobenzene	1.0
Phenanthrene	0.05
Naphthalene	<0.01
Benzene	<0.01
Styrene	<0.01

[a] Data from Lovelock, Zlatkis, and Becker (34).
[b] The electron absorption coefficient of chlorobenzene is taken as unity.

Since aromatics absorb so strongly in the ultraviolet region, the combination of gas chromatography with ultraviolet absorption spectrophotometry allows the construction of a simple apparatus for measurement of small concentrations of aromatic hydrocarbons (35–37). Kaye (36) prefers to use the far-ultraviolet region (below 1700 Å) because more characteristic spectra can be obtained from gas samples in this spectral region. In application for the continuous monitoring of a chromatographic apparatus, the gaseous effluent is radiated with a selective wavelength and the radiation split into two beams, one of which passes through the sample cell, the other serving as the reference. A simple plant process gas chromatograph built on this design by Merritt, Comendant, Abrams, and Smith (37) is illustrated diagrammatically in Figure 2.3 and a typical recorder chart for the analysis of a stream containing benzene and toluene is shown in Figure 2.4.

SEPARATION OF AROMATIC COMPOUNDS BY LIQUID CHROMATOGRAPHY

As is described in Chapter 21 one of the preferred applications of liquid–liquid column chromatography is to aromatic compounds since ultraviolet

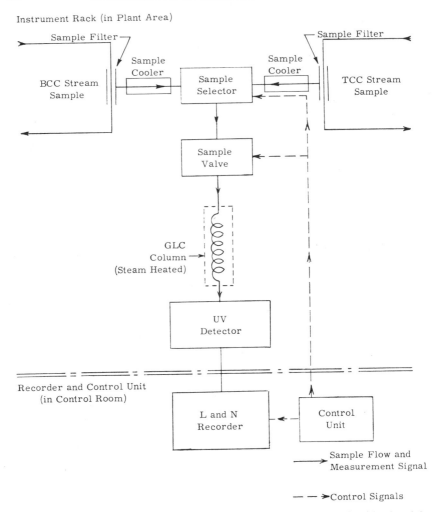

Figure 2.3. Simplified block diagram of process gas chromatograph with ultraviolet detector. From Merritt, Comendant, Abrams and Smith (37). Copyright 1963 by the American Chemical Society. Reprinted by permission of the copyright owner.

detectors are relatively simple to use for gas or liquid streams. Some applications have been reported by Kirkland (38), Sie and Rijnders (39, 40), and Jentoft and Gouw (41). Jentoft and Gouw have developed a high resolution liquid chromatographic apparatus for the analysis of high molecular weight compounds or those that are thermally unstable and cannot be analyzed by gas chromatography. Sie and Rijnders have also been concerned with the determination of materials too high boiling for gas chromatography and have

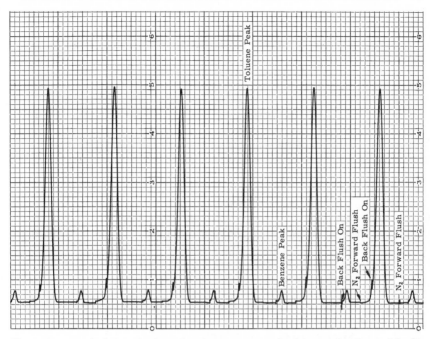

Figure 2.4. Typical record chart from process gas chromatograph. From Merritt, Comendant, Abrams and Smith (37). Copyright 1963 by the American Chemical Society. Reprinted by permission of the copyright owner.

developed a separation technique with a supercritical fluid as the mobile phase. An example of the rapid separation of an aromatic mixture by their technique is shown in Figure 21.3. Untreated alumina of 120/140 mesh was used as the stationary phase and n-pentane as the mobile phase. The temperature was 213° and the pressure 50 kg/cm². An ultraviolet absorption detector was used in these experiments.

REFERENCES

1. G. Briegleb, *Elektronen-Donator-Acceptor-Komplexe*, Springer, Berlin, 1961.
2. A. E. Gillam and E. S. Stern, *Electron Absorption Spectroscopy*, E. Arnold, London, 1957.
3. R. A. Burdett, L. W. Taylor, and L. C. Jones, in *Molecular Spectroscopy*, The Institute of Petroleum, London, 1955, pp. 30–42.
4. E. Clar, *Polycyclic Hydrocarbons*, Volumes 1 and 2, Academic, New York, 1964.
5. D. P. Stevenson and H. M. McConnell, *Spectrochim. Acta*, **12**, 262 (1958).
6. D. G. Marketos, *Anal. Chem.*, **41**, 195 (1969).
6a. Method D 1840, American Society for Testing and Materials, *Standards*, Part 17, October, 1969.

7. B. L. Van Duuren, *Chem. Rev.*, **63**, 325 (1963).
8. B. L. Van Duuren, *J. Natl. Cancer Inst.*, **21**, 623 (1958).
9. B. L. Van Duuren, *Anal. Chem.*, **32**, 1436 (1960).
10. J. H. Chaudet and W. I. Kaye, *ibid.*, **33**, 113 (1961).
11. B. J. Mair and T. J. Mayer, *ibid.*, **36**, 351 (1964).
12. N. F. Chamberlain, *ibid.*, **31**, 56 (1959).
13. H. S. Knight and S. Groennings, *ibid.*, **28**, 1949 (1956).
14. J. C. Suatoni, *ibid.*, **39**, 1505 (1967).
15. W. Lijinsky, *ibid.*, **32**, 684 (1960).
16. W. Lijinsky, C. R. Raha, and J. Keeling, *ibid.*, **33**, 810 (1961).
17. E. Sawicki, T. W. Stanley, and W. C. Elbert, *J. Chromatog.*, **26**, 72 (1967).
18. E. Sawicki, W. Elbert, T. W. Stanley, T. R. Hauser, and F. T. Fox, *Anal. Chem.*, **32**, 810 (1960).
19. W. J. Carnes, *ibid.*, **36**, 1197 (1964).
20. J. Q. Walker and D. L. Ahlberg, *ibid.*, **35**, 2022 (1963).
21. C. A. Clemons, P. W. Leach, and A. P. Altshuller, *ibid.*, **35**, 1546 (1963).
22. S. H. Langer, C. Zahn, and G. Pantazoplos, *J. Chromatog.*, **3**, 154 (1960).
23. A. R. Cooper, C. W. P. Crowne, and P. G. Farrell, *ibid.*, **29**, 1 (1967).
24. H. Miyake, M. Mitooka, and T. Matsumato, *Bull. Chem. Soc. Japan*, **38**, 1062 (1965).
25. R. D. Schwartz, R. G. Mathews, and D. J. Brasseaux, *J. Gas Chromatog.*, **5**, 251 (1967).
26. A. O. S. Maczek and C. S. G. Phillips, *J. Chromatog.*, **29**, 15 (1967).
27. J. Van Rysselberge and M. Van Der Stricht, *Nature*, **193**, 1281 (1962).
28. S. F. Spencer, *Anal. Chem.*, **35**, 592 (1963).
29. J. V. Mortimer and P. L. Gent, *Nature*, **197**, 789 (1963).
30. E. W. Cieplinski, *Anal. Chem.*, **37**, 1160 (1965).
31. F. J. Kabot and L. S. Ettre, *ibid.*, **36**, 250 (1964).
32. W. Lijinsky, I. Domsky, G. Mason, H. Y. Ramahi, and T. Safavi, *ibid.*, **35**, 952 (1963).
33. H. J. Dawson, Jr., *ibid.*, **36**, 1852 (1964).
34. J. E. Lovelock, A. Zlatkis, and R. S. Becker, *Nature*, **193**, 540 (1962).
35. R. A. W. Johnstone and A. G. Douglas, *Chem. and Ind.*, (*London*), **1959**, 154.
36. W. Kaye, *Anal. Chem.*, **34**, 287 (1962).
37. J. Merritt, F. Comendant, S. T. Abrams, and V. N. Smith, *ibid.*, **35**, 1461 (1963).
38. J. J. Kirkland, *ibid.*, **40**, 391 (1968); *J. Chromatog. Sci.*, **7**, 7 (1969).
39. S. T. Sie and G. W. A. Rijnders, *Anal. Chim. Acta*, **38**, 31 (1967).
40. S. T. Sie and G. W. A. Rijnders, *Separation Sci.*, **2**(6) 699, 729, 755 (1967).
41. R. E. Jentoft and T. H. Gouw, *Anal. Chem.*, **40**, 923, 1787 (1968).

DETERMINATION OF OLEFINIC UNSATURATION

Olefinic unsaturation is encountered by the analytical chemist not only in many hydrocarbon samples but very frequently with chemicals of many types of which perhaps the monomers used in the commercial preparation of polymers represent the largest number. These will include such diverse materials as styrene, methyl methacrylate, acrolein, acrylonitrile, vinyl acetate, butadiene, and isoprene, to name just a few. Olefinic polymers are themselves of great importance. The great diversity of types of materials containing olefinic unsaturation as well as the high order of chemical reactivity associated with the double bond accounts for the large number and variety of analytical methods that have been used for the determination of unsaturation. An exceptionally thorough review of the determination of olefinic unsaturation was published some years ago by Polgár and Jungnickel (1). In the course of preparing their review they examined over 2000 articles on this subject, of which some 700 were included in their critical evaluation of the methods.

Nearly all the chemical methods involve the addition of a reagent to the double bond; some of the principal features of the more significant methods are summarized in Table 3.1. The chemistry of the reactions at and around the double bond is complex, and it is important to understand the possibilities and limitations to determine the best choice of analytical method. The reactivity of the olefinic group derives from its high concentration of electrons. These attract electrophilic substances such as halogen and ozone. The reaction of Br_2 with a symmetrical olefin in a polar solvent involves the initial partial polarization of the bromine molecule followed by the formation of a π-complex of positive charge with the Br attached in an intermediate manner. The final step is the reaction of the negatively charged bromine atom to yield the dibromide. The full reaction has the net effect of the addition of one molecule of Br_2 to the olefin. The idea that halogen consumption values give a quantitative measure of olefinic unsaturation is based upon the assumption

Table 3.1. Principal Features of Methods for Determination of Olefinic Unsaturation

Method	Determination	Applicability	Limitations
Bromine in carbon tetrachloride	Total olefin content: in hydrocarbons	Gasolines kerosines	Branched olefins give high results.
Bromide–bromate	in hydrocarbons and nonhydrocarbons	Olefinic groups in alcohols halides, esters	Polynuclear aromatics and sulfur compounds are reactive. Phenyl ethers may be partially substituted.
Potassium tribromide	in nonhydrocarbons	Olefinic groups in alcohols, esters, ethers, carbonyl compounds	Phenol reacts quantitatively to give tribromophenol.
Iodine monochloride	Total olefin content in high molecular weight material	Fatty oils, polymers	Similar to bromination methods
Hydrogenation	Total olefin content in hydrocarbons	Wide general applicability. Branched olefins give accurate results.	Sulfur compounds may poison catalyst
Ozonolysis	Double-bond position	General	Product yields not often quantitative
Infrared absorption	Olefin types	General	Quantitative use limited since absorptivities variable. Tetrasubstituted olefins not determined.
Nuclear magnetic resonance	Olefin types	General, useful for polymers	Tetrasubstituted olefins not determined
Ultraviolet absorption	Conjugated olefins	For simple mixtures	Interference from vinylacetylene, some polynuclear aromatics
Gas chromatography	Individual olefins	Volatile compounds	Large numbers of isomeric olefins above C_8

that addition takes place rapidly, giving rise to stable end products, and that halogen substitution is a slow and insignificant process. Unfortunately, substitution reactions are significant, especially with branched olefins. An inspection of the data in Table 3.2 shows that, although the halogenation methods do provide nearly quantitative results on simple olefins, branched materials generally give high results. Natural olefin mixtures, such as those in petroleum fractions, can be expected to give high results in some of the halogenation methods.

The halogen reagent most commonly used is Br_2 or the interhalogen compound ICl, since Cl_2 is too reactive and causes severe substitution, whereas I_2 is generally too low in reactivity. Many solvents, including carbon tetrachloride, acetic acid, and water, have been employed. Since the halogen addition reaction is not instantaneous, the techniques generally involve adding excess reagent and determining the amount remaining after the completion of the reaction by addition of aqueous KI and titration of the liberated iodine with standard aqueous sodium thiosulfate solution. The difference in titration of the sample reaction mixture from the blank provides the measure of the olefin content. To overcome the effects of substitution, it is possible to analyze a sample at several reaction times and extrapolate the results to zero time.

Those methods considered to be most useful for determination of unsaturation are listed in Table 3.1. The four halogenation methods are given in detail in this chapter. In the case of the other methods and techniques, references and background information are provided to allow the reader to assess the value of the technique and find the sources of the necessary equipment or facilities.

Among the recommended methods, the Bromine in Carbon Tetrachloride method is recommended for hydrocarbons in the gasoline and kerosine ranges. It is a variation of a method published many years ago by McIlhiney (2) and calls for reaction with bromine in carbon tetrachloride at ice temperature. The excess bromine is determined iodometrically. Several determinations are made for different times and the data are extrapolated to zero time if there is a significant difference in the values. The Bromide–Bromate method has been used for many years (3, 4) and has a number of features to recommend it, including simplicity and speed. The method has been widely used, in several versions, in the petroleum industry and is particularly valuable for the determination of unsaturation in nonhydrocarbon organic mixtures such as alcohols, amines, chlorides, acids, and esters, which are miscible with aqueous acetic acid. Bromine is produced from the reaction of bromide ion with bromate under acid conditions. The reaction is carried out at room temperature for a short period of time and the remaining bromine is determined iodometrically after addition of excess potassium iodide solution. The

Table 3.2. Extent of Reaction (%) of Pure Materials in Chemical Methods for Determination of Olefinic Unsaturation

Compound	Bromine in carbon tetrachloride	Bromide–bromate	Potassium tribromide	Iodine monochloride	Hydrogenation
		Hydrocarbons			
1-Pentene	101	100, 102			
2-Pentene	97	96		100	
1-Hexene	100			100.3	
1-Octene	100	99			100.6[a], 99.6, 100.4, 100.6 100.6, 100.8[f]
1-Decene	99	98, 99			101.4[a]
Hexadecene	97	100		100.0	99.6[a]
2,3-Dimethyl-1-butene	115	115			100
2,3,3-Trimethyl-1-butene	99	119			100
3-Methyl-2-isopropyl-1-butene		116			100
4,4-Dimethyl-2-pentene		99			100
3,4,4-Trimethyl-2-pentene		120			100
2,4,4-Trimethyl-pentene-1		102			100.1[b]
2,4,4-Trimethyl-pentene-2		102			100.3[b]
Cyclopentene		99, 100	100		
Cyclohexene	99	99	97	99.1	99, 100, 101[g] 99.0, 99.0
Methylcyclohexene	99	100			99.5, 99.6, 100.2[f]
Benzene	<0.01[c]	<0.01[c]		<0.1[c]	0[h]
Ethylbenzene	<0.01[c]	0.1[c]			
α-Methylnaphthalene		1.0[c]			
Anthracene	85	130[c]			
n-Heptane	<0.01[c]	<0.05[c]			No reaction
2,2,4-Trimethyl pentane	<0.01[c]	0.03[c]			No reaction
		Acids			
Oleic acid				100	99.0, 100.5
Acrylic acid	5		96.5, 97.4		
Methacrylic acid			99.0, 99.5		

Table 3.2. (*continued*)

Compound	Bromine in carbon tetrachloride	Bromide–bromate	Potassium tribromide	Iodine monochloride	Hydro-genation
Elaidic acid				100.1[a]	100.6[a]
Maleic acid		99			99.5[d]
		Alcohols			
Allyl alcohol		99	99		
Methallyl alcohol	80	102	102		
Methyl alcohol		<0.1[c]	<0.02[c]		
Glycerol			<0.02[c]		
		Carbonyls			
Acrolein	26	99	100		
Acetaldehyde		Reacts	5[c]		
Methyl isopropenyl ketone		96	99		
Acetone	High reactivity	High reactivity	0.2[c]	Reacts	
Cyclohexanone	<0.1		0.1[c]		
		Esters			
Ethyl oleate				98.8[a]	99.3[a], 99.0, 99.5, 99.5, 100.1, 100.3[f]
Dimethyl fumarate					100.2[d]
Dimethyl maleate					100[d]
		Ethers			
Vinyl phenyl ether	116		348	111	99.2
Allyl phenyl ether	138		185		97.5
α-Allyl glyceryl ether		99	100		97.1
Diethyl ether		<0.1[c]	0.1[c]		
Glycerol α-phenyl ether	59, 80[c]		105, 109[c]	12[c]	<0.5
		Phenols			
Phenol		100[e]	100[e]		

(*Continued overleaf*)

Table 3.2. (*continued*)

Compound	Bromine in carbon tetrachloride	Bromine– bromate	Potassium tribromide	Iodine monochloride	Hydro- genation
		Sulfur compounds			
Thiophene	30–55[c]	102–115[c]	110[c]	40[c]	0[h]
2-Methylthiophene	50–60[c]	200–250[c]	120[c]	54[c]	
n-Amyl mercaptan	Reacts	230[c]			0[h]
Diethyl sulfide	Reacts	120[c]			
Tetrahydrothiophene	Reacts	110[c]			

[a] W. J. C. de Kok, H. I. Waterman, and H. A. van Westen, *J. Soc. Chem. Ind.*, **55**, 2257 (1936).

[b] C. A. Brown, S. C. Sethi, and H. C. Brown, *Anal. Chem.*, **39**, 823 (1967).

[c] Results calculated on an assumed reaction of one molecule of Br_2 or ICl per molecule.

[d] F. C. Pack, R. W. Planck, and F. G. Dollear, *J. Am. Oil Chemists' Soc.*, **29**, 227 (1952).

[e] Results calculated on the basic of consumption of six Br_2 atoms.

[f] H. C. Brown, K. Sivasankaran, and C. A. Brown, *J. Org. Chem.*, **28**, 214 (1963).

[g] A. F. Colson, *Analyst*, **79**, 298 (1954).

[h] J. L. S. Curtis and M. O. Baker, *Anal. Chem.*, **42**, 278 (1970).

Potassium Tribromide method is useful for the determination of unsaturation in nonhydrocarbon organic materials under somewhat milder conditions than the comparable Bromide–Bromate method. The method (1) uses an aqueous reagent prepared from bromine and potassium bromide. The reaction with the sample is conducted at ice temperature in an evacuated bottle to prevent loss of bromine. The Iodine Monochloride method is generally used for determination of unsaturation of fats, drying oils, and polymers. The method recommended here is derived from the procedure originally published by Wijs (5) and has had considerable use in industry, being incorporated into standard methods in a number of areas (6–8). The iodine monochloride reagent is prepared in acetic acid and the reaction carried out in that solvent or in admixture with chloroform. After completion of the reaction, the excess halogenating agent is converted into triiodide with potassium iodide and determined in the usual manner.

Calculation of the results from the determination of unsaturation can be done as percentage of an indicated structure or, commonly, in terms of *bromine number* or *iodine number*. The halogen numbers signify the quantity of bromine or iodine which have been consumed by 100 g of the sample by reaction under the conditions of the method.

Determination of unsaturation by hydrogenation has been studied by many investigators (1), generally using platinum-metal catalysts. A particularly interesting development is the self-contained reduction apparatus developed by Brown, Sivasankaran, and Brown (9–11), in which the hydrogen is generated within the apparatus by decomposition of sodium borohydride. The hydrogenation catalyst is finely divided platinum prepared from the *in situ* reduction of chloroplatinic acid with sodium borohydride. This catalyst is not only very active for the hydrogenation of the olefinic double bond at room temperature but also catalyzes the decomposition of sodium borohydride to produce quantitatively the hydrogen required. An apparatus was constructed such that the buret containing the standard ethanolic sodium borohydride solution automatically delivered borohydride into the reaction flask whenever the internal pressure dropped as much as 5–10 mm below atmospheric. The finely divided platinum is a highly active catalyst for the hydrolysis of sodium borohydride (12) to produce gaseous hydrogen. It was found that the amount of borohydride consumed corresponded quantitatively to the amount of unsaturated material taken. Many replicated data obtained in a thorough examination indicate an accuracy and precision of the order of $\pm 0.5\%$. Apparatus for conducting the hydrogenation by the method of Brown and his coworkers is now commercially available. In using catalytic hydrogenation reactions, it is important to avoid poisoning the catalyst. Sulfur compounds are notorious in their effectiveness in destroying the catalytic activity of the noble metals and should not be present to an appreciable concentration in samples for analysis. Curtis and Baker (12a) found that catalyst poisoning was so severe that this hydrogenation technique was inapplicable to many practical petroleum fractions. Some samples which reacted with bromine consumed no hydrogen because of catalyst poisoning apparently due to small amounts of sulfur-containing compounds. They were able to counteract the poisoning by using larger amounts of platinum catalyst and, when this was done, quantitative results were obtained for a considerable number of olefins. Of the sulfur compounds examined, the disulfides were most deleterious to the catalyst and the thiophenes least. Curtis and Baker also recommend calculating the extent of hydrogenation of olefinic linkages from a plot of the volume of sodium borohydride solution consumed versus time. In petroleum fractions a slow reaction often occurs after saturation of the olefin groups due presumably to partial hydrogenation of aromatic structures. This is illustrated for indene in Figure 3.1 and for a series of petroleum fractions in Figure 3.2.

A condensed list of the results obtained with pure materials by the recommended methods is given in Table 3.2 and summarized in Table 3.1. The examples in Table 3.2 were chosen to provide a representative indication of the behavior of the more significant types of materials in the methods. *Saturated hydrocarbons* are generally nonreactive, as are the simpler *aromatics*. However, the polynuclear aromatic hydrocarbons can be reactive with halogenation reagents, as indicated by the data on anthracene. *Unbranched*

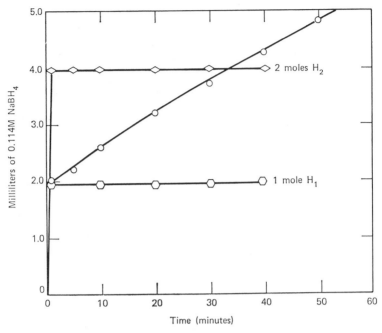

Figure 3.1. Hydrogenation of Olefins. From Curtis and Baker (12a). Copyright 1970 by the American Chemical Society. Reprinted by permission of the copyright owner. ○, 1-octene; ◇, 1,3 pentadiene; ○, indene.

olefins and *cyclic olefins* give results that are reasonably quantitative in the chemical methods. *Branched olefins*, however, tend to give high results in the halogenation methods due to substitution reactions that consume some of the halogenating agent. The hydrogenation methods provide accurate results for the determination of the olefin content of branched materials because no such destructive side reaction is present in the chemically simpler hydrogenation step carried on under mild conditions. In the application of the halogenation methods to nonhydrocarbons rather severe errors are observed with many *sulfur compounds*, since combined sulfur in its lower valence states is oxidized by the halogenation reagents. The extent of reaction is variable and depends upon the severity of the conditions. Simple organic *acids, alcohols,* and *ethers* behave as predicted in that the saturated materials are nonreactive and the olefinic bond is essentially quantitatively accounted for in the unsaturated members of these series. A significant error is found with the phenyl ethers, however, in that the phenyl group itself is halogenated, but hydrogenation under mild conditions provides the correct results with phenyl ethers since the aromatic ring is not reduced. With *carbonyl* compounds, errors can

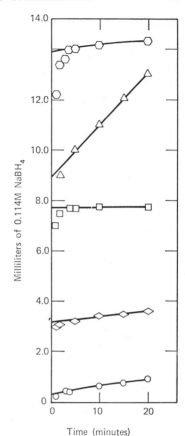

occur with the lower, more reactive homologs. Acetone and acetaldehyde are quite reactive in the Bromide–Bromate method but interfere to a considerably lesser extent in the Potassium Tribromide method. The simplicity of conducting the halogenation methods has long been their principal attraction and, where useful results are obtained, these methods are attractive. However, their limitations should be carefully kept in mind and the alternative hydrogenation or spectroscopic methods considered for many applications.

DETERMINATION OF UNSATURATION IN HYDROCARBONS

Bromine in Carbon Tetrachloride Method

Apparatus

Ice bath, a cylindrical metal pot, about 6 in. in height and diameter, containing an ice–water slurry. The pot should be provided with a light-shielding cover.

Reagents

Bromination reagent, Br_2 in CCl_4, standard $0.2N$.
Carbon tetrachloride, CP grade or equivalent.
Potassium iodide solution, 20% aqueous.
Sodium thiosulfate solution, standard $0.1N$.

Sampling

If the approximate bromine number of the sample is not known, make a pre-liminary determination as follows: add 0.2 ml of sample to 1 ml of carbon tetra-chloride in a 25-ml Erlenmeyer flask. Add crushed ice and titrate with bromination reagent until the color of the bromine persists for 2 min. Calculate the approximate bromine number by multiplying the milliliters of reagent used by 12.

If the bromine number is greater than 10, add a weight of sample in grams calculated from the formula 120/(bromine number) into a 50-ml volumetric flask containing approximately 20 ml of carbon tetrachloride. Dilute to the mark with carbon tetrachloride and mix thoroughly. Transfer a 10-ml aliquot of this solution into each of three 500-ml glass-stoppered Erlenmeyer flasks containing 15 ml of carbon tetrachloride, mix, and proceed as described below.

If the bromine number is less than 10, introduce a weighed amount of sample, calculated from the formula 24/(bromine number) (but not more than 20 g) into each of three 500-ml glass-stoppered Erlenmeyer flasks containing 25 ml of carbon tetrachloride, mix, and proceed as described below.

Procedure

To each 500-ml Erlenmeyer flask add approximately 100 ml of distilled water. Cool for 10 min by inserting each flask in a pot containing a slurry of ice and water.

Calculate the approximate volume of brominating reagent required to brominate the sample and to provide a correct excess from the following equation:

$$\text{volume of reagent, ml} = \frac{(\text{bromine number})(\text{weight of sample in aliquot})}{1.6} + 17$$

Cover the flask in the pot with the light shield and add the total calculated volume of brominating reagent. Swirl the flask gently during the addition and add the reagent as it drains from the buret, slowing the addition at the last to allow control of the exact amount to be added. As soon as the reagent has been added, stopper the flask and place the pot containing the flask in a dark cabinet to shield it further from the light. Then add the same amount of bromination reagent to the second and then to the third flasks in like manner, *timing the reaction from the beginning of the addition of the bromination reagent.* Record the volume of brominating reagent added to each flask to the nearest 0.01 ml. Allow the first flask a 30-min reaction time, the second flask a 20-min reaction time, and the third flask a 10-min reaction time.

Fifteen seconds before the end of each reaction time, remove the pot containing the flask from the cabinet, and at the exact end of the reaction period, ±5 sec, remove the stopper from the flask (leaving the light shield and the flask in place in the pot) and immediately add 15 ml of potassium iodide solution. Then, remove the shield from the flask, restopper the flask, remove the flask from the pot, and immediately shake it vigorously. Titrate the liberated iodine to the starch end point with standard thiosulfate solution, shaking vigorously at frequent intervals as the end point is approached.

If the titration with thiosulfate is less than 30 ml, the excess of brominating reagent present during the reaction was too low (many times resulting in a low bromine number), and the determination must be repeated with the correct reagent excess.

Calculation

$$\text{Bromine number, g/100 g} = \frac{(VN - vn)(8)}{W}$$

where V = volume of bromination reagent, ml
 N = normality of the bromination reagent
 v = volume of sodium thiosulfate solution, ml
 n = normality of the sodium thiosulfate solution
 W = weight of sample, g, in the aliquot portion analyzed

If determinations at different reaction times show a trend in bromine number outside the repeatability of the method, obtain the bromine number of the sample extrapolated to zero time.

DETERMINATION OF UNSATURATION IN ORGANIC MATERIALS

BROMIDE–BROMATE METHOD

Apparatus

Mechanical shaker.
Bromination bottle (Figure 3.3), available from several suppliers.

Reagents

Acetic acid, CP glacial.
Bromide–bromate reagent, standard 0.2N.
Potassium iodide solution, 20% aqueous.
Sodium thiosulfate solution, standard 0.1N.
Starch indicator solution.
Sulfuric acid solution, 10%.

Procedure

Introduce 10 ml of glacial acetic acid into a 50-ml volumetric flask and add a weight of sample calculated from the formula 120/(bromine number). If the bromine

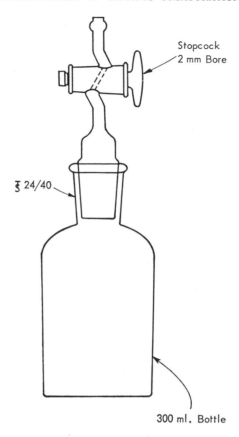

Stopcock
2 mm Bore

⅊ 24/40

300 ml. Bottle

Figure 3.3.   Bromination bottle.

number is less than 10, use 25 ml of sample. Dilute to volume at room temperature with glacial acetic acid and mix thoroughly.

Place 10 ml of distilled water in a bromination bottle, stopper it, and evacuate it to a pressure of ⅓ atm or lower. By means of a pipet, transfer a 10-ml aliquot of the acetic acid solution of the sample into the evacuated bottle by inserting the tip of the pipet into a short piece of clean rubber tubing connected to the stopcock of the bottle stopper and opening the stopcock to an extent sufficient to draw the liquid from the pipet at its normal drainage rate. When the level of the liquid in the pipet reaches the top of the rubber tubing, close the stopcock and let the pipet drain for 15 sec. Withdraw the pipet and allow the remainder of the liquid to drain into the rubber tubing, then flush the tubing and stopcock by drawing 2–5 ml of glacial acetic acid into the bottle from a buret, taking care not to lose the vacuum.

Draw into the evacuated bromination bottle a volume of bromination reagent calculated to be 15 ml in excess of that required to react with the sample, using the equation

$$\text{volume, ml} = 15 + \frac{(\text{bromine number})(\text{sample weight, g})}{1.6}$$

Immediately draw into the bottle a volume of 10% sulfuric acid solution equal to the volume of bromination reagent added. Shield the bottle from strong light and shake it, preferably in a mechanical shaker, for 5 min ± 10 sec, measured from the time at which the sulfuric acid solution was added.

Stop the reaction by drawing into the bottle 15 ml of 20% potassium iodide solution followed by approximately 100 ml of distilled water. Remove the stopper and wash the inside with water. Titrate the liberated iodine immediately with standard sodium thiosulfate solution until the brown color fades to a pale yellow. Add 2 ml of starch indicator solution and continue the titration to the blue starch end point.

Repeat the determination using a sample of the same size but 10 min reaction time.

If the results of the first two analyses differ by more than 1%, make a third test using a 15-min reaction time.

Calculation

Use the corresponding section of the Bromine in Carbon Tetrachloride method.

DETERMINATION OF UNSATURATION IN ORGANIC MATERIALS

POTASSIUM TRIBROMIDE METHOD

Apparatus

Mechanical shaker.
Bromination bottle (Figure 3.3).

Reagents

Bromination reagent, Br_2 in KBr, standard 0.2N, aqueous.
Diluent, a water-miscible organic solvent such as ethyl alcohol (Formula 3A) or CP acetone. Make a blank determination on each lot of the diluent according to the procedure described below. Calculate the milliequivalents of bromine consumed by 10 ml of the diluent. Average the two determinations.
Potassium iodide solution, 20% aqueous.
Sodium thiosulfate solution, standard 0.1N.
Starch indicator solution.

Procedure

If the approximate bromine number is not known to 20% or better, a preliminary determination should be made. Place 0.2 ml of sample into a 25-ml

Erlenmeyer flask containing 1 ml of ethyl alcohol. Add crushed ice and slowly, with constant agitation, add bromination reagent until the color of the mixture remains the same as that of the reagent for 2 min. Calculate the approximate bromine number of the sample by multiplying the milliliters of reagent used by 12.

Introduce 10 ml of ethyl alcohol into a 50-ml volumetric flask and add a weight of sample in grams calculated from the formula 120/(bromine number). If the bromine number is less than 10, use 25 ml of sample. Dilute to volume at room temperature with diluent and mix thoroughly.

Fill two bromination bottles two-thirds full with crushed ice and allow the water to drain out by inverting the bottles in a shallow pan. Stopper the bottles and evacuate to a pressure of $\frac{1}{3}$ atm or lower. By means of a pipet, transfer 10-ml aliquots of the diluted sample into each of the evacuated bottles by inserting the tip of the pipet into the short piece of clean rubber tubing connected to the stopcock of the bottle stopper and opening the stopcock enough to draw the liquid from the pipet at its normal drainage rate. When the level of the liquid in the pipet reaches the top of the rubber tubing, allow it to continue half-way into the rubber tubing, close the stopcock, let the pipet drain for 15 sec, withdraw the pipet, and allow the remainder of the liquid to drain into the rubber tubing. Then, by first pinching the tubing with the fingers (to maintain the vacuum in the bottle) and then opening the stopcock, suck this last portion of the sample into the bottle. Repeat this operation twice. Finally close the stopcock and then flush the tubing and stopcock in like manner by drawing 2 ml of diluent into the bottle from a pipet.

Into one of the evacuated bottles measure from the buret a volume of bromination reagent 17 ml in excess of that required to react with the sample. Into the other bottle measure a volume of bromination reagent 22 ml in excess. Calculate the volume of bromination reagent required to react with the sample from the formula:

bromination reagent, ml

$$= \frac{(\text{approximate bromine number})(\text{weight of sample in aliquot, g})}{1.6}$$

Use the following technique for introducing the bromination reagent into the bromination bottles: Connect the tip of the buret to the stopcock of the bottle stopper by means of the short piece of rubber tubing. Open the stopcock of the bromination bottle, then close it. Open the stopcock of the buret completely, then slowly open the stopcock of the bromination bottle so that the buret drains at its normal rate. As the bromine solution is being introduced into the bromination bottle, shake the bottle intermittently to permit thorough contact with the sample, taking great care not to pull the rubber tubing connection from the buret. When the required volume of reagent has been drawn in, close the stopcock of the bottle stopper. Close the buret stopcock and carefully remove the connecting rubber tubing from the buret tip, immediately pinching the top of the rubber tubing shut with the fingers to prevent any loss of bromine. Open the stopcock to withdraw the bromine solution remaining in the tubing, then close the stopcock and admit air into the rubber tubing by quickly opening and closing the fingers. Repeat this operation twice. Flush the tubing and stopcock in the same manner with 2–3 ml of distilled water, taking care to maintain all the vacuum possible in the bottle.

Shake the bottle in the mechanical shaker for 20 min ±15 sec, counting from the time the bromine was first introduced into the bottle. If an ampule is used for sampling, break the ampule after the bromination reagent is added and measure the reaction period from the time the ampule is broken.

Ten seconds before the end of the reaction period, remove the bottle from the shaker, and at the end of the reaction period draw in 15 ml of 20% potassium iodide solution and shake well. Wash down the rubber tubing and the inside of the hollow stopper by drawing a stream of water in from a wash bottle. Remove the stopper of the bottle and wash the inside with a stream of water. Titrate the liberated iodine with standard sodium thiosulfate solution until the brown color fades to pale yellow. Add 2 ml of starch indicator solution and continue the titration to the starch end point.

If the back-titration with $0.1N$ thiosulfate solution is less than 30 and 40 ml for the calculated 17- and 22-ml excesses, respectively, repeat the determination with the correct excesses.

Calculation

$$\text{Bromine number, g/100 g} = \frac{(VN - vn - B)(8)}{W}$$

where V = volume of bromination reagent added, ml
N = normality of the bromination reagent
v = volume of sodium thiosulfate solution used, ml
n = normality of the sodium thiosulfate solution
B = quantity of bromine consumed by 10 ml of diluent, milli equivalents
W = weight of sample, g, taken for analysis

DETERMINATION OF IODINE NUMBER

IODINE MONOCHLORIDE METHOD

Reagent

Acetic acid, CP glacial.
Chloroform, CP
Iodine monochloride (Wijs) solution, approximately $0.2N$. Dissolve 16.2 g of iodine monochloride in enough glacial acetic acid to make 1 liter of solution.
Potassium iodide solution, 20% aqueous.
Sodium thiosulfate solution, standard $0.1N$.
Starch indicator solution, 1%.

Procedure

Weigh out a quantity of sample, calculated from the formula 30/(iodine number) (but not more than 5 g), using a Lunge weighing pipet for liquids or a small weighing dish for solids and semisolids, and place it in a 500-ml glass-stoppered Erlenmeyer flask containing 10 ml of chloroform or glacial acetic acid. Swirl the flask until the sample is entirely dissolved. By means of a pipet, add 25 ml of iodine monochloride solution, allow the pipet to drain for a fixed time, and again swirl the mixture gently. Place the flask in a dark place and allow the reaction to continue at uniform temperature for 1 hr. During this period swirl the flask gently every 10 min.

After 1 hr, add 15 ml of potassium iodide solution and 100 ml of water to the flask. Shake vigorously and titrate the liberated iodine to the starch end point with standard thiosulfate solution.

Make two blank determinations in an identical manner and using the same 25-ml pipet, but omit the sample. Allow the blanks to stand with the test mixture for the same length of time.

Calculation

Calculate the iodine number in grams of iodine per 100 g of sample from the following equation:

$$\text{iodine number, g/100 g} = \frac{(B - S)(N)(12.7)}{W}$$

where B = volume of standard thiosulfate solution, ml, used for the blank

S = volume of standard thiosulfate solution, ml used for the sample

N = normality of the thiosulfate solution

W = weight of sample, g.

DETERMINATION OF OLEFIN TYPES

Table 3.3 illustrates the behavior of several types of olefins in the halogenation and spectroscopic methods. The halogenation methods provide essentially no differentiation among olefin types but do provide a value for total olefin content, whereas the spectroscopic methods allow differentiation among several types. Because of the widely varying molar absorptivity and the limited applicability to the internal olefins, infrared absorption spectroscopy cannot always provide a good overall quantitative figure for total olefin content when used alone. Since proton NMR essentially counts protons, the data obtained are quantitative and do not require calibration except to indicate the location of the resonance. A useful survey of the proton NMR technique to obtain quantitative measurements of hydrogen types was published a few years ago by Jungnickel and Forbes (13), some of whose data are reprinted in Table 3.4. In a series of saturates, olefins, and aromatics the chemical shift (δ) is distinctly different for protons of the several types and their integrated intensities are demonstrated to be essentially quantitative with the system employed.

The success of the instrumental methods in providing a rapid and accurate differentiation among olefin types has made obsolete the earlier chemical methods that attempted to do this but were slow, cumbersome, and did not always give sufficiently definitive results.

Table 3.3. Behavior of Types of Olefin Groups in Several Methods

Type	Terminology	Chemical methods, %	Infrared		NMR
			Absorption maxima, μ	Molar absorptivity liters/mole-cm	Chemical shift (δ) and coupling (J)
$RCH=CH_2$*	"Vinyl"	100 ± 1	10.05 and 10.98	ca. 50 and 140	δ = 4.8–5.0 ppm
$RR'C=CH_2$*	"Vinylidene"	100 ± 2	11.25	150	δ = 4.6–4.8 ppm
trans-RCH*$=CH$*R'	"Internal"	100 ± 2	10.35	110	δ = 5.3–5.5 ppm J = 14–16 Hz
cis-RCH*$=CH$*R'	"Internal"	100 ± 2	14.0–14.6, variable	Low variable	δ = 5.3–5.5 ppm J = 10–13 Hz
$RR'C=CH$*R''	"Trisubstituted internal"	100 ± 5	11.9–12.7, variable	Low variable	δ = 5.0–5.3 ppm
$RR'C=CR''R'''$	"Tetrasubstituted internal"	100 ± 5	Not determinable	—	Determined only from allylic group

Table 3.4. Results of Integration of Proton NMR Spectra of Pure Hydrocarbons[a]

Compound	Purity, wt %	Proton type	Chemical shift[b] δ, ppm	Per cent hydrogen Theory	Per cent hydrogen Found	Dev. from theory
CH₃–△–CH₃	99.77	—CH₃	1.03	60.0	59.9	−0.1
		Ring	0.25	40.0	40.1	+0.1
H₂C=CH–C(CH₃)₂–CH₃	>99	=CH—	5.75	8.3	8.4	+0.1
		=CH₂	4.83	16.7	16.5	−0.2
		Alkyl	1.00	75.0	75.1	+0.1
CH₃–CH=CH–CH₂–CH₂–CH₂–CH₃	99.86	=CH—	5.3	14.3	14.2	−0.1
		Alkyl	0.9–1.9	85.7	85.8	+0.1
cyclohexane =CH–CH₃	99.86	=CH—	5.05	7.1	7.0	−0.1
		Alkyl	1.5–2.1	92.9	93.0	+0.1
cyclopentene –CH₃	99.9	=CH—	5.20	10.0	10.0	0.0
		Alkyl	1.7–2.2	90.0	90.0	0.0
cyclopentane –CH=CH₂	99.9+	=CH—	5.66	8.3	8.3	0.0
		=CH₂	4.83	16.7	16.7	0.0
		Alkyl	1.5–2.4	75.0	75.0	0.0
benzene –CH₂CH₃	99.8	Aromatic	7.05	50.0	50.0	0.0
		Ar–CH₂—	2.53	20.0	19.8	−0.2
		—CH₃	1.15	30.0	30.2	+0.2
tetralin	99.86	Aromatic	6.85	33.3	33.6	+0.3
		α–CH₂—	2.60	33.3	33.6	+0.3
		β–CH₂—	1.66	33.3	32.8	−0.5
benzene –CH₂–CH=CH₂	~95	Aromatic	7.05	50.0	52.2	+2.2
		=CH—	5.8	10.0	9.4	−0.6
		=CH₂	5.0	20.0	19.2	−0.8
		Ar–CH₂–C=	3.25	20.0	19.2	−0.8

[a] From Jungnickel and Forbes (13). Data obtained with a Varian A-60 and a sample concentration of ≃ 30 vol % in CCl₄. Copyright 1963 by the American Chemical Society. Reprinted by permission of the copyright owner.

DETERMINATION OF OLEFINS BY ELECTRONIC ABSORPTION SPECTROSCOPY

The determination of unconjugated olefins by electronic absorption spectroscopy has been limited since their principal bands are below 2000 Å, a region that is not conveniently available with the common spectrophotometers. In work with specialized apparatus, Jones and Taylor (14) found it possible to measure the electronic absorption spectra of monoolefins and found that the simpler monoolefins are generally characterized by a broad absorption band with maximum absorptivity of some 10^4 liters/mole-cm in the wavelength region of 1720–1950 Å. Another approach to utilizing electronic absorption spectroscopy to differentiate unconjugated olefins has been to measure the spectra of their charge-transfer complexes. As an example of this approach, Bauer (15) observed a large shift in wavelength of olefins complexed with tetracyanoethylene. The greatest shift was found with the tetrasubstituted olefins. Tetramethylethylene formed a complex with tetracyanoethylene in which the absorption maximum was in the vicinity of 5350 Å. The wavelength variation of the complexes was 2000 Å compared to only some 200 Å for the olefins themselves. Only limited use has so far been made of this interesting technique.

With conjugated dienes, direct measurement of the absorption spectra shows strong absorption in the region 2200–4000 Å. Since the monoolefins do not absorb appreciably in this region, the common ultraviolet absorption spectrophotometers provide a useful determination of conjugated dienes even in olefin mixtures. A selected list of data indicating the usefulness of this measurement in distinguishing conjugation is given in Table 3.5. A typical application of the method is the determination of 1,3-butadiene in a C_4 hydrocarbon mixture by measurement of the absorption in the region 2260–2410 Å (16). Paraffins and olefins in the carbon number range of C_4 and less do not affect the results other than in diluting the sample. Vinyl acetylene and 1,2-butadiene, however, do interfere. The ultraviolet method was used extensively some years ago in the analysis of the intermediates for production of synthetic rubber, but at the present time this analysis is more generally done in the commercial plants by gas chromatography in which each of the components can be analyzed without interference. Gas chromatography is particularly useful since process analyzers, based on the chromatographic principle, provide successful control of plant operation.

ANALYSIS OF POLYMERIC OLEFINS

Analysis of polymers containing olefinic bonds can be made with a number of the techniques described for the lower molecular weight members of this

Table 3.5. Absorption of Some Unsaturated Hydrocarbons in the Ultraviolet Region 2200–4000 Å[a]

Compound	Absorption maxima, Å	Molar absorptivity, liters/mole-cm
Isoprene (2-methyl-1,3-butadiene)	2235	2.1×10^4
1-*cis*-3-Pentadiene	2270	2.0×10^4
1-*trans*-3-Pentadiene	2230	2.4×10^4
1,3-Cyclopentadiene	2410	3.2×10^3
cis-3-Hexene	—[b]	0.9[c]
2,5-Dimethyl-2-hexene	—[b]	6.2[c]
Benzene	2550	2.0×10^2
Toluene	2620	2.1×10^2

[a] Data from American Petroleum Institute Research Project 44; measurements made in isooctane.
[b] No maxima in this region.
[c] Absorption at 2200 Å.

series. An instructive example is the case of polyisoprene, which is available in several structural forms: hevea (natural rubber), balata (gutta-percha), and synthetic. These three forms are all high molecular weight polymers of isoprene and could occur in any one or several of the structures illustrated.

(1,4-*cis*) hevea   (1,4-*trans*) balata

(1,2)   (3,4)

Total unsaturation values can be obtained on stereoregular rubber samples by the iodine monochloride method. A satisfactory solvent is *p*-dichlorobenzene. Some values on typical samples are given in Table 3.6. Some years ago a thorough study of the application of the iodine monochloride method to the

Table 3.6

Rubber sample	Double bonds, % of theory (iodine monochloride)
Balata (A)	102.2
(B)	98
Hevea	95.5
Synthetic	
1,4-cis (A)	99.5
(B)	99.5
(C)	102.4
(D)	99.5
(E)	99.8

determination of total unsaturation in several synthetic rubbers and in natural rubber was made by Lee, Kolthoff, and Mairs (17). They observed some complicating side reactions, including substitution but they found it possible to make corrections and obtain precise results. It should be noted, however, that in rubber samples that have been converted to cyclized structures, which produces branching, the iodine monochloride method will give quite high results due to a large degree of substitution during the halogenation reaction (18).

The structure types of the several polyisoprenes have been determined by a combination of infrared and NMR spectroscopy. Infrared studies had indicated that the natural polyisoprenes were essentially pure 1,4 polymers with hevea being *cis* and balata being *trans*. Until the application of high resolution NMR to these systems it was not entirely certain that there was not a few percent of the alternate structure in each product. The work of Golub, Fuqua, and Bhacca (19) with a Varian 100-MHz NMR unit showed that there was no evidence for any 3,4 units in the NMR spectra of the natural polyisoprenes. It was also possible to determine that hevea and balata were each at least 99% pure *cis* and *trans* isomer, respectively. Somewhat similar studies have been made by Chen (20, 21), who has examined butadiene-isoprene copolymers and polyisoprenes in the NMR. It was suggested that the determination of mixtures of the isomeric forms could be determined in synthetic samples by NMR.

A statement (22) that perhaps 5% of the C_5 units in natural polyisoprene are combined as a 3,4 structure was based on finding small amounts of formic acid after ozonolysis and oxidative hydrolysis. Bevilacqua (23) points out that oxidative results must be interpreted with caution when based on products obtained in low yields. He notes that formic acid had been observed as a product in the reaction of polyisoprene with molecular oxygen itself and could well be an expected result from any oxidative process. It is not always recognized that rubber samples are easily oxidized by air and that those samples coming to an analyst may already have a small but appreciable amount of combined oxygen.

DETERMINATION OF DOUBLE-BOND POSITION BY OXIDATIVE CLEAVAGE REACTIONS

There is a large literature on techniques for the oxidative cleavage of unsaturated compounds and determination of the products for evidence concerning the structure of the original compounds. A number of reagents have been used for this purpose, including potassium permanganate, either directly (24, 25), or in admixture with alkaline periodate (26–28), osmium tetroxide (29), ruthenium tetroxide (30), and ozone (31). The most extensive investigations of double-bond oxidation have been made by ozonolysis. This reaction has been thoroughly studied by Criegee and his coworkers (32, 33), who have outlined the mechanism and described the products obtained. A large number of investigations have utilized the ozonolysis technique, with different schemes for the analysis of the products, to provide information on the position of unsaturation in the molecule. Although extensively used for many years, there have been certain dissatisfactions with the ozonolysis procedures (1, 34), which included the inconvenience and danger of generating ozone, the instability and explosiveness of the ozonides, and the occasional observations of abnormal products (35–37).

In recent years a number of these difficulties have been overcome, especially by workers in lipid chemistry. A number of improvements have been made in techniques to convert the ozonides to analyzable species (34, 38, 39). Since the sample requirements for gas chromatography are so small, there is no longer any danger in handling the microgram quantity of the ozonides. In a particularly interesting method reported by Nickell and Privett (40), a solution of the ozonolysis product is pyrolyzed in an attachment to the port of a GLC instrument. A specific reductive catalyst is employed in the pyrolysis under such conditions that the ozonides produce aldehydes that are then determined by gas chromatography in the usual way. A microanalyzer reported by Beroza and Bierl (41) has a sample requirement of as little as 1–5 μg. The ozonolysis is conducted in carbon disulfide as solvent and completed in a few minutes at $-70°$C. The ozonides were reduced by triphenyl phosphine and analyzed by gas chromatography. Yields of aldehydes from cleavage of olefins was 70–95 % with sample weights in the range 40–110 μg.

Another application of ozonolysis was published some years ago in which ozone was employed as a titrimetric reagent for determination of the amount of olefinic unsaturation (42). An electrolytic ozone generator was used to produce ozone in low concentration in oxygen. A constant stream of the dilute

ozone was passed through a chloroform solution of the sample kept at low temperature. A colored indicator was also included in the reaction mixture. When the olefinic compound had completely reacted with ozone, the indicator was oxidized and the color destroyed. A calculation of the unsaturation value was obtained from the determined rate of ozone production and the time observed before the indicator was destroyed.

ANALYSIS OF OLEFINS BY GAS CHROMATOGRAPHY

The isomeric complexity of hydrocarbons, which increases so rapidly with increase in carbon number, has with the olefinic compounds another large multiplication factor in that the double bond can be at various of the chain positions and can also give *cis* and *trans* modifications. Polgár, Holst, and Groennings (43) determined the relative retention volumes of olefins in gas chromatography. Despite their use of a high resolution capillary column they were unable to separate a number of close-boiling C_7 olefins, yet under the same conditions all the C_7 saturates were separated. The retention volumes determined by Pogár, Holst, and Groennings are given in Table 3.7. A close inspection of the data reveals that there is some overlap of the olefins of different carbon number, especially with the cyclic olefins, which have a distinctly higher retention volume. It is clear that the complexity of the olefins can be reduced by saturation and determination of the saturate composition to provide information on the carbon skeleton. Consequently, it is often recommended that complex olefin mixtures be examined at one stage in their analysis as their hydrogenated products to determine the carbon skeletons. If more information is then required, the use of infrared or NMR spectroscopy can reveal the general arrangements of the double bonds and it

Table 3.7.   Adjusted Retention Volumes of Olefins Relative to *n*-Hexane[a,b]

Components in order of emergence	Boiling point °C	Relative retention	Components in order of emergence	Boiling point °C	Relative retention
Ethylene	−103.71	0.003	3,4-Dimethyl-1-		
Propylene	−47.70	0.034	pentene	80.80	1.52
2-Methylpropene	−6.90⎫		*cis*-4,4-Dimethyl-2-		
1-Butene	−6.26⎭	0.11	pentene	80.43	1.53
trans-2-Butene	−0.88	0.14	2,4-Dimethyl-1-		
cis-2-Butene	3.72	0.18	pentene	81.61	1.60

[a] Column: Silicone SF-96 on glass capillary. Temperature, 24°C.

[b] From Polgár, Holst, and Groennings (43). Copyright 1962 by the American Chemical Society. Reprinted by permission of the copyright owner.

Table 3.7. (*continued*)

Components in order of emergence	Boiling point °C	Relative retention	Components in order of emergence	Boiling point °C	Relative retention
3-Methyl-1-butene	20.06	0.22	1-Methylcyclopentene	75.49	1.63
1-Pentene	29.97	0.31	3-Methyl-1-hexene	83.90	1.68
2-Methyl-1-butene	31.16	0.34	3-Ethyl-1-pentene	84.11	1.73
trans-2-Pentene	36.35	0.38	2,4-Dimethyl-2-pentene	83.30	1.77
3,3-Dimethyl-1-butene	41.25	0.40	5-Methyl-1-hexene	85.31	
cis-2-Pentene	36.94	0.41	2,3-Dimethyl-1-pentene	84.28	1.80
2-Methyl-2-butene	38.57	0.44	trans-2-Methyl-3-hexene	85.90	1.87
Cyclopentene	44.24	0.60	4-Methyl-1-hexene	86.73	1.92
4-Methyl-1-pentene	53.87	0.63	cis-4-Methyl-2-hexene	86.31	
3-Methyl-1-pentene	54.18	0.64	2-Ethyl-3-methyl-1-butene	86.37	1.97
2,3-Dimethyl-1-butene	55.62	0.70	trans-4-Methyl-2-hexene	87.56	
cis-4-Methyl-2-pentene	56.39	0.71	trans-5-Methyl-2-hexene	88.11	2.02
trans-4-Methyl-2-pentene	58.61	0.74	Cyclohexene	82.98	2.08
2-Methyl-1-pentene	62.11	0.88	cis-3,4-Dimethyl-2-pentene	89.25	2.25
1-Hexene	63.49	0.89	2-Methyl-1-hexene	92.00	2.42
2-Ethyl-1-butene	64.68	0.99	trans-3,4-Dimethyl-2-pentene	91.50	2.46
n-Hexane	68.74	1.00	1-Heptene	93.64	
trans-3-Hexene	67.09	1.03	2-Ethyl-1-pentene	94.0	2.50
cis-3-Hexene	66.45	1.03	trans-3-Methyl-3-hexene	93.54	2.65
trans-2-Hexene	67.88	1.05	trans-3-Heptene	95.67	2.76
3-Methylcyclopentene	64.91		cis-3-Heptene	95.75	2.84
2-Methyl-2-pentene	67.31	1.08	trans-3-Methyl-2-hexene	95.18	2.84
4,4-Dimethyl-1-pentene	72.52		2-Methyl-2-hexene	95.41	2.87
trans-3-Methyl-2-pentene	67.70	1.11	cis-3-Methyl-3-hexene	95.40	2.90
4-Methylcyclopentene	65.67	1.12	trans-2-Heptene	97.95	2.95
cis-2-Hexene	68.89	1.16	3-Ethyl-2-pentene	96.01	2.97
cis-3-Methyl-2-pentene	70.46	1.23	cis-3-Methyl-2-hexene	97.26	3.07
trans-4,4-Dimethyl-2-pentene	76.74	1.31	2,3-Dimethyl-2-pentene	97.40	
3,3-Dimethyl-1-pentene	77.48	1.36	cis-2-Heptene	98.41	3.19
2,3-Dimethyl-2-butene	73.21	1.37			
2,3,3-Trimethyl-1-butene	77.89	1.40			

is often possible to calculate the structures present without the need for exhaustive and time-consuming determination of individual components. For those occasions when a detailed examination is required of olefins in close-boiling mixtures the use of gas chromatography with silver nitrate–ethylene glycol as the partition phase can be recommended. A determination has been made (44) of the equilibrium constants of the silver nitrate–olefin complexes using gas chromatography for the measuring technique. Table 3.8

Table 3.8. Value of Equilibrium and Partition Coefficients for Olefins and Other Hydrocarbons[a,b]

Compound	K_1	K_L	Compound	K_1	K_L
Ethylene	22.3	0.1	Allene	0.8	1.6
Propene	9.1	0.4	Methylallene	0.8	3.5
1-Butene	7.7	0.9	1,3-Butadiene	4.2	2.2
1-Pentene	4.9	1.9	1,4-Pentadiene	10.2	2.9
1-Hexene	4.3	3.5	1,5-Hexadiene	28.8	5.1
1-Heptene	3.2	7.3	1,6-Heptadiene	14.7	9.9
1-Octene	2.6	13.1	1,7-Octadiene	11.3	19.4
3-Methyl-1-butene	5.1	1.5	1,8-Nonadiene	10.4	36.5
3,3-Dimethyl-1-butene	3.6	2.2	1,9-Decadiene	7.8	76.3
3-Methyl-1-pentene	3.4	2.8	*trans*-1,3-Pentadiene	3.5	5.1
3-Ethyl-1-pentene	1.4	5.2	*cis*-1,3-Pentadiene	4.4	6.1
4-Methyl-1-pentene	2.8	2.7	Isoprene	3.1	4.4
3-Methyl-1-hexene	2.7	5.3	2,3-Dimethyl-1,3-butadiene	1.9	8.8
4-Methyl-1-hexene	2.3	6.0	2,4-Dimethyl-1,3-pentadiene	1.6	12.8
5-Methyl-1-hexene	3.1	5.9	2,5-Dimethyl-2,4-hexadiene	0.8	47.3
			2-Methyl-1,5-hexadiene	22.1	10.2
cis-2-Butene	5.4	1.1	2,5-Dimethyl-1,5-hexadiene	13.3	19.4
cis-2-Pentene	4.3	2.3	*trans*-1,3,5-Hexatriene	5.1	19.4
cis-2-Hexene	3.1	4.3	*cis*-1,3,5-Hexatriene	4.7	22.7
cis-2-Heptene	2.6	8.1	Methylenecyclobutane	5.8	5.3
cis-2-Octene	2.2	14.6	Cyclopentene	7.3	5.8
cis-3-Hexene	3.9	4.1	1-Methylcyclopentene	1.9	8.9
cis-3-Heptene	2.7	7.6	1-Methylcyclopentene	2.1	9.0
cis-4-Methyl-2-pentene	3.1	2.8	Methylenecyclopentane	4.0	10.2
cis-4,4-Dimethyl-2-pentene	2.7	5.3	1-Ethylcyclopentene	2.3	16.0
cis-2,2-Dimethyl-3-hexene	2.5	8.9	Ethylidenecyclopentane	0.7	21.8
			Allylcyclopentane	3.9	24.9
trans-2-Butene	1.4	1.0	Cyclopentadiene	4.6	10.7
trans-2-Pentene	1.1	2.3	Cyclohexene	3.6	14.7

[a] K_1 = equilibrium constant (l./mole) for formation of silver nitrate-olefin complex in ethylene glycol. K_L = partition coefficient for compound on pure ethylene glycol compound.

[b] From Muhs and Weiss (44). Copyright 1962 by the American Chemical Society. Reprinted by permission of the copyright owner.

Table 3.8. (*continued*)

Compound	K_1	K_L	Compound	K_1	K_L
trans-2-Hexene	0.8	4.0	1-Methylcyclohexene	0.5	21.3
trans-2-Heptene	0.6	7.6	3-Methylcyclohexene	3.5	16.5
trans-2-Octene	0.4	14.6	4-Methylcyclohexene	3.8	14.2
trans-3-Hexene	1.0	4.1	Methylenecyclohexane	6.0	18.7
trans-3-Heptene	0.6	7.6	1-Ethylcyclohexene	0.5	35.9
trans-4-Octene	0.5	13.4	Ethylidenecyclohexane	1.6	39.6
trans-4-Methyl-2-pentene	0.7	3.4	Vinylcyclohexane	5.9	27.1
trans-2-Methyl-3-hexene	0.6	5.5	4,4-Dimethyl-1-cyclohexene	1.4	21.2
trans-4,4-Dimethyl-2-pentene	0.4	4.4	Allylcyclohexane	3.2	46.7
trans-2,2-Dimethyl-3-hexene	0.3	7.9	1,3-Cyclohexadiene	8.9	22.9
trans-2,5-Dimethyl-3-hexene	0.2	6.5	1,4-Cyclohexadiene	4.9	33.2
			1-Methyl-1,4-cyclohexadiene	3.3	52.4
2-Methyl-1-propene	3.9	0.9	4-Vinyl-1-cyclohexene	11.2	45.5
2-Methyl-1-butene	3.0	2.3	Dipentene	5.9	126.0
2-Methyl-1-pentene	2.1	3.7	α-Phellandrene	5.1	108.0
2,3-Dimethyl-1-butene	2.4	3.2	Cycloheptene	12.8	27.0
2,3,3-Trimethyl-1-butene	1.8	5.4	Cycloheptatriene	7.6	89.2
2-Ethyl-1-butene	3.5	4.2	*cis*-Cycloöctene	14.4	56.1
2-Ethyl-1-hexene	2.1	12.7	*trans*-Cycloöctene	>1000	56.1
			1,3-Cycloöctadiene	3.2	78.7
2-Methyl-2-butene	0.8	2.2	1,4-Cycloöctadiene	14.4	90.7
2-Methyl-2-pentene	0.6	4.2	1,5-Cycloöctadiene	75	144
cis-3-Methyl-2-pentene	0.7	4.2	Cycloöctatetraene	91	211
trans-3-Methyl-2-pentene	0.7	4.4	2-Norbornene	62	17.7
2,3-Dimethyl-2-butene	0.1	4.5	2,5-Norbornadiene	33.7	27.8
			2-Methylenenorbornane	4.3	35.1
2-Hexyne	2.0	18.3	Camphene	3.1	61.2
3-Hexyne	2.6	15.2	α-Pinene	1.1	47.4
2-Heptyne	1.6	34.0	β-Pinene	3.7	84.5
3-Heptyne	2.1	25.1	Benzene	0.1	47.8
2-Octyne	1.2	65.2	Toluene	0.1	78.9
4-Octyne	1.5	43.8			

gives information on the equilibrium constant (K_1) for the formation of the silver nitrate–olefin constant in ethylene glycol. Also given is the partition coefficient (K_L) for the compound on the pure ethylene glycol column. The observed partition coefficient (H) on a silver nitrate–ethylene glycol column can be readily calculated from K_1 and K_L and the molar concentration of silver nitrate [$AgNO_3$]$_L$ in ethylene glycol by the following expression:

$$H = K_L + K_1 K_L [AgNO_3]_L$$

Careful inspection of these data offers many possibilities for separation of otherwise difficultly separable materials. Some examples are separation of *cis* and *trans* isomers, of positional isomers in large ring systems, and of non-conjugated dienes.

REFERENCES

1. A. G. Polgár and J. L. Jungnickel, *Organic Analysis*, Vol. III, Interscience, New York, 1956, pp. 203–386.
2. P. C. McIlhiney, *J. Am. Chem. Soc.*, **21**, 1084 (1899).
3. A. W. Francis, *Ind. Eng. Chem.*, **18**, 821, 1095 (1926).
4. W. Vaubel, *Z. Angew. Chem.*, **23**, 2078 (1910).
5. J. J. A. Wijs, *Ber.*, **31**, 750 (1898).
6. Method Tg 1-64, American Oil Chemists Society, *Official and Tentative Methods*, Chicago, Illinois.
7. Method D-460, American Society for Testing and Materials, *Standards*, Part 22, 1969, Sections 47–49.
8. Association of Official Agricultural Chemists, *Official Methods of Analysis*, 1965, Washington, D.C., p. 418.
9. H. C. Brown, K. Sivasankaran, and C. A. Brown, *J. Org. Chem.*, **28**, 214 (1963).
10. C. A. Brown and H. C. Brown, *J. Am. Chem. Soc.*, **84**, 2829 (1962).
11. C. A. Brown, S. C. Sethi, and H. C. Brown, *Anal. Chem.*, **39**, 823 (1967).
12. H. C. Brown and C. A. Brown, *J. Am. Chem. Soc.*, **84**, 1494 (1962).
12a. J. L. S. Curtis and M. O. Baker, *Anal. Chem.*, **42**, 278 (1970).
13. J. L. Jungnickel and J. W. Forbes, *ibid.*, **35**, 938 (1963).
14. L. C. Jones, Jr., and L. W. Taylor, *ibid.*, **27**, 228 (1955).
15. R. H. Bauer, *ibid.*, **35**, 107 (1963).
16. Method D-1096, American Society for Testing and Materials, Part 18, 1969.
17. T. S. Lee, I. M. Kolthoff, and M. A. Mairs, *J. Poly. Sci.*, **3**, 66 (1948).
18. D. F. Lee, J. Scanlan, and W. F. Watson, *Proc. Roy. Soc. (London)*, Ser. A, **273**, 345 (1963).
19. M. A. Golub, S. A. Fuqua, and N. S. Bhacca, *J. Am. Chem. Soc.*, **84**, 4981 (1962).
20. H. Y. Chen, *Anal. Chem.*, **34**, 1134 (1962).
21. H. Y. Chen, *J. Polymer Sci.*, B **4** (11), 891 (1966).
22. S. N. Chakaravarty and A. K. Sircar, *J. Appl. Polymer Sci.*, **11**, 37 (1967).
23. E. M. Bevilacqua, *J. Polymer Sci.*, B, **5**, 601 (1967).
24. P. H. Begemann, J. G. Keppler, and H. A. Boekenoogen, *Rec. Trav. Chim.*, **69**, 439 (1950).
25. J. G. Keppler, *ibid.*, **76**, 49 (1957).
26. R. U. Lemieux and E. von Rudloff, *Can. J. Chem.*, **33**, 1701 (1955).
27. A. P. Tullock and B. M. Craig, *J. Am. Oil Chemists' Soc.*, **41**, 322 (1964).
28. E. P. Jones and V. L. Davison, *ibid.*, **42**, 121 (1965).
29. R. Pappo, D. S. Allen, Jr., R. U. Lemieux, and W. S. Johnson, *J. Org. Chem.*, **21**, 478 (1956).
30. L. M. Berkowitz and P. N. Rylander, *J. Am. Chem. Soc.*, **80**, 6682 (1958).
31. C. D. Harries, *Untersuchungen uber Ozon und Seine Einwirkung auf Organische Verbindungen*, J. Springer, Berlin (1916).
32. R. Criegee and G. Wenner, *Annalen*, **564**, 9 (1949).

33. R. Criegee and G. Lohaus, *Ber.*, **86,** 1 (1953).
34. O. S. Privett and E. C. Nickell, *J. Am. Oil Chemists' Soc.*, **43,** 393 (1966).
35. W. G. Young, A. C. McKinnis, I. D. Webb, and J. D. Roberts, *J. Am. Chem. Soc.*, **68,** 293 (1946).
36. M. Stoll and A. Rouve, *Helv. Chim. Acta*, **27,** 950 (1944).
37. E. Spath, M. Pailer, and G. Gregely, *Ber.*, **73,** 795 (1940).
38. R. A. Stein and N. Nicolaides, *J. Lipid Res.*, **3,** 476 (1962).
39. R. A. Stein, *J. Am. Oil Chemists' Soc.*, **42,** 326 (1965).
40. E. C. Nickell and O. S. Privett, *Lipids*, **1,** 166 (1966).
41. M. Beroza and B. A. Bierl, *Anal. Chem.*, **38,** 1976 (1966), **39,** 1131 (1967).
42. H. Boer and E. C. Kooyman, *Anal. Chim. Acta*, **5,** 550 (1951).
43. A. G. Polgár, J. J. Holst, and S. Groennings, *Anal. Chem.*, **34,** 1226 (1962).
44. M. A. Muhs and F. T. Weiss, *J. Am. Chem. Soc.*, **84,** 4697 (1962).

DETERMINATION OF ACETYLENES

Acetylenic hydrocarbons are distinguished from the double-bonded olefins in a number of reactions. The triple bond is less reactive to halogenation than the double bond and consequently the halogenation methods do not generally apply. The most useful and distinctive difference is in the reactivity of the acetylenic hydrogen in α-acetylenes to form metal derivatives by reaction with either copper or silver salts. Since this reaction is specific to acetylenic hydrogen and is not shown by olefins or dialkyl acetylenes, it can be used as a method of analysis as in the following reaction:

$$R\text{—}C\equiv CH + AgNO_3 \rightarrow R\text{—}C\equiv C\text{—}Ag + HNO_3$$

Titration of the acid produced is taken as the measure of the acetylenic hydrogen. It is also possible to hydrate the triple bond

$$R\text{—}C\equiv C\text{—}R' + H_2O \xrightarrow{\text{catalyst}} R\text{—}\underset{\displaystyle \underset{O}{\|}}{C}\text{—}CH_2\text{—}R'$$

and then to determine the ketone so produced.

The determination of acetylenic hydrogen by reaction with alcoholic silver nitrate has been widely employed. The titration procedure for measuring the extent of this reaction was first utilized by Hill and Tyson many years ago (1). The American Society for Testing and Materials recommends the use of this method for determination of α-acetylenes in butadiene and butane–butene mixtures (2). Use of silver perchlorate as the reagent was shown to be effective by Barnes (3), who obtained essentially quantitative results with a number of organic compounds containing both acetylenic and hydroxyl functional groups but did obtain low results with some acetylenic hydrocarbons due perhaps to slow reactivity or poor solubility.

The silver nitrate method is recommended for the determination of acetylene in the range between 10 and 1000 ppm in gases. Acetylene is absorbed from the gas sample in alcoholic silver nitrate solution and the increase in acidity is measured by titration with standard base. Saturated and olefinic hydrocarbons, non-alpha acetylenes, oxygen, and nitrogen do not interfere.

DETERMINATION OF SMALL CONCENTRATIONS OF ACETYLENE IN GASES

SILVER NITRATE METHOD

Apparatus

Gas washing bottle, 125-ml, with extra coarse fritted cylinder. Two required.
Buret, 10-ml, graduated in 0.05-ml divisions.
Wet test meter.

Reagents

Sodium hydroxide solution, standard 0.05N.
Methyl red indicator solution, 0.2 g in 10 ml of 95% ethanol.
Alcoholic silver nitrate solution; dissolve 50 g of CP $AgNO_3$ in about 100 ml of distilled water and dilute to 1 liter with 95% ethanol. Store in the dark. This solution is somewhat unstable and should be discarded when it becomes cloudy.

Procedure

Using a graduated cylinder, place 40 ml of alcoholic silver nitrate solution in each of two 125-ml gas washing bottles. Connect the bottles in series with the sample source and connect the outlet tube with the wet test meter. Protect the gas washing bottles from strong light. Pass the gas sample through the apparatus at a rate of 150–250 ml/min to a total volume of 10–20 liters. Record the volume, barometric pressure, and temperature.

Transfer the contents of the two bottles to a 250-ml flask and titrate with 0.05N sodium hydroxide to the methyl red end point.

Carry out a blank determination on 80 ml of the alcoholic silver nitrate solution, titrating as directed above.

> **DANGER!** Silver acetylide precipitates should be destroyed while wet by decomposing with an excess of acid ferrous sulfate solution. The acetylides should not be allowed to accumulate or dry because of the danger of explosion.

Calculation

Calculate acetylene content from the following equations:

$$\text{acetylene, ppm} = \frac{(S - B)(N)(273 + t)}{(P - p)V} \times 31{,}200$$

At 25°C and 760 mm, this reduces to

$$\text{acetylene, ppm} = \frac{(S - B)(N)}{V} \times 12{,}500$$

where S = ml of NaOH solution for the sample

B = ml of NaOH solution for the blank

N = normality of the NaOH solution

t = room temperature, $°C$

P = barometric pressure, mm Hg

p = vapor pressure of water at $t°C$, mm Hg

V = volume of sample, liters

The hydration technique for determination of mono- and diallylacetylenes has also been extensively investigated. Wagner, Goldstein, and Peters (4) published a procedure involving the reaction of the acetylenes with methanol in the presence of a catalyst to procedure ketals, which were subsequently hydrolyzed to ketones. The ketones were distilled from the aqueous reaction mixture and determined by the usual hydroxylamine hydrochloride method. Although the method did not give quantitative results, recoveries were generally found to range from 89 to 95%, making it possible to obtain useful approximate analyses at that time. Siggia (5) utilized a hydration procedure with a mercuric catalyst in an acidic medium and determined the ketones produced, after neutralization of the reaction mixture, by direct addition of hydroxylamine hydrochloride. The precision and the accuracy were found to be of the order of ±2% on a variety of acetylenic compounds. Scoggins and Price (6) found that the hydration of acetylenes could be followed by conversion of the ketones to the 2,4-dinitrophenylhydrazones. The hydrazones were extracted from the reaction mixture and measured with a spectrophotometer. The method was shown to be applicable in the range 5–500 ppm.

Considerable attention has been paid to the development of methods for the determination of acetylenes in low concentrations. Siggia and Stahl (7) published a spectrophotometric technique involving the initial formation of mercuric acetate complexes to give products with molar absorptivities varying between 4×10^2 and 30×10^2, making it necessary to calibrate with the compound being examined. Hobart, Bjork, and Katz (8) reported on the measurement of the colored, reduced copper derivative (Ilsovay reagent) for the determination of acetylene. The molar absorptivity of the reduced product was in the range of 4×10^3 liters/mole-cm.

DETERMINATION OF ACETYLENES BY GAS CHROMATOGRAPHY

The ultimate sensitivity of the chemical methods for determination of trace concentrations of acetylenes is considerably surpassed by the gas chromatographic techniques. The gas chromatographic methods can avoid interference from other materials in the sample and they also provide information on the individual components. Therefore, they are generally to be favored for trace analysis and are applicable to dialkyl acetylenes as well as those with an active hydrogen. With a correct choice of column packing and operating conditions it has been found possible to determine acetylene itself below the ppm level in ethylene (9) and in mixed C_4 hydrocarbons (10). Pollard (11) described conditions for the gas chromatographic determination of low concentrations of the 1- and 2-butynes and 1-butene-3-yne (vinyl acetylene) in C_4 hydrocarbons. The high level of accuracy and speed in the determination of these components at concentrations in the range of 30–1000 ppm were so satisfactory that Pollard chose the gas chromatographic method to replace the previous chemical methods which were not so sensitive and were much more laborious. The disadvantage of gas chromatography for acetylenes is that the detailed procedure must be worked out for each type of sample. At the part per million level, many hydrocarbon streams will be found to contain numerous components and the acetylenes must be placed where there is no interference by a proper choice of solvent polarity. This problem becomes more severe at higher carbon numbers because of the multiplicity of isomers.

DETERMINATION OF ACETYLENIC HYDROGEN BY GAS-FORMING REACTIONS

The active hydrogen in α-acetylenes can react with the Grignard or lithium aluminum hydride reagents to produce a measurable gas in the usual active hydrogen methods. The lithium aluminum hydride method detailed in Chapter 8 can be employed for the determination of acetylenic hydrogen in the absence of active hydrogen from other materials. Müller and Merz (12) recently published an extensive investigation of the determination of monosubstituted acetylenes by a new gasometric method involving reaction with an aluminum alkyl derivative earlier reported by Merz (13). The reagent has the formula $Na(Al(C_2H_5)_2H_2)$ and is soluble in hydrocarbons and some polar solvents such as anisole and pyridine. The apparatus employed is of conventional design with a micro gas buret. The reagent is prepared according to the following reaction:

$$Al(C_2H_5)_2Cl + 2NaH \rightarrow NaCl + Na[Al(C_2H_5)_2H_2]$$

The product, in anisole solution, after being freed of sodium chloride by centrifuging, is stored under oxygen-free nitrogen and is ready for use. Müller and Merz examined a considerable number of acetylenes, both substituted and unsubstituted, and found that the C≡C—H group did not produce measurable H_2 at 0°C but did react quantitatively at 90°C. Hydroxyl groups did react quantitatively at 0°C and consequently it was possible to determine the two groups in compounds containing the two functions.

DETERMINATION OF THE ACETYLENIC HYDROGEN BY PROTON MAGNETIC RESONANCE

The detection of the protons of various types in acetylenic molecules can be assisted by use of nuclear magnetic resonance spectrometers. Because of the proximity of the triple bond, the resonance position of the acetylenic hydrogen is most generally at a different position from those of other protons in the molecule, as is illustrated for some hydrocarbons in Table 4.1. It is important to note, however, that the position of resonance is not always at the same place nor is it always at a different position from other protons. For instance, propyne does not afford differences within the usual error of measurement. Other functional groups in the molecule may affect the position of resonance, as is the case with phenylacetylene (Table 4.1). However, a very small variation was found with a group of acetylene derivatives containing N, O, or the halogens as substituents in various functions, as was illustrated by work reported by Hatton and Richards (15), some of whose data are given in Table 4.2.

Table 4.1. Shift of Proton Absorption Position in NMR Spectra of Some Acetylenic Hydrocarbons[a]

Compound	Proton type	Chemical shift[b] δ, ppm
H—C≡C—CH$_3$	≡CH	1.80
	≡C—CH$_3$	1.80
HC≡C—CH$_2$—CH$_3$	≡CH	1.78
	≡C—CH$_2$—	2.17
	—CH$_3$	1.14
H—C≡C—(CH$_2$)$_7$—CH$_3$	≡CH	1.74
	≡C—CH$_2$—	2.10
	—(CH$_2$)$_n$	1.30
	—CH$_3$	0.88
⬡—C≡CH	≡CH	3.05
	C$_6$H$_5$	7.3–7.6

[a] From J. L. Jungnickel (14), data obtained with Varian A-60.
[b] From tetramethylsilane.

DETERMINATION OF ACETYLENES

Table 4.2.   Shift of Proton Absorption Position in NMR Spectra
of Some Acetylenic Derivatives[a]

Compound	Chemical shift of $C{\equiv}CH^{b}$, ppm
$HC{\equiv}C{\cdot}CH_2Cl$	−1.19 liquid
$HC{\equiv}C{\cdot}CH_2Br$	−1.31 liquid
$HC{\equiv}C{\cdot}CH_2OH$	−1.32 liquid
$HC{\equiv}C{\cdot}CH_2{-}O{-}$⬡	−1.19 liquid
$HC{\equiv}C{\cdot}CH_2{-}N(CH_3)_2$	−1.02 liquid
$HC{\equiv}C{\cdot}CH(CH_3)NHCH(CH_3)_2$	−1.21 liquid
$HC{\equiv}C{\cdot}CH(OH){\cdot}CH_3$	−1.23 liquid
$HC{\equiv}C{\cdot}CH(OH){\cdot}C_6H_5$	−1.02 CCl$_4$ solution

[a] From J. V. Hatton and R. E. Richards (15).
[b] From cyclohexane.

REFERENCES

1. A. J. Hill and F. Tyson, *J. Am. Chem. Soc.*, **50**, 172 (1928).
2. American Society for Testing and Materials, *Standards*, Part 18, Designation D1020-61, 1969.
3. L. Barnes, *Anal. Chem.*, **31**, 405 (1959).
4. C. D. Wagner, T. Goldstein, and E. D. Peters, *ibid.*, **19**, 103 (1947).
5. S. Siggia, *ibid.*, **28**, 1481 (1956).
6. M. W. Scoggins and H. A. Price, *ibid.*, **35**, 48 (1963).
7. S. Siggia and C. R. Stahl, *ibid.*, **35**, 1740 (1963).
8. E. W. Hobart, R. C. Bjork, and R. Katz, *ibid.*, **39**, 224 (1967).
9. R. A. L. Paylor and R. Feinland, *ibid.*, **33**, 808 (1961).
10. H. S. Knight and F. T. Weiss, *ibid.*, **34**, 749 (1962).
11. S. A. Pollard, *ibid.*, **36**, 999 (1964).
12. K. Müller and W. Merz, *Z. Anal. Chem.*, **239**, 151 (1968).
13. W. Merz, *ibid.*, **181**, 147 (1961).
14. J. L. Jungnickel, unpublished data from Shell Development Co.
15. J. V. Hatton and R. E. Richards, *Trans. Faraday Soc.*, **56**, 315 (1960).

5

DETERMINATION OF ACIDS

The variety of acids that comes to the attention of the analytical chemist is indeed large and will include the strong mineral acids used in processing organic chemicals and refining petroleum products, the weak carboxylic acids widely manufactured and converted into commercial products, and the very weakly acidic phenols. Because of the wide diversity of materials, a large number of analytical methods have been published. The titration methods fall into two categories, aqueous and nonaqueous, with the non-aqueous methods generally having the larger scope and utility. There are, in addition, some important chromatographic and spectroscopic methods used for the analysis of acids. A useful review (1) covers the general literature.

The strength of acids is compared with regard to their dissociation constants (K_a), which can be expressed as

$$K_a = \frac{[H^+][A^-]}{[HA]}$$

or as the negative logarithm of the dissociation constant, pK_a. Use of the term pK_a provides a consistency in interrelations between acid and bases. A listing of some of the common acids with their dissociation constants expressed as pK_a is given in Table 5.1. These data are taken principally from compilations by Albert and Serjeant (2) and by Kortüm, Vogel, and Andrussow (3), who issued a compilation of data as part of the activities of the International Union of Pure and Applied Chemistry. The common acids fall into four general categories, with the strong inorganic acids having low pK_a's or perhaps values even negative. The low or negative values which arise from the high dissociation of these very strong acids are only approximate but do serve to indicate the relative strength of the acids. The next category are the organic acids that have an acid strength bordering on the inorganic acids and includes the sulfonic acids and the polynitro and polyhalogen organic acids. The common carboxylic acids, such as acetic and propionic acids, are generally considered "weak" acids and fall into the third group with pK_a's ranging from 3.5 to 5. The "very weak" acids such as the naphthols and phenols, with pK_a's near 10, fall into the lowest class indicated. Kolthoff and

63

Table 5.1. Dissociation Constants of Some Acids and Behavior in Titration to Phenolphthalein

Acid	$pK_a{}^a$	Percent titration to phenolphthalein end point
Hydrogen bromide	-9^b	
Perchloric	-8^b	
Sulfuric	0.4^c	100%
$(HSO_4{}^-)$	1.92^c	
Trichloroacetic	0.66^b	
Benzenesulfonic	0.70^d	
Trinitrophenol	0.71^b	
Dichloroacetic	1.25^b	100%
Chloroacetic	2.87^b	
Bromoacetic	2.90^b	
Formic	3.75^b	
Benzoic	4.18^b	
Acetic	4.76^b	100%
Valeric	4.86^b	
Trimethylacetic	5.05^b	
α-Naphthol	9.30^e	
Phenol	9.99^e	Only partial with indistinct
p-Cresol	10.26^e	shading of end point.
o-Cresol	10.28^e	
2,4,6-Trimethylphenol	10.88^e	

[a] Values at or near 25°C in water.
[b] From Albert and Serjeant (2).
[c] N. A. Lange, *Handbook of Chemistry*, McGraw-Hill, New York, 1967.
[d] R. C. Weast, *Handbook of Chemistry and Physics*, Chemical Rubber Co., Cleveland, Ohio, 1967.
[e] From Kortüm, Vogel, and Andrussow (3).

Stenger (4) provide a thorough review of the theory and procedures employed in the titration of acids, as well as other materials in their classic text. The principal features of the recommended methods are given in Table 5.2.

DETERMINATION OF TOTAL ACIDITY

Aqueous titration of acids is limited to the mineral acids and the organic acids that are soluble in water and have acid dissociation constants at least as low as $pK_a = 8$. Organic acids for which aqueous titration can be used include formic, acetic, propionic, benzenesulfonic, and toluenesulfonic acids.

Table 5.2. Principal Features of Methods for Determination of Acids

Method	Determination	Applicability	Limitations
Phenolphthalein indicator	Total acidity for acids with $pK_a < 8$	Inorganic and organic acids	Does not differentiate among acids
Aniline precipitation	Free H_2SO_4	Spent acids from petroleum processing	Method limited to H_2SO_4
Nonaqueous potassium hydroxide	Differential determination of mineral acids and carboxylic acids	Mineral and organic acid mixtures	Very weak acids give poor inflections
Tetrabutylammonium hydroxide	Differential determination of mineral acids, carboxylic acids, and phenols	Has widest range of all methods; applies to very weak acids	Titrant expensive and may decompose on standing if not refrigerated
Methylation-GLC	Individual acids	Wide range of mono- and polycarboxylic acids	Requires pretreatment with diazomethane
Colorimetric, pinacyanol	Low concentrations of long-chain acid salts in water	Higher molecular weight carboxylic acid salts	Variable molar absorptivity
Sodium iodide–Fischer reagent	Acid anhydrides	Generally useful with limited interference from other functional groups	Sterically hindered anhydrides give low results: Maleic anhydride reacts violently with pyridine

Standard aqueous sodium hydroxide is the usual titrant and phenolphthalein the indicator. Since phenolphthalein changes from colorless to pink in going from pH 8 to pH 10, it can be accurately used to indicate the end point for titration of mineral acids and carboxylic acids with a strong base, but very weak acids, such as the phenols, cannot be titrated in this way because their pH changes are very small in water and other hydroxyl-containing solvents. The simple aqueous titration system is often satisfactory, but isopropyl alcohol can also be used as solvent with the same results and, since many more organic acids are soluble in alcohol than in water, the recommended method for determination of the acid content of organic materials uses isopropyl alcohol as the solvent.

DETERMINATION OF THE ACID CONTENT
OF ORGANIC MATERIALS

Phenolphthalein Indicator Method

Reagents

Phenolphthalein indicator solution, 1% in 60% alcohol.
Sodium hydroxide solution, standard 0.1 and 0.5N, alcoholic.
Isopropyl alcohol, 99% grade.

Procedure

Add 25 ml of isopropyl alcohol, which has previously been neutralized to phenolphthalein, to a 250-ml glass-stoppered Erlenmeyer flask. Weigh a quantity of sample comprising less than 10 g into the flask. Weigh liquid materials from a Lunge weighing bottle; weigh solid materials directly into the flask. Determine the acid present by titration to the phenolphthalein end point with either 0.1 or 0.5N standard alcoholic sodium hydroxide solution, using the weaker base when the acid content is low. Keep the liquid sufficiently cool during titration to avoid fading of the end-point color.

Calculation

$$\text{Acid value, equiv/100 g} = \frac{(A)(N)}{10W}$$

where A = volume of base used in the titration, ml
$\quad\quad N$ = normality of the base
$\quad\quad W$ = weight of sample, g

DIFFERENTIAL DETERMINATION OF ACIDITY

A number of procedures are available for the resolution of acids of differing dissociation constants and for the determination of very weak acids. The most useful of these involve potentiometric titration in nonaqueous systems; much research is presently underway in this area.

However, for a specific analysis often called upon—the determination of free sulfuric acid in spent organic acids—there is available such a simple and useful method, developed many years ago (5), that it is included in this chapter as a recommended method. It depends upon the insolubility of aniline sulfate in chloroform and involves treating the acid sample with a warm solution of aniline in chloroform. The precipitated aniline sulfate, after being washed with chloroform, is dried, dissolved in water, and titrated with standard base to the phenolphthalein end point. Interference from other organic acids generally is small, because their aniline salts are soluble in chloroform. The alkyl sulfate monoesters, ethane-, propane-, and butane-sulfonic acids do not interfere. Methanesulfonic acid does interfere because its aniline salt is insoluble, but this is an unlikely contaminant in spent acids. The recommended Aniline Precipitation method is taken from a publication describing its application to the analysis of spent acids from petroleum processes (6).

DETERMINATION OF FREE SULFURIC ACID

ANILINE PRECIPITATION METHOD

Reagents

Aniline solution, 10 vol % in chloroform.
Sodium hydroxide solution, standard 0.5N, carbonate-free.
Phenolphthalein indicator solution, 1% alcoholic.

Procedure

Weigh approximately 1 g of the acid sample into a 125-ml Erlenmeyer flask. Chill the flask in an ice bath and add 0.2 ml of water from a pipet. Remove the flask from the ice bath and, with constant swirling, slowly add 50 ml of a boiling 10% solution of aniline in chloroform. Conduct this operation in an efficient hood because of the toxicity of the reagents. Break up any large lumps of aniline sulfate with a glass rod and allow the mixture to cool to room temperature.

Attach a glass funnel equipped with a fine fritted disk to a filter flask, transfer the reaction mixture to this funnel and filter off the liquid by application of a moderate vacuum. Wash the reaction flask with a 10- to 15-ml portion of chloroform and add the washings to the funnel. It is not necessary to remove all the precipitate from the flask, as it will be recovered later in the procedure. Triturate the precipitate in the funnel with the glass rod and draw the washings through the filter by continued application of vacuum. Continue washing with chloroform until the last washings are colorless, using a minimum of 40 ml. Then allow air to draw through the filter to evaporate the remaining chloroform.

Discard the filtrate and attach the filter to a clean 500-ml filter flask. Moisten and triturate the precipitate with 2 or 3 ml of acetone and apply vacuum until the precipitate is dry. (Acetone is used to remove the last traces of chloroform, which would cause spattering on addition of hot water.) The acetone is retained with the subsequent aqueous filtrate, as it may contain a small amount of dissolved aniline sulfate. Add 10–15 ml of hot water to the original reaction flask to dissolve any precipitate that may not have been washed out. Use this washing, plus an additional 100–150 ml of hot water, to dissolve the precipitate on the filter, drawing the washings into the flask by means of vacuum.

Titrate the contents of the filter flask with standard $0.5N$ sodium hydroxide solution to the phenolphthalein end point.

Calculation

Calculate the free sulfuric acid as follows:

$$\text{free sulfuric acid, wt \%} = \frac{(V)(N)(49.04)}{10W}$$

where V = volume of sodium hydroxide, ml
N = normality of the sodium hydroxide
W = weight of sample, g

Many mixtures of inorganic and organic acids or dibasic acids that provide only one inflection in water may give two or more sharp inflections in certain nonaqueous solvents. Practical procedures for conducting such nonaqueous titrations have been published by Harlow and Wyld (7, 8), Fritz (9), Streuli (10), van der Heijde and Dahmen (11, 12), Cundiff and Markunas (13), and Lykken, Porter, Ruliffson, and Tuemmler (14). The theoretical interpretation has been thoroughly discussed in publications by Kolthoff and Bruckenstein (15, 16), and excellent general reviews have been published in recent years (17, 18). Perhaps the most significant concept is that the solvent should itself have an extremely weakly acidic character so that it does not compete for the basic titrant. Often the solvent can be a weak base but it must have sufficient conductivity to allow electrode measurements to be made with the usual pH meters. It is possible with certain nonaqueous solvents to perform accurate titrations on materials of much lower acid (or basic) strength than is possible in water; for instance, phenols can be accurately titrated in pyridine. Certain nonaqueous solvents also allow much better resolution of acids of different strength than water does. A clear-cut illustration of the effect of nonaqueous media on the behavior of acids is taken from the work of Harlow and Wyld (7) and is shown in Figure 5.1. When sulfuric acid is titrated in water, a single inflection is obtained, both hydrogens behaving as strong acids. When alcohol is added to the titration solution, the strength of the second hydrogen is reduced relative to the first, and this makes

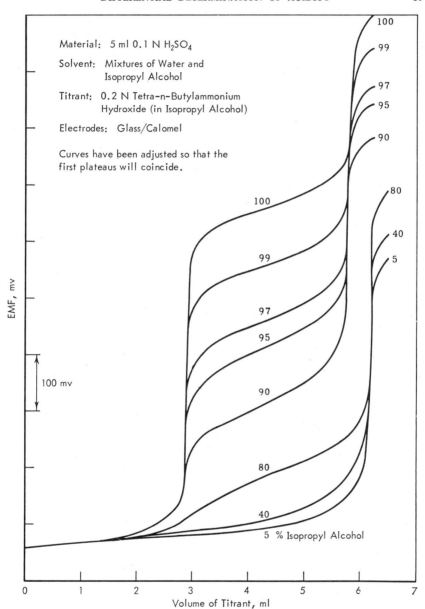

Material: 5 ml 0.1 N H_2SO_4

Solvent: Mixtures of Water and Isopropyl Alcohol

Titrant: 0.2 N Tetra-n-Butylammonium Hydroxide (in Isopropyl Alcohol)

Electrodes: Glass/Calomel

Curves have been adjusted so that the first plateaus will coincide.

100 mv

5 % Isopropyl Alcohol

Volume of Titrant, ml

EMF, mv

Figure 5.1. Titration of sulfuric acid in water-isopropyl alcohol mixtures. From Harlow and Wyld (7). Copyright 1958 by the American Chemical Society. Reprinted by permission of copyright owner.

it possible to obtain a separate titration of the two. It has been found that good resolution can be obtained at any isopropyl content above 90%.

A number of solvents can be employed to titrate weak acids in such a way as to distinguish among those of differing acid strengths. A commonly used method, ASTM D 664 (19), involves dissolving the sample in a mixture of toluene and isopropyl alcohol and conducting the titration potentiometrically with alcoholic potassium hydroxide, using a glass indicating electrode and

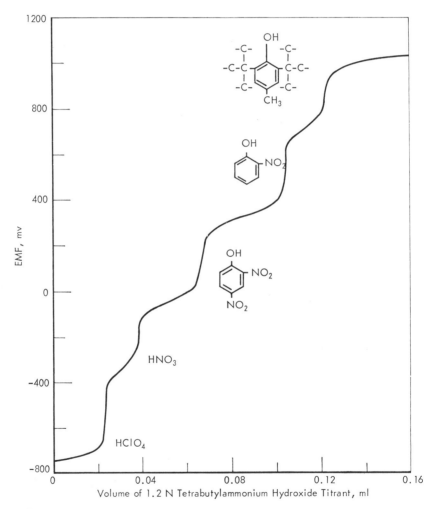

Figure 5.2. Titration of a mixture of acids using 3-methylsulfolane solvent. From Morman and Harlow (24). Copyright 1967 by the American Chemical Society. Reprinted by permission of the copyright owner.

calomel reference electrode. The titration curve is generally plotted manually or recorded automatically. The solvent system of ASTM D 664 allows a separation to be made between strong mineral acids and carboxylic acids, and with certain other solvents it is possible to cover even a larger range of acidities.

Two recommended methods are given in this chapter for the differential determination of weak acidities. One (the Nonaqueous Potassium Hydroxide method) employs the solvent system and titrant of ASTM D 664 and is to be used for the titration of carboxylic acids and their mixtures with mineral acids. The second method employs tetra-*n*-butylammonium hydroxide as the titrant and pyridine as solvent and is recommended for the titration of very weak acids such as the phenols. This method is based on the publication of Harlow, Noble, and Wyld (20) and permits a classification of acids into the general categories very weak, weak, and strong. The electrodes used in this method are the same as those in ASTM D 664 except that the calomel reference electrode is filled with $1M$ tetra-*n*-butylammonium chloride solution rather than KCl, to overcome the introduction of K^+ which would interfere with the glass electrode potential. The reduced scale titration cell is taken from the work of Deal and Wyld (21). Although the nonaqueous tetrabutylammonium hydroxide method is quite useful, this titrant is somewhat expensive both in initial cost of salt and in the time involved in conversion to the base. In addition, the titrant is not stable for long periods of time.

A number of other nonaqueous solvents have been used successfully for the titration of very weak acids. These include tetramethylguanidine (22), methyl isobutyl ketone (23), and, in particular, the sulfolanes. A publication by Morman and Harlow (24) shows that sulfolanes, 3-methylsulfolane, and 2,4-dimethylsulfolane provide a wide potential range for the differentiation of acids and bases. A good inflection point was found in the titration of the hindered, weakly acid phenol, 2,6-di-*tert*-butyl-4-methyl phenol, in admixture with a series of acids of varying strengths, as can be seen from Figure 5.2.

DETERMINATION OF STRONG AND WEAK ACIDITY

NON-AQUEOUS POTASSIUM HYDROXIDE METHOD

Apparatus

pH meter, with an accuracy of ± 0.005 V and operable on an input current of less than 5×10^{-12} A.

Glass electrode, pencil-type, 125–180 mm in length and 8–14 mm in diameter.

Calomel electrode, pencil-type with sleeve-type junction, 125–180 mm in length and 8–14 mm in diameter.

Buret, a 10-ml buret graduated in 0.05-ml divisions. The tip should extend 100–130 mm beyond the stopcock.

Titration beaker, 250-ml, tall-form electrolytic beaker.
Stirrer, magnetic, variable speed.
Titration stand.

Reagents

Titration solvent: add 500 ml of toluene and 5 ml of water to 495 ml of anhydrous isopropyl alcohol. Determine the titration blank.
Potassium hydroxide solution, standard alcoholic, 0.1*N* and 0.2*N*.

Procedure

Preparation of Electrodes. Before and after using, wipe the glass electrode thoroughly with a clean cloth or a soft absorbent tissue and rinse with water. Wipe the calomel reference electrode with a cloth or tissue, carefully remove the ground-glass sleeve, and thoroughly wipe both ground surfaces. Replace the sleeve loosely and allow a few drops of electrolyte to drain through to flush the ground-glass joint. Wet the ground surfaces thoroughly with electrolyte, set the sleeve firmly in place, rinse the electrode with water, and dry with a clean tissue.

Into a 250-ml titration beaker, introduce a weighed quantity of sample and add 100 ml of titration solvent. Prepare the electrodes as directed. Place the beaker on the titration stand and adjust its position so that the electrodes are about half immersed. Start the stirrer, and stir throughout the determination at a rate sufficient to produce vigorous agitation without spattering and without stirring air into the solution. Titrate potentiometrically with standard base, adding small increments through the end point.

Calculation

Prepare a titration curve by plotting volume of titrant against the corresponding meter readings.

Sample Gives One Titration Inflection. When there appears to be only one titration inflection for the sample, use the difference between the blank titration and the titration end point to calculate the volume of standard base equivalent to the acid present in the sample.

Sample Gives Two or More Titration Inflections. Use the difference between consecutive end points in the titration curve as the volume of standard base equivalent to each type of acidity.

Calculate the acidity as follows:

$$\text{acidity, equiv}/100\text{g} = \frac{(V)(N)}{10W}$$

where V = volume of standard base, ml, used in titrating each type of acidity
  N = normality of base used
  W = weight of sample, g

DETERMINATION OF VERY WEAK ACIDITY

TETRABUTYLAMMONIUM HYDROXIDE METHOD

Apparatus

Meter, pH, or Titrometer.

Glass electrode, pencil-type, 125–180 mm in length and 8–14 mm in diameter.

Calomel reference electrode, pencil-type, 125–180 mm in length and 8–14 mm in diameter with sleeve-type junction. The calomel reference electrode should be filled with $1M$ tetra-*n*-butylammonium chloride solution instead of the saturated potassium chloride solution.

Magnetic stirrer.

Buret, a 5-ml microburet calibrated in 0.01-ml increments.

Titration beaker and beaker cover, a special reduced-scale beaker marked at 20-ml volume and beaker cover are described in Figure 24.2.

Reagents

Pyridine, reagent grade.

Tetra-n-butylammonium hydroxide (TBAH), standard 0.2N alcoholic. The titrant should be stored under nitrogen in a refrigerator. All transfers should be carried out under an atmosphere of nitrogen.

Tetra-n-butylammonium chloride, 1.0M aqueous, polarographic grade. Available from Southwestern Analytical Chemicals, Austin 2, Texas.

Nitrogen, free of carbon dioxide, supplied at a pressure of about 6 psig.

Procedure

Sample Titration. Into a special reduced-scale titration beaker introduce directly or by aliquot a quantity of sample weighed to 0.1 mg and containing 0.15–0.20 meq of acid (e.g., phenolic hydroxyl).

Add pyridine to the sample to the 20-ml mark of the titration beaker.

Place the beaker under clean electrodes that have been wiped nearly dry with tissue. Start the magnetic stirrer and stir until the sample is dissolved. Continue stirring throughout the determination at a rate sufficient to produce vigorous agitation without spattering. Pass a slow stream of nitrogen into the vapor space of the beaker during the entire titration.

Fill the 5-ml microburet with 0.2N alcoholic TBAH. Place in position in the titration assembly. Record the initial buret and meter (cell potential) readings. Add carefully 0.01-ml portions of the TBAH and after a constant potential has been established, record the buret and meter readings. If little change in potential occurs, titrant may be added in larger portions of 0.02–0.05 ml (such that potential changes are no greater than 10 mV) until a break is approached, at which time addition of 0.01-ml increments should be resumed. Stop the titration about 0.3 ml after completion of the final break, making 0.05-ml additions after the break is passed.

Consider the cell potential constant if the meter reading changes less than 2 mV in 30 sec. Make the next addition of titrant without delay.

Blank Titration

Make a blank titration of the solvent(s) used for the sample, including any added as an aliquot.

Calculation

Use section from previous method.

DETERMINATION OF ACIDS THROUGH ULTRAVIOLET ABSORPTION SPECTROSCOPY

The ionization of acids or bases materially alters the electronic configuration in the vicinity of the active groups and consequently produces a change in the ultraviolet spectra, which has suggested the technique of spectrophotometric titration. A thorough review of the technique in its application to the titration of weak acids been given by Goddu and Hume (25), who were particularly concerned with the titration of substituted phenols in aqueous media. The strong absorption of the phenolate ions in the region of the near ultraviolet was used to follow the course of the titration in a modified Beckman Model B spectrophotometer. A typical titration curve of a phenol with sodium hydroxide will show a smoothly rising absorbance as phenol is converted to the more strongly absorbing phenolate ion. Subsequent to the end point, further addition of base makes no change in the absorbance. A simple plot provides an accurate determination of the base required for titration of the weak acid. Good results are obtained with weak acids in solutions as dilute as $10^{-3}M$ but errors begin to be large when dilutions approach $10^{-4}M$. Hummerlstedt and Hume (26) have also shown that, when photometric titrations are conducted in isopropyl alcohol with tetra-n-butylammonium hydroxide as the titrant, differentiation between substituted phenols can be obtained. To obtain clear-cut resolution, a change in the wave-length setting was made to coincide with the absorption maximum of the compound being titrated.

DETERMINATION OF ACIDS BY GAS CHROMATOGRAPHY

Although it is possible to perform gas chromatographic separations on the lower monocarboxylic acids directly, their polar nature tends to give rise to absorption on many column packings, leading to tailing and consequent poor repeatability of analysis. The dibasic acids are extremely difficult to chromatograph directly. A considerable effort has been expended in exploring column materials to obtain a system for the analysis of the volatile fatty acids, particularly in aqueous systems. The most satisfactory packing material on which investigations have been published is the Porapak synthetic polymer beads developed by Hollis (27). These beads have partition properties similar to liquid surfaces without the attendant problems of polarity, and consequently Hollis was able to obtain symmetrical curves for the low molecular weight monobasic acids, as well as other polar materials. More recently, Mahadevan and Stenroos (28) obtained excellent results for the separation of the C_1–C_5 monobasic acids in low concentrations in water by use of a commercial Porapak that they coated with small amounts of 85% H_3PO_4.

For the gas chromatographic analysis of the higher fatty acids and of dicarboxylic acids, direct analysis is generally not satisfactory and it is preferable to convert the acids into a more volatile derivative before analysis. Methylation with diazomethane has been used for this purpose by a considerable number of workers (29–31). Although other reagents have been used for preparation of methyl esters prior to chromatography, it is the opinion of the author as well as that of others who have reviewed the available procedures (32, 33) that diazomethane is to be preferred. This reagent possesses the advantages of having only a gaseous by-product, producing high yields of the desired product and providing a simple quantitative procedure for the recovery of the esters. Consequently the recommended method given in this section utilizes diazomethane as the reagent for the methylation–GLC analysis of organic acids. The methyl esters are particularly well separated on a capillary column coated with a polyphenyl ether–DC 710 Silicone mixture (1/5). With programmed temperatures up to 200°C, C_{15} carboxylic acid methyl esters are eluted in 60 min.

An alternative method of preparing methyl esters involves the pyrolysis of tetramethylammonium salts of the acids to yield trimethylamine and the methyl ester (34–37). The amine salts can be pyrolyzed in the injection port of the gas chromatographic unit. The repeatability is good and the method has been shown to be quite widely applicable. However, there are some limitations in that it does not apply to oxalic and malonic acids or to some hydroxy acids. It was pointed out by Bailey (36) that ethyl or butyl esters of acids can also be easily formed by decomposition of the corresponding tetraalkylammonium salts.

ANALYSIS OF CARBOXYLIC ACIDS

METHYLATION–GLC METHOD

Reagents

Nitrosomethylurea: prepare approximately 100 g in accordance with *Organic Syntheses*, A. H. Blatt, Ed., Coll. Vol. II, Wiley, New York, 1943, p. 461, and store in a refrigerator.

Potassium hydroxide, 40% aqueous.

Preparation of Diazomethane

CAUTION! Conduct the preparation and use of diazomethane in a well-ventilated hood and wear rubber gloves. Diazomethane is a highly toxic yellow gas. The undiluted compound and concentrated solutions can explode violently, expecially if impurities are present or in contact with rough surfaces. Dilute solutions, as prepared below, are safe in that respect. However, the gas and solutions can be absorbed through the skin, particularly by the mucous membranes; therefore use adequate ventilation and protect the skin.

For the preparation of 40 meq (approx. 1.7 g) of diazomethane, place 56 ml of ethyl ether and 18 ml of 40% KOH in a 250-ml Erlenmeyer flask. Cool the flask to ice temperature. Keep the flask cool and add in small portions with vigorous swirling 5.6 g of powdered nitrosomethylurea as rapidly as the solid dissolves (2–5 min). After addition is completed, decant the yellow ether layer into an ice-cold 50-ml graduated cylinder containing 5 ml of KOH pellets. The cylinder must be kept submerged in an ice bath to prevent evaporation of the reagent. This quantity of reagent is sufficient for 3–10 samples as described below.

Methylation

Weigh 0.200–0.500 g of the carboxylic acid sample into a 6-dram screw-cap vial. Dissolve the sample with gentle heating if necessary in 2–3 ml of ether. Cool the vial to ice temperature and add the diazomethane solution in small increments with swirling. Continue the addition of reagent until the evolution of gas ceases and the solution remains yellow. Evaporate the mixture to approximately 2 ml, with the aid of a nitrogen stream.

GLC Separation

The choice of column and operating conditions depends on the nature of the sample. If the sample contains no materials sufficiently volatile to be hidden by the ether peak and no nonvolatile materials that will remain on the column, the component percentages can be obtained directly from the GLC curve. If this is not the case, a weighed amount of a suitable pure material (marker) can be added to the ether solution of the methylated weighed sample. The added compound must be chosen to emerge in a peak separated from the sample peaks. The technique must be calibrated with known mixtures of pure compounds to ascertain emergence times and weight–area factors.

Preparation of GLC Column

Capillary tubing, for preparing GC columns, 0.061–0.064 in. o.d. × 0.009–0.011 in. i.d., 347 seamless, 15 micro finish inside. Handy and Harman Tube Co., Inc., Norristown, Pennsylvania.

Silicone DC 710, available from Dow Corning Corp., Midland, Michigan. Heat the material under vacuum to top off about 30% of the sample. Use the 70% bottoms cut for coating GC columns.

Polyphenyl ether, 6P5E, Monsanto Chemical Co.

Clean a 150-ft length of the capillary column and coat with a solution containing 0.20 g of polyphenyl ether and 1.0 g of DC 710 Silicone in 9 g of a 50:50 (v/v) mixture of acetone and diethyl ether. Purge the column with carrier gas at room temperature and condition it by purging at 200°C for 3 hr.

GC Apparatus Preparation

Adjust the column temperature to 150 C. Adjust the carrier gas pressure at the column inlet to give an average linear gas velocity through the columns of 15 cm/sec. To measure the linear gas velocity, inject a sample of natural gas into the sample vaporizer and note the time required for the methane to reach the detector. Divide the length of the column in centimeters by the time required for the methane to pass through the column to obtain the average linear velocity.

Adjust the auxiliary helium flow to the detector to give the maximum detector response by repeatedly introducing a constant amount of sample into the sample vaporizer while varying the auxiliary gas flows.

Set the temperature program to give a column temperature rise from 150°C to 200°C in 1 hr.

Both the hydrogen and helium flow rates affect detector response. These gas flows are limited by the diameter of the burner tip, which is usually 0.01–0.03 in. i.d. Maximum response is obtained at high hydrogen flow rates, but too high a rate causes excessive detector noise. Therefore, it is best to set the hydrogen flow at some relatively high rate (35–50 ml/min) and then adjust the auxiliary helium flow to give the maximum response. The ratio of helium-to-hydrogen flow rate will then approximate 1.75.

Most commercial gas chromatographs are not designed for introducing auxiliary helium. This can be done through a tube connected to the hydrogen inlet to the detector.

GC Analysis Procedure

Inject a sample into the vaporizer of such a size that it does not seriously overload the column for separating the major components but is adequate for detecting components present in concentrations as low as 0.1%. Set the temperature program and attenuate the detector signal to give suitable chromatographic peaks for measurement.

Measure the peak areas on the chromatogram and correct these for detector attenuation. Do not include the early solvent peak.

Calculation

To calculate the weight percent of each component, divide the value obtained for that component by the sum of the values for all components shown in the chromatogram and multiply by 100.

DETERMINATION OF ACIDS BY ION EXCHANGE

Ion exchange can be easily employed to separate organic acids from inorganic cations and nonionics with the technique described in Chapter 21. This allows, in many cases, a simplification in analysis since the carboxylic acids can be displaced from the resin by elution with reagents that will not interfere in the subsequent analysis. Ion-exchange resins can also be used in the chromatographic process known as "ion exclusion." When aqueous

Table 5.3.   Emergence Data for Acids Relative to Acetic Acid by Ion Exclusion–Partition Chromatography[a]

Acid	Ratio acid/acetic	Acid	Ratio acid/acetic
Sulfuric	0.57	Adipic	1.0
Toluenesulfonic	0.57	Fumaric	1.0
Sulfurous	0.58	Glutaric	1.0
5-Sulfosalicylic	0.58	Chloroacetic	1.0
Sulfamic	0.58	Acetic	1.00
Hydrochloric	0.59	Levulinic	1.0
Acetylenedicarboxylic	0.59	Nadic	1.0
Trichloroacetic	0.60	L-Pyroglutamic	1.13
Mucic	0.60	Methylene-bismercaptoacetic	1.15
L-Cysteic	0.61	Propionic	1.17
Maleic	0.61–0.71	Tetrahydrophthallic	1.21
Oxalic	0.62	Acrylic	1.23
Phosphoric	0.63	Carbonic	1.26
Citric	0.64	Isobutyric	1.32
Nitroform	0.67	Butyric	1.45
Itaconic	0.70	Mandelic	1.49
Pyruvic	0.71	Pivalic	1.49
Malonic	0.72	α-Hydroxybutyric	1.57
α-Ketobutyric	0.74	Methacrylic	1.63
Glyceric	0.75	Isovaleric	1.66
Boric	0.75–0.79	Tertinary butylacetic	1.67
α-Ketovaleric	0.79	Crotonic	1.95
Cyanuric	0.80	Valeric	2.09
Dichloroacetic	0.81	Furoic	2.09
Mercaptosuccinic	0.82	Cyclohexanecarboxylic	3.26
Succinic	0.82	2,4-Dihydroxybenzoic	3.80
Glycolic	0.82	p-Hydroxybenzoic	4.46
Lactic	0.84	Hydrocinnamic	5.40
Formic	0.91	Benzohydroxamic	5.95

[a] From Harlow and Morman (38). Copyright 1964 by the American Chemical Society. Reprinted by permission of the copyright owner.

solutions containing mixtures of inorganic and organic acids are passed through such an ion-exclusion column, separations take place according to the properties of the acid. A thorough study of this type of separation was published by Harlow and Morman (38), from whose work the data in Table 5.3 are taken. The ratio of emergence times are listed relative to that of acetic acid and it can be seen from these data that the highly ionized strong acids come through quickly. The mineral acids and sulfonic acids come through first and are not individually separated. The dibasic, oxygenated, and chlorinated acids generally emerge earlier than the corresponding simple or monocarboxylic acids of the same carbon numbers. Harlow and Morman (38) published a description of a simple and ingenious apparatus for this analysis that involves automatic titration and recording of data.

DETERMINATION OF LOW CONCENTRATIONS OF THE HIGHER FATTY ACIDS

The analyst may be called upon for the determination of ppm concentrations of carboxylic acid salts (soaps) in aqueous effluents. Some years ago Mukerjee (39) suggested the use of pinacyanol, a water-soluble cationic dye, for this purpose. In this method, the dye and the carboxylic acid anion react at pH 9.0 to form a colored complex that can be extracted into an organic solvent. The color of the organic phase (bromobenzene), measured in a spectrophotometer, is proportional to the content of the carboxylic acid in the sample. The recommended method is taken from this publication and its application to some carboxylate acid salts is shown in Table 5.4. The lower molecular weight acids showed no response but sodium octanoate showed a low response that varied greatly with the concentration being examined. Calibration curves for sodium laurate leveled off at higher concentrations, making it advisable to conduct the analysis on solutions of the acids at low concentrations where the calibration curve is more nearly linear. The high level of molar absorptivity for the higher members of the homologous series

Table 5.4. Response of Carboxylic Acid Salts in the Colorimetric Pinacyanol Method

Sodium carboxylate	Molar absorptivity, liters/mole-cm
Butyrate	0
Hexanoate	0
Octanoate	$2.0–4.6 \times 10^3$
Decanoate	$1.7–2.2 \times 10^4$
Laurate	$3.5–5.0 \times 10^4$

allows the determination of the corresponding soaps at ppm levels, but the method is not applicable to acids containing less than eight carbon atoms.

DETERMINATION OF LOW CONCENTRATIONS OF FATTY ACIDS

COLORIMETRIC PINACYANOL METHOD

Apparatus

Spectrophotometer: any spectrophotometer or photoelectric colorimeter equipped with a filter transmitting light at 6200 Å may be used.

Reagents

Bromobenzene, CP.

Borate buffer solution: place 6.184 g of boric acid and the equivalent of 42.60 ml of 1.000N hydroxide in a graduated cylinder. Dissolve and dilute to 200 ml with water.

Pinacyanol solution: dissolve 40 ml of pinacyanol chloride in 1 liter of distilled water.

Standardization

Prepare standards using a stock solution containing a known amount of the particular material to be measured. The standards should contain 0.1–0.5 μmoles of fatty acid salt. Continue as directed below.

Obtain a corrected absorbance for each standard. Plot the correct absorbances against quantity of material in each standard, as μg.

Procedure

Place a sample containing 0.1–0.5 μmoles of fatty acid salt in a 125-ml separatory funnel. Add water to bring the total volume to 50 ml. Add 1 ml of 1N sulfuric acid and extract with 10 ml of bromobenzene. Allow the phases to separate and drain the extract into a 60-ml separatory funnel containing 10 ml of pinacyanol solution and 5 ml of borate buffer solution. Mix the contents of the second funnel and allow it to stand 10 min for phase separation. Meanwhile, add a second 10-ml portion of bromobenzene to the first separatory funnel, mix, and allow to settle. Swirl the second funnel to homogenize the color in the lower phase and drain the lower phase into a 25-ml volumetric flask. Drain the lower layer from the first funnel into the second funnel and repeat the extraction procedure in the second funnel. Drain the lower layer into the volumetric flask. Add bromobenzene to the mark in the flask and mix the contents.

Make two blank determinations on the reagents by repeating the entire procedure but omitting the sample.

Within an hour measure the absorbance at 6200 Å in a 1-cm cell, relative to distilled water.

Calculation

Correct the absorbance of the sample solution by subtracting the average of the reagent blanks.

Obtain the quantity of fatty acid salt present from the calibration curve. Calculate the concentration of the fatty acid salt by means of the following expression:

$$\text{fatty acid salt, ppm} = \frac{F}{S}$$

where F = weight of fatty acid salt obtained from calibration curve, μg, and S = volume of sample taken, ml.

DETERMINATION OF ACID ANHYDRIDES

The most useful method available for the determination of the anhydrides of organic acids involves the sodium iodide catalyzed hydration of the anhydride followed by determination of the water consumed by titration with Fischer reagent. This method, published by Smith, Bryant, and Mitchell (40), has been found quite widely applicable. There is no interference from organic acids, esters, ketones, or low concentrations of most acidic organic compounds (40). The recommended method is taken from that of Smith, Bryant, and Mitchell with few changes because the original procedure has been found satisfactory with a large variety of samples. It applies well both to low molecular weight materials and to those samples containing resins and polymers and has become one of the standard, useful methods of the laboratory. Several limitations of the method must be considered, however. Some anhydrides, because of steric hindrance, may be hydrolyzed with difficulty and yield low results; camphoric anhydride gives only about 1% reaction. Maleic anhydride interferes by reacting violently with the pyridine reagent and must not be present in a sample.

DETERMINATION OF ACID ANHYDRIDE

SODIUM IODIDE–FISCHER REAGENT METHOD

Apparatus

Atmospheric oven, explosion-proof, capable of being maintained at $60 \pm 1°C$. *Buret assembly*, an all-glass buret system.

Reagents

Ethylene glycol–pyridine mixture.
Fischer reagent.
Pyridine–sodium iodide solution: dissolve 100 g of CP sodium iodide in sufficient CP pyridine to make 1 liter of solution. Pipet 25 ml of this solution into a 100-ml

volumetric flask containing 10 ml of methanol that has been brought to the orange-red end-point color with Fischer reagent. Calculate the additional volume of water to be added to each liter of solution by means of the expression

$$\text{water to be added, ml} = 9 - \frac{(V)(F)}{25}$$

where V = volume of Fischer reagent, ml, required to titrate 25 ml of solution, and F = equivalency factor for Fischer reagent, mg of water per ml of reagent.

Add the calculated amount of water to each liter of pyridine–sodium iodide solution prepared. The solution darkens on standing, but the extent of discoloration can be decreased by storing the preparation under an atmosphere of nitrogen.

Procedure

Clean and dry two 250-ml glass-stoppered volumetric flasks and draw laboratory air through them at a brisk rate until equilibrium has been reached.

By means of a dry pipet introduce 25 ml of pyridine–sodium iodide solution into each of the flasks. To one flask add an amount of sample to contain not more than 9 mmoles of anhydride. Separate the stoppers from the ground joints of the flasks with a small strip of paper and heat the flasks at 60 ± 1°C for 90 min. At the end of this time, remove the reaction flasks from the oven and allow them to cool spontaneously to room temperature.

Add 20 ml of glycol–pyridine mixture and titrate the contents of each flask to the same end-point color with Fischer reagent.

Determine the water content of the sample.

Calculation

Calculate the anhydride content of the sample by means of the expression

$$\text{anhydride, moles/100 g} = \frac{(B - S)(F)}{(W_1)(180.2)} + \frac{(C)(F)}{(W_2)(180.2)}$$

where B = volume of Fischer reagent, ml, required to titrate blank on the reagents
S = volume of Fischer reagent, ml, required to titrate the hydrolyzed sample mixture
C = volume of Fischer reagent, ml, required to titrate free water in the sample
F = equivalency factor for Fischer reagent, mg of water per ml of reagent,
W_1 = weight of sample, g, taken for hydrolysis
W_2 = weight of sample, g, taken for determination of free water

REFERENCES

1. S. Veibel, in *Treatise on Analytical Chemistry*, Part II, Vol. 13, I. M. Kolthoff and P. J. Elving, Eds., Interscience, New York, 1966, pp. 223–299.
2. A. Albert and E. P. Serjeant, *Ionization Constants of Acids and Bases*, Methuen and Co., London, 1962.

3. G. Kortüm, W. Vogel, and K. Andrussow, *Dissociation Constants of Organic Acids in Aqueous Solution*, Butterworths, London, 1961.
4. I. M. Kolthoff and V. A. Stenger, *Volumetric Analysis*, Vol. II, Interscience, New York, 1947, pp. 49–155.
5. F. S. Bacon, *Ind. Eng. Chem.*, *Anal. Ed.*, **1**, 89 (1929).
6. F. T. Weiss, J. L. Jungnickel, E. D. Peters, and F. W. Heath, *Anal. Chem.*, **25**, 277 (1953).
7. G. A. Harlow and G. E. A. Wyld, *ibid.*, **30**, 69 (1958).
8. G. A. Harlow and G. E. A. Wyld, *ibid.*, **34**, 172 (1962).
9. J. S. Fritz, *ibid.*, **24**, 306, 674 (1952).
10. C. A. Streuli, *ibid.*, **28**, 130 (1956).
11. H. B. van der Heijde and E. A. M. F. Dahmen, *Anal. Chim. Acta*, **16**, 378 (1957).
12. H. B. van der Heijde, *ibid.*, **17**, 512 (1957).
13. R. H. Cundiff and P. C. Markunas, *Anal. Chem.*, **28**, 792 (1956).
14. L. Lykken, P. Porter, H. D. Ruliffson, and F. D. Tuemmler, *Ind. Eng. Chem.*, *Anal. Ed.*, **16**, 219 (1944).
15. I. M. Kolthoff and S. Bruckenstein, *J. Am. Chem. Soc.*, **78**, 1 (1956).
16. S. Bruckenstein and A. Saito, *ibid.*, **87**, 698 (1965).
17. I. Gyenes, *Titration in Non-Aqueous Media*, Van Nostrand, Princeton, N.J., 1967.
18. W. Huber, *Titrations in Nonaqueous Solvents*, Academic Press, New York, 1967.
19. American Society for Testing and Materials, *Standards*, Part 17, 1969.
20. G. A. Harlow, C. M. Noble, and G. E. A. Wyld, *Anal. Chem.*, **28**, 787 (1956).
21. V. Z. Deal and G. E. A. Wyld, *ibid.*, **27**, 47 (1955).
22. J. A. Caruso, G. G. Jones, and A. I. Popov, *Anal. Chim. Acta*, **40**, 49 (1968).
23. D. B. Bruss and G. E. A. Wyld, *Anal. Chem.*, **29**, 232 (1957).
24. D. H. Morman and G. A. Harlow, *ibid.*, **39**, 1869 (1967).
25. R. F. Goddu and D. N. Hume, *ibid.*, **26**, 1679, 1740 (1954).
26. L. E. I. Hummelstedt and D. N. Hume, *ibid.*, **32**, 1792 (1960).
27. O. L. Hollis, *ibid.*, **38**, 309 (1966).
28. V. Mahadevan and L. Stenroos, *ibid.*, **39**, 1652 (1967).
29. A. T. James and A. J. P. Martin, *Biochem. J.*, **63**, 144 (1956).
30. H. Schlenk and J. L. Gellerman, *Anal. Chem.*, **32**, 1412 (1960).
31. M. G. Horning, K. L. Knox, C. E. Dalgliesh, and E. C. Horning, *Anal. Biochem.*, **17**, 244 (1966).
32. P. G. Simmonds, B. C. Pettitt, and A. Zlatkis, *Anal. Chem.*, **39**, 163 (1967).
33. M. L. Vorbeck, L. R. Mattick, F. A. Lee, and C. S. Pederson, *ibid.*, **33**, 1512 (1961).
34. E. W. Robb and J. J. Westbrook III, *ibid.*, **35**, 1644 (1963).
35. D. T. Downing, *ibid.*, **39**, 218 (1967).
36. J. J. Bailey, *ibid.*, **39**, 1485 (1967).
37. D. T. Downing and R. S. Greene, *ibid.*, **40**, 827 (1968).
38. G. A. Harlow and D. H. Morman, *ibid.*, **36**, 2438 (1964).
39. P. Mukerjee, *ibid.*, **28**, 870 (1956).
40. D. M. Smith, W. M. D. Bryant, and J. Mitchell, Jr., *J. Am. Chem. Soc.*, **63**, 1700 (1941).

DETERMINATION OF CARBONYL COMPOUNDS

The carbonyl compounds include the aldehydes $R{-}\overset{\overset{O}{\|}}{C}{-}H$ and the ketones $R{-}\overset{\overset{O}{\|}}{C}{-}R$ whose reactions are quite similar with many analytical reagents. Since the acetals $RCH(OR)_2$ are immediately derived from aldehydes, their determination is also included in this chapter. The chemistry of the carbonyl compounds has been intensively investigated for many years and excellent reviews (1, 2) have been written covering the basic principles of the methods used for the analysis of these materials. An outline of the principal features of the methods discussed for the determination of the carbonyl compounds is given in Table 6.1, from which it can be seen that methods are available for the determination of the carbonyl group for assay and for trace analysis and for determination of aldehydes and acetals. Recommended methods are given for most of these determinations.

The methods in most common use for the determination of the carbonyl group involve carbonyl addition reactions, of which the most widely applied procedures are based on the reaction with hydroxylamine hydrochloride:

$$R{-}\overset{}{\underset{|}{C}}{=}O + H_2NOH{\cdot}HCl \rightleftharpoons R\overset{}{\underset{|}{C}}{=}NOH + HCl + H_2O$$

This reaction produces both HCl and H_2O and the determination of the carbonyl group can be followed by measurement of either product. The hydroxylamine hydrochloride method has been applied in several forms for some years and a thorough review of the early procedures has been made by Bryant and Smith (3), who found them generally of limited usefulness. They point out that the basic weakness of the reaction is that it does not go to quantitative conversion but they found that it could be forced essentially to completion by adding an excess of the weak base pyridine and conducting the reaction in an aqueous–alcoholic solvent. Their method received considerable use for a few years but does have a disadvantage in that pyridine exerts a buffering action that makes the end point somewhat difficult to discern.

Table 6.1. Principal Features of Methods for Determination of Carbonyl Compounds

Method	Determination	Applicability	Limitations
Aqueous hydroxylamine	Carbonyl group	Lower molecular weight carbonyl compounds	Conversion not always quantitative
Fischer reagent	Carbonyl group	Generally applicable for assay purposes	Requires Fischer reagents
Dinitrophenyl hydrazine, colorimetric	Traces of carbonyl compounds	Range: 20 ppm and above	Not suited for assay
Sodium bisulfite	Aldehydes	Lower aliphatic aldehydes	Acetone and methyl ketones react partially and give indistinct end points
Argentimetric	Aldehydes	Aliphatic and aromatic aldehydes	High results found with acrolein
Methyl-benzothiazolone hydrazone	Traces of aliphatic aldehydes	Range: ppm and lower	Only aliphatic aldehydes determined
Chromotropic acid	Traces of formaldehyde	Range: ppm and lower; specific for formaldehyde	Not suited for assay
Ultraviolet absorption	Carbonyl group	Conjugated compounds	Needs calibration
Infrared absorption	Carbonyl group	General, particularly useful for polymers	Needs calibration
Hydrolysis	Acetals plus carbonyl	Aliphatic acetals	Variable reactivity requires exploration for new materials

Table 6.2. Extent of Recovery (%) of Aldehydes and Ketones in the Hydroxylamine Hydrochloride Methods

Compounds	Aqueous hydroxylamine	Fischer–carbonyl
Formaldehyde	99.5, 99.6, 99.7, 100.1	
Acetaldehyde	99.0	99.7, 99.8
Furfuraldehyde	99.4	99.3
Glyceraldehyde	96.3	100
β-Methoxypropionaldehyde		99.6, 99.8
Propionaldehyde	98.8	
β-Ethoxypropionaldehyde	99.6, 99.7	
Benzaldehyde	100.3	100.0
Acetone	98.7	99.6
Methyl ethyl ketone	98.2	
Acetophenone		99.4, 99.7
Benzophenone		99.0, 99.1
Cyclohexanone	98.7	99.6, 99.8
Cyclopentanone	98.2	98.6
Isophorone		99.3, 100.0
4-Methyl-2-hexanone		100.1

Because of the exceptional flexibility of the hydroxylamine hydrochloride method, a number of successful modifications have been devised for application to particular problems. In this chapter two hydroxylamine methods are recommended. One, the Aqueous Hydroxylamine method, is a simply applied acidimetric technique for water-soluble carbonyl compounds. The apparatus and reagents are easily obtained but the method is limited in that the conversion is not completely quantitative. For instance, acetone reacts to 98.7% and methyl ethyl ketone to 98.2%. Under identical conditions, these analyses are repeatable and the method is quite useful. The other recommended hydroxylamine method involves determination of the water liberated from the reaction by the Fischer titration technique. It was developed by Mitchell, Smith, and Bryant (4) and, because of the use of pyridine to displace the equilibrium, the results are quantitative, as can be seen from the data in Table 6.2. This method is recommended for general use and has displaced, to a considerable extent, the earlier acidimetric technique (3).

Information on the extent of interference of other functional groups in the hydroxylamine methods is shown in Table 6.3. Some *acetals* are easily hydrolyzed to the corresponding aldhydes, and, as described later, a method for the analysis of acetals is based on this reaction. In the Fischer method, any

Table 6.3. Reaction of Other Functional Groups in the Hydroxylamine Hydrochloride Methods

Compound	Aqueous hydroxylamine	Fischer–carbonyl
Acetals		
Diethoxymethane	<0.1%	<0.1%
1,1-Dimethoxyethane	100%	0.7, 0.7%
1,1-Diethoxyethane	100%	1.5%
Acids		
Formic	3%	12.6, 13.1%
Acetic	5%	0.5, 0.6%
Fumaric		5.1, 5.4%
Adipic		0.9%
Benzoic		<0.3, <0.3%
Esters		
Ethyl acetate	} No Reaction	0.2, 0.3%
Methyl benzoate	}	<0.1%
Epoxides		
Ethylene oxide	} { Interference by	3%
Propylene oxide	} { consuming HCl	4%
Glycidyl phenyl ether	} 46%	49%
Peroxides		
tert-Butyl hydroperoxide	Interferes	160, 165%
2,2-Bis(*tert*-butylperoxy)butane		39, 45%
Di-*tert*-butyl peroxide		<1%

hydrolysis stoichiometrically consumes the water that would have been produced on oximation and, subsequently, acetals do not respond. The Fischer method can be used for determination of aldehydes in acetals and the low values observed may represent aldehyde impurities. *Organic acids* generally interfere in the aqueous method by buffering the end point, but in the Fischer method there is generally no interference from acids except when destructive side reactions occur as in the dehydration of formic acid. The simple *esters* do not present an interference in either method. *Epoxides* interfere severely in the aqueous method by consuming HCl and, of course, this leads to low results in the analysis of mixtures of carbonyl compounds and epoxides. Reactive *peroxides* also interfere in both methods.

DETERMINATION OF WATER-SOLUBLE CARBONYL COMPOUNDS

AQUEOUS HYDROXYLAMINE METHOD

Apparatus

Color comparison tubes, Nessler-type, matched, 50-ml, low-form.

Color comparator: a rack, which will permit visual comparison of diffused light after passage through the color comparison tubes in the direction of their longitudinal axes.

Glass ampules, thin-walled.

Reagents

Bromophenol blue indicator solution, 0.1 % in 30 % denatured alcohol.

Hydroxylamine reagent, 2.5 %, aqueous. Dissolve 25 g of CP hydroxylamine hydrochloride in 1 liter of distilled water.

Methyl orange–Xylene cyanole indicator solution: dissolve 0.1 g of methyl orange and 0.14 g of xylene cyanole FF in 500 ml of 50 % ethyl alcohol.

Sodium hydroxide solution, standard 0.5N, carbonate-free.

Procedure

To 150 ml of hydroxylamine hydrochloride reagent, add 1.0 ml of methyl orange–xylene cyanole indicator solution and titrate with 0.5N sodium hydroxide solution to the steel grey end-point color. View the color by transmitted light, using an artificial daylight source if strong diffused natural daylight is not available. Place 100 ml of the neutralized solution in a 250-ml glass-stoppered bottle and retain the remaining 50 ml for use as a color standard.

To the 100 ml of neutralized solution, add a quantity of sample corresponding to approximately 0.013 mole of carbonyl radical. If the volatility of the sample is high or the carbonyl content is high, weigh the required amount in a glass ampule; for more dilute solutions and for less volatile samples, weigh the sample from a Lunge weighing bottle or measure volumetrically, reducing the amount if lower accuracy is satisfactory or if the volume to be added is excessively large.

To fill the ampule, warm the bulb gently in a small flame and insert the open capillary beneath the surface of the sample. When the required amount has been drawn in, remove the capillary from the sample and seal by placing momentarily in a flame. Use of a 5-ml graduated cylinder as a sample container during this operation is helpful in estimating the amount of sample drawn into the bulb.

Add a number of clean 5-mm glass beads if the sample was weighed in an ampule; moisten the stopper of the bottle to effect a seal, and shake the bottle until the contents are thoroughly mixed (or until the bulb and stem of the ampule are completely broken up). Titrate immediately with standard 0.5N sodium hydroxide solution to a light pink color slightly short of the end point. If the sample contains water-insoluble components, again shake and titrate; repeat until the indicator color no longer exhibits rapid fading. Filter the entire mixture through a water-wetted rapid filter paper to remove glass beads and chips and any water-insoluble material that may be producing a turbidity.

If formaldehyde is present, heat the mixture for about 15 min at approximately 40°C, then cool to room temperature and titrate as described.

Prepare the color standard by diluting the retained 50 ml of neutralized hydroxylamine hydrochloride solution with a volume of distilled water equal to approximately one-half the sum of the volume of sodium hydroxide solution and sample added.

Proceed with the titration, adding the sodium hydroxide solution dropwise to the filtered mixture and mixing well after each one-drop addition. Continue the titration until the color of the mixture matches that of the blank when viewed by transmitted light from a natural or artificial daylight source.

The accuracy of the determination can be improved by making the final endpoint color comparison in 50-ml Nessler tubes by viewing in the direction of their longitudinal axes and, if strong diffused daylight is available, by substituting 0.2 ml of bromophenol blue indicator for the methyl orange–xylene cyanole and titrating until a greenish-blue color slightly short of the end point is reached.

To make certain that the reaction has reached equilibrium, allow the mixture to stand several minutes.

To obtain a correction for strong acids present in the original sample, weigh or measure a 10-ml sample into 100 ml of distilled water and titrate with standard 0.5N sodium hydroxide solution to the methyl orange–xylene cyanole end point.

Calculation

$$\text{Carbonyl value, equiv/100 g} = \frac{(V - A)(N)}{(10)(W)}$$

where V = total volume of sodium hydroxide solution, ml, used to titrate liberated acid

A = volume of sodium hydroxide solution, ml, used to titrate strong acids originally present

N = normality of the sodium hydroxide solution

W = weight of sample, g

DETERMINATION OF CARBONYL

Fischer Reagent Method

Apparatus

Atmospheric oven, explosion-proof, capable of being maintained at 60 ± 1°C.

Reagents

Hydroxylamine hydrochloride reagent, 0.5N, in methanol. Prepare by dissolving 35 g of CP anhydrous hydroxylamine hydrochloride in 1 liter of CP absolute methanol.

Sulfur dioxide and pyridine in methanol (See Chapter 23).

Fischer reagent (See Chapter 23).

Procedure

Pipet 50 ml of hydroxylamine hydrochloride reagent and 10 ml of pyridine into a clean, dry 250-ml glass-stoppered volumetric flask. Weigh or pipet into the flask a quantity of sample containing not more than 0.012 mole of carbonyl plus water. If desired, the sample may be dissolved in pyridine or other inert solvent and an aliquot of the solution taken for analysis. Put a small strip of paper under the stopper and place the flask in an oven at $60 \pm 1°C$ for 2 hr or, in the case of more slowly reacting materials, for a longer time to produce complete reaction. To ascertain whether sufficient reaction time has been allowed, react two samples of the same size for different lengths of time, say, 3 and 4 hr; checking results indicate maximum or complete reaction.

At the end of the heating period, remove the flask from the oven and allow to cool to room temperature spontaneously. Then add from a pipet 50 ml of the sulfur dioxide and pyridine in methanol solution and allow to stand at room temperature for 10 min to 1 hr. Titrate the reaction mixture with Fischer reagent to the orange-red end point.

Make a blank determination, omitting sample, to determine the combined water and carbonyl content of the reagents. Titrate the blank with Fischer reagent to the same end-point color as the sample reaction mixture.

Determine the initial free water in the sample or, if the sample was diluted with pyridine or other solvent and an aliquot was used, in the corresponding solution by titration with Fischer reagent.

Calculation

$$\text{Carbonyl Value, equiv/100 g} = \frac{(S - B)(F)}{(W_1)(10)(18.02)} - \frac{(C)(F)}{(W_2)(10)(18.02)}$$

where S = volume of Fischer reagent required for sample, ml

B = volume of Fischer reagent required for reagent blank, ml

C = volume of Fischer reagent required for free water in sample, ml

F = standardization factor for Fischer reagent, in mg of water equivalent to 1 ml of reagent.

W_1 = weight of sample reacted, g

W_2 = weight of sample taken for free water determination, g

When duplicate aliquots of a solution of the sample are taken for reaction and free water determination, $W_1 = W_2 = W$ and the expression becomes

$$\text{carbonyl value, equiv/100 g} = \frac{(S - B - C)(F)}{(W)(10)(18.02)}$$

DETERMINATION OF TRACE CONCENTRATIONS OF CARBONYL COMPOUNDS

A practical and sensitive method for the accurate determination of traces of aldehydes or ketones involves the condensation of the carbonyl group with

Table 6.4. Absorptivities Obtained for Pure Carbonyl Compounds in the Dinitrophenylhydrazine-Colorimetric Method

Compound	Molar absorptivity at 4800 Å, liters/mole-cm
Decanal	9,800
Dodecanal	9,500
2-Undecanone	10,400
2-Tridecanone	9,900

2,4-dinitrophenylhydrazine followed by addition of alcoholic KOH to the reaction mixture to form the deeply red quinoidal derivative of the hydrazone. A number of variations of the basic method have been published, including a particularly useful one by Jordan and Veatch (5), who employ a mixed hydrocarbon–alcohol solvent to permit application to organic materials of higher molecular weight. With such carbonyl compounds as butanone-2, cyclohexanone, acetophenone, and heptaldehyde, good recoveries were obtained on sample sizes of 20–150 μg. The recommended method is based on the publication of Jordan and Veatch (5) and some data illustrating its application are given in Table 6.4. The absorptivities of ketones and aldehydes are in the vicinity of 10,000 liters/mole-cm at the point of maximum absorption (4800 Å), which means that the method is quite sensitive—as little as 20 ppm of carbonyl can be determined.

Jordan (6) has continued with the previously described technique and extended it so that saturated and unsaturated α,β-unsaturated carbonyl compounds are determined as the dinitrophenylhydrazones in alkaline solution at two selected wavelengths. Characteristic shapes are different for the saturated and unsaturated carbonyl compounds and measurements at 4260 and 4800 Å, with prepared calibration curves, permit the determination of both types of materials at submilligram levels.

DETERMINATION OF TRACE CARBONYL

DINITROPHENYLHYDRAZINE COLORIMETRIC METHOD

Apparatus

Spectrophotometer, equipped with a blue-sensitive phototube for use at 4800 Å. Two or more glass cells, cylindrical in shape, and having a 1-cm light path, are required.

Glassware, as needed, must be free of any contamination by carbonyl compounds. Wash glassware with water and alcohol (do not use acetone) and dry in an oven.

Water bath, capable of being maintained at 55 ± 1°C, and of sufficient depth to hold 25-ml volumetric flasks immersed to the top of the flasks.

Reagents

Ethanol, absolute.

n-Hexane.

2,4-Dinitrophenylhydrazine reagent: place 0.2 g of 2,4-dinitrophenylhydrazine in a mixing cylinder with 50 ml of absolute ethanol and shake the mixture for 5 min. Let settle and decant the liquid into a 2-ounce bottle. Add 2.5 ml of concentrated HCl and mix.

Mixed solvent: mix 30 ml of *n*-hexane with 70 ml of absolute ethanol.

Potassium hydroxide reagent: dissolve 11.8 g of CP potassium hydroxide in 50 ml of water and dilute to 200 ml with absolute ethanol.

Dodecanal (dodecyl aldehyde, lauric aldehyde): this compound may be purchased from Aldrich Chemical Co. or J. T. Baker Chemical Co.

Dodecanal 2,4-dinitrophenylhydrazone: prepare this derivative as follows: Place 2 g of 2,4-dinitrophenylhydrazine and 1.9 g of dodecanal in 100 ml of absolute ethanol and heat on a steam bath to dissolve. Slowly add 2 ml of concentrated hydrochloric acid with stirring. The hydrazone precipitates immediately. Cool the mixture and filter using vacuum. Recrystallize the solid from ethanol and dry in a vacuum oven at 60°C. This product is stable and may be stored at room temperature.

Standard hydrazone solution: prepare a standard solution by dissolving 10 mg of dodecanal 2,4-dinitrophenylhydrazone in 50 ml of ethanol. This solution is unstable and should be prepared daily. One milliliter of this solution is equivalent to 15.4 μg of carbonyl calculated as C=O.

Procedure

Weigh a sample containing 15–90 μg of carbonyl (calculated as C=O) into a 25-ml volumetric flask. Add 5 ml of mixed solvent and 2 ml of dinitrophenyl-hydrazine reagent. Place the flask in a 55 ± 1°C heating bath, loosely stoppered, and heat for 30 min. Cool rapidly to room temperature.

Dilute to the mark with potassium hydroxide reagent. Mix well and read the absorbance at 4800 Å exactly 30 min after diluting to the mark. Use 1-cm cells.

Accompany the samples with two reagent blanks and with two standards using 1 ml and 2 ml of the standard hydrazone solution. Add all reagents and carry through the procedure concurrently with the samples.

Calculations

Subtract the average of the two blank absorbance readings from each of the sample absorbances. Prepare a calibration curve plotting the net absorbance of the standards against micrograms of carbonyl calculated as C=O. From this curve find the micrograms of carbonyl in each sample. Calculate the carbonyl content as follows:

$$\text{carbonyl, wt \%, calculated as C=O} = \frac{C}{W} \times 10^{-4}$$

where C = micrograms of C=O found from curve, and W = weight of sample taken, g.

DETERMINATION OF ALDEHYDES BY MEANS OF REACTION WITH AQUEOUS BISULFITE

Bisulfite in aqueous solution reacts reversibly with the carbonyl group of aldehydes and certain ketones to yield an α-hydroxysulfonic acid salt.

$$R_1{-}C{=}O + HSO_3^- \rightleftharpoons R_1{-}\overset{\overset{\displaystyle SO_3^-}{\displaystyle |}}{\underset{\underset{\displaystyle R_2}{\displaystyle |}}{C}}{-}OH$$

The dissociation constants of the various bisulfite addition products are of the order of 10^{-6} to 10^{-7} for aliphatic aldehydes, 10^{-3} to 10^{-4} for aromatic aldehydes, and 10^{-2} to 10^{-3} for methyl ketones (7). The bisulfite reaction, therefore, has analytical importance as a means for determination of aldehydes and a large literature has developed in which the various possibilities have been examined and utilized (8–13).

The addition reaction with aldehydes can be followed by measuring the unreacted excess of bisulfite either by means of oxidation with iodine (8) or by titration with standard base (11). Since the equilibrium can be reversed by the addition of sodium bicarbonate it is possible to determine the combined bisulfite in the following way: The excess bisulfite is first removed by titration with iodine and the complex is then decomposed with bicarbonate. The liberated bisulfite is determined by titration with standard iodine solution. This is the technique used in the recommended method.

An examination of the chemistry and equilibria involved with the bisulfite methods leads to the following conclusions:

1. The lower aliphatic aldehydes can be determined accurately by the bisulfite methods.

2. Ketones are generally not determined.

3. Acetones and some other methyl ketones react partially with bisulfite, causing indistinct end points in the determination of aldehydes.

The limitation due to the blurring of the end point with small amounts of methyl ketones is especially noticeable in the acidimetric method, in which as little as 20 mole % of acetone in acetaldehyde produces an indistinct end point.

Since the choice of other, more reliable carbonyl methods is presently so large, the bisulfite methods have today only limited applicability. The recommended method is most useful for the analysis of simple aldehydes in water-soluble samples free of interferences. A particular application is the specification testing for traces of acetaldehyde in ethylene oxide product (14).

DETERMINATION OF ALDEHYDES IN WATER-SOLUBLE SAMPLES

SODIUM BISULFITE METHOD

Reagents

Iodine solution, standard 0.1*N*. Dissolve 12.69 g of CP iodine in a solution of 24 g of CP potassium iodide in 200 ml of distilled water and dilute to 1 liter. Store the solution in a clean, brown, glass-stoppered bottle.

Iodine solution, stand 0.01*N*. Prepare this solution by accurate dilution of the standard 0.1*N* solution. Store in a clean, brown, glass-stoppered bottle and make a fresh solution at least every three days.

Sodium bicarbonate.

Sodium bisulfite solution, 0.1 %: dissolve 0.50 g of CP sodium bisulfite in distilled water, make up to 500 ml and mix well. Make a fresh solution every day.

Starch indicator solution.

Procedure

With the help of a measuring cylinder, pour 100 ml of the sodium bisulfite solution into a 250-ml conical flask and allow the flask to stand in an ice bath for 15 min.

Add 25 ml of the sample and mix well.

For samples expected to contain more than 200 ppm of aldehyde, the ratio of bisulfite to sample should be increased proportionally, which can conveniently be done by reducing the sample size.

Add 1 ml of starch indicator solution to the conical flask and titrate quickly with 0.1*N* iodine solution to within an estimated 0.5 ml of the end point. Complete the titration with 0.01*N* iodine solution to the first permanent blue end point.

Add 1 g of sodium bicarbonate, mix well, and titrate with the 0.01*N* iodine solution until the blue color at the end point persists for 5 min.

Calculation and Reporting

Calculate the aldehyde content of the sample, as acetaldehyde, by the following equation:

$$\text{acetaldehyde, wt \%} = \frac{(T)(N)(22)}{(10)(V)(d)}$$

where T = volume of iodine solution used for titration after addition of sodium bicarbonate, ml

N = normality of the standard iodine solution

V = volume of sample taken, ml

d = density of sample under test

DETERMINATION OF ALDEHYDES IN THE PRESENCE OF KETONES

Since the bisulfite method cannot be accurately applied to aldehydes if appreciable amounts of methyl ketones are present, considerable effort has been applied to finding more suitable methods for this important determination. This search has taken a number of routes; for instance, dimedon(5,5-dimethyldihydroresorcinol) specifically reacts with aldehydes to give a precipitate (15–17) but the reaction is not quantitative for aldehydes higher than acetaldehyde. A method has been based on the reaction of aldehydes with ammonia (18, 19) but has the disadvantage that aldehydes other than formaldehyde react rather slowly. Individual aldehydes and ketones have been determined by chromatographic separation of their 2,4-dinitrophenyl-hydrazone derivatives (20) but the method is slow and laborious. Oxidative techniques have also been commonly investigated. The use of hypoiodite allows the oxidation of aldehydes (21) but the reaction is not specific because methyl ketones are also oxidized to iodoform. The most common oxidation reagents are the ammoniacal silver complex and silver oxide. Although the ammoniacal silver complex (Tollens' reagent) has been employed widely for a qualitative test for the aldehyde group since the original publications of Tollens (22), the reaction is not entirely quantitative, according to Ponndorf (23). In addition, the ammoniacal silver complex produces explosive materials in reactions with organic compounds. The substitution of silver oxide for the ammoniacal silver complex lead to Ponndorf's development (23) of a practical and quantitative method for the specific determination of the aldehyde group.

Some years ago, Siegel and Weiss (24) reviewed the available methods for determination of the aldehyde function and concluded that the method of Ponndorf was generally suitable. In this method aldehydes react with silver oxide according to the following equation:

$$\underset{\text{H}}{\overset{\text{H}}{R-\underset{|}{C}=O}} + Ag_2O \longrightarrow \overset{O}{\overset{\|}{RC}}-OH + 2Ag$$

$$2\overset{O}{\overset{\|}{RC}}-OH + Ag_2O \longrightarrow 2\overset{O}{\overset{\|}{RC}}-OAg + H_2O$$

The amount of silver oxide reduced can be taken as a direct measure of the aldehyde present. In the Ponndorf method, the silver oxide is formed *in situ* by addition of sodium hydroxide to the reaction mixture containing dilute silver nitrate. Since the reaction mixture is kept dilute with respect to the sample and is made strongly alkaline only in the last stages of the oxidation, side reactions such as the Cannizzaro or aldol condensations are kept to a minimum. At the completion of the reaction, the unreacted silver oxide is dissolved with acid and the metallic silver is separated from the reaction mixture by filtration. The amount of silver oxide reduced, obtained by difference between the titration of the filtrates from the sample and blank determinations, is the measure of the aldehyde content of the sample.

The recommended method in this chapter is based on the original work of Ponndorf (23) but contains several modifications to make the method more rapid and convenient, including a final titration with thiocyanate reagent. Data on the recovery of aldehydes are listed in Table 6.5 that show that quantitative results are commonly obtained except for the unsaturated aldehyde acrolein. Ketones generally do not interfere, although cyclohex-anone reacted to the extent of 2% (Table 6.6). The behavior of other functional groups is shown in Table 6.7. *Esters, carboxylic acids*, and *monohydroxyl alcohols* do not interfere. It should be noted that while formic acid reduces salts of mercury and copper, no such reducing action is observed in the argentimetric procedure. *Polyhydroxyl compounds* interfere, but this inter-ference is overcome by separating the aldehyde from the glycol with steam distillation followed by determination of the aldehyde in the distillate. *Acetals* interfere to the extent of 0.04–2.2%, calculated as acetaldehyde; α-*Epoxides*, tested by using propylene oxide as a representative compound, caused no interference.

Table 6.5. Determination of Aldehydes[a]

Aldehyde	Aldehyde recovery, wt %
Formaldehyde	98.5
	98.4
Acetaldehyde	98.5
	98.5
	98.5
Propionaldehyde	99.8
	99.8
	99.1
n-Butyraldehyde	101.8
	101.5
Valeraldehyde	98.9
	100.1
n-Hexaldehyde	99.8
	100.8
Acrolein	104.9
	104.4
Benzaldehyde	99.9
	98.4

[a] Data from Siegel and Weiss (24).

Table 6.6. Determination of Aldehydes in the Presence of Ketones by Argentimetric Method[a]

Ketone present	Aldehyde present	Ketone added, wt %	Aldehyde, wt %	
			Added	Found
Acetone	None	100	0.0	<0.1
	Acetaldehyde	99.8	0.2	0.4
		99.7	0.3	0.4
		94.7	5.3	5.3, 5.2
		73.3	26.7	25.8, 25.6
		40.7	59.3	56.3, 54.7
	Propionaldehyde	90.9	9.1	9.2, 9.2
		60.1	39.9	39.8, 40.2
Methyl ethyl ketone		100	0.0	<0.2
	Acetaldehyde	99.7	0.3	0.8, 0.7, 0.6, 0.7
	Propionaldehyde	87.0	13.0	13.4, 13.7
		65.5	34.5	34.5, 34.7
		9.3	91.7	91.2, 90.3
Diethyl ketone		100	0.0	<0.2
Methyl isobutyl ketone		100	0.0	<0.2
Methyl isopropyl ketone		100	0.0	<0.2
Methyl n-amyl ketone		100	0.0	<0.3
Diisobutyl ketone		100	0.0	<0.3
Ethyl n-butyl ketone		100	0.0	<0.3
Cyclohexanone		100	0.0	2

[a] From Siegel and Weiss (24). Copyright 1954 by the American Chemical Society. Reproduced by permission of the copyright owner.

DETERMINATION OF ALDEHYDES IN THE PRESENCE OF KETONES

ARGENTIMETRIC METHOD

Apparatus

Shaking machine, of suitable construction to accommodate two or more 100-ml or 250-ml volumetric flasks.

Water bath, maintained at $60 \pm 2°C$.

Reagents

Ammonium thiocyanate solution, standard $0.05N$, aqueous.

Ferric alum indicator solution. Dissolve 350 g of CP ferric ammonium sulfate crystals in 1 liter of water and add 200 ml of aerated 30% nitric acid.

Silver nitrate solution, $0.1N$, aqueous.

Table 6.7. Results Obtained in the Determination of Aldehyde in the Presence of Various Substances by the Argentimetric Method[a]

Substance tested	Substance added, wt %	Propionaldehyde Added wt %	Propionaldehyde Found, wt %
Methyl alcohol	99.7	0.28	0.27
Ethyl alcohol	99.7	0.28	0.27
Isopropyl alcohol	99.7	0.28	0.25
	99.5	0.56	0.55
Ethylene glycol	100.0	0.0	0.2[b]
	97.7	2.3	4.2[b]
	99.2	0.77	3[b]
	99.4	0.63	2[b]
Triethylene glycol	99.8	0.23	0.26[b]
Mannitol	100.0	0.0	22.0
	100.0	0.0	0.1[c]
	89.8	10.2	9.4[c]
Formic acid	33.0	67.1	66.2
Acetic acid	97.9	2.1	1.9
Propionic acid	97.8	2.2	1.8
Lactic acid	97.5	2.5	2.5
n-Caprylic acid	97.6	2.4	2.3
Ethyl acetate	97.6	2.4	2.3
Diallyl phthalate	97.8	2.2	2.1
Benzyl benzoate	98.1	1.9	1.8
Diallyl maleate	97.8	2.2	3.0
Methyl benzoate	98.0	2.0	1.9
Methylal	100.0	0.0	0.04[e]
n-Propylal	100.0	0.0	0.2[e]
	64.3	35.7[d]	36.2
Dimethyl acetal	100.0	0.0	1.1[e]
	68.2	31.8[d]	32.3
Diethyl acetal	99.4	0.0	2.0[e]
	70.4	29.6[d]	30.2
Di-n-butyl acetal	97.3	0.0	0.4[e]
	72.3	27.7[d]	28.6
Propylene oxide	88.4	11.6	11.9
	88.8	11.2	11.4

[a] From Siegel and Weiss (24). Copyright 1954 by the American Chemical Society. Reproduced by permission of the copyright owner.

[b] Calculated as butyraldehyde, wt %.

[c] Results obtained by the steam distillation of the aldehyde.

[d] Acetaldehyde substituted for propionaldehyde.

[e] Results calculated as acetaldehyde, wt %.

Sodium hydroxide solution, 0.5N and 6N, aqueous,
Sulfuric acid solution, 18N.

General Procedure

Pipet 25.0 ml of 0.1N silver nitrate solution into a 100-ml volumetric flask pre-viously cleaned with cleaning acid. Add a quantity of sample containing approxi-mately 0.5 mmole of aldehyde. If the sample is volatile or the carbonyl content is high, weigh the required amount in a glass ampule. If desired, the sample containing 5 mmoles of aldehyde may be dissolved in 100 ml of water or alcohol and a 10-ml aliquot of the solution taken for analysis.

Add 5 ml of 0.5N sodium hydroxide solution slowly with swirling and shake the mixture on a shaking machine for 15 min. At the end of this time, add an additional 2 ml of 0.5N sodium hydroxide solution and continue the shaking for 10 min. Add 10 ml of 6N sodium hydroxide solution and repeat the shaking. Acidify the reaction mixture slowly with 5 ml of 18N sulfuric acid solution. After allowing the mixture to cool to room temperature, dilute to the mark with distilled water. Filter the mixture through a dry No. 41 Whatman filter paper into a 400-ml beaker.

Pipet 50.0 ml of the filtrate into a 500-ml glass-stoppered Erlenmeyer flask and add 4 ml of ferric alum indicator. Swirl the flask and titrate with 0.05N thiocyanate solution until the end point is approached, as indicated by a more slowly fading red color. Stopper the flask, shake vigorously for 20–30 sec, and continue the titration until one drop produces a reddish coloration that does not fade upon swirling or vigorous shaking.

Carry out a blank determination by following the procedure as described but omitting the sample.

Calculations

$$\text{Aldehyde content, equiv/100 g} = \frac{(B - V)(N)}{10W}$$

where B = volume of thiocyanate solution used for blank determination, ml
V = volume of thiocyanate solution used for sample determination, ml
N = normality of the thiocyanate solution
W = weight of sample, g

DETERMINATION OF TRACES OF ALIPHATIC ALDEHYDES

Aliphatic aldehydes react with 3-methyl-2-benzothiazolone hydrazone hydrochloride (MBTH) in the presence of ferric chloride, to form a blue condensed derivative (25). In a thorough development of this method, the investigators at the Robert A. Taft Center of the Public Health Service showed that the technique could be successfully applied to a considerable number of aliphatic aldehydes at a high level of sensitivity. The mechanism of the reaction was shown to follow the following steps:

1. Reaction of the aldehyde with the hydrazone, A, to form the azine B.
2. Oxidation of a part of the unreacted A to the reactive cation C.
3. Formation of the blue condensed cation, D.

$$ (A) + CH_2O \longrightarrow (B) $$

$$ \xrightarrow[H^+]{(O)} (C) $$

$$ B + C \xrightarrow{(O)} (D) $$

The colored cation D, as prepared in the analytical procedure from formaldehyde, has dual maxima at 6350 and 6700 Å with equal molar absorptivity (6.5×10^4 liters/mole-cm). The behavior of a number of aldehydes in the spectrophotometric method is shown in Table 6.8, from which it can be seen that the molar absorptivities vary from compound to compound but that the absorptivities for the first four listed are moderately close if the longer wavelength is taken for comparison. Consequently, the method is useful for the general determination of traces of aldehydes. Additional investigations have been made for the purpose of increasing the sensitivity (26) and the efficiency of collection of the aldehydes in air samples (27). The recommended method given in this chapter is derived from "Selected Methods" of the U.S. Public Health Service (28) and can be used for the determination of as little as 0.002 ppm of aldehydes in air.

DETERMINATION OF ALIPHATIC ALDEHYDES

METHYL BENZOTHIAZOLONE HYDRAZONE METHOD

Apparatus

Spectrophotometer, equipped with 1- and 5-cm cells.

Absorber containing a fritted bubbler of 40- to 80-μ porosity (Corning coarse frit) and having a capacity of at least 75 ml.

Table 6.8. Behavior of Some Aldehydes in the 3-Methyl-2-benzothiazolone Hydrazone Method[a]

Compound	Absorption maxima, mμ	Molar absorptivity $\times$ 10^{-4}, liters/mole-cm
Formaldehyde	635	6.5
	670	6.5
Acetaldehyde	635(S)	4.8
	666	5.1
Propionaldehyde	635(S)	5.2
	666	5.7
n-Butyraldehyde	636(S)	4.8
	668	5.2
Isobutyraldehyde	634(S)	2.1
	664	2.3
Glyoxal	634(S)	2.7
	664	2.8
Acrolein	634	2.3
	667	2.3
Pyruvaldehyde	635	3.8
	668	3.8
Glyceraldehyde	636(S)	5.4
	662	5.8
Crotonaldehyde	636(S)	2.5
	665	2.7

S = shoulder

[a] Data from Sawicki, Hauser, Stanley, and Elbert (25).

Air-metering and flow-control devices capable of measuring and regulating air flows with an accuracy of $\pm 2\%$.

Air pump capable of pulling air through the sampling assembly at a rate of 0.5 liter/min for 24 hr.

Reagents

Collecting reagent, a 0.05% aqueous 3-methyl-2-benzothiazolone hydrazone hydrochloride (MBTH) solution. This colorless solution should be filtered by gravity if slightly turbid and is stable for at least 1 week. Stability may be increased by storing in a dark bottle in the cold.

Oxidizing reagent, an aqueous solution containing 1.6% sulfamic acid and 1.0% ferric chloride is used. Both reagents should be ACS reagent grade.

Formaldehyde solution: accurately dilute 2.7 ml of commercially available 37–39% aqueous ACS reagent grade formaldehyde to 1 liter with distilled water. This solution will contain approximately 1 g of formaldehyde per liter. Standardize this solution by the aqueous hydroxylamine method.

Standardization

Prepare five test solutions ranging from 0.1 to 0.7 μg of formaldehyde per milliliter of 0.05% MBTH. After it has stood for 1 hr, place 10 ml of each test solution in a test tube, and add 2 ml of the oxidizing reagent. After mixing, allow the tube to stand for at least 12 min for complete color development. Determine the absorbance at 6280 Å against an appropriate blank. Plot absorbance versus micrograms of formaldehyde per milliliter of test solution to obtain the calibration curve.

Procedure

Assemble a sampling train in the following order: absorber, trap to protect the flow device, flow-metering device, flow-control device, and air pump. (The flow-control and flow-metering devices may be one piece of equipment, such as a precalibrated limiting orifice.) After adding 35 ml of the collecting reagent in the absorber, draw air through the system at a rate of approximately 0.5 liter/min for 24 hr. When sampling is completed, adjust the volume of the collecting reagent back to the original 35 ml with distilled water and allow to stand for 1 hr. This insures complete reaction of the aliphatic aldehydes with the MBTH. Pipet 10 ml of the sample into a test tube, add 2 ml of the oxidizing reagent, and mix thoroughly. After it has stood for 12 min, measure absorbance at 6280 Å against an appropriate blank prepared from nonaerated laboratory reagents. The amount of aliphatic aldehydes (reported as formaldehyde) per milliliter of test solution is determined from the absorbance–concentration curve.

Calculation

$$\text{ppm (total aldehyde as CH}_2\text{O)} = 0.814 \, \frac{VC}{FT}$$

where V = total volume of collecting reagent = 35 ml
C = μg aldehyde found (as CH$_2$O) per ml collecting reagent
F = airflow-sampling rate, liters/min
T = total sampling time, min
0.814 = total μl that 1 μg CH$_2$O will occupy at 25°C and 760 mm Hg

DETERMINATION OF FORMALDEHYDE

The determination of the individual carbonyl compounds is often best accomplished by gas chromatography over large ranges of concentration. Formaldehyde can also be determined by gas chromatography (29, 30), but there is available such a particularly sensitive and useful colorimetric method (31) for its specific determination that this technique is also recommended. The recommended method included in this chapter involves the use of chromotropic acid (1,8-dihydroxynaphthalene-3,6-disulfonic acid) as the reagent. The heating of this reagent in acid solution with formaldehyde produces a deep purple color which can be accurately measured spectrophotometrically at a wavelength of 5700 Å. The molar absorptivity of the product is 1.9 × 10^4

liters/mole-cm and the method is sensitive to as little as 0.1 ppm of formaldehyde in aqueous solutions. The method has been examined by a number of investigators (32–36), who have clearly pointed out its wide utility. Bricker and his coworkers showed that very little interference would be encountered even with large ratios of alcohols or ketones and that the common aldehydes produced only a minor interference. Altshuller, Miller, and Sleva (36) showed that the chromotropic acid method was particularly useful for the specific determination of formaldehyde in polluted air or in combustion gases because nitrogen dioxide and most aldehydes and ketones did not interfere significantly. The slight interference from olefins and aromatic hydrocarbons could be overcome by using an aqueous sodium bisulfite solution as the collecting medium. The method has been adopted by the U.S. Public Health Service (28) to measure formaldehyde in the air concentration range of 0.01–200 ppm and it has been used to determine formaldehyde in city atmospheres (37, 38). Los Angeles air was found to contain 0.005–0.15 ppm of formaldehyde.

The recommended method given in this chapter is taken from the more recent publications in the literature and was designed for use on aqueous solutions of formaldehyde. Some of the data obtained by the recommended method are given in Table 6.9 and show the high specificity indicated by the earlier worker of Bricker. Quantitative recovery from solutions containing as little as 0.536 μg/ml offer the high sensitivity required for the trace determination of formaldehyde.

Table 6.9. Effects of Other Compounds on Determination of Formaldehyde by Chromotropic Acid

Material added			Formaldehyde	
Compound	μg/ml	Wt ratio to formaldehyde	Added, μg/ml	Recovery, %
None			0.536	99.7
			0.536	100.3
			0.536	100.6
Acetaldehyde	25.0	47:1	0.536	101.5
	2.5	4.7:1	0.536	100.8
Propionaldehyde	2.5	4.7:1	0.536	102.5
Acrolein	2.5	4.7:1	0.536	102.0
Acetone	3200.0	4400:1	0.719	100.7
Methanol	3600.0	5000:1	0.719	101.4
Ethanol	3070.0	4200:1	0.719	100.1
tert-Butanol	6.96	9.7:1	0.719	95.8
Pyridine	7000.0	9700:1	0.719	90.4

DETERMINATION OF FORMALDEHYDE

COLORIMETRIC CHROMOTROPIC ACID METHOD

Apparatus

Micropipets, Kirk-type, covering the range from 10 to 1000 μliters. Available from Microchemical Specialties Co., Berkeley, California.

Spectrophotometer, equipped with 1- and 5-cm cells.

Steam bath designed so that 50-ml volumetric flasks may, except for the upper portion of the neck, be entirely enclosed by the bath and protected from light.

Reagents

Sulfuric acid, CP concentrated.

Benzene, CP.

Sodium bisulfite solution, 0.02N: to prepare 1 liter of solution dissolve 2 g of powdered CP sodium metabisulfite in 1 liter of distilled water. This solution should be prepared fresh daily.

Chromotropic acid reagent: to prepare approximately 1 liter of reagent, dissolve 4.0 g of chromotropic acid (1,8-dihydroxynaphthalene-3,6-disulfonic acid), Eastman Kodak, practical grade, in 100 ml of distilled water and filter the solution into a 2-liter flask. Place 300 ml of water in another 2-liter flask and slowly add 700 ml of cold concentrated sulfuric acid *with continuous chilling and gentle swirling*. Add the chilled acid solution to the filtered chromotropic acid solution in small increments with stirring and cooling. Store under nitrogen in a dark, glass-stoppered bottle. The reagent should be freshly prepared when the blank determination becomes greater than 0.25 absorbance unit in a 5-cm cell.

Standard formaldehyde solution, approximately 0.060 mg/ml: first, prepare a solution of formaldehyde to contain approximately 6 mg/ml by weighing 8.5 g of formaldehyde solution (35–40%) into a 500-ml volumetric flask, diluting to the mark with water, and mixing. Transfer the solution to a 500-ml brown glass, screw-cap bottle. Establish the actual formaldehyde content of the solution by the aqueous hydroxylamine method. With a micropipet, pipet 1.00 ml of the standardized formaldehyde solution to a 100-ml volumetric flask, dilute to the mark with 0.02N sodium bisulfite solution, and mix. This solution should have a formaldehyde concentration of approximately 0.06 mg/ml; the actual concentration is calculated using the data obtained above. This solution can be used for several months.

Calibration of Apparatus

With micropipets introduce exactly 0, 0.100, 0.200, 0.400, 0.600, 0.800, and 1.00 ml of the standard formaldehyde solution (approx. 0.060 mg/ml) into separate dry 50-ml volumetric flasks. Add sufficient sodium bisulfite solution to make a total volume of 5 ml and proceed as directed below. Read the absorbance (at 570 mμ) of the solutions containing 0, 0.100, 0.200, and 0.400 ml of the standard formaldehyde solution in 5-cm cells and those containing 0, 0.400, 0.600, 0.800, and 1.00 ml in 1-cm cells. Correct each absorbance by subtracting the absorbance of the 0 ml standard and calculate each absorptivity as follows:

$$a = \frac{(A)(V)}{(b)(w)}$$

where a = absorptivity
  A = absorbance
  b = cell length, cm
  V = volume of solution in which color is developed, ml
  w = weight of component being determined in the colored solution, mg

Average the absorptivities and use the average absorptivity in calculating formaldehyde content. The method gives an absorptivity of about 620 liters/g-cm.

Procedure

Accurately weigh an appropriate amount of sample into a 100-ml volumetric flask, dilute to the mark with sodium bisulfite solution, and mix thoroughly.

Transfer a 1- to 5-ml aliquot containing 5–30 μg of formaldehyde into a clean, dry 50-ml volumetric flask. If less than 5 ml of the sample solution is taken, add sodium bisulfite solution to bring the volume to 5 ml.

From a buret add 40 ml of chromotropic acid reagent while swirling the contents of the flask. Heat the unstoppered flask inside a steam bath, protected from light, for 30 min. When the amount of formaldehyde is less than 20% of the total aldehyde content of the sample, heat the sample for only 15 min. Remove the flask from the steam bath, allow to come almost to room temperature, dilute to the mark with distilled water, and mix. Allow the flask to come to room temperature, again make up to the mark with distilled water, and mix thoroughly. Measure the absorbance of the solution relative to distilled water at 570 mμ in a 1- or 5-cm absorption cell with a Beckman Model B spectrophotometer. Choose the absorption cell that will give an absorbance reading between 0.2 and 2.0.

Make a blank determination using 5 ml of sodium bisulfite solution in place of the sample.

Calculation

Subtract the absorbance found for the blank determination from that found for sample. Calculate the formaldehyde content of the sample directly from the corrected absorbance using the established absorptivity as follows:

$$\text{Formaldehyde content, wt \%} = \frac{(A)(D)}{(a)(b)(w)(10)}$$

where a = absorptivity
  A = absorbance
  b = cell length, cm
  D = the sample dilution factor
  w = weight of sample, g

The sample dilution factor D, as used in the above calculations, is best illustrated by an example:

A sample is diluted to 100 ml, and 5 ml of this solution is taken for acid decomposition and finally diluted to 25 ml for color development. The sample dilution factor is as follows:

$$D = \frac{(100)(25)}{5} = 500$$

DETERMINATION OF ACROLEIN

A number of reagents for the specific determination of acrolein have been reported, but, in general, most of these appear to have rather limited applicability, including tryptophan (39), phloroglucinol (40), and m-dinitrobenzene (41). The use of 4-hexylresorcinol as a color-forming reagent (42), however, has permitted the development of a sensitive spectrophotometric method for the determination of low concentrations of acrolein in liquid mixtures and in gaseous samples. The spectrophotometric method was developed by Cohen and Altshuller (43) and has been adopted by the U.S. Public Health Service (28) to measure acrolein in the atmosphere. In the application to the measurement of contaminants in the Los Angeles atmosphere (37), the average acrolein concentration was found to be 0.007 ppm.

The reagent for color development contains 4-hexylresorcinol, mercuric chloride, and trichloroacetic acid in aqueous alcohol. The color-forming reaction is completed during a 15-min heating period at 60°C, producing a strong absorption maximum at 6050 Å that is used for determination of the concentration of acrolein in the sample. Cohen and Altshuller (43) investigated a number of chemical compounds for possible interference and found that saturated aliphatic aldehydes and ketones, even in very large excess, did not produce any significant absorptivity at 6050 Å. In some cases, condensation products were formed with the reagent, but the absorptivities were low and the maxima occurred at other wavelengths. Other α, β-unsaturated aldehydes do generally react with 4-hexylresorcinol to form products with moderate absorptivity but the maxima are considerably shifted and this provides little interference. Of other materials examined, olefins, acetylenes, aromatics, phenols, esters, alcohols, sulfur dioxide, and nitrogen dioxide do not cause interference in the determination of acrolein.

DETERMINATION OF CARBONYL COMPOUNDS BY ULTRAVIOLET ABSORPTION SPECTROSCOPY

The ultraviolet spectra of the simple monocarbonyl compounds, in dilute solution, show a wide absorption envelope in the general range of 2600–3000 Å with molar absorptivities in the region of 20 liters/mole-cm. This low

Table 6.10. Absorptivities of Some Carbonyl Compounds in the Ultraviolet Region between 2000 and 4000 Å[a]

Compound	Principal absorption maximum, Å	Molar absorptivity, liters/mole-cm	Solvent
Acetaldehyde	2905	16	Isooctane
Propionaldehyde	2930	20	Isooctane
Acrolein	2100	1.3×10^4	Water
Crotonaldehyde	2130	1.5×10^4	Isooctane
	2240	1.6×10^4	Water
Acetone	2650	16	Water
Methyl isobutyl ketone	2840	19.5	Isooctane
Methyl vinyl ketone	2120	1.02×10^4	Water
2,4-Pentanedione	2710	1.04×10^4	Isooctane
Quinone	2460	2.2×10^4	Water

[a] Data from American Petroleum Institute Research Project 44.

molar absorptivity does not make the ultraviolet a useful region for determination of the monocarbonyl compounds. The absorption spectra of carbonyl compounds conjugated either with an olefinic bond or a second carbonyl group shows a considerable difference. A comparison of the principal maxima observed between 2000 and 4000 Å is given in Table 6.10. The conjugated compounds have molar absorptivities in the vicinity of 10^4, which makes the ultraviolet region attractive for determination of the conjugated carbonyl compounds. An interesting example of this measurement is the work of Garrett, Johnson, and Alway (44), who compared the ultraviolet spectrometric curves of those steroids that had a ring structure in which a keto group was conjugated with either one or two double bonds in the ring.

DETERMINATION OF CARBONYL COMPOUNDS BY INFRARED ABSORPTION SPECTROSCOPY

According to Bellamy (45), the carbonyl group exhibits strong absorption in the region of 5.5–6.0 μ, with the exact position dependent upon the molecular structure. Absorption at slightly higher wavelengths is found for structures in which chelation or ionization takes place and distinct differences are noticed between saturated carbonyls and those with α, β unsaturations. An infrared spectrophotometric method for the determination of free carbonyl in polyacrolein illustrates some particularly useful spectroscopic techniques. Forbes and Schissler (46) were faced with the problem of determining free carbonyl in an insoluble polymer that reacted with chemical reagents to yield values for *free* plus *combined* carbonyl content. The infrared method was a good choice and involves suspending the sample in Fluorolube and measuring the absorptivity for the carbonyl stretching band at 5.83 μ. To obtain quantitative values for the free carbonyl content it was necessary to obtain a calibration because the absorptivity of the free carbonyl group in polyacrolein cannot be obtained directly from the infrared spectrum, as no independent method for free carbonyl had been developed. To surmount this problem, poly-α-methylstyrene-acrolein copolymer was selected as a model for the carbonyl group in polyacrolein. The NMR spectrum of the copolymer showed no hydroxyl (exchangeable hydrogen) and agreed with the aldehyde content found by a chemical method. Also, in the copolymer, the acrolein unit carbonyl is of the same type as the free carbonyl groups in polyacrolein. Therefore, from a comparison of the intensity of the carbonyl absorption band in the infrared spectrum with the carbonyl value from chemical methods, an absorptivity for the carbonyl stretching mode can be calculated.

A sample of poly-α-methylstyrene-acrolein copolymer (PAMS-A) containing 0.446 equiv carbonyl per 100 g of polymer was used for calibration. The copolymer was powdered and mulled in a Wig-L-Bug with Fluorolube S-30. The resulting emulsions were run in a 0.107_8-mm infrared cell with NaCl windows. The molar absorptivity, ε, of the carbonyl group was calculated in the following manner for each experiment. A linear baseline from 5.5 to 6.7 μ was used and a correction for the Fluorolube absorption was made:

$$\text{volume of Fluorolube} = \frac{\text{weight of Fluorolube}}{\text{density of Fluorolube}}$$

$$\text{Concentration of PAMS-A} = \frac{\text{weight of PAMS-A}}{\text{volume of Fluorolube}}$$

$$\varepsilon = \frac{\text{(absorbance)(equivalent weight per C=O)}}{\text{(concentration)(pathlength in cm)}}$$

where the equivalent weight per C=O of polymer (PAMS-A) used is 224 and the density of Fluorolube is 1.958 at 25°C. The data are given in Table 6.11.

Table 6.11

Concn. PAMS-A g/liter of Fluorolube	ε (calc) liter/mole-cm	Deviation liter/mole-cm
43.7	80.6	+0.6
59.8	79.7	−0.3
81.6	81.3	+1.3
89.4	77.0	−3.0
106.0	81.2	+1.2
Average	80	±1.3

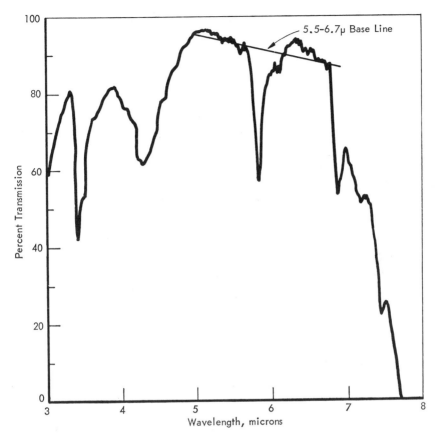

Figure 6.1. Spectrum of typical polyacrolein in fluorolube. From Forbes and Schissler (46).

Figure 6.1 shows a typical spectrum of polyacrolein for which the calculation for free carbonyl is as follows:

Free Carbonyl. ε for the C=O stretching vibration of free carbonyl in polyacrolein is 80 liters/mole-cm at 5.83 μ. Therefore

$$\text{g/equiv C=O} = \frac{(\text{sample concentration})(80)}{(\text{absorbance at 5.83 } \mu)}$$

DETERMINATION OF ACETALS

Acetals are the condensation products of aldehydes with alcohols and are converted to the aldehydes by hydrolysis under acidic conditions.

$$\text{RCH(OR)}_2 + \text{H}_2\text{O} \rightarrow \text{RCHO} \pm 2\text{ROH}$$

Table 6.12. Rates of Hydrolysis of some Acetals in 1.0N
Hydrochloric Acid at 25°C[a]

Acetal	K_{25}
Dimethoxymethane (methylal)	0.00153
Diethyoxymethane (ethylal)	0.0130
Diisopropoxymethane	0.0723
Di-*n*-propylmethane	0.0144
Di-*n*-butoxymethane	0.0143
Diisobutoxymethane	0.0992
Di-*sec*-butoxymethane	0.0992

[a] Data from Skrabal and coworkers (47, 48).

The hydrolysis rates of a number of acetals were measured many years ago by Skrabal (47, 48) and his coworkers. Some of their data, measured at 25°C in 1.0N aqueous hydrochloric acid solution and listed in Table 6.12, show that the acetals have a wide range of hydrolysis rates and that methylal, as the lowest member of the series, has the slowest rate. The hydrolysis of acetals has allowed the development of simple methods for their analysis. A number of these methods have been reviewed by Mitchell (49), who presented considerable data on their application to typical acetals. The hydroxylamine hydrochloride reagent can be used in a direct procedure either with or without added acid, depending on the reactivity of the acetals being analyzed, since the pH of the hydroxylamine hydrochloride reagent solution is about 2.5. In these methods the acetals hydrolyze and, together with any free carbonyl compounds, react with hydroxylamine hydrochloride to form the oximes and liberate acid. Titration of the acid is taken as the measure of free plus combined carbonyl (50–52). A separate determination of free carbonyl can be made, from which combined carbonyl can be determined. The recommended method for the determination of free plus combined

Table 6.13. Determination of Acetals by the Hydrolysis Method

Acetal	Extent of recovery, %	Acid normality	Time, hr	Temp, °C
1,1-Dimethoxyethane	100.1, 100.1	0.1	1	60
1,1-Diethoxyethane	99.3, 99.3	0.1	1	60
Dimethoxymethane	89.6, 91.0	0.1	2	60
	96.3, 97.2	0.5	2	60
Diethoxylmethane	96.4, 97.4	0.1	1	60
	98.6, 98.7	0.1	2	60
	98.6, 98.7	0.1	4	60

carbonyl is a variation of the published techniques and involves heating the reaction mixture at 60° with a hydroxylamine hydrochloride reagent containing a small, added concentration of hydrochloric acid (53). Some data by this method are given in Table 6.13, from which it can be seen that essentially quantitative results are obtained for the more reactive acetals with 0.1N acid in a heating period of 1 hr at 60°C while more severe conditions are required for the less reactive acetals.

DETERMINATION OF FREE AND COMBINED CARBONYL

Hydrolysis Method

Apparatus

Reaction bottle, heavy-walled, 250- to 500-ml, with screw cap, crown cap, or spherical joint closure. The caps should be lined with Teflon inserts.
Water bath, maintained at 60 ± 2°C.

Reagents

Hydroxylamine hydrochloride–0.1N acid reagent: mix 100 ml of distilled water, 8.5 ml of 12N hydrochloric acid, 25 g of CP hydroxylamine hydrochloride and 8 ml of methyl orange–xylene cyanole indicator solution. Dilute to 1 liter with distilled water.
Hydroxylamine hydrochloride–0.5N acid reagent: mix 100 ml of water, 42 ml of 12N hydrochloric acid, 100 g of CP hydroxylamine hydrochloride, and 33 ml of methyl orange–xylene cyanole indicator solution. Dilute to 1 liter with distilled water.
Methyl orange–xylene cyanole indicator solution: dissolve 0.1 g of methyl orange and 0.14 g of xylene cyanole FF in 500 ml of 50% ethyl alcohol.
Sodium hydroxide solution, standard 0.5N.

General Procedure

Pipet 100 ml of hydroxylamine hydrochloride–0.1N acid reagent into each of two reaction bottles. Retain one for use as a blank. To the other reaction bottle, add a quantity of sample corresponding to approximately 0.012 mole of carbonyl plus acetal compound. Limit the maximum sample size to 10 g. Cap both bottles and heat for 1 hr at 60°C. Cool to room temperature. Remove the caps from both bottles and rinse the cap and bottle neck of each with a small quantity of water.

Titrate the blank with 0.5N sodium hydroxide solution to a steel grey end point. Similarly titrate the sample with 0.5N sodium hydroxide solution to a light pink color slightly short of the end point. To the blank now add a volume of distilled water equal to the difference between the sample and blank titrations. Proceed with the titration until the color of the sample mixture matches that of the blank. Let the sample stand for about 15 min and, if the end point has faded, titrate again to the color of the blank.

To obtain a correction for strong acids or bases present in the original sample, weigh or measure a sample into 100 ml of distilled water that has been previously brought to the methyl orange–xylene cyanole end point, and titrate again to the same end point color.

Dimethoxymethane (Methylal) Procedure

Pipet 25 ml of hydroxylamine hydrochloride–0.5N acid reagent into each of two reaction bottles. Cap and retain one for use as a blank. To the other, add a quantity of sample corresponding to approximately 0.012 mole of carbonyl plus acetal compound. Limit the maximum sample size to 10 g. For pure dimethoxymethane, use about 0.9 g and weigh in a sealed glass ampule. Introduce some clean glass beads into the bottle containing the sample. Cap and shake the bottle until the bulb and stem of the ampule are broken. Heat both blank and sample bottles at 60°C for 2 hr. Cool to room temperature. Remove the caps from both bottles and rinse the cap and bottle neck of each with 75 ml of distilled water.
Titrate the sample and a corresponding blank.

Calculations

$$\text{Total carbonyl value, equiv/100 g} = \frac{(S - B)(N)}{10W} - A$$

where A = acidity to methyl orange–xylene cyanole end point, equiv/100 g
S = volume of sodium hydroxide solution, ml, used to titrate sample
B = volume of sodium hydroxide solution, ml, used to titrate blank
N = normality of sodium hydroxide solution
W = weight of sample, g

DETERMINATION OF CARBONYL COMPOUNDS BY POLAROGRAPHIC REDUCTION

The determination of the carbonyl group can be made directly or after formation of derivatives (54) by polarographic techniques. There are a large number of examples in the literature of the determination of carbonyl compounds, including such typical materials as citral in lemon grass oil (55) and crotonaldehyde in vinyl acetate (56). The conversion of carbonly compounds to hydrazones (57) or to imines (58, 59) has been found helpful in producing more sharply defined polarographic waves at a favorable voltage. The direct polarographic determination of aldehydes is feasible because they reduce readily at voltages below the supporting electrolytes, but aliphatic ketones reduce directly at too high a potential. The imines formed from aliphatic diamines reduce smoothly at approximately −1.6 V vs. S.C.E. for the aldimines and −1.8 V vs. S.C.E. for the ketimines (58). The variable reactivity of glyceraldehyde, dihydroxyacetone, and methylglyoxal toward imine formation has been used in a polarographic method for their determination (60). The polarography of ketosteroids has been found useful to indicate the structure of these complex materials (61, 62). Polarography has been found useful in the analysis of the complex materials that arise from the low-temperature oxidation of hydrocarbons (63). Formaldehyde can be determined in an alkaline solution that has been treated with titanium tetrachloride to remove hydrogen peroxide, and acetaldehyde can be determined in the presence of dimedon, which reacts with formaldehyde. Barnes and Zuman (64) have published a detailed study of the reductive behavior of cinnamaldehyde and 3-phenylpropionaldehyde at several ranges of pH values.

REFERENCES

1. J. Mitchell, Jr., in *Organic Analysis*, Vol. I, Interscience, New York, 1953, pp. 243–307.
2. J. G. Hanna and S. Siggia, in *Treatise on Analytical Chemistry*, I. M. Kolthoff and P. J. Elving, Eds., Part II, Vol. 13, Interscience, New York, 1966, pp. 131–213.
3. W. M. D. Bryant and D. M. Smith, *J. Am. Chem. Soc.*, **57**, 57 (1935).
4. J. Mitchell, Jr., D. M. Smith, and W. M. D. Bryant, *J. Am. Chem. Soc.*, **63**, 573 (1941).
5. D. E. Jordan and F. C. Veatch, *Anal. Chem.*, **36**, 120 (1964).
6. D. E. Jordan, *Anal. Chim. Acta*, **37**, 379 (1967).
7. I. M. Kolthoff and V. A. Stenger, *Volumetric Analysis*, Vol. I, Interscience, New York, 1942, p. 215.
8. M. Ripper, *Monatsch.*, **21**, 1079 (1900).
9. K. Täufel and C. Wagner, *Z. Anal. Chem.*, **68**, 25 (1926).
10. E. W. Adams and H. Adkins, *J. Am. Chem. Soc.*, **47**, 1358 (1925).
11. S. Siggia and W. Maxcy, *Anal. Chem.*, **19**, 1023 (1947).
12. I. M. Kolthoff and V. A. Stenger, *Volumetric Analysis*, Vol. II, Interscience, New York, 1947, p. 220.
13. C. Kleber, *Z. Anal. Chem.*, **44**, 442 (1905).
14. Shell Chemical Company, Ltd., *Alkylene Oxides*, London, 1962, p. 68.
15. D. Vorländer, *Z. Anal. Chem.*, **77**, 241, 321 (1929).
16. G. W. Gaffney, W. A. Williams, and H. McKennis, Jr., *Anal. Chem.*, **26**, 588 (1954).
17. J. H. Yoe and L. C. Reid, *Ind. Eng. Chem., Anal. Ed.*, **13**, 238 (1941).
18. A. Castiglioni, *Z. Anal. Chem.*, **119**, 287 (1940).
19. F. Mack and R. Herrmann, *ibid.*, **62**, 129 (1923).
20. B. E. Gordon, F. Wopat, H. D. Burnham, and L. C. Jones, Jr., *Anal. Chem.*, **23**, 1754 (1951).
21. H. R. Rogers, *Ind. Eng. Chem., Anal. Ed.*, **16**, 319 (1944).
22. B. Tollens, *Ber.*, **15**, 1828 (1882); **16**, 917, 921 (1883).
23. W. Ponndorf, *ibid.*, **64**, 1913 (1931).
24. H. Siegel and F. T. Weiss, *Anal. Chem.*, **26**, 917 (1954).

25. E. Sawicki, T. R. Hauser, T. W. Stanley, and W. Elbert, *ibid.*, **33**, 93 (1961).
26. T. R. Hauser and R. L. Cummins, *ibid.*, **36**, 679 (1964).
27. I. R. Cohen and A. P. Altshuller, *ibid.*, **38**, 1418 (1966).
28. "Selected Methods for the Measurement of Air Pollutants," Public Health Service Publication 999-AP-11, Robert A. Taft Sanitary Engineering Center, Cincinnati, Ohio, 1965.
29. K. J. Bombaugh and W. C. Bull, *Anal. Chem.*, **34**, 1237 (1962).
30. R. S. Mann and K. W. Hahn, *ibid.*, **39**, 1314 (1967).
31. E. Eegrive, *Z. Anal. Chem.*, **110**, 22 (1937).
32. C. E. Bricker and H. R. Johnson, *Ind. Eng. Chem. Anal. Ed.*, **17**, 400 (1945).
33. C. E. Bricker and K. H. Roberts, *Anal. Chem.*, **21**, 1331 (1949).
34. C. E. Bricker and A. H. Vail, *ibid.*, **22**, 720 (1950).
35. P. W. West and B. Sen, *Z. Anal. Chem.*, **153**, 177 (1956).
36. A. P. Altshuller, D. L. Miller, and S. F. Sleva, *Anal. Chem.*, **33**, 621 (1961).
37. A. P. Altshuller and S. P. McPherson, *J. Air Pollution Control Assoc.*, **13**, 109 (1963).
38. A. P. Altshuller, I. R. Cohen, M. E. Meyer, and A. F. Wartburg, Jr., *Anal. Chim. Acta*, **25**, 101 (1961).
39. S. J. Circle, L. Stone, and C. S. Boruff, *Ind. Eng. Chem., Anal. Ed.*, **17**, 259 (1945).
40. I. L. Uzdina, *Chim. Ind. (Paris)*, **40**, 260 (1938).
41. I. Antener, *Mitt. Lebensm. Hyg.*, **28**, 305 (1937).
42. L. Rosenthaler and G. Vegezzi, *Z. Lebensm. Untersuch m. Forschung.*, **99**, 352 (1954).
43. I. R. Cohen and A. P. Altshuller, *Anal. Chem.*, **33**, 726 (1961).
44. E. R. Garrett, J. L. Johnson, and C. D. Alway, *ibid.*, **34**, 1472 (1962).
45. L. J. Bellamy, *The Infra-red Spectra of Complex Molecules*, 2nd ed., Wiley, New York, 1958.
46. J. W. Forbes and D. O. Schissler, *J. Polymer Sci.*, Part C, **8**, 61 (1965).
47. A. Skrabal and M. Zlatewa, *Z. Physik. Chem.* **119**, 305 (1926).
48. A. Skrabal and H. H. Eger, *ibid.*, **122**, 349 (1926).
49. J. Mitchell, Jr., in *Organic Analysis*, Vol. I, Interscience, New York, 1953, pp. 309–328.
50. D. M. Smith and J. Mitchell, Jr., *Anal. Chem.*, **22**, 750 (1950).
51. S. Siggia, *Quantitative Organic Analysis via Functional Groups*, Wiley, New York, 1949, pp. 59–64.
52. S. Hähnel and M. Lennerstrand, *Svensk. Kem. Tidskr.*, **53**, 336 (1941); *Chem. Abstr.* **36**, 62 (1942).
53. E. D. Peters, A. G. Polgár, and W. Lee, unpublished work from Shell Development Co.
54. P. Zuman, *Organic Polarographic Analysis*, Macmillan, New York, 1964.
55. A. P. Shakunthala and M. S. V. Pathy, *J. Electroanal. Chem.*, **14**, 123 (1967).
56. J. Pasciak, *Z. Anal. Chem.*, **213**, 111 (1965).
57. V. Prelog and O. Hafliger, *Helv. Chim. Acta*, **32**, 2088 (1949).
58. M. E. Hall, *Anal. Chem.*, **31**, 2007 (1959).
59. R. E. Van Atta and D. R. Jamieson, *ibid.*, **31**, 1217 (1959).

60. M. Fedoronko, J. Königstein, and K. Linek, *J. Electroanal. Chem.*, **14**, 357 (1967).
61. P. Kabasakalian and J. McGlotten, *Anal. Chem.*, **34**, 1441 (1962).
62. A. I. Cohen, *ibid.*, **35**, 129 (1963).
63. S. Sandler and Y. H. Chung, *ibid.*, **30**, 1252 (1958).
64. D. Barnes and P. Zuman, *Trans. Faraday Soc.*, **65**, 1668, 1681 (1969).

DETERMINATION OF ESTERS

The classical saponification method for determination of the ester function has a long and useful history (1). The recommended method is the time-honored one that involves refluxing the material to be analyzed with alcoholic potassium hydroxide, followed by titration of the remaining caustic with standard acid. The method is widely applicable to a variety of esters, as can be seen from the results in Table 7.1. In general a reflux period of 1 hr is sufficient for many compounds but 3 hr is often used. An occasional limitation of the method is the interference from some other functional groups, such as aldehydes and peroxides, as shown in Table 7.2. Particularly severe interference is found with some aldehydes even when using precautions to exclude air. Aldehydes are known to be reactive toward self-condensation under alkaline conditions and this reaction can consume caustic. Reactive peroxides also can consume caustic but ketones and epoxides are relatively

Table 7.1. Extent of Recovery of Esters in the Saponification Method

| | Recovery, wt % | | |
Compound	0.5 hr	1 hr	3 hr
Allyl propionate	99.5, 99.6		
Benzyl benzoate		99.2, 99.4	99.4, 100.0
Allyl toluate		100.0	
Allyl acetate		99.9	
Ethyl crotonate	99.3		
Methyl benzoate		99.8, 100.1	99.8
n-Butyl phthalate		99.6	100.0
β-Butyrolactone			100.1
ω-Caprolactone			99.3
Dibutyl isophthalate	91	99.6	
Bis(4-octyl) sebacate		98.6	100.2
Bis(2-octyl) sebacate			99.6, 100.2
n-Octyl stearate		72	98.5, 100.8
Dioctyl phthalate			100.0, 100.2
Triisocaproate of 1,2,6-hexanetriol			99.7, 99.8
Methylsultone			100.0
Methyl abietate		14.4	40.5

Table 7.2. Behavior of Other Functional Groups in Ester Saponification

Compound	Apparent ester content, wt %		Comments
	30 min Reflux	1 hr Reflux	
Aldehydes			
Formaldehyde		11.4	N_2 atmosphere
Acetaldehyde	3.0, 3.1		N_2 atmosphere; reaction mixture darkened
Benzaldehyde	15.8, 16.4, 16.7		N_2 atmosphere
Crotonaldehyde	75, 77		N_2 atmosphere
Ketones			
Methyl ethyl ketone	≤0.03		
Methyl *n*-amyl ketone	≤0.1		
Mesityl oxide	0.3		N_2 atmosphere
α-Epoxides			
Allyl glycidyl ether		0.5	
Phenyl glycidyl ether		0.3	
Glycidyl benzoate	100.0, 100.2[a]		
Peroxides			
tert-Butyl hydroperoxide	31.9		
2,2-Bis(*tert*-butyl peroxy) butane	3.2		

[a] Value agrees with ester function present.

stable and do not interfere. If organic halides are present, these will also be saponified; however, a correction can be made by determination of the concentration of halide ion in the titration mixture after the analysis for remaining base has been completed.

Although the common esters are usually determinable by the procedure recommended, esters with a high degree of steric hinderance, generally due to branching, give low results in the usual procedure but more difficult saponifiable materials can be determined by methods that involve reactions at higher temperatures. A useful procedure is that published by Redemann and Lucas (2), which utilized a temperature of 150°C with KOH in diethylene glycol as the reagent and required the displacement of air with nitrogen to prevent errors due to oxidation. This procedure gave quantitative results with methyl abietate upon heating for 1 hr at 170°C. Jordan (3) reviewed the techniques available for the quantitative saponification of highly hindered esters and presented a method that gave excellent results on a series of complex, hindered esters. In Jordan's method (3) the reaction is conducted at the reflux temperature of hexyl alcohol (bp 155°C), containing sodium hydroxide for saponification and a low concentration of sodium perchlorate to act as a catalyst. Vinson, Fritz, and Kingsbury (4) found that aqueous dimethyl sulfoxide was an unusually effective solvent in promoting the high rate of alkaline hydrolysis with potassium hydroxide as the base and required only some 5 min heating on a steam bath for the quantitative saponification of most esters. Many hindered esters could be quantitatively analyzed but, with those most heavily hindered, it was not possible to obtain meaningful results because long heating at high temperatures under basic conditions appeared to initiate partial decomposition of the dimethyl sulfoxide solvent. Measurements of the rates of ester hydrolysis have been of importance over many years in studies of the effect of structure on the reactivity of organic compounds. A classic survey of this field of physical organic chemistry is provided by Hammett (5). The alkaline hydrolysis of esters has been shown to be initiated through a rupture on the acid side of the ether bond by experiments conducted in water enriched in ^{18}O. This and other evidence has led to the proposal of a mechanism for saponification of carboxylic esters in which the initial step is the addition of hydroxyl ion to the carbonyl carbon followed by the breaking away of the —OR group:

$$R'-C\overset{O}{\underset{OR}{}} + (OH)^- \rightleftarrows \left[R'-\overset{OH}{\underset{OR}{C}}-OH \right] \longrightarrow R'-C\overset{O}{\underset{OH}{}} + (OR)^-$$

The rates of the saponification are greatly affected by changes in either of the alkyl groups, R' or R. A tabulation of some relative rate constants for alkaline saponification at 25°C in water solution are given in Table 7.3. In each series the rates are relative to R being CH_3. The lowest rate is that of the compound with the bulky *tert*-butyl group, showing the effect of steric hindrance, whereas vinyl esters are quite unstable and this structure produces the highest relative rate. Data on the rates of ester saponification and other organic reactions have been summarized by Mark and Rechnitz, who consider the uses of kinetics in analysis (6).

DETERMINATION OF CARBOXYLIC ESTERS

SAPONIFICATION METHOD

Reagents

Alcoholic caustic reagent: dissolve 85 g of CP potassium hydroxide pellets in 240 ml of CP methanol, warming if necessary to effect solution. Cool, filter into a 2-liter graduated mixing cylinder, and add 125 ml of distilled water and 635 ml of 99% isopropyl alcohol. Mix thoroughly, then determine the normality by titration

Table 7.3. Relative Rates of Saponification of Esters[a]

R	CH_3COOR[b] in aqueous solutions at 25°C, dilute NaOH	$RCOOC_2H_5$[c] in 87.8% ethanol at 30°C, dilute NaOH
CH_3-	1	1
C_2H_5-	0.601	0.470
$i\text{-}C_3H_7-$	0.148	0.100
$t\text{-}C_4H_9-$	0.0084	0.0105
$n\text{-}C_3H_7-$	0.549	0.274
$CH_2{=}CH-$	57.7	
⬡—	7.63	0.1019
⬡—CH_2-	1.10	1.322

[a] Data from Hammett (5).

[b] Original data from A. Skrabal and A. M. Hugetz, *Monatsh.*, **47**, 17 (1924).

[c] Original data from K. Kindler, *Annalen*, **450**, 1 (1926); **452**, 90 (1927).

of a 25-ml portion with standard 0.5N acid. Adjust the normality to 0.95N by dilution with 99% isopropyl alcohol. After adjusting, transfer the solution to a rubber-stoppered bottle and store under nitrogen.

Nitric acid, standard 0.5N.

Isopropyl alcohol, 99%.

Phenolphthalein indicator solution, 1% alcoholic.

Potassium hydroxide solution, standard 0.1N alcoholic.

Dispense in such a manner that the solution is protected from atmospheric carbon dioxide by means of a guard tube containing soda lime and such that it does not come in contact with cork, rubber, or saponifiable stopcock grease.

Procedure

Place 25 ml of isopropyl alcohol and a few drops of phenolphthalein indicator solution in a 250-ml saponification flask. Cool the flask in an ice or ice–salt slurry and weigh into it a quantity of sample in which the total saponifiable material (esters plus saponifiable halogen compounds) does not exceed 21 meq and, for greatest precision, is not less than 18 meq. Make all weighings to the nearest 0.01 g, using a Lunge-type weighing bottle for liquid samples.

Neutralize any free acidity in the sample by titrating to the phenolphthalein end point with standard alcoholic potassium hydroxide solution, keeping the solution sufficiently cool to prevent fading of the end point.

Pipet 25 ± 0.1 ml of the alcoholic caustic reagent into the flask, add a few Carborundum boiling stones, and attach the flask to the reflux condenser, moistening the glass-joint connection with a few drops of water to prevent sticking. Reflux for a period of from 30 min to 3 hr, depending on the type of material. If potassium salts precipitate during the refluxing, add a sufficient quantity of water through the condenser to effect solution.

When the mixture has refluxed for the required period, rinse the condenser with a little water, collecting the rinsings in the flask. Disconnect the flask from the condenser, cool to room temperature, and titrate to the phenolphthalein end point with $0.5N$ nitric acid.

Carry out a blank titration in the manner described above, using the same volume of alcoholic caustic reagent but omitting the sample.

Calculation

$$\text{Ester value, equiv/100 g} = \frac{N(B - A)}{10W}$$

where A = volume of acid, ml, used in the sample titration
$\quad\quad B$ = average volume of acid used in the blank titrations
$\quad\quad N$ = normality of the acid
$\quad\quad W$ = weight of sample, g

COLORIMETRIC DETERMINATION OF ESTERS

The hydroxamic acid reaction has been used for the determination of esters by engaging the following reactions:

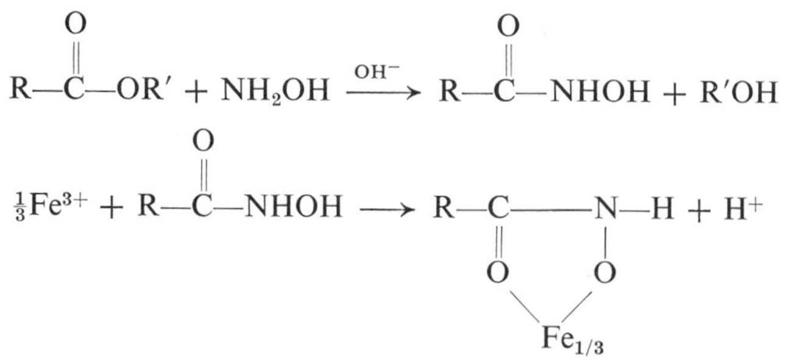

$$R-\overset{\overset{\displaystyle O}{\|}}{C}-OR' + NH_2OH \xrightarrow{OH^-} R-\overset{\overset{\displaystyle O}{\|}}{C}-NHOH + R'OH$$

$$\tfrac{1}{3}Fe^{3+} + R-\overset{\overset{\displaystyle O}{\|}}{C}-NHOH \longrightarrow R-C\text{——}N-H + H^+$$

The ferric chelate of hydroxamic acid is deeply colored and has been used by Feigl, Anger, and Frehden (7) both as a spot test for esters and for their determination. A thorough investigation of the variables of the method was published by Goddu, LeBlanc, and Wright (8), who recommend procedures for application to esters and to anhydrides and lactones, which are also determined by this technique. Esters are determined by refluxing the sample with an alkaline solution of hydroxylamine in methanol for 5 min. After this reaction period, the mixture is allowed to cool and is treated with an alcoholic solution of ferric perchlorate to develop the color. Anhydrides and lactones are considerably more reactive with hydroxylamine than are simple esters and for these more reactive compounds a nearly neutral solution (phenolphthalein end point) of hydroxylamine is used. Of the esters tested with neutral hydroxylamine, only phenolic esters, peroxyesters, lactones, and formates reacted (8). Tests on other materials showed that acid chlorides react but that acids, amides, and nitriles do not interfere. The determination of amides by this reaction (Chapter 15) requires a heating period of several hours.

The data in Table 7.4 show some results on typical esters. The ferric hydroxamates formed from most aliphatic acid esters have an absorption maxima generally at 5300 Å and somewhat different positions of the maxima are found with esters or aromatic acids. The molar absorptivities have been recalculated for multifunctional esters on an equivalent basis. The equivalent absorptivities varied from 0.77 to 1.21, which would make it necessary to calibrate with the particular ester being determined. Lehmann and Wilhelm

Table 7.4. Behavior of Some Esters in the Ferric Hydroxamate Method[a]

| Ester | Properties of ferric hydroxamate | |
	Absorption maxima, Å	Molar absorptivity × 10^{-3} liters/mole-cm
Ethyl formate	5200	1.06
Ethyl acetate	5300	1.10
Ethyl propionate	5300	1.02
n-Amyl n-butyrate	5300	0.91
Methyl oleate	5300	1.00
Methyl benzoate	5500	1.13
n-Butyl benzoate	5500	1.08
Benzyl benzoate	5500	1.13
Methyl p-toluate	5500	0.94
Dimethyl malonate	5200	0.86[b]
Dimethyl maleate	5200	0.77[b]
Dimethyl adipate	5300	1.02[b]
Dimethyl o-phthalate	5400	0.74[b]
Dimethyl isophthalate	5400	1.21[b]
Triacetin	5300	1.11[b]

[a] Data from Goddu, LeBlanc, and Wright (8).

[b] The molar absorptivity observed has been divided by number of equivalents of ester group to provide the value indicated.

(9) recommended the hydroxamate method for the determination of phthalate esters in plasticizers.

DETERMINATION OF ESTERS BY GAS CHROMATOGRAPHY

The ester function is sufficiently nonpolar and thermally stable to make gas chromatography an attractive technique for the separation and determination of esters as individual compounds. In fact, as described in Chapter 5, it is often preferable to determine acids by gas chromatography after their conversion to the corresponding methyl esters and many publications have appeared recommending gas chromatographic procedures for the separation of esters. It is possible to discuss only a limited number of these publications in this chapter. Hornstein and Crowe (10) reported that good resolution of the methyl esters of the $C_{12}-C_{18}$ fatty acids was obtained using treated Chromosorb R and Celite 545 as column supports. These supports had been "silanized" with dimethyldichlorosilane prior to their being coated with polyvinylacetate for the partitioning phase. Nestler and Zinkel (11) recommended diethyleneglycol succinate as the polar liquid phase for the separation of the methyl esters of the resin acids. Several investigators have utilized a transesterification technique to simplify the analysis of polymeric materials containing the ester function. The reaction with a typical polymer is essentially the following:

$$RO \left[-\overset{\overset{\displaystyle O}{\|}}{C} -(CH_2)_4 -\overset{\overset{\displaystyle O}{\|}}{C} -O-CH_2-CH_2-O- \right]_n -H + CH_3OH \xrightarrow{\text{catalyst}}$$

$$ROH + CH_3 -\overset{\overset{\displaystyle O}{\|}}{OC} -(CH_2)_4 -\overset{\overset{\displaystyle O}{\|}}{C} -OCH_3 + HO-CH_2-CH_2-OH$$

Percival (12) carried out the transesterification by refluxing a dried sample of the resin with 100 ml of absolute methanol containing 0.1 g of sodium methoxide. Jankowski and Garner (13) used a transesterification reagent prepared from a $1M$ solution of sodium methoxide in methanol mixed with an equal volume of methyl acetate. The reflux period required with this reagent was considerably less than with the reagent containing the lower concentration of sodium methoxide. A thorough review of the transesterification techniques was given by Rawlinson and Deeley (14), who concluded that these techniques provide a rapid method for the systematic qualitative analysis of polymeric esters. The sensitivity is high and minor components can be detected. The methods, however, are not quantitative in their application to complex materials although it is possible to estimate the composition through comparisons with the behavior of known materials.

REFERENCES

1. R. T. Hall and W. E. Shaefer, *Organic Analysis*, Vol. 2, Interscience, New York, 1954, pp. 19–70.
2. C. E. Redemann and H. J. Lucas, *Ind. Eng. Chem., Anal. Ed.*, **9**, 521 (1937).
3. D. E. Jordan, *Anal. Chem.*, **36**, 2134 (1964).
4. J. A. Vinson, J. S. Fritz, and C. A. Kingsbury, *Talanta*, **13**, 1673 (1966).
5. L. P. Hammett, *Physical Organic Chemistry*, McGraw-Hill, New York, 1940.
6. H. B. Mark, Jr. and G. A. Rechnitz, *Kinetics in Analytical Chemistry*, Interscience, New York, 1968.
7. F. Feigl, V. Anger, and O. Frehden, *Mikrochemie*, **15**, 12 (1934).
8. R. F. Goddu, N. F. LeBlanc, and C. M. Wright, *Anal. Chem.*, **27**, 1251 (1955).
9. G. Lehmann and G. Wilhelm, *Z. Anal. Chem.* **238**, 415 (1968).
10. I. Hornstein and P. F. Crowe, *Anal. Chem.*, **33**, 310 (1961).
11. F. H. M. Nestler and D. F. Zinkel, *ibid.*, **35**, 1747 (1963); **39**, 1118 (1967).
12. D. F. Percival, *ibid.*, **35**, 236 (1963).
13. S. J. Jankowski and P. Garner, *ibid.*, **37**, 1709 (1965).
14. J. Rawlinson and E. L. Deeley, *J. Oil Colour Chemists' Assoc.*, **50**, 373 (1967).

DETERMINATION OF THE HYDROXYL GROUP

Accurate methods for determining alcoholic and phenolic hydroxyl groups represent perhaps the largest single demand on the industrial organic analytical chemist because of the many alcohols and phenols and the corresponding derivatives presently being manufactured. It is frequently necessary to determine hydroxyl in the presence of one or more of the following types of compounds: ketones, aldehydes, amines, acids, amides, or water. As a result of the demand for this type of analysis, a variety of methods have been developed or adapted for the quantitative determination of the hydroxyl group in alcohols and phenols. For the specific determination of polyhydroxy compounds see Chapter 9; for phenols see Chapter 10.

GENERAL METHODS FOR DETERMINATION OF THE HYDROXYL GROUP

The classical general method for the determination of the hydroxyl group is that published many years ago by Verley and Bölsing (1), who used acetic anhydride as the acetylating agent and pyridine as a catalyst. After a period of heating, the excess acetic anhydride was decomposed with water and the acid remaining was titrated with standard aqueous alkali. A corresponding blank analysis was made without sample. The difference between the quantity of acid in the blank and the sample was taken as the measure of the acid used in reacting with the hydroxyl group, as shown in the equations of Table 8.1. Other reagents that have been employed in variations of this method include acetyl chloride (2) and phthalic anhydride (3), to each of which pyridine is added to convert the reagent into an oxocarbonium complex (4) by a reaction similar to the following:

Table 8.1.   Reactions in the Determination of the Hydroxyl
Group

$$ROH + (CH_3CO)_2O \xrightarrow{\text{pyridine}} CH_3COOH + CH_3COOR$$
$$H_2O + (CH_3CO)_2O \rightarrow 2CH_3COOH$$

$$ROH + CH_3COOH \xrightarrow{BF_3} CH_3COOR + H_2O$$

$$\underset{\substack{| \\ CH_2 \\ | \\ R}}{R-\overset{R}{\underset{|}{C}}-OH} \xrightarrow{BF_3} \underset{\substack{\| \\ CH \\ | \\ R}}{R-\overset{R}{\underset{|}{C}}} + H_2O$$

$$LiAlH_4 + 4ROH \rightarrow 4H_2 + (RO)_4(LiAl)$$
$$CH_3MgI + ROH \rightarrow CH_4 + MgIOR$$

The oxocarbonium complex is a highly active acetylating reagent and converts alcohols to esters under comparatively mild conditions.

These procedures and their modifications have been successfully applied to a wide variety of hydroxylated materials including fats, hydroxylated fatty acids, oils, sugars, cellulose derivatives, phenols, and mono- and polyhydric alcohols. The phthalic anhydride reagent is particularly useful for the determination of hydroxyl in hydroxy acids since the acid function in the latter is prone to form difficult hydrolyzable mixed anhydrides upon reaction with acetic anhydride or acetyl chloride.

Another useful hydroxyl method involves the reaction of alcohols with acetic acid catalyzed by boron trifluoride. This procedure is intended for determination of the total alcoholic hydroxyl content of samples that may contain tertiary aliphatic and alicyclic alcohols. The alcohol produces the ester and an equivalent amount of water. In the method of Bryant, Mitchell, and Smith (5) the amount of water formed is then measured by Fischer titration. Under the conditions of the method, tertiary alcohols may be partially esterified and partially dehydrated but in either case one mole of water is produced for each mole of alcoholic group present. Amines will form complexes with BF_3 but otherwise do not interfere, since if required, an additional amount of catalyst can be added to reactivate the catalyst.

The lithium aluminum hydride reagent has been widely used for the determination of active hydrogen in organic compounds and is uniquely applicable to determination of hydroxyl in the presence of epoxide groups, as in epoxy resins (6). Its reaction with alcoholic or phenolic hydroxyl closely resembles that of the Grignard reagent and it also will react with many of the same functional groups that interfere with the use of Grignard as an alcohol determinant. Indeed, its reactions are generally even more vigorous at ordinary temperatures than those of the Grignard reagent.

Because of this high reactivity, LiAlH$_4$ will react quantitatively with hydroxyl groups at 0°C, a temperature at which many of the interfering reactions are greatly lessened. For this reason, the LiAlH$_4$ reagent will give more nearly quantitative results than the Grignard reagent and is to be preferred. A review of these two techniques has been published by the author (7) giving detailed comparisons and applications of the methods. A procedure employing the lithium aluminum hydride reaction followed by a gas chromatographic measurement of the hydrogen produced offers considerable promise of increasing speed and precision. Such a development has been reported by Chumachenko, Tverdyukova, and Leenson (8), who found their combined procedure gave fairly accurate results in the determination of the active hydrogen content of a considerable variety of organic compounds.

The phenolic hydroxyl group has the facility of being determinable by a variety of methods due to the large chemical reactivity imparted to the molecule through this group.

COMPARATIVE BEHAVIOR OF HYDROXYL TYPES IN THE PRINCIPAL GENERAL METHODS

There is a great variety of choices in the several general hydroxyl methods in application to compounds bearing different types of hydroxyl groups.

Table 8.2. Summary of the Behavior of Types of Hydroxyl Compounds in the Principal General Methods

| Type | Extent of reaction, % | | | | Infrared (2.86 μ) molar absorptivities, liters/mole-cm |
	Acetylation, acetic anhydride or acetyl chloride	Phthalation	BF$_3$–Fischer	LiAlH$_4$	
Primary R—CH$_2$—OH	100 ± 0.2	100 ± 0.3	100 ± 0.3	100 ± 0.4	60–80
Secondary R—CH—R | OH	100 ± 0.3	99 ± 0.5	100 ± 0.3	100 ± 0.4	60–80
Tertiary R | R—C—R | OH	5–20	3–10	100 ± 0.3	100 ± 0.5	60–80
Phenolic	100% for simple phenols, low for hindered phenols	Slight reaction	Low recovery	100 ± 0.4	50–150 (2.7–3.0 μ)

Table 8.2 illustrates, in summary form, the widely different applicability of the methods while more detailed data are given in Table 8.3. The accuracy of the methods is greatest with *primary alcohols*. Slightly lower accuracy is found with *secondary alcohols* in the phthalic anhydride method. *Tertiary alcohols* dehydrate, at least partially, under esterification conditions; consequently, the acidimetric methods give low results but correct values can be obtained by use of the BF_3–Fischer method in which the water production from both esterification and dehydration is measured. Correct results are also obtained by the $LiAlH_4$ method, which operates under chemically milder conditions. *Simple phenols* are determined with ease by the $LiAlH_4$ and the acetylation methods, but not by the phthalic anhydride or the BF_3–Fischer methods. Steric effects limit the reactivity of phenols with bulky substituents in the acetylation methods but not in the $LiAlH_4$ technique. *Polyhydroxy* compounds can be determined by the acetylation methods although it is usually preferable to employ periodate oxidation with the α, β-polyols as discussed in Chapter 9, because of the higher accuracy and specificity of the oxidation technique. The phthalic anhydride method generally gives low results with polyhydroxy compounds, probably because of steric limitation with the bulky reagent. Low results are likewise found by the $LiAlH_4$ reagent, due generally to the precipitation of the partially reacted salts of the polyhydroxy compounds. In the *infrared method* for hydroxyl determination, aliphatic alcohols all show an absorption maximum at 2.86 μ, which is often used for their determination; however, molar absorptivities for the several classifications vary over a 25 % range, making it impossible to use the infrared directly for quantitative analysis. Once the infrared spectrophotometer has been calibrated for an alcohol type, using either pure alcohols or a sample assayed by a chemical method, the method of analysis is rapid, although it generally does not have the high precision that is provided by chemical methods. There are a few other concerns regarding the accuracy of the infrared method for alcohols; the hydroxyl group in water interferes and consequently samples must be dried and hydrogen-bonding materially alters the position of the maximum and its absorptivity. For complex mixtures or with polymers containing the hydroxyl function, it is necessary to investigate carefully the several possibilities before deciding upon the method of choice.

INTERFERENCE OF OTHER FUNCTIONAL GROUPS IN THE PRINCIPAL GENERAL HYDROXYL METHODS

The vigorous acidic reagents employed in many of the hydroxyl methods caused interference from other functional groups. Since the $LiAlH_4$ reagent is basic and the reaction is generally conducted at $0°C$, interferences are found to be small with this reagent and consequently, despite the somewhat

Table 8.3. Extent of Recovery (%) of Alcohols and Phenols in the General Hydroxyl Methods

Compound	Acetyl chloride method	Acetic anhydride method	Phthalic anhydride method	BF$_3$–Fischer method	LiAlH$_4$ method
Primary and secondary alcohols					
Methyl alcohol	99.1		100.1, 100.2	99.5[a]	
Ethyl alcohol			99.9	99.9[a]	
Benzyl alcohol	99.8, 100.2	99.4, 99.5	100.1, 100.3, 100.5	98.4[a]	100.2, 100.8
sec-Butyl alcohol	99.7, 99.8	99.4, 99.5, 99.7	98.2		97.5
Isopropyl alcohol	99.5, 100		98.8		
Methyl isobutyl carbinol	99.1, 99.7	99.6, 99.8	98.0, 98.4		103
Methallyl alcohol	99.5, 99.8		99.5, 99.7, 99.9		
Cyclohexanol	99.4, 99.5, 99.8		98.7, 98.7, 99.3		98, 101
n-Octyl alcohol	100.1	100.0, 100.2			98.5, 98.9, 99.2, 99.2, 99.3
4-Methyl-4-penten-2-ol	98.5				98.3
Cetyl alcohol	99.0, 99.5	99.2, 99.5	99.0, 99.1		
Tertiary alcohols					
tert-Butyl alcohol	18	6	6.5	100.0[a]	
Diacetone alcohol			3		
tert-Amyl alcohol	5.7 (0.5 hr) 11.0 (1 hr)			98.9 100.2[a]	97.5
Polyhydric alcohols					
Ethylene glycol		99.1	99.3	99.3[a]	99.0
Glycerol		99.4, 99.5	98.2	98.0[a]	88
Glycerol α-monoethyl ether	99.7, 100.0	99.6, 99.8	97.1, 97.2		
Mannitol		99.7	85		
Phenols					
Phenol	99.9, 99.9		1.0, 1.2	low recovery	99.8, 100.0
p-Cresol	100.5, 100.5		>0.5		
3,5-Xylenol	99.5, 99.5				
2,6-Di-tert-butyl-4-methyl phenol	7.9	5			100.0, 100.4
Bisphenol A					99.6

[a] Data from Bryant, Mitchell, and Smith (5), corrected for water content of samples.

complex apparatus and procedures required, the method finds considerable use. The simpler methods involving the formation of esters are each subject to some areas of interference and these should be carefully considered to avoid erroneous results. Table 8.4 provides a summary of the extent of interference of functions other than hydroxyl, while Table 8.5 gives more extensive data on the behavior of many compounds. *High molecular weight acids* form mixed anhydrides with acetyl chloride and acetic anhydride that do not break down readily upon hydrolysis of the acetylation reagent, thus giving high and erroneous results, but this is not observed with the phthalic anhydride reagent nor with the BF$_3$–Fischer method. *Aldehydes* condense with all the acetylation reagents but generally do not interfere in the phthalic anhydride or LiAlH$_4$ methods. *Ketones* are nonreactive except to the vigorous, acidic BF$_3$–Fischer reagent where reactive ketones will condense to produce water and, consequently, register a value for apparent hydroxyl content. *Epoxides* produce a severe interference in all the chemical methods with the exception of the LiAlH$_4$ technique, which makes this method useful for the analysis of mixtures containing both the hydroxyl and epoxide function. *Esters* and *ethers* are generally stable except that secondary or unsaturated ethers are reactive to the BF$_3$–Fischer reagent. *Amines* and *amides* present a picture of variable reactivity in the hydroxyl methods. Since primary and secondary amines and single amides possess a reactive hydrogen, these show reactivity with some of the reagents. Thus they generally indicate active hydrogen with the LiAlH$_4$ reagent although the reaction may be slow and incomplete with some compounds that apparently form insoluble salts. To avoid interference from the amine function it is possible to employ the

Table 8.4. Summary of the Interference of Other Functional Groups in the General Hydroxyl Methods

Function	Acetylation	Phthalation	BF$_3$–Fischer	LiAlH$_4$
Acids	Interference from high molecular weight acids	None	None	Stoichiometric reaction
Aldehydes	Interference	Generally none	Interference	None
Ketones	None	None	Variable interference	None
Epoxides	Interference	Interference	Interference	None
Amines	Partial to complete reaction	Variable reaction	None	Partial to complete reaction
Ethers	None	None	Variable interference	None

Table 8.5. Percent Reaction of Other Functional Groups in the General Hydroxyl Methods

Compound	Acetyl chloride	Acetic anhydride	Phthalic anhydride	BF_3– Fischer	$LiAlH_4$
		Acids			
Benzoic acid			<0.1		100
Valeric acid	16, 17				100
Stearic acid				0.6	100
12-Hydroxystearic acid		55[a]	<0.1[a]	<0.1[a]	100[a]
Naphthenic acids	95	40	<0.1		
		Acetals			
Dimethoxymethane	<0.5	<0.5	<0.5	170	
Diethoxymethane	<0.3	<0.3	<0.3	175	2.2
1,1-Dimethoxyethane	<0.5	<0.5		181	
		Aldehydes			
Formaldehyde	48	52	12		
Propionaldehyde	15	19, 35[b]	0.3, 0.4		
Hexaldehyde		22			0.1, 0.2
Benzaldehyde	−0.5	−2	1.0	1.1	0.3
		Ketones			
Acetone	<0.5	none	none	26	<0.1
Methyl isobutyl ketone				2.3	<0.1
Mesityl oxide	0.1				
Acetophenone					0.8
Cyclohexanone				50, 70[c]	
		Ethers			
Diethyl ether	none	none		0.2	none
Dioxane	none	none		<0.1	none
Diallyl ether				11, 12	
Diisopropyl ether				68	
Glycerol isopropyl ether				47	
		Epoxides			
Epichlorhydrin	6, 7	37	Severe decom-	39, 46[b]	<0.2
Glycidyl phenyl ether	8	17	position with	20, 57[b]	<0.1
Glycidyl isopropyl ether			deep black reaction		

Table 8.5. (*continued*)

Compound	Acetyl chloride	Acetic anhydride	Phthalic anhydride	BF$_3$– Fischer	LiAlH$_4$
		Esters			
Ethyl acetate	none	none	none		<0.1
Diallyl adipate				<0.1	
Ethylbenzoate					<0.1
		Amines			
Allyl amine				0.1	
Aniline				2.8	60–90[d]
Ethanol amine				<0.1[a]	
Tetramethylpiperidine	45	98.9, 99.0			
Piperidine					103
		Amides			
Acetamide	115	99		0.7, 0.9	100.5, 101
Acetanilide					98
		Peroxides			
tert-Butyl hydroperoxide			95		195, 197
Di-*tert*-butyl peroxide			<0.1		7, 8
		Sulfur Compounds			
Dodecyl mercaptan	95	96		96	102, 103
Diethyl sulfide					0

[a] Value for nonhydroxyl functional group only.
[b] Results obtained with varying sample weights.
[c] Bryant, Mitchell, and Smith (5).
[d] Very slow reaction.

BF$_3$–Fischer method using a double strength reagent to overcome the effect of the amine group.

RECOMMENDED METHODS

Five procedures involving the use of chemical reagents are given with detailed instructions as recommended methods for general determination of the hydroxyl group. These are the: Acetyl Chloride method, the Acetic Anhydride method, the Phthalic Anhydride method, the Boron Trifluoride–Fischer Reagent method, and the Lithium Aluminum Hydride method. A

Table 8.6.   Principal Features of Methods for Determination of Hydroxyl Compounds

Method	Determination	Applicability	Limitations
Acetyl chloride	Hydroxyl group	Primary and secondary alcohols and phenols	Tertiary alcohols not determined
Acetic anhydride	Hydroxyl group	Primary and secondary alcohols and phenols	Tertiary alcohols not determined
Phthalic anhydride	Hydroxyl group	Primary and secondary alcohols	Tertiary alcohols, phenols not determined
BF_3–Fischer reagent	Hydroxyl group	Determines primary, secondary, and tertiary alcohols	Phenols not determined
Lithium aluminum hydride	Active hydrogen	General for active hydrogen	Requires correction for acid, water, other active hydrogen
Methylol–Fischer	Methylol group	Polymers and low molecular weight compounds	Of specific but limited application
Trimethylsilyl ether–gas chromatography	Individual alcohols	Useful to compounds even in steroid range; has high resolution	Not applicable to polymers
Infrared absorption	Hydroxyl group	General; particularly useful for polymers	Needs calibration; avoidance of hydrogen bonding
Deuterium exchange	Active hydrogen	Rapid, general method for active hydrogen	Accuracy is not high
Proton nuclear magnetic resonance	Hydroxyl group	To examine complex compounds or systems	Requires NMR instrument
Periodate oxidation	Vicinal hydroxyl groups	For polyhydroxy alcohols—see Chapter 9	
Phenolic compounds		For specific and general methods, see Chapter 10	

choice among these methods should be made for application to most of the common organic samples. This chapter also provides recommended methods for other types of hydroxyl determination: the specific determination of the methylol group, the preparation and gas chromatography of the trimethylsilyl ethers, and the determination of alcohol hydroxyl by nuclear magnetic resonance. Table 8.6 summarizes in outline form the scope of the many methods for the determination of the hydroxyl compounds. Detailed coverage of the polyhydroxy alcohols and the phenols are given in Chapters 9 and 10.

ACID-CATALYZED ACETYLATION METHODS

Although the more common acetylation methods for determination of the hydroxyl group employ pyridine as the catalyst, it is also possible to catalyze the acetylation reaction with a strong acid. Some examples of this are described by Fritz and Schenk (9), who used perchloric acid, Stetzler and Smullin (10), who used p-toluenesulfonic acid, and Pietrzyk and Belisle (11), who compared the effectiveness of the catalytic properties of these two acids with 2,4-dinitrobenzenesulfonic acid. These techniques are quite rapid; however, acid catalysts may cause interferences that are not significant when pyridine is the catalyst. The BF_3–Fischer method, which employs BF_3 as the acid catalyst, suffers from considerable interferences with ketones and acetals (see Table 8.5) whereas the base-catalyzed methods do not have this deficiency. Fritz and Schenk point out that acetone, cyclohexanone, and cyclopentanone interfere in perchloric acid-catalyzed acetylations carried out in ethyl acetate solution, even when conducted at 0°C. Reducing the acid strength by using pyridine as the solvent reduces the extent of interference but also slows the rate of the acetylation reaction. Stetzler and Smullin (10) found that an acetylation reagent prepared from acetic anhydride and $0.2M$ perchloric acid in ethyl acetate solution was unsatisfactory for the determination of the hydroxyl function in polyoxyalkylene ethers because this reagent attacked the ether groups in the polyether chain, even at room temperature, to yield high and erroneous hydroxyl values. A similar reagent in which p-toluene-sulfonic acid was the catalyst gave a quantitative acetylation in 10–15 min at 50°C without any evidence of attack on the ether group. The work of Pietrzyk and Belisle (11) has shown that 2,4-dinitrobenzenesulfonic acid has an acid strength close to that of perchloric acid. Use of this sulfonic acid as a catalyst in ethyl acetate solution gave a rapid acetylation of the hydroxyl function with acetic anhydride. With simple alcohols essentially quantitative results were obtained and on a number of polyethers. The results agree with those obtained by the acetic anhydride–pyridine method. However, on several commercial polyoxyalkylene ethers a side reaction, presumably due to the opening of an ether bond, caused high apparent hydroxyl values that increased with time.

OTHER ESTERIFICATION METHODS FOR HYDROXYL GROUP DETERMINATION

In addition to the more common esterification reagents for the titrimetric determination of the hydroxyl function, which have been described above, certain other reagents have also been examined. Methoxyacetic anhydride was suggested as a substitute for acetic anhydride many years ago (12) but little further use has been reported of this reagent for the quantitative determination of the hydroxyl group. Pyromellitic dianhydride has been examined as an esterification reagent and found to have certain advantages over acetic anhydride and phthalic anhydride (13–15) because it has a low reactivity to aldehydes and phenols. A difficulty reported in the use of pyromellitic dianhydride is its limited solubility in pyridine, which is normally used to catalyze the reaction. This difficulty has been overcome either by employing dimethyl sulfoxide as the major solvent or by preparing the esterification reagent from the dianhydride in dimethylformamide and using imidazole as the catalyst (15). The imidazole-catalyzed method gives good accuracy and precision in the determination of the hydroxyl content of primary and secondary monohydroxyl and dihydroxyl alcohols as well as good precision in the analysis of several commercial polyols (15). As is described further in this chapter, nitrobenzoyl chlorides and phenylazo-salicylic acids are used as reagents to produce esters for a colorimetric determination and the chloro- and fluoroacetates of alcohols can be prepared for more detailed examination by nuclear magnetic resonance or gas chromatography.

DETERMINATION OF HYDROXYL

ACETYL CHLORIDE METHOD

Apparatus

Water bath, of suitable construction to maintain two or more 250-ml volumetric flasks at a temperature of 40 ± 1°C.

Reagents

Acetyl chloride solution, 1.9 ± 0.1M in CP anhydrous toluene.
Phenolphthalein indicator solution, 1% in 60% alcohol.
Pyridine, CP anhydrous.
Sodium hydroxide solution, standard 1.0N, carbonate-free.
Toluene, CP anhydrous.

Procedure

Introduce 20 ml of acetyl chloride solution into a dry 250-ml glass-stoppered volumetric flask and cool to ice temperature by inserting into an ice–water slurry. Add 5 ml of pyridine, stopper, and shake vigorously to break down large pieces of coagulated solids. Remove the flask from the bath and immediately add a sufficient quantity of sample so that approximately one-half but not more than two-thirds of the acetyl chloride is consumed (including that consumed by any water in the sample).

The sample should be added in such a manner that none adheres to the neck of the flask. It is satisfactory, however, to wash down the neck with not more than 5 ml of toluene in order to dissolve small amounts of sample.

Shake the flask vigorously and place in a water bath at 40 ± 1°C. Loosen the stopper momentarily to expel air, stopper firmly, and allow to heat for 30 min, shaking vigorously at 10-min intervals. At the end of the heating period, transfer the flask to an ice bath. When cool, add about 25 ml of chilled distilled water and shake vigorously to hydrolyze all excess reagent. Titrate immediately to the phenolphthalein end point with standard $1N$ sodium hydroxide solution, keeping the temperature below 20°C. For samples that produce fading of the indicator color due to hydrolysis of the ester keep the mixture at ice temperature throughout the titration.

Make a blank determination for each group of samples according to the above procedure; if desired, the heating may be eliminated.

Test the sample for free acidity and if applicable, determine the amount by titration to the phenolphthalein end point.

Calculation

$$\text{Hydroxyl value, equiv/100 g} = \frac{(B - S)(N)}{10W} + A$$

where B = volume of sodium hydroxide solution consumed by blank, ml
S = volume of sodium hydroxide solution consumed by sample, ml
N = normality of the sodium hydroxide solution
W = weight of sample, g
A = free acidity, equiv/100 g.

If a single known alcohol is present, the alcohol content may be expressed as weight percent by multiplying the hydroxyl value by the equivalent weight of the alcohol.

DETERMINATION OF HYDROXYL

Acetic Anhydride Method

Reagents

Acetic anhydride reagent, 1.35*M*. Mix 0.5 ml of water with 800 ml of anhydrous pyridine, then add 130 ml of acetic anhydride and mix thoroughly.
Phenolphthalein indicator solution, 1 % in 60 % alcohol.
Sodium hydroxide solution, standard 1.0*N*, carbonate-free.
Toluene, CP anhydrous.

Procedure

Pipet 25 ml of the acetic anhydride reagent into a dry 250-ml glass-stoppered Erlenmeyer flask and add 3–4 g of sample.

Protect the mixture from strong light by covering the flask with a metal protective cover to prevent darkening of the solution. Attach the covered flask to a clean, dry reflux condenser equipped with a water-cooled standard taper joint, moistening the connection with toluene. Heat the flask on a hot plate for 3 hr at such a heat that the mixture is refluxed at a very slow rate.

At the end of the refluxing period, surround the flask, with condenser attached, with an ice bath and, when cool, add 25 ml of previously chilled toluene through the condenser, swirling the flask to mix; then add 25 ml of chilled distilled water.

Disconnect the condenser, rinse the ground joint with distilled water, collecting the washings in the flask, and stopper the flask.

Immediately titrate the contents of the flask with standard $1.0N$ sodium hydroxide solution to the phenolphthalein end point, keeping the flask cool during the titration. Stopper and shake the flask vigorously when nearing the end point.

Make a blank determination, omitting the sample. It is not desirable to reflux the blank, but the flask should be cooled and the chilled water added soon after introducing the reagent to prevent volatilization.

Test the sample for free acidity, and if appreciable, determine by titration to the phenolphthalein end point.

Calculations

Use corresponding section of the Acetyl Chloride Method.

DETERMINATION OF ALCOHOLIC HYDROXYL

Phthalic Anhydride Method

Apparatus

Pressure bottles: Pyrex bottles with crown-cap closure, approximately 400-ml capacity.

Crown caps, fitted with Teflon inserts.

Water bath, protected, 100°C. The design should be such that a number of bottles may be placed in cold water, the bath closed and heated to 100°C for a given period, and then cooled within a period of 20–30 min after draining the water.

Reagents

Phthalic anhydride reagent: weigh 60 g of CP phthalic anhydride, to the nearest half-gram, in a 500-ml glass-stoppered, graduated mixing cylinder. Dissolve the phthalic anhydride in approximately 450 ml of CP pyridine and fill to the 500-ml mark with CP pyridine.

Phenolphthalein indicator solution.

Sodium hydroxide solution, standard 0.1 and $0.5N$, carbonate-free.

Procedure

Pipet 25 ml of the phthalic anhydride solution into a clean, dry pressure bottle. Add a known weight of sample containing 0.008–0.010 equiv of hydroxyl but in general limit the maximum amount of sample to 10 g.

If water is present in the sample, reduce the sample size so that no more than 0.012 equiv of hydroxyl *plus* water are taken.

Seal the bottle and place in the water bath. Close the bath, fill with tap water, and heat with steam as rapidly as possible to boiling (5–10 min).

One hour after boiling starts, drain the boiling water from the bath as rapidly as possible. Raise the lid of the bath a few inches to allow free circulation of air to permit more rapid cooling.

CAUTION! The contents of the bottle are under pressure and any attempt to hasten cooling by removing from the bath or adding cold water may cause the bottle to explode. Do not handle bottles until room temperature is reached.

Open the bottle and rinse the inside of the cap with water, collecting the rinsings in the bottle. Add approximately 50 ml of distilled water in all and titrate immediately with standard 0.5N sodium hydroxide solution using 1 ml of phenolphthalein in acetone as indicator.

Make a blank determination and also determine the free acidity of the sample.

Calculation

Use corresponding section of the earlier method.

DETERMINATION OF ALCOHOLIC HYDROXYL

BF$_3$–FISCHER REAGENT METHOD

Apparatus

Buret assemblies, two all-glass buret systems as shown in Figure 24.1.
Safety oven (explosion proof), capable of maintaining a temperature of 67 ± 1°C.
Volumetric flasks, 250 ml, glass-stoppered.

Reagents

Acetic acid, CP, glacial. If the water content of the acid is appreciably more than 0.1 %, mix the acid with the amount of CP acetic anhydride required to reduce the water content to 0.1 %. Allow to stand for 1 day before use.

Boron trifluoride, 97 %, obtainable in small cylinders from the Matheson Gas Products, East Rutherford, N.J.

Boron trifluoride reagent, double strength. Connect a needle valve (Hoke No. 341) to a cylinder of boron trifluoride gas. The valve and fittings must have a pressure rating of 3000 psi; the fittings used for hydrogen sulfide and hydrogen chloride may be used. Connect the exit of the needle valve through a trap to a piece of glass tubing of sufficient length to reach to the bottom of a 1-liter Pyrex mixing cylinder. Neoprene or Tygon tubing is satisfactory for the connections. The trap can be made from a small Erlenmeyer flask and a two-hole rubber stopper. *Boron trifluoride is extremely toxic.* Make sure that adequate protection is provided for the face and hands and carry out the following operations in a well-ventilated hood. Place 800 ml of acetic acid (0.1 % water by analysis) in a 1-liter Pyrex graduated cylinder, and pass boron trifluoride gas into the acid until an increase in weight of 200 g (approximately 120 ml) has been obtained. When cool, dilute the mixture to 1 liter with acetic acid and store in a glass-stoppered bottle.

Boron trifluoride reagent, single strength. Mix equal portions of the double strength reagent and acetic acid and store in a glass-stoppered bottle.

Fischer reagent.

Glycol–pyridine solution: prepare by mixing 1 part CP anhydrous pyridine with 4 parts of CP anhydrous ethylene glycol. Mix thoroughly and dispense from buret assembly.

Pyridine, CP, anhydrous (less than 0.1% water).

Procedure (in Absence of Amines)

Pipet 20 ml of the single strength reagent into a 250-ml glass-stoppered volumetric flask. Carry out this operation in a well-ventilated hood.

Introduce a weighed sample of such size that a total titration of, preferably, 20–30 ml but not more than 50 ml will be obtained. If the alcohol content is low, the sample size should not be increased beyond that which will dissolve completely in the reagent; do not use more than 10 ml unless a greater amount is proven to give higher accuracy. If desired, the sample may be dissolved in anhydrous acetic acid and aliquot portions used for the hydroxyl test and for the water determination required for correction.

Insert the stopper into the flask, after placing a thin strip of paper between the stopper and flask to allow venting, and heat the mixture for 2 hr at 67°C. Cool in a water bath to 20 ± 5°C, add 10 ml of CP anhydrous pyridine from a pipet and again bring to water bath temperature. Add 10 ml of anhydrous glycol–pyridine mixture from a protected buret and titrate with Fischer reagent to the orange-red point.

Make a blank determination on the reagents in parallel with the sample.

Determine the water content of the original sample.

Special Procedure (in the Presence of Amines)

Pipet 20 ml of the *double strength reagent* into a 250-ml glass-stoppered volumetric flask. Continue the treatment of sample and blanks as described above, except add 20 ml of pyridine instead of 10 ml.

Determine the water content of the original sample.

Calculation

$$\text{Hydroxyl value, equiv/100 g} = \frac{(S - B)(F)}{(W)(10)(18.02)} - \frac{A}{18.02}$$

where S = volume of Fischer reagent required to titrate the reacted sample, ml

      B = volume of Fischer reagent required to titrate the blank, ml

      F = equivalency factor for Fischer reagent, mg water per ml reagent

      W = weight of sample, g

      A = water content of original sample, %

DETERMINATION OF HYDROXYL

Lithium Aluminum Hydride Method

Apparatus

Gas-measuring system for measuring evolved hydrogen is illustrated in Figure 8.1, and consists of a 100-ml water-jacketed gas buret graduated in 0.2-ml divisions and equipped with a four-way *L*-bore stopcock, a leveling tube located in a position adjacent to the gas buret, a mercury lift connected at the top by means of a three-way cock to vacuum and air services and at the bottom to the buret and leveling tube by means of steel needle valves and plastic tubing, and hypotubing (14 gage stainless steel) connected to the gas buret by means of a metal spherical joint and looped as shown in Figure 8.1.

Thermometer, covering the normal variations in room temperature.

Reaction flask, round bottom, with a standard taper joint, having a capacity of approximately 50 ml, with a side arm of approximately 10-ml capacity, as illustrated in Figure 8.2. A standard taper joint is provided on the top of the side arm. The flask is attached to the system by means of an adapter.

Reagent preparation and storage flasks, consisting of two 250-ml conical flasks, one for preparation of reagent, having a standard taper joint and stopper, and the other for storage of reagent, sealed at the top. On opposite sides of each flask are sealed a standard taper joint and a stopcock as shown in Figure 8.3. A special connecting piece is provided for filtration of the reagent from one flask to the other.

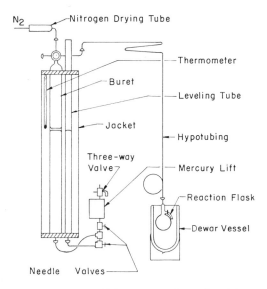

Figure 8.1. Lithium aluminum hydride apparatus. Reproduced by permission of the Shell Method Series.

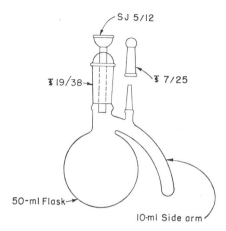

Figure 8.2. Reaction Flask. Reproduced by permission of the Shell Method Series.

Storage and dispensing apparatus for tetrahydrofuran, consisting of a 1-liter Pyrex bottle having a 29/42 standard taper joint into which two pieces of glass tubing are sealed as shown in Figure 8.4. One piece of tubing, 12-mm i.d., has a standard taper joint sealed at the top into which a pipet is inserted; the pipet is provided with a stopcock and a small Drierite tube. The other piece of tubing, 6-mm i.d., is connected to a Drierite tube, small glass *T*-tube, and the source of nitrogen. With nitrogen flowing, the solvent is forced into the pipet by placing a finger over the open end of the *T*-tube.

Rubber serum stoppers, sleeve type, for insertion in a 19/38 standard taper joint.

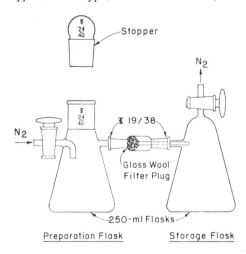

Figure 8.3. Reagent preparation. Reproduced by permission of the Shell Method Series.

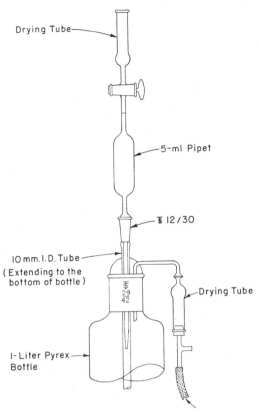

Figure 8.4. Solvent storage and dispensing system. Reproduced by permission of the Shell Method Series.

Hypodermic syringe and needle, a 5-ml glass hypodermic syringe and plunger, graduated in 0.2-ml subdivisions, and stainless steel needle.

Steel balls, approximately $\frac{3}{8}$-in. diameter.

Reagents

Lithium aluminum hydride reagent, saturated solution in tetrahydrofuran. Connect the flasks as shown in Figure 8.3 with a glass filter plug inserted in the connecting piece and flush completely with nitrogen. Add approximately 11 g of lithium aluminum hydride and 100 ml of dry tetrahydrofuran to the reagent preparation flask. Stopper the flask and, with the stopcocks open, swirl vigorously. After most of the lithium aluminum hydride has dissolved, close the stopcock and allow the solution to stand overnight. Filter the reagent into the storage flask, maintaining slight nitrogen pressure to facilitate the transfer. Disassemble the apparatus and close the storage flask by inserting a serum stopper into the standard taper joint.

CAUTION!   During preparation of the reagent wear a face mask and keep the reagent off the skin. The hazards involved and precautions to be observed in the use and disposal of lithium aluminum hydride are described in page 144.

Tetrahydrofuran: to purify, add 1 liter of tetrahydrofuran to a 2-liter round-bottom flask fitted with a standard taper joint. Displace the air from the flask with dry nitrogen and maintain a slow stream of nitrogen over the solvent. Add lithium aluminum hydride in small increments with swirling. Continue the addition until an excess is present, as indicated by the absence of further gas evolution (10–20 g will usually suffice). Connect the flask to a distilling head and condenser, and distil the tetrahydrofuran in a hood, using a mantle-type heater. Tetrahydrofuran boils at approximately 68°C and is highly flammable.

Discard the first 50 ml of distillate, and collect approximately 800 ml in a 1-liter Pyrex dispensing bottle (Figure 8.4) from which air is excluded by a slow stream of dry nitrogen. Discontinue the distillation when approximately 100 ml of liquid remains in the flask. Protect the distillate from moisture by a Drierite tube immediately upon completion of the distillation.

Apparatus Preparation

Assemble the apparatus as shown in Figure 8.1; bend the hypotubing as shown. Solder a 5/12 steel outer spherical joint to the upper end of the hypotubing and attach to the glass spherical joint of the gas buret, using sealing wax. Clamp the hypotubing at some convenient place along the top to prevent undue strain on the joint where the hypotubing is joined to the gas buret. Solder a 5/12 steel inner spherical joint to the other end of the hypotubing and attach the glass adapter (Figure 8.2), using sealing wax. Paint the outside of the spherical joints, where the metal–glass seals are made, with a thin coating of glyptal.

Place a layer of purified tetrahydrofuran in the buret so that the gas is always saturated with this solvent. This tetrahydrofuran should be replaced weekly with fresh material. Do not allow the tetrahydrofuran to come into contact with the buret stopcock, as it will dissolve the lubricant.

Each day, before performing any analyses, test the apparatus for leaks. Raise the mercury in the buret to a convenient level near the top, attach a flask to the apparatus, and turn the stopcock to connect with the flask. Lower the mercury column as far as it will go and note the buret reading; allow it to stand for 3–4 min and again note the reading. If a volume change is observed, carefully relubricate the buret stopcock and ground glass joints and test again. Read the top level of tetrahydrofuran in the buret when measuring the volume.

Dry all glassware in an oven at 110°C for 30 min, and cool under a stream of dry nitrogen prior to use.

Sample

Use an amount of sample calculated to yield 60–80 ml of hydrogen; maximum sample sizes for typical anhydrous samples are given below. Limit the size of sample to 0.5 g unless the behavior of the material with respect to side reactions is known.

Estimated hydroxyl content, equiv/100 g	Sample size, g
0.1	2.0
0.5	0.4
1.0	0.2

Procedure

General Procedure. Into a dry reaction flask previously flushed with dry nitrogen, weigh, to the nearest milligram, the appropriate amount of sample as given above. Add 5.0 ml of tetrahydrofuran, stopper the flask, and swirl gently until the material has dissolved. By means of a hypodermic syringe, add 5 ml of lithium aluminum hydride reagent into the side arm of the flask through the standard taper joint on the top of the side arm and cap the standard taper joint.

The syringe should be dismantled and set aside for cleaning immediately after use.

Flush the gas-measuring apparatus with nitrogen for approximately 5 min, uncap the joints on the reaction flask, and immediately attach the flask to the system. Allow nitrogen to pass through for approximately 1 min at a slow rate, shut off the nitrogen, and cap the small joint on the side arm. Turn the buret stopcock to connect with the reaction flask, immerse the flask completely in an ice slurry kept in a Dewar flask, and balance the levels of mercury. Allow several minutes for the system to equilibrate; equilibrium is established when the levels of mercury in the buret and leveling tube remain constant for approximately 5 min. Turn the buret stopcock to connect with the atmosphere and force the liquid level in the buret up to the zero mark, expelling the nitrogen from the buret into the atmosphere.

Turn the buret stopcock to connect with the reaction flask, set the three-way valve of the mercury lift on "Vacuum," and open the lower needle valve. Raise the reaction flask out of the ice bath, open the upper needle valve on the mercury lift slightly, and tip the flask so that a portion of the reagent in the side arm flows into the sample solution. Swirl the flask and continue adding reagent in small increments, with swirling, until all has been used. Maintain the system as near atmospheric pressure as possible at all times.

When all gas evolution has creased, replace the reaction flask in the ice bath, close the upper needle valve, and equilibrate for 10 min; establish atmospheric pressure in the buret. When the mercury levels in the buret and leveling tube remain constant for 5 min, read and record the buret volume, jacket temperature, and barometric pressure.

Resin Procedure. Into a dry reaction flask previously flushed with dry nitrogen, weigh to the nearest milligram the appropriate amount of sample as given earlier. Introduce a steel ball in the flask, add 5.0 ml of tetrahydrofuran, swirl gently to dissolve the sample, and add an additional 5.0 ml of tetrahydrofuran. By means of a hypodermic syringe, introduce 5 ml of lithium aluminum hydride reagent into the side arm of the flask, cap the standard taper joint, and proceed as directed above.

Mix the solution thoroughly, swirling the flask in such a manner that the steel ball will aid in dispersing any precipitate that is formed. Immerse the flask in the ice bath, allow several minutes for equilibration, establish atmospheric pressure in the buret, and record the gas volume and jacket temperature. Allow the mixture to react until a constant volume is obtained; in general, resins require reaction times of 1–2.5 hr. The contents of the flask should be thoroughly mixed several times during the reaction and gas volume readings taken every 15–30 min. When analyzing materials that require extended reaction times it is advisable to leave the three-way valve to the "Vacuum" position between volume readings.

BLANK. Make a blank determination exactly as described above, omitting the sample, and using the same volume of tetrahydrofuran as used for the sample determination.

WATER. Determine the water content of the sample the same day the hydroxyl value is determined.

ACIDITY. Determine the acidity of the material by titration with standard base to the phenolphthalein end point.

Calculation

$$\text{Hydroxyl value, equiv/100 g} = \frac{(S - B)(1.604)(P - Q)}{(T + 273)(W)(1000)} - \left(\frac{C}{9} + D\right)$$

where S = volume of gas evolved by the sample, ml

B = volume of gas evolved by the blank, ml

P = atmospheric pressure, mm

Q = vapor pressure of tetrahydrofuran, mm, from the following table:

Temp., °C	Vapor pressure of tetrahydrofuran, mm Hg
10	92
15	116
20	142
25	173
30	214

T = jacket temperature, °C

W = weight of sample, g

C = water content of the sample, wt %

D = acid content of the sample, equiv/100 g

1.604 = reciprocal of the gas constant

9 = equivalent weight of water in this determination

Safety Precautions in the Use of Lithium Aluminum Hydride

Lithium aluminum hydride is a solid that is stable in dry air at room temperature. It decomposes with liberation of hydrogen at temperatures above 125°C and burns with a hot flame when ignited. It reacts violently with water, alcohols, and acids with the release of hydrogen. In general, it reacts with most classes of organic compounds except hydrocarbons and ethers.

The hazards to bear in mind when using lithium aluminum hydride concern fire or personal injury.

Fire. The solid is extremely flammable. In addition, it reacts violently with many materials to produce hydrogen, a flammable gas explosive over a wide concentration range. These factors combine to make the material extremely hazardous unless handled with caution. Fires can be initiated by

contact with water or other reactive materials;

frictional heat generated during grinding or crushing;

static electricity generated by agitation in an insulated enclosure, for example, when pouring the powder through a glass funnel;

sparks produced by forceful contact with hard metals.

Personal contact. By virtue of the extreme reactivity of the material, it will produce severe caustic burns upon the skin. Obviously, inhalation of the dust is harmful because of severe damage to the lungs and air passages.

Handle the storage can with care; do not shake it. Work in a hood isolated from flammable liquids and keep water or other reactive materials away.

When handling the solid material or solutions, wear goggles. Keep the solid and solutions off the skin.

Have at hand a supply of powdered calcium carbonate or limestone for smothering fires and for covering any spilled solutions of lithium aluminum hydride. Do not use any conventional fire extinguisher for lithium aluminum hydride fires.

Open the storage can carefully and immediately displace the gas in the can with dry nitrogen. Transfer the quantity of solid required to another dry vessel, flush the storage can with dry nitrogen, and replace the cover immediately.

Large lumps may be broken by cautious pounding with a nonsparking (aluminum, brass) instrument in a dry metal vessel other than the storage can. Avoid breathing the dust.

When preparing solutions of lithium aluminum hydride, flush out the vessel containing the solvent with nitrogen prior to adding the solid. Add the solid in small quantities and maintain an atmosphere of nitrogen in the vessel.

When necessary to dispose of a solution containing lithium aluminum hydride, the reagent should be destroyed by diluting it with ethyl ether, gradually mixing the ether solution with a 10% solution of isopropyl alcohol in ether, and finally pouring the mixture slowly into a large excess of water. This procedure is advisable since violent spattering results upon adding the reagent to water.

SPECIFIC METHODS FOR DETERMINATION OF HYDROXYL COMPOUNDS

DETERMINATION OF METHYLOL GROUPS IN PHENOLIC RESINS

An intermediate step in the production of the phenol-formaldehyde resins is the formation of condensed structures containing the methylol function

$$-\!\!\!\bigcirc\!\!\!-CH_2OH$$

The methylol group then proceeds to condense further with other phenolic molecules, leading to resinous products. When working with this type of polymer, it is generally necessary to have some measurement of the methylol content. Procedures for this determination have been published based upon the condensation reaction of the methylol group and phenol to form water as one of the products. In the work of Martin (16) the sample was reacted with phenol in benzene solution with p-toluenesulfonic acid as a catalyst.

$$\langle\!\rangle\!-\!CH_2OH + \langle\!\rangle\!-\!OH \longrightarrow \langle\!\rangle\!-\!CH_2\!\!\overset{OH}{\langle\!\rangle} + H_2O$$

The water produced was continuously distilled from the mixtures as a benzene azeotrope and measured in a calibrated receiver. Using the same reaction but employing the Karl Fischer reagent for measurement of the evolved water, Stenmark and Weiss (17) found it possible to effect a 50-fold reduction in sample size. With the Fischer reagent technique it was found preferable to use xylene as the solvent and boron trifluoride as the catalyst. The recommended method included here and the data given are taken from the work of Stenmark and Weiss.

Some data on the behavior of pure compounds are shown in Table 8.7. Essentially quantitative recoveries were observed with the methylol compounds examined. Dibenzyl ethers reacted to produce almost 1 mole of

Table 8.7. Reactivity of Pure Compounds in the Fischer–Methylol Method

Compound	Reaction, %
Benzyl alcohol	99.0, 99.6, 99.6
p-Hydroxybenzyl alcohol	99.6, 100.2
o-Hydroxybenzyl alcohol	99.2, 99.4
Benzhydrol	99.6, 100.0
Benzyl ethyl ether	3.6, 3.7
Dibenzyl ether	96.3, 96.5
Bis(2-hydroxybenzyl)ether	97.2, 97.8
Formaldehyde	101.0, 101.0
Acetaldehyde	99.5, 100.5
Benzaldehyde	100.4, 100.4
Acetone	7.3
Methyl isobutyl ketone	0.2

water per mole, possibly via a two-step reaction as follows:

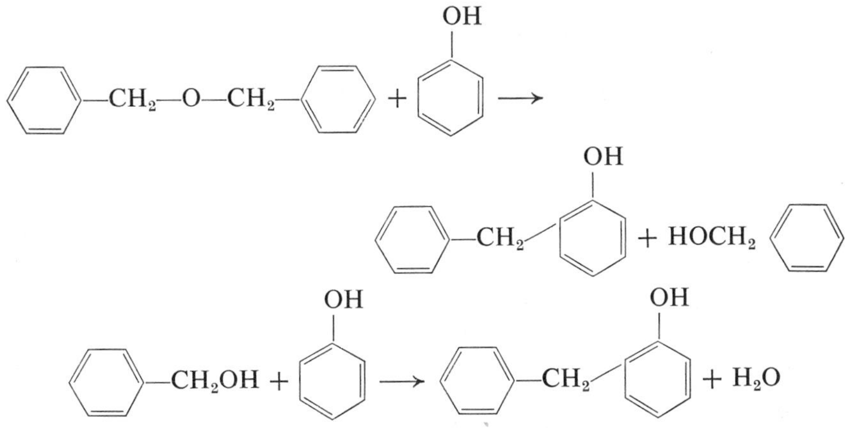

In view of the presence of considerable unreacted formaldehyde in the phenolic resins under consideration, the stoichiometry of the reaction of aldehydes in the method was tested and in addition the reactions of other materials were also studied. The results of these tests (Table 8.7) show that formaldehyde, acetaldehyde, and benzaldehyde react to form 1 mole of water per mole of aldehyde, in excellent agreement with theory. Because of the observed stoichiometry, the methylol content of phenolic resins can be obtained by application of a correction for carbonyl content. The ketones tested, acetone and methyl isobutyl ketone, reacted to the extent of 7.3 and 0.2%, respectively; this low reactivity is not a serious handicap, as ketones are not constituents of the phenolic resins under consideration.

An example of the application of the method, in conjunction with other functional methods, is shown by the data in Table 8.8 on three phenol-formaldehyde resins of low molecular weight ("resols"). These resins had been prepared with excess formaldehyde under alkaline conditions and were stored in a refrigerator at $-15°C$ to prevent further polymerization. Water was determined by titration with Fischer reagent after reaction of the interfering aldehyde groups with hydrocyanic acid and the carbonyl content was determined by the Fischer–carbonyl method.

In order to gain further information about the constitution of these materials and as a further check on the accuracy of these procedures, the resins were also analyzed for total hydroxyl, phenolic hydroxyl, and total oxygen. Total hydroxyl was determined by lithium aluminum hydride and phenolic hydroxyl by potentiometric titration. Total oxygen was determined by a modified Unterzaucher method: In every case the Unterzaucher values

Table 8.8. Functional Oxygen Balance Obtained for Phenolic Resins

Functional group, equiv/100 g	Resin 1	Resin 2	Resin 3
Carbonyl	0.007	0.133	0.407
Water	0.109	0.243	0.048
Methylol plus dibenzyl ethers	0.345, 0.348, 0.348	0.691, 0.680	0.819, 0.820
Phenolic hydroxyl[a]	0.79	0.67	0.68
Total functional oxygen	1.26	1.81[b]	1.96
Total oxygen[c]	1.30, 1.30	1.76, 1.79	1.97
Total hydroxyl[d]	1.03	1.28	1.42
Phenolic hydroxyl	0.79	0.67	0.68
Alcoholic hydroxyl	0.24	0.61	0.74
Methylol plus dibenzyl ethers[e]	0.35	0.69	0.82
Dibenzyl ethers[e]	0.11	0.08	0.08

[a] Potentiometric titration.
[b] Includes 0.07 equiv/100 g of ethoxyl by Zeisel method.
[c] Modified Unterzaucher.
[d] Lithium aluminum hydride determination.
[e] Calculated as difference between above two values.

agreed well with the total functional oxygen obtained by adding the values for carbonyl, water, methylol, and phenolic hydroxyl. The alcoholic hydroxyl is determined as the difference between total hydroxyl and the phenolic hydroxyl. In the resins studied the alcoholic hydroxyl should equal the methylol content. Thus an estimate of the dibenzyl ether content is obtained as the difference between the alcoholic hydroxyl values and the methylol plus dibenzyl ether values.

DETERMINATION OF METHYLOL GROUPS

FISCHER REAGENT METHOD

Apparatus

Buret assembly, all-glass.
Safety oven, explosion-proof, capable of maintaining a temperature of 60 ± 1°C.

Reagents

Boron trifluoride–phenol complex (26% BF$_3$), obtainable from General Chemical Division of Allied Chemical and Dye Corporation, New York.
Fischer reagent.
Ethylene glycol–pyridine mixture.
Phenol, CP, crystals.
Phenol–boron trifluoride reagent: add 20 ml of CP xylene and 10 ml of boron

trifluoride–phenol complex to 40 g of phenol in a 125-ml glass-stoppered flask. Heat the flask on a hot plate and swirl the contents to effect solution.

> **CAUTION!** Boron trifluoride is extremely toxic and phenol is a severe skin irritant. Use rubber gloves and a face mask during preparation of the reagent. If phenol or the reagent is spilled on the skin, wash immediately with water, then with alcohol.

Phenol–xylene solution: add 100 ml of CP xylene to 200 g of phenol in a 500-ml glass-stoppered flask. Heat the flask on a hot plate and swirl the content to effect solution.

Pyridine, CP anhydrous.

Xylene, CP.

Procedure

Weigh a sample containing 6–9 mmoles of methylol plus water into a clean, dry 250-ml volumetric flask. Pipet 20 ml of phenol–xylene solution into the flask and dissolve the sample. Pipet 5 ml of the phenol–boron trifluoride reagent into the flask. Carry out this operation in a well-ventilated hood.

Swirl the flask to mix and heat the mixture for 3 hr at 60°C.

At the end of the reaction period, cool the mixture to room temperature and add 10 ml of anhydrous glycol–pyridine mixture from a protected buret. Titrate the mixture to the orange-red end point with Fischer reagent.

Make a blank determination on the reagents in an identical manner but omit the sample.

Determine the water content of the original sample.

Determine the carbonyl content of the original sample by the Fischer–carbonyl method.

Calculation

$$\text{Methylol content, equiv/100 g} = \frac{(A - B)(F)}{(W)(10)(18.02)} - C - \frac{D}{18.02}$$

where A = volume of Fischer reagent required for methylol determination on sample, ml

B = volume of Fischer reagent required for reagent blank in methylol determination, ml

F = standardization factor for Fischer reagent in mg of water equivalent to 1 ml of reagent

W = weight of sample taken for methylol determination, g

C = carbonyl content, equiv/100 g

D = water content, wt %

DETERMINATION OF HYDROXYLIC COMPOUNDS BY GAS CHROMATOGRAPHY

Gas chromatography is an excellent means for separating and determining the alcohols. Since, however, the hydroxyl function imparts polarity to the molecule, some tailing is generally observed with the usual substrates and means should be taken to overcome this effect to obtain good resolution and accurate analysis. Improved resolution can be obtained by utilizing nonpolar column packings; Hollis (18) used porous polyaromatic polymer beads, which are now commercially available. With such gas chromatographic columns it is possible to achieve high resolution of mixtures of alcohols, glycols, and other polar compounds. An alternative approach that has become very popular is to convert the polar hydroxyl function into a nonpolar function by the quantitative formation of an appropriate derivative, such as the acetates (19), the trifluoroacetates (20, 21), and, especially useful, the silyl ethers, whose preparation and properties have been examined by many investigators. Early work at the U.S. Bureau of Mines showed that the conversion of alcohols or phenols to their trimethylsilyl ethers provided considerably improved mass spectra (22, 23). Their work also led to the investigation of the suitability of these ethers as improved derivatives of phenols for separation by gas chromatography (24).

The trimethylsilyl group can be easily introduced into a series of compounds containing active hydrogen, including hydroxyl, carboxylic acid, mercaptan, and amine. The ether-forming reaction with trimethylchlorosilane follows the indicated course.

$$CH_3-\underset{\underset{CH_3}{|}}{\overset{\overset{CH_3}{|}}{Si}}-Cl + ROH \longrightarrow R-O-\underset{\underset{CH_3}{|}}{\overset{\overset{CH_3}{|}}{Si}}-CH_3 + HCl$$

Hexamethyldisilazane can also be used as a converting reagent without producing acid.

$$(CH_3)_3Si-\underset{}{\overset{\overset{H}{|}}{N}}-Si(CH_3)_3 + 2ROH \longrightarrow 2ROSi(CH_3)_3 + NH_3$$

A number of analysts prefer to use a combination of the two ether-forming reagents so that the reaction mixture remains neutral through the reaction of the NH_3 and HCl to form NH_4Cl. Formation of the ethers and NH_4Cl is complete within a few minutes. A portion of the whole reaction mixture, including the suspended NH_4Cl, is injected directly into a gas chromatographic apparatus. The power of this technique is illustrated by the work of Makita and Wells (25) on the separation of the bile acids and by a number of authors (26) for the gas chromatographic separation of the sugars. The recommended method for this determination is taken from a number of the literature sources.

DETERMINATION OF ALCOHOLS AND PHENOLS

Trimethylsilyl Ether–Gas Chromatographic Method

Apparatus

Either a *packed* or a *capillary column* can be used. Better resolution will generally result with a capillary column. A suitable partitioning phase is prepared from 0.5 g of SF 96 Silicone plus 20 mg of GAS-QUAT L (available from Lachat Chemical Co., 20200 Ashland Ave., Chicago Heights, Illinois). This mixture can be used to coat a capillary column by dissolving the reagents in 10 ml of chloroform. A programmed-temperature chromatographic apparatus is most suitable for a wide boiling range mixture.

Reagents

Hexamethyldisilazane (HMDS), purified grade, Pierce Chemical Company, Rockford, Illinois. Store the vial in a closed wide-mouth bottle containing a layer of indicating Drierite.

Trimethylchlorosilane (TMCS), specially purified grade, Pierce Chemical Company.

Drierite, indicating, 10–20 mesh, anhydrous $CaSO_4$. W. A. Hammond Drierite Company, Xenia, Ohio.

Trimethylsilylation Procedure

Weigh a sample containing 0.4–0.9 mmole of alcohol into a dry 1-dram vial having a screw cap with an aluminum foil liner. Using a syringe and hypodermic needle withdraw 0.2 ml of hexamethyldisilazane (HMDS) from the elastomer-capped vial and add it to the sample. Cap the sample vial securely and shake the contents to dissolve the sample in the HMDS. Withdraw 0.1 ml of trimethyl-chlorosilane (TMCS) from the supply vessel, using a micropipet or syringe as needed, and add it to the sample. Cap the sample vial securely and shake the contents vigorously for 1 min to ensure mixing of the reactants. The reaction mixture will be viscous during the first few minutes because of precipitated NH_4Cl.

Prepare a blank on the reagents occasionally, particularly when a fresh reagent stock vial is started, by following the procedure above, omitting the sample.

During the above operations minimize the exposure of the reagents to atmospheric moisture. Use dry glassware, syringes, etc., and make transfers with the minimum of delay. Cap the sample reaction mixture immediately after adding reagents. If the TMCS is in a screw-capped bottle, cap it as soon as possible after withdrawing a portion. Put both reagent vessels back into the storage bottles containing Drierite and close them as soon as practicable.

Allow the reaction mixture of sample plus HMDS and TMCS to stand 10 min or longer before taking a portion for chromatography. Securely capped mixtures can be left at least a day without affecting the results. If the sample size is small (e.g., 0.4 mmole) the minimum reaction time can be reduced to 5 min.

Rinse out syringes and micropipets with acetone promptly after use and dry by sucking a stream of air through them.

GC Analysis Procedure

Inject a sample into the vaporizer of such a size that it does not seriously overload the column for separating the major components but is adequate for detecting components present in concentrations as low as 0.1 %.

Calculation

Measure the peak areas on the chromatogram and correct these for detector attenuation. Omit any peaks attributable to the reagents. Apply any necessary calibration factors to the peaks and calculate the weight percent of each component by dividing its peak area by the sum of the peak areas for all components and multiply by 100.

DETERMINATION OF THE HYDROXYL GROUP BY COLORIMETRIC MEANS

Several procedures have been published for the colorimetric determination of the alcoholic hydroxyl group. These have included the use of the following reagents: 3,5-dinitrobenzoyl chloride (27), 5-(p-sulfamylphenylazo)-salicyclic acid (28), and ceric salts (29–31). The 3,5-dinitrobenzoyl chloride method is one of the more specific and accurate techniques and involves the formation of the esters of the alcohols with the reagent catalyzed by pyridine. The reaction mixture is treated with aqueous hydrochloric acid and the esters extracted with n-hexane. After several steps to purify the ester solution the esters are converted to a red quinoidal ion by treatment with a solution of dimethylformamide and propylenediamide and the intensity of the color at 5250 Å taken as a function of the alcohol concentration. The method was found sensitive to microgram quantities of aliphatic monohydroxyl alcohols. Ethylene glycol and diethylene glycol failed to produce any color and only some 50% reaction was found with several other diols. Belcher, Dryhurst, and MacDonald (32) explored the application of the colorimetric 3,5-dinitrobenzoyl chloride method for the submicro determination of the hydroxyl group. They found it satisfactory for most simple aliphatic alcohols including isopropyl and isobutyl alcohols, decanol, dodecanol, and octa-decanol and noted that methanol consistently gave results some 20% low based on the calibration curve obtained with ethanol. Hydroxyl compounds with an aromatic ring in the molecule, such as benzyl alcohol and benz-hydrol, gave low and inconsistent results.

One of the more interesting colorimetric methods recently suggested for this determination was published by Gutnikov and Schenk (33), who converted the alcohols initially into the corresponding acetate esters and then utilized for familiar ferric hydroxamate colorimetric technique (see Chapter 7). The acetylation reagent consisted of acetic anhydride dissolved in pyridine and used perchloric acid as catalyst. After the acetylation was complete, the excess acetic anhydride was destroyed by treating the reaction mixture with a 25% aqueous pyridine solution as the hydrolysis reagent. The ferric hydroxamate chelate was prepared by reaction first with hydroxylamine and then with ferric perchlorate and the absorbance of the sample was measured at 5240 Å. Through this course of reactions, the same end product, acethydroxamic acid, is formed from the hydroxamation of all the alcohols. It would be expected that the molar absorptivities of all the alcohols would be the same, but this is not the case since the values range from 1140 to 1180 liters/mole-cm with some secondary alcohols, to a high value of 1340 with methanol. The variation in absorptivity must result from the variation in the extent of the reactions. In contrast to the dinitrobenzoyl chloride method, the ferric hydroxamate method provides satisfactory results in the analysis of benzyl alcohol and ethylene glycol.

DETERMINATION OF THE HYDROXYL GROUP BY INFRARED ABSORPTION SPECTROSCOPY

A major problem in the application of the spectroscopic methods for analysis of the hydroxyl group is caused by the large extent of hydrogen bonding, which leads to the association of molecules in solution and strongly affects the position and intensity of the hydroxyl absorption. In the direct determination of the hydroxyl group by conventional infrared spectroscopy, use can be made of the intensity of absorption of the band near 2.86 μ, which is associated with the stretching frequency of the O—H bond. Because the location and intensity of this band varies with the nature and degree of hydrogen bonding, the system in which the hydroxyl content is determined requires that hydrogen bonding remain constant. To satisfy this condition, dilute solutions in such polar solvents as methyl ethyl ketone or tetrahydrofuran are employed. The infrared method can be calibrated with a material whose hydroxyl content is known by a stoichiometric method such as the acetic anhydride or acetyl chloride technique. A suitable standard for determination of low concentrations of the hydroxyl group can be a polyalkylene oxide of low degree of polymerization. It is important to note that small amounts of water affect the determination of the hydroxyl function since water not only can change the hydrogen bonding properties of the

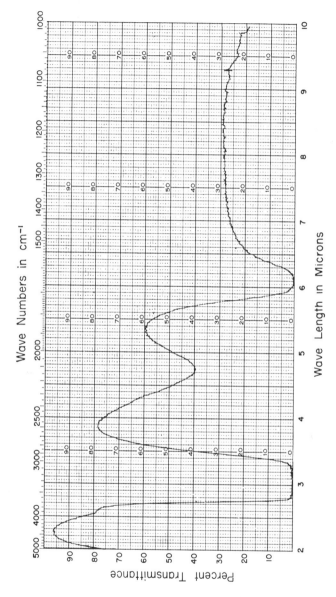

Figure 8.5. Infrared absorption spectrum of water (H₂O), 0.025 mm CELL.

system but also contributes to the absorption. The apparent hydroxyl content increases in the presence of water; however, the increase is not directly related to the amount of water present. It has been found that the adverse effects of water could be avoided by drying the solvent and the solutions with Type 3A molecular sieve.

An excellent review of techniques for determination of functional groups by infrared absorption spectroscopy is given by Bellamy in his widely used text (34).

An interesting and important specific application of the infrared technique for measurement of the hydroxyl group is through its property of containing an active hydrogen group. For instance, the alcoholic proton will exchange with deuterium from deuterium oxide by the following reactions:

$$ROH + D_2O \rightleftharpoons ROD + DOH$$

$$H_2O + D_2O \rightleftharpoons 2DOH$$

By using a large excess (greater than 30:1) of deuterium to active hydrogen, the equilibria are shifted strongly to production of the DOH species.

One of the early applications of this technique was carried out by dissolving the sample in deuterium oxide and determining the change in composition of the water obtained by distillation (35, 36). The possibility of utilizing infrared absorption measurements for following the exchange of active hydrogen with deuterium from deuterium oxide was first suggested in 1949 by Gore, Barnes, and Petersen (37). DOH is determined in D_2O by infrared absorption measurement of the 2.97 μ band characteristic of the —OH group. The distinctive differences between the infrared absorption spectra of H_2O and D_2O are shown in Figures 8.5 and 8.6. The essential difference is that the bands for D_2O appear at longer wavelengths than do the corresponding bands of H_2O; therefore, the OH group can be easily observed in the presence of the OD group. The characteristic OH band at 2.97 μ is observed in the D_2O sample due to a slight water contamination.

The D_2O exchange and infrared measurement of DOH have been combined by Harp and Eiffert (38) into a useful technique for determining the active hydrogen content of both water-soluble and insoluble materials. Results obtained from the analysis of known compounds by Harp and Eiffert are shown in Table 8.9 from analyses made on a Perkin–Elmer Model 21 infrared spectrophotometer using a 0.025-cm cell for the soluble compounds and a 0.05-mm cell for the insoluble materials. The recommended Deuterium Exchange method is taken from their publication. It is rapid and has general utility; its limitation is that the accuracy is not high. A more complete review of chemical and physical methods for determination of active hydrogen in organic materials was published some years ago (7) in which a number of isotopic exchange techniques are considered.

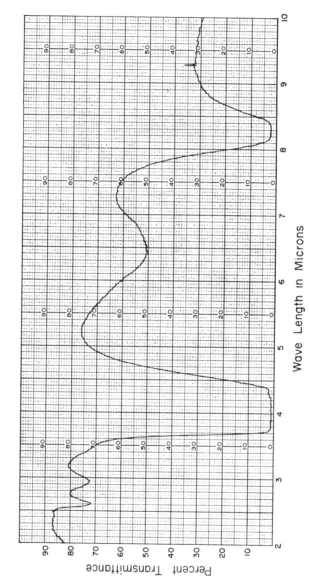

Figure 8.6. Infrared absorption spectrum of deuterium oxide (D_2O) 0.025 mm CELL.

Table 8.9.   Active Hydrogen Values Determined by the Deuterium
Isotope Exchange Method[a]

	Active hydrogen per mole	
Material	Theory	Found
Water-soluble		
Urea	4.00	4.12, 3.95
Potassium acid phthalate	1.00	0.95
2-Amino-2-hydroxymethyl-1,3-propanediol	5.00	4.80
Water-insoluble		
Aniline	2.00	2.01, 1.98
Cetyl alcohol	1.00	0.99
Fluorene	0.00	0
2-Methyl-2-pentene	0.00	0
2-*tert*-Butyl-6-methylphenol in		
hydrocarbon solution	1.0	0.98

[a] Data from Harp and Eiffert (38).

DETERMINATION OF HYDROXYL

DEUTERIUM EXCHANGE METHOD

Apparatus

Spectrophotometer, any commercial model equipped with cells of thin-walled fused quartz. Cells with an internal spacing of 0.025 and 0.050 mm and window thickness of 1 mm are recommended.

Reagents

Deuterium oxide, 99.5% pure. Because of the hygroscopic nature of D_2O, preparation and transfer of samples should be done in a dry box. Samples should be stored in glass vessels with rubber serum caps from which transfers can be made with hypodermic syringes. Equilibrate all sample-handling equipment with D_2O.

Instrument Calibration

Water is a convenient source of active hydrogen and is used to prepare calibration samples covering the range of 0–50 to 0–25 g of water per liter for cells of 0.025 or 0.050 mm thickness, respectively. Weigh a known amount of water into a 5-ml volumetric flask, stopper the flask with a rubber serum stopper, and then, in a dry box, add the D_2O by means of a hypodermic syringe. Determine the absorbance, equal to log $[T_0/T]$, for the calibration solutions, where T_0 is the transmittance at 2.30 μ and T is the transmittance at 2.97 μ, both measured relative to air. The transmittance at 2.30 μ was selected as the baseline reference point, because D_2O has maximum transmittance here, as do most of the samples to be analyzed. Blank corrections on D_2O are necessary for all absorbance measurements because even the best commercial D_2O has some residual OH absorption. From the measurements made, prepare the usual calibration curve of corrected absorbance vs. concentration of active hydrogen, in moles per liter, for use in the analysis of unknown samples.

Procedure—Soluble Samples

Weigh a portion of the sample into a 5-ml volumetric flask and then fill it to volume with D_2O, using the precautions described above to avoid moisture contamination. Water-soluble materials exchange rapidly and it is only necessary to provide good mixing to obtain equilibrium. Measure the transmittance of the sample–D_2O solution at 2.30 and 2.97 μ and from this calculate the absorbance of the solution as described above. Apply a correction for the cell blank and the residual DOH absorbance in the D_2O used. This corrected absorbance is used to find the concentration of —OH groups from the calibration curve.

Procedure—Insoluble Samples

The techniques for water-insoluble materials are similar to those used for soluble samples. For liquids, known weights of sample and D_2O are placed together in a stoppered flask and shaken long enough to assure complete exchange. If the sample is a solid or a viscous liquid, it should be dissolved in, or diluted with, a dry, nonreactive solvent such as benzene, hexane, or carbon tetrachloride. If emulsions form during the contacting step it may be necessary to centrifuge to obtain a clear D_2O phase. After the D_2O phase is separated, its absorbance is measured as described above. The active hydrogen content is calculated in a similar fashion, except that the volume of the solution in the calculation is only the volume of the D_2O phase.

Calculation

Calculate the active hydrogen content as follows:

$$\text{active hydrogen content per mole} = \frac{\text{moles of DOH per liter of solution}}{\text{moles of sample per liter of solution}}$$

DETERMINATION OF THE HYDROXYL GROUP BY NUCLEAR MAGNETIC RESONANCE (NMR)

Thorough studies carried out on the NMR spectra of alcohols and phenols have shown that the absorption position varies within a wide area and is dependent upon solvent, concentration, and temperature (39, 40, 41). When the system is simple it is possible to determine the hydroxyl group resonance directly by integration of high resolution NMR. Jungnickel and Forbes (42) found good accuracy in this measurement with a number of functional groups. In complex systems, however, the hydroxyl function, if present in low concentrations, can be obscured in the general proton spectra. This problem can be overcome and the hydroxyl proton identified and determined quantitatively by shifting the hydroxyl resonance to an otherwise empty region of the spectrum through the addition of an acid, such as formic acid. The exchange between the hydroxyl protons in the sample and the exchangeable proton from formic acid results in only one resonance line. The position of this line is intermediate between the two normal resonance positions and depends upon the relative concentrations of the two species. The integral for the shifted hydroxyl line must be corrected for the amount of acid proton added, which can be done very simply because the formic acid also produces a C—H resonance line equivalent in magnitude to that of the acid proton resonance line. The NMR measurement is made with the instrument operated in the integration mode and since the magnetic resonance absorption is identical for all protons, a simple ratio of integration values provides the amount of hydroxyl protons relative to the total amount of protons. Consequently, no calibration is necessary for the relative determination. If the absolute concentration of hydroxyl protons is to be determined, calibration with any compound or solution of known concentration of protons may be made. A useful solvent for the NMR analysis of alcohols is deuterochloroform. Because of the large effect of water, it is best to dry the solution of the sample over Type 3A molecular sieve. Since this technique is based on measurement of exchangeable protons, other exchangeable functions, such as amines, will also be counted.

Some data obtained in the determination of the hydroxyl function in several compounds are given in Table 8.10. With simple alcohols, in which the hydroxyl group was directly observable, a simple integration was all that was required and the results show good accuracy. For more complex materials, in which the hydroxyl resonance was obscured, formic acid was added

Table 8.10. Results Obtained in the Determination of Hydroxyl Groups by Nuclear Magnetic Resonance

Compound	Hydroxyl H as % of total H		Theory or alternate method
	Direct NMR	After addition of formic acid	
Ethyl alcohol	16.6		16.7
Butyl alcohol	9.8[a]		10.0
Hexanediol	14.4		14.3
Poly(butadiene monoxide)		4.3, 4.5	4.5[b]

[a] From Jungnickel and Forbes (42).

[b] By calculation from results of BF_3–Fischer method.

Table 8.11. Results of Integration of Proton NMR Spectra of Pure Compounds[a]

Compound	Purity, wt %	Proton type	Chemical shift, δ, ppm	Percent hydrogen Theory	Percent hydrogen Found	Dev. from theory
CH_3—CH_2OH	99.94	—OH —CH_3 —CH_2—	4.90 1.17 3.60	16.7 50.0 33.3	17.2 49.3 33.5	+0.5 −0.7 +0.2
CH_3—CH_2—CH_2—CH_2OH	E.K. White Label	OH O—CH_2— Alkyl	4.7 3.5 0.8–1.7	10.0 20.0 70.0	9.8 19.9 70.3	−0.2 −0.1 +0.3
CH_3—CH_2—CH_2—O—CH_2—CH_2—CH_3	E.K. Anal. Distilled	—CH_2—O β—CH_2— CH_3—	3.30 1.50 0.90	28.6 28.6 42.8	28.8 30.0 41.2	+0.2 +1.4 −1.6
CH_3—CH_2—CH_2—CH_2—O—CH_2—CH_2—CH_2—CH_3	99+ %	O—CH_2 Alkyl	3.3 0.9–1.4	22.2 77.8	21.8 78.2	−0.4 +0.4
H_2C—CH—CH_3 (epoxide, O)	E.K. White Label	O—CH_2— Alkyl	2.2–2.8 1.22	50.0 50.0	49.8 50.2	−0.2 +0.2
$CH_3(CH_2)_5$—C(=O)—O—$(CH_2)_3$—CH_3	>99.5	CO—O—CH_2— All other	4.00 0.9–2.2	9.1 90.9	9.1 90.9	0.0 0.0
CH_3CH_2—C(=O)—CH_3CH_2	E.K. Distilled	CO—CH_2— —CH_3	2.35 1.0	40.0 60.0	39.9 60.1	−0.1 +0.1

[a] From Jungnickel and Forbes (42), data obtained on Varian A-60 at concentrations ca. 30%. Copyright 1963 by The American Chemical Society. Reprinted by permission of the copyright owner.

and the results were found to be in good agreement with the chemical methods for hydroxyl determination.

A number of other interesting and useful applications of NMR analysis have been published for determination of the hydroxyl group. A somewhat similar use of the deuterium exchange reaction can be made in nuclear magnetic resonance spectroscopy except that, with this technique, conversion of ROH to ROD eliminates the effect of active hydrogen since deuterium does not have a magnetic moment in the same spectral region. Consequently, the experiment measures the difference in magnetic spectra. A detailed experimental procedure employing nuclear magnetic resonance to follow this exchange reaction has been published by Paulsen and Cooke (43), who report active hydrogen measurement in a number of organic compounds. A survey of the use of the proton NMR technique to obtain quantitative measurements of types of protons was published by Jungnickel and Forbes (42), who showed that electronic integration gave quite accurate values for a variety of chemical types of hydrogen in organic compounds. Some of their data, illustrated in Table 8.11, illustrate that distinctly different chemical shifts are observed for a group of alcohols, ethers, and several other functions depending upon the environment but that the integrated intensities are nearly quantitative in each case.

DETERMINATION OF ALCOHOLIC HYDROXYL

NUCLEAR MAGNETIC RESONANCE METHOD

Apparatus

High resolution NMR spectrometer.

Reagents

Formic acid, CP.
Deuterochloroform.

Procedure

A small amount of formic acid is added to a solution of the sample in deuterochloroform or other suitable solvent and the NMR spectrum is obtained. The hydroxyl resonance is shifted in the direction of that of the acid hydrogen of formic acid in proportion to the amounts of each type of exchangeable hydrogen present. Enough formic acid is added to shift the resonance to an otherwise empty region of the spectrum. The spectrum is then integrated to yield the areas under all bands. The area under the hydroxyl band is corrected for the amount of formic acid added by comparison with the area under the band due to the formyl hydrogen of formic acid.

Calculation

$$\text{Hydroxyl hydrogen, } \% = \frac{A_{OH} - A_{CH}}{A_{total}} \times 100$$

where A_{OH} = integrated area under the shifted hydroxyl band
A_{CH} = integrated area due to C—H resonance of formic acid
A_{total} = integrated areas due to all protons

DETERMINATION OF PRIMARY, SECONDARY AND TERTIARY HYDROXYL GROUPS BY NMR

The characterization of these specific types of alcohols has been investigated by Chapman and King (44) using dimethyl sulfoxide as the solvent. They point out that the hydroxyl proton in methanol gives a quartet and that primary, secondary, and tertiary alcohols give well-resolved triplets, doublets, and singlets, respectively. The formation of derivatives of the alcohols can in some cases increase the amount of information (45). Manatt (46) prepared the trifluoroacetates and examined their ^{19}F magnetic resonance spectra in a Varian high resolution spectrometer with special facilities for this resonance and found high sensitivity; he noted that the order of shielding was primary < secondary < tertiary. A similar study of the use of derivatives was made by Babiec, Barrante, and Vickers (47) with the dichloroacetate esters. They found it advantageous to examine the proton resonance of the dichloroacetyl group since it gave a sharp line, well resolved from most alkyl and aryl resonances. Since the proton resonance is being observed, the more common proton magnetic resonance spectrometer can be used and it provides, in the usual scan, information on the primary, secondary, and tertiary alcohol derivatives in the system. Babiec et al. applied the technique to a number of simple alcohols and also to polyether polymers and reported that the types of hydroxyl groups present in the polyethers could be resolved. The use of NMR for resolution of the alcohol types seems to offer the possibility of a rapid and sensitive method, although more work is necessary to define its accuracy and precision. This determination has been made by chemical methods that depended upon the more rapid reaction of primary alcohols, compared to secondary, with such reagents as acetic anhydride (48), phenyl isocyanate (49), or triphenylchloromethane (50). Hendrickson (50) has commented on the chemical methods and points out the appreciable time required to make the many determinations to define the rate curves. He avoids this with the triphenylchloromethane reagent by following the disappearance of the —OH band in the infrared absorption spectrum and found the method useful with polyglycols having primary hydroxyl contents of 2–42% of total hydroxyl.

REFERENCES

1. A. Verley and F. Bölsing, *Ber. Chem. Ges.*, **34**, 3354 (1901).
2. D. M. Smith and W. M. D. Bryant, *J. Am. Chem. Soc.*, **57**, 61 (1935).
3. P. J. Elving and B. Warshowsky, *Anal. Chem.*, **19**, 1006 (1947).
4. G. A. Olah and M. B. Comisarow, *J. Am. Chem. Soc.*, **88**, 4442 (1966).
5. W. M. D. Bryant, J. Mitchell, Jr., and D. M. Smith, *J. Am. Chem. Soc.*, **62**, 1 (1940).
6. G. A. Stenmark and F. T. Weiss, *Anal. Chem.*, **28**, 1784 (1956).
7. F. T. Weiss, in *Treatise on Analytical Chemistry*, Part II, I. M. Kolthoff and P. J. Elving, Eds., Vol. 13, Interscience, New York, 1966, pp. 33–95.
8. M. N. Chumachenko, L. B. Tverdyukova, and F. G. Leenson, *Zh. Analit. Khim.*, **21**, 617 (1966). See also E. J. Norton, L. Turner and D. G. Salmon, *Analyst*, **95**, 80 (1970).
9. J. S. Fritz and G. H. Schenk, *Anal. Chem.*, **31**, 1808 (1959).
10. R. S. Stetzler and C. F. Smullin, *ibid.*, **34**, 194 (1962).
11. D. J. Pietrzyk and J. Belisle, *ibid.*, **38**, 1508 (1966); **38**, 969 (1966).
12. D. W. Hill, *J. Am. Chem. Soc.*, **56**, 993 (1934).
13. S. Siggia, J. G. Hanna, and R. Culmo, *Anal. Chem.*, **33**, 900 (1961).
14. R. Harper, S. Siggia, and J. G. Hanna, *ibid.*, **37**, 600 (1965).
15. B. H. M. Kingston, J. J. Garey, and W. B. Hellwig, *ibid.*, **41**, 86 (1969).
16. R. Martin, *ibid.*, **23**, 883 (1951).
17. G. A. Stenmark and F. T. Weiss, *ibid.*, **28**, 260 (1956).
18. O. L. Hollis, *ibid.*, **38**, 309 (1966).
19. M. W. Anders and G. J. Mannering, *ibid.*, **34**, 730 (1962).
20. B. Freedman, *J. Am. Oil Chemists' Soc.*, **44**, 113 (1967).
21. R. A. Morrissette and W. E. Link, *J. Gas Chromatog.*, **3**, 67 (1965).
22. A. G. Sharkey, Jr., R. A. Friedel, and S. H. Langer, *Anal. Chem.*, **29**, 770 (1957).
23. S. H. Langer, R. A. Friedel, I. Wender, and A. G. Sharkey, Jr., *ibid.*, **30**, 1353 (1958).
24. S. H. Langer, P. Pantages, and I. Wender, *Chem. Ind. (London)*, **1958**, 1664.
25. M. Makita and W. W. Wells, *Anal. Biochem.*, **5**, 523 (1963).
26. C. C. Sweeley, R. Bentley, M. Makita, and W. W. Wells, *J. Am. Chem. Soc.*, **85**, 2497 (1963); D. C. DeJongh, T. Radford, J. D. Hribar, S. Hanessian, M. Bieber, G. Dawson, and C. C. Sweeley, *ibid.*, **91**, 1728 (1969).
27. D. P. Johnson and F. E. Critchfield, *Anal. Chem.*, **32**, 865 (1960).
28. M. Pesez, *Ann. Pharm. France*, **14**, 555 (1956).
29. V. W. Reid and R. K. Truelove, *Analyst*, **77**, 325 (1952).
30. F. R. Duke and G. F. Smith, *Ind. Eng. Chem., Anal. Ed.*, **12**, 201 (1940).
31. F. R. Duke, *ibid.*, **17**, 572 (1945).
32. R. Belcher, G. Dryhurst, and A. M. G. MacDonald, *Anal. Chim. Acta*, **38**, 435 (1967).
33. G. Gutnikov and G. H. Schenk, *Anal. Chem.*, **34**, 1316 (1962).
34. L. J. Bellamy, *The Infra-red Spectra of Complex Molecules*, 2nd ed., Wiley, New York, 1958.

35. K. F. Bonhoeffer and G. W. Brown, *Z. Physik. Chem.*, **B23**, 171 (1933).
36. W. H. Hamill and W. Freudenberg, *J. Am. Chem. Soc.*, **57**, 1427 (1935).
37. R. C. Gore, R. B. Barnes, and E. Petersen, *Anal. Chem.*, **21**, 382 (1949).
38. W. R. Harp, Jr., and R. C. Eiffert, *ibid.*, **32**, 794 (1960).
39. C. M. Huggins, G. C. Pimentel, and J. N. Shoolery, *J. Phys. Chem.*, **60**, 1311 (1956).
40. M. Saunders and J. B. Hyne, *J. Chem. Phys.*, **29**, 253 (1958).
41. C. P. Rader, *J. Am. Chem. Soc.*, **91**, 3248 (1969).
42. J. L. Jungnickel and J. W. Forbes, *Anal. Chem.*, **35**, 938 (1963).
43. P. J. Paulsen and W. D. Cooke, *ibid.*, **36**, 1721 (1964).
44. O. L. Chapman and R. W. King, *J. Am. Chem. Soc.*, **86**, 1256 (1964).
45. A. Mathias, *Anal. Chim. Acta*, **31**, 598 (1964).
46. S. L. Manatt, *J. Am. Chem. Soc.*, **88**, 1323 (1966).
47. J. S. Babiec, Jr., J. R. Barrante, and G. D. Vickers, *Anal. Chem.*, **40**, 610 (1968).
48. S. Siggia and J. G. Hanna, *ibid.*, **33**, 896 (1961).
49. J. G. Hanna and S. Siggia, *J. Polymer Sci.*, **56**, 297 (1962).
50. J. G. Hendrickson, *Anal. Chem.*, **36**, 126 (1964).

DETERMINATION OF POLYHYDROXYL ALCOHOLS

Polyhydroxy alcohols, such as ethylene glycol, propylene glycol, glycerol, and their derivatives, as well as the sugars and the carbohydrates, are materials of such importance that their analysis deserves specific attention. The most generally useful method for the analysis of α-glycols is the Malaprade periodic acid oxidation, in which the carbon–carbon bond of the glycol function is cleaved.

Oxidation with periodate is a fairly specific reaction for the analysis of compounds containing hydroxyl groups on adjacent carbon atoms (α-glycols). Vicinal polyols are oxidized to aldehydes and formic acid:

$$R-\underset{OH}{CH}-\left[\underset{OH}{CH}\right]_n-\underset{OH}{CH}-R' + (n+1)IO_4^- \longrightarrow$$

$$RCHO + R'CHO + nHCOOH + (n+1)IO_3^- + H_2O$$

Vicinal diols ($n = 0$) yield only aldehydes; thus, ethylene glycol produces only formaldehyde, and 1,2-propylene glycol produces formaldehyde and acetaldehyde. Vicinal triols ($n = 1$) and higher polyols ($n \geq 2$) yield formic acid in addition to aldehydes. Thus, each molecule of glycerol is oxidized to two molecules of formaldehyde and one molecule of formic acid:

$$CH_2OH-CHOH-CH_2OH + 2IO_4^- \rightarrow$$

$$2CH_2O + HCOOH + 2IO_3^- + H_2O$$

Analytical use of this reaction was introduced in 1928 by Malaprade (1). Other methods for determination of glycols and glycerol, such as the acetylation and dichromate methods, have now been largely supplanted by methods based on oxidation with periodate. Since the acetylation determines total hydroxyl content and the dichromate methods measure total oxidizable substances, these methods are subject to extensive interferences. Measurement of the amount of periodate reduced to iodate by the sample is more specific, since it determines the α-glycol function. Extensive studies of the mechanism of the oxidation of α-glycols have been carried out by Buist and his coworkers (2, 3), who have shown that the oxidation proceeds through a cyclic periodate ester.

Two recommended methods are given in this chapter for the general determination of α-glycol groups by periodate oxidation, one method for water-soluble and the other for water-insoluble samples. Both methods utilize a final iodiometric titration in which periodate and iodate are converted to iodine by the following reactions:

$$8H^+ + IO_4^- + 7I^- \rightarrow 4H_2O + 4I_2$$
$$6H^+ + IO_3^- + 5I^- \rightarrow 3H_2O + 3I_2$$

The amount of periodate consumed in the oxidation of the α-glycol is determined by the reduction in the iodine produced from a corresponding blank titration. The more widely used method is that for water-soluble α-glycols, which are the more commonly encountered. Some typical data indicating the utility of the method are given in Table 9.1, which show that quantitative results are readily obtained on a variety of compounds containing the α-glycol function.

Although the Malaprade oxidation is often considered as an example of a specific reaction for α-glycols, there may be some interference with certain other groups, especially if they are neighbors to a hydroxyl or other functional group. For instance, as is shown in Table 9.2, glycolic acid shows slight reactivity, the ethanolamines undergo considerable oxidation, and diacetyl, with adjoining carbonyl groups, is appreciably oxidized. The readily oxidized, water-soluble unsaturates acrolein and allyl acetate are quite reactive. The simple compounds formaldehyde, ethanol, acetone, and dioxane are nonreactive. Phenols interfere by reaction with periodate, which can be especially severe in acid systems in the absence of water, as has been shown by Stenmark (4). A comprehensive review of periodate oxidations, published by Dyer (5), covers application to many organic and biological materials. The periodate method recommended for water-insoluble samples, taken from that published by Stenmark (4), involves the use of chloroform as the sample solvent and an alcoholic solution of a quaternary ammonium

Table 9.1. Extent of Reaction of α-Glycols in the Aqueous Periodic Acid Method

Compound	Reaction, %
Ethylene glycol	99.0, 99.9
Glycerol	99.5
Glyceraldehyde	97.8, 98.0, 99.0
Glycerol α-monochlorhydrin	100.0
Glycerol α-allyl ether	100.6, 101.0
Glycerol α-ethyl ether	99.8, 99.1
Glycerol α-phenyl ether	98.8, 99.6

Table 9.2. Extent of Reaction of Other Functional Groups in the Aqueous Periodic Acid Method

Compound	Reaction, %[a]
Diacetyl	79.5
Dihydroxy acetone	96
Glycolic acid	1.0
Monoethanolamine	14.3 (0.5 hr, room temperature)
	28.7 (2 hr, 60°C)
	52.2 (5 hr, 100°C)
Diethanolamine	11.9 (0.5 hr, room temperature)
Acrolein	Rapidly fading end point
Allyl acetate	122
Formaldehyde	0.00
Ethanol	0.00
Acetone	0.00
Dioxane	0.00

[a] Calculated as equivalent to ethylene glycol (2 equiv/mole).

periodate as the reagent. This method gives accurate results with pure glycols and is sensitive to small concentrations of glycol groups in epoxy resins. Other functional groups, such as epoxy and phenol, interfere to a minor extent or not appreciably. Some data by this method are given in Table 9.3.

Table 9.3. Reaction of Glycols and Epoxides in the Quaternary Ammonium Periodate Method[a]

Compound	Recovery, %
Ethylene glycol	100.0, 99.3
Glycerol	100.0, 102.3
Glycerol α-phenyl ether	98.8, 97.6
Glycerol α-monochlorhydrin	99.6, 98.8
Epichlorhydrin	<0.2
Allyl glycidyl ether	0.4, 0.2

[a] Data from Stenmark (4).

DETERMINATION OF WATER-SOLUBLE α-GLYCOLS

PERIODIC ACID METHOD

Reagents

Potassium periodate reagent, 0.2*N*. Dissolve 5.64 g of reagent grade potassium periodate and 1.61 g of 85% potassium hydroxide in 200 ml of hot distilled water and dilute to 1 liter. To test the purity of the reagent, prepare a solution containing

100 mg of ethylene glycol per 10 ml and make a test using a 10-ml portion of the solution in a manner described below. The net titration represents the total amount of periodate available for the reaction with glycol.

Starch indicator solution, 0.2% aqueous, mercuric iodide inhibited.

Acetic acid solution, 12%, aqueous.

Sulfuric acid solution, 10%.

Potassium iodide solution, 20%, aqueous.

Standard sodium thiosulfate solution, 0.1N. Dispense this reagent from a 50-ml precision buret.

Procedure

Prepare a dilute aqueous solution of the sample such that 10 ml contains not more than the equivalent of 0.44 mmole of an α-glycol or 0.22 mmole of glycerol. Pipet 10 ml of the glycol solution and 25 ml of the 0.20N potassium periodate reagent into a thoroughly cleaned flask containing 10 ml of 12% acetic acid solution. If the glycol solution is weaker than the strength specified above, a larger portion, up to 50 ml, may be used, provided not more than the specified amount of glycol is present. Allow the mixture to stand for 30 min; then add 5 ml of 10% sulfuric acid and 10 ml of 20% potassium iodide solution. Titrate with 0.1N sodium thiosulfate to the starch end point.

Make a blank test on the reagents in a similar manner.

Calculation

$$\text{α-Glycol content, wt } \% = \frac{(B - S)(N)(M)}{(W)(10F)}$$

$$\text{α-Glycol, moles/100 g} = \frac{(B - S)(N)}{20W}$$

where B = volume of sodium thiosulfate solution used for blank determination, ml

S = volume of sodium thiosulfate solution used for titration of reacted sample, ml

N = normality of sodium thiosulfate solution

W = weight of sample, g

M = molecular weight of determined glycol

$F = 2(n + 1)$ = number of equivalents of periodic acid consumed per mole of the glycol. For example: for ethylene glycol, $F = 2$, and for glycerol, $F = 4$.

DETERMINATION OF WATER-INSOLUBLE α-GLYCOLS

Quaternary Ammonium Periodate Method

Reagents

Prepare the *benzyl trimethyl ammonium periodate* reagent by dissolving 2.5 g of periodic acid, H_5IO_6, in 475 ml of methanol. Add enough benzyl trimethyl ammonium hydroxide to neutralize the acid. Add 15 ml of glacial acetic acid and 5 ml of water.

Potassium iodide, 20% aqueous.

Starch indicator solution, 0.2%, aqueous.

Chloroform, CP.

Sodium thiosulfate, 0.1N.

Sulfuric acid, 10%. Mix 61 ml of 95% sulfuric acid with 800 ml of cold water. Dilute to 1 liter.

Procedure

Add 25 ml of chloroform to a 250-ml glass-stoppered bottle from a graduate. Weigh a 0.3–0.5-g sample that contains not more than 0.3 mmole of α-glycol. Place the sample in the bottle, and after solution, cool the mixture in an ice bath. With a pipet add exactly 25 ml of periodate reagent, swirl the mixture, and let it stand in a 40° water bath for 90 min. At the end of the reaction period add 100 ml of ice water. Stopper the bottle and shake it vigorously for 30 sec. Add 5 ml of 10% sulfuric acid and 15 ml of 20% potassium iodide. Titrate with 0.1N thiosulfate to the starch end point. As the end point is approached, stopper the bottle and shake it frequently and vigorously. Run a blank in an identical manner, but omit the sample. (The sample titration volume must be at least 80% of the blank titration volume in order to ensure an adequate excess of reagent.)

Calculation

$$\alpha\text{-Glycol content, moles/100 g} = \frac{(B - S)(N)}{20W}$$

where B = volume of sodium thiosulfate required to titrate the blank, ml

S = volume of sodium thiosulfate required to titrate the sample, ml

N = normality of the sodium thiosulfate

W = weight of the sample, g.

SPECIFIC DETERMINATION OF GLYCEROL

A more specific method for determination of glycerol is based on measurement of the formic acid produced by oxidation with periodate. Simple monohydroxyl alcohols do not react; vicinal diols do not produce acid upon oxidation with periodate. Compounds that interfere include those containing three or more vicinal hydroxyl groups, e.g., 1,2,3-trihydroxybutane, erythritol, sorbitol, mannitol, and the sugars. Interference also may arise from compounds containing a carbonyl group attached to a carbon atom carrying a hydroxyl group, e.g., glycolaldehyde, glyceraldehyde, and dihydroxyacetone, and from those containing two adjacent carbonyl groups, e.g., glyoxal and pyruvaldehyde. The oxidation of α-glycols with periodate is rapid and quantitative in neutral or slightly acidic solution. To obtain the high level of accuracy of which this determination is capable, a number of investigators have more thoroughly studied its variables. Since oxidation is to take place under neutral or slightly acidic conditions, the solubility of the periodate reagent is important. The potassium salt is only sparingly soluble in water (0.5 g/100 ml at 25°C) and is normally caused to dissolve by addition of potassium hydroxide. Sodium metaperiodate, $NaIO_4$, has a relatively high solubility in water (11.4 g/100 ml at 25°C) and consequently is the preferred reagent. It has been shown by Erskine, Strouts, Walley, and Lazarus (6) that erratic results in the determination of glycerol by the periodate–acidimetric method can be caused by exposure to strong light, presumably due to the action of sodium periodate on the formaldehyde and formic acid produced by oxidation of glycerol with periodate. A study of the effect of reaction time has shown that the reaction is rapid, being nearly complete in 30 sec (Table 9.4). A reaction time of 10 min appears to be a good choice for the recommended method included here.

Since periodic acid is polybasic, sodium periodate reacts with alkali to form a disodium salt. Consequently, formic acid from oxidation of glycerol is difficult to determine accurately in the presence of excess periodate remaining after reaction of glycerol. A means for avoiding the interference of the unconsumed periodate is to reduce it to iodate by adding an excess of an α-glycol such as ethylene glycol:

$$(CH_2OH)_2 + IO_4^- \rightarrow 2CH_2O + IO_3^- + H_2O$$

The formaldehyde and iodate formed are neutral and do not interfere in the titration with base. The use of ethylene glycol or 1,2-propylene glycol in this

Table 9.4. Rate of Reaction of Glycerol with Sodium Periodate[a]

Reaction time[b]	Glycerol found, wt %
30 sec	99.64
1 min	99.69
2 min	99.62, 99.67
5 min	99.64, 99.72
10 min	99.77
15 min	99.77, 99.80
30 min	99.85, 99.85
1 hr	99.82, 99.88

[a] Sample: Recrystallized glycerol, 99.8 wt % pure (based on melting point and water content).
[b] Time between addition of sodium periodate and addition of ethylene glycol to reduce unconsumed periodate.

manner was suggested, apparently independently, by several investigators (7–9), and has been adopted in the American Oil Chemists' Society method for the determination of glycerol (10). A satisfactory color indicator is either cresol red or phenolphthalein. The recommended method is based principally on the publication of the American Oil Chemists but contains some simplifications that arose from the observations described above.

The high level of accuracy of the method is shown by the data in Table 9.4. The values for the determination when carried on for 10–15 min are 99.77, 99.77, and 99.80%, compared to a known purity of 99.8% for the sample.

DETERMINATION OF GLYCEROL

Sodium Periodate–Acidimetric Method

Reagents

Ethylene glycol solution, 50%. Dissolve 50 ml of ethylene glycol in sufficient distilled water to make 100 ml. The glycerol content of the ethylene glycol used, as determined by analyzing a 0.4-g sample, should not exceed 0.5%.

Phenolphthalein indicator solution, 1% in 60% ethyl alcohol.

Sodium hydroxide solution, standard, $0.1N$, carbonate-free.

Sodium periodate solution, 5%. Dissolve 50 g of sodium metaperiodate, ACS reagent grade, in 1 liter of distilled water. Do not heat to dissolve the sodium periodate. A small amount of white, powdery residue may remain undissolved. If so, decant or filter through a sintered glass filter. Do not use filter paper; it reacts with periodate. Prepare this solution fresh each week.

Procedure

By means of a Lunge weighing bottle with a wide tip, or a medicine dropper and a vial, weigh a sample containing not more than 0.35 g of glycerol (preferably, at least 0.25 g) nor more than 8 meq of total α-glycol (ethylene glycol = 1 equiv/mole, glycerol = 2 equiv/mole) into a 250-ml Erlenmeyer flask. Add sufficient distilled water to bring the volume to approximately 50 ml. Dissolve the sample by gentle agitation, add 3 drops of phenolphthalein indicator solution, and carefully neutralize with $0.1N$ sodium hydroxide or sulfuric acid as required.

If appreciable CO_3^{2-} and HCO_3^- is present in the sample, first acidify with sulfuric acid to the methyl orange end point and purge with a stream of nitrogen for 15 min to remove carbon dioxide. After carbon dioxide has been removed, titrate to the phenolphthalein end point as directed above.

Add 50 ml of sodium periodate solution to the neutralized sample solution and swirl. Let the mixture stand for 10 min in a place not exposed to direct sunlight or bright artificial light. Then add 10 ml of 50% glycol solution, swirl, and let stand for an additional 5 min.

Add 3 drops of phenolphthalein indicator solution and titrate to the end point with standard $0.1N$ sodium hydroxide solution.

Make a blank determination omitting the sample. The blank titration should be of the order of 0.2–0.3 ml; if it exceeds 0.5 ml, repeat the determination using a freshly prepared sodium periodate solution and/or a different lot of ethylene glycol.

Calculation

$$\text{Glycerol, wt }\% = \frac{(S - B)(N)(92.1)}{10W}$$

where S = volume of sodium hydroxide solution, ml, used in titrating the sample
B = volume of sodium hydroxide solution, ml, used in titrating the blank
N = normality of the sodium hydroxide solution
W = weight of sample, g
92.1 = molecular weight of glycerol

ANALYSIS OF GLYCOLS BY CHROMATOGRAPHY

Paper chromatography has been employed by Siegel, Bullock, and Carter (11) to separate, identify, and determine the components in commercial diglycerol concentrates. It was found that the principal components were the α,α'- and α,β-diglycerols. There were also other polyglycerols containing α-glycol groups that were presumably materials higher than the dimer. Sahasrabudhe (12) applied thin-layer and gas chromatographic techniques for the determination of the components of polyglycerols and their fatty acid esters. The polyglycerols were converted to the trimethylsilyl ethers prior to analysis by gas chromatography. Diglycerol can occur in many forms and in addition to the α,α' and α,β found by Siegel, Bullock, and Carter, there are cyclic structures with possibilities of stereoisomerism so that chromatographic separations give complex patterns. Dallas and Stewart (13) carried out thin-layer chromatography of polyglycerols using synthetic, authentic samples as standards. Complicated glyceride mixtures containing α-monoglycerides can be analyzed by conversion of the α-monoglycerides to the cyclic phenylboronic acid esters. The boronic acid esters can be fractionated by gas chromatography (14). Simpler glycols can be separated directly by gas chromatography on solid supports containing a selected polar stationary phase (15, 16) or after conversion to the silyl ethers as described in Chapter 8. More complex polyols can be readily analyzed as the silyl ethers (17).

REFERENCES

1. L. Malaprade, *Bull. Soc. Chim.*, *Ser.* 4, **43**, 683 (1928).
2. G. J. Buist and J. D. Lewis, *J. Chem. Soc. Ser. B*, **1968**, 90.
3. G. J. Buist, C. A. Bunton, and J. Lomas, *ibid.*, **1966**, 1099.
4. G. A. Stenmark, *Anal. Chem.*, **30**, 381 (1958).

5. J. R. Dyer, in *Methods of Biochemical Analysis*, Vol. 3, D. Glick, Ed., Interscience, New York, 1956.

6. J. W. B. Erskine, C. R. N. Strouts, G. Walley, and W. Lazarus, *Analyst*, **78**, 630 (1953).

7. R. Colson, *Oleagineaux*, **5**, 701 (1950); *Chem. Abstr.*, **45**, 4467 (1951).

8. S. H. Newberger and C. F. Bruening, *J. Assoc. Offic. Agr. Chemists*, **30**, 651 (1947).

9. A. Troy and W. G. Alsop, *J. Am. Oil Chemists' Soc.*, **25**, 394 (1948).

10. American Oil Chemists' Society, Official Method 6-51, "Official and Tentative Methods of the American Oil Chemists' Society."

11. H. Siegel, A. B. Bullock, and G. B. Carter, *Anal. Chem.*, **36**, 502 (1964).

12. M. R. Sahasrabudhe, *J. Am. Oil Chemists' Soc.*, **44**, 376 (1967).

13. M. S. J. Dallas and M. F. Stewart, *Analyst*, **92**, 634 (1967).

14. G. Kresze and F. Schäuffelhut, *Z. Anal. Chem.*, **229**, 401 (1967).

15. H. G. Nadeau and D. M. Oaks, *Anal. Chem.*, **32**, 1760 (1960).

16. B. A. Swinehart, *ibid.*, **40**, 427 (1968).

17. M. R. Sahasrabudhe and R. K. Chadha, *J. Am. Oil Chemists' Soc.*, **46**, 8 (1969).

DETERMINATION OF PHENOLS

Organic materials possessing a phenolic hydroxyl group may vary widely in their degree of analytical complexity. Fortunately, many reliable methods are available both for the analysis of phenol products and for the determination of the phenolic group occurring in trace impurities. The essential characteristics of the principal methods for the analysis of phenols are listed in Table 10.1 in which the methods are classified under two general headings: One grouping fits the methods that are dependent upon the properties of the hydroxyl group, and under the second classification are the methods that are based on the properties of the molecule. To some extent, these classifications are somewhat arbitrary but they are still useful in indicating the limitations and applicability of the methods. The phenolic hydroxyl group behaves toward a number of the functional reagents as a typical hydroxyl and consequently can be accurately assayed by some of the methods used for the determination of that functional group. Because the phenolic hydroxyl is weakly acidic it can also be determined by titration with a quaternary ammonium hydroxide in a nonaqueous solvent. The position of absorption in infrared and NMR is different from that of the alcoholic hydroxyl groups but the measurement technique is the same. The methods under the first classification are all described elsewhere, in the chapters indicated, in some cases as recommended methods.

The set of techniques based on molecular properties include the chromatographic techniques, which allow the specific determination of individual phenols, as well as those techniques that are specifically applicable to phenols because of the highly reactive nature of the aromatic ring activated by the phenolic group. The activation is clearly pronounced when one compares benzene, which is quite unreactive to bromine, to phenol, which is so rapidly converted to the tribromide that this is one of the methods that have been used for assaying the purity of phenol itself. The most sensitive methods for the determination of the phenols are in the category of those techniques based on molecular properties. The colorimetric amino-antipyrine method is among the most sensitive but the variable reactivity of the substituted phenols is such that the materials to be analyzed must be carefully examined to determine the applicability of the color-forming reaction. Use of

Table 10.1.   Characteristics of Methods Used for Determination of Phenols

Type of determination	Method	Chapter listed	Accuracy expected	Sensitivity, g (approximate)
Methods Based on Properties of Hydroxyl Function				
Acetylation	Acetyl chloride	8	$100 \pm 0.5\%$ (unless hindered)	10^{-3} to 10^{-4}
Acidimetric	Tetrabutylammonium hydroxide (nonaqueous media)	5	$100 \pm 0.5\%$	10^{-3} to 10^{-4}
	Photometric titration	5	$100 \pm 1\%$	10^{-4} to 10^{-5}
Active hydrogen	$LiAlH_4$	8	$100 \pm 0.4\%$	10^{-3}
Infrared absorption spectroscopy		8	$100 \pm 2\%$	10^{-4} to 10^{-5}
Nuclear magnetic resonance		8	$100 \pm 3\%$	10^{-3} to 10^{-5}
Methods Based on Molecular Properties				
Chromatography	Gas chromatography	21	$100 \pm 3\%$	10^{-7} to 10^{-8}
	Thin-layer and paper chromatography		$100 \pm 10\%$	10^{-6} to 10^{-7}
Bromination	Bromide—bromate	3	$100 \pm 0.5\%$ (limited use)	10^{-4}
Colorimetric	4-Aminoantipyrine	10	Variable	10^{-7}
Ultraviolet		10	$100 \pm 5\%$	10^{-6}

ultraviolet absorption spectroscopy, either directly or by photometric titration, is a generally suitable method, especially for aqueous systems, and gas chromatography can also be advantageous with many products for both direct and trace analysis.

The most suitable general assay procedures for phenolic compounds are those based on reaction with the hydroxyl function. Of these, the acetyl chloride method is convenient and generally accurate except for hindered phenols. Application data, described in more detail in Chapter 8, show that quantitative results are obtained by the acetyl chloride method for simple phenolic structures such as phenol, cresols, and xylenol, whereas highly hindered phenols such as 2,6-di-*tert*-butyl-4-methyl phenol give very low results. In the analysis of this hindered phenol, however, the lithium aluminum hydride method provides quantitative results. In addition to these methods, direct acidimetric titration using tetrabutylammonium hydroxide titrant in nonaqueous media can be used as a generally reliable measure of phenol content since this method (Chapter 5) provides a significant titration break between acids of different strengths and enables phenols to be distinguished from mineral and carboxylic acids.

The determination of phenol (hydroxybenzene) itself by bromination has long been recommended (1) and is still considered a useful analysis for the assay of preparations of phenol. The variability of the reaction of substituted phenols with bromine, however, prevents this from being considered as a general method for the analysis of phenols. The most useful bromination technique was that originally published by Koppeschaar (2) and involves the use of an acidified aqueous solution of potassium bromide and bromate to produce the brominating reagent in a method similar to that in Chapter 3. The applicability and limitations of the bromination method for determination of phenols has been examined by a number of investigators and some of the published data are shown in Table 10.2. Certain phenols react stoichiometrically; these include phenol, *m*-cresol, resorcinol, and several of the chlorinated and nitrated phenols. However, the *ortho-* and *para*-substituted cresols and xylenols react in a nonstoichiometric manner. Other limitations are in the partial displacement of the nitro group by bromine in some compounds and, of course, reaction of any olefinic materials in the samples with bromine.

To increase the sensitivity and reduce the effect of interfering materials, a

Table 10.2. Extent of Reaction of Various Phenols with Bromine Reactions in acidic aqueous media with $KBr-KBrO_3$ reagent at room temperature

Compound	Atoms of bromine consumed per molecule	Reaction conditions	Ref.
Phenol	6	5 min	[a]
m-Cresol	6	1 min	[b]
o-Cresol	4.40, 4.42	10 min	[c]
p-Cresol	4.54	10 min	[c]
p-Chlorophenol	4	30 min	[b]
p-Nitrophenol	4	30 min	[b]
	4	10 hr	[d]
Resorcinol	6	1 min	[b]
2,6-Dimethylphenol	4.84, 5.00	10 min	[c]
2,3,5-Trimethylphenol	4.24	10 min	[c]
Picric acid	0.03	5 min	[d]
	0.70	10 hr	[d]
	1.47	20 hr	[d]
2,4-Dinitroresorcinol	0.70	10 min	[d]
	11.68	20 hr	[d]

[a] Chapter 3.
[b] A. R. Day and W. T. Taggart, *Ind. Eng. Chem.*, **20**, 545 (1928).
[c] M. M. Sprung, *Ind. Eng. Chem., Anal. Ed.*, **13**, 35 (1941).
[d] L. D. Johnson, W. M. McNabb, and E. C. Wagner, *Anal. Chem.*, **27**, 1494 (1955).

preliminary separation is frequently employed to concentrate the phenols. Some of the separating procedures that have been utilized include steam distillation (3), extraction of the phenols from acidified aqueous solutions with an organic solvent and subsequent reextraction of the phenol with aqueous caustic (4), and the use of ion-exchange resins (5, 6).

DETERMINATION OF PHENOLS BY CHROMATOGRAPHY

Phenols of lower molecular weight are directly and easily determined by gas chromatography. Many examples of this analysis have been published, including the analysis of the C_6–C_8 monohydric phenols (7), the determination of phenolic inhibitors in food products (8), and the determination of phenol in urine as a check on exposure to benzene (9). The formation of derivatives such as the silyl or pentafluorobenzyl ethers (10) are important to increase the volatility and to provide more sensitive or specific analysis. A recommended trimethylsilyl ether method is given in Chapter 8. Gas chromatography has also been used to determine the distribution of the individual phenols in industrial waste waters in ppm concentrations (11–13). Since it is not always possible to obtain good results in the analysis of high molecular weight phenols by gas chromatography, investigators have used paper chromatography (14, 15) and thin-layer chromatography (16, 17) for the identification and determination of many types of phenolic compounds. The acidic properties of the phenols has made it possible to employ ion-exchange chromatography (5, 6). Munday and Eaves (5) were able to separate alkyl phenols from gasoline by percolating the gasoline over a commercial anion exchanger in the basic form (5) and desorbing the phenols with dilute aqueous ammonium carbonate solution. Snyder and Buell (18) proposed an integrated separation scheme for the determination of nitrogen and oxygen compounds, including phenols, in petroleum fractions that involve the use of ion-exchange resins as well as adsorption on alumina, silica gel, or charcoal. A freeze-concentration process has been recommended by Baker (19) to increase the concentration of phenols and other organics prior to analysis by gas chromatography.

COLORIMETRIC METHODS FOR DETERMINATION OF PHENOLS

One of the more commonly used colorimetric methods for the determination of traces of phenols in waste waters and effluents involves the use of 4-aminoantipyrine reagent. The reactions involved in the formation of color, established by Emerson and his coworkers, who developed the method some years ago (20, 21), are illustrated by equation 10.1. The coupled product of this reaction is deep red and the method is general for those phenols that do not have an alkyl or aryl substituent in the position *para* to the phenolic

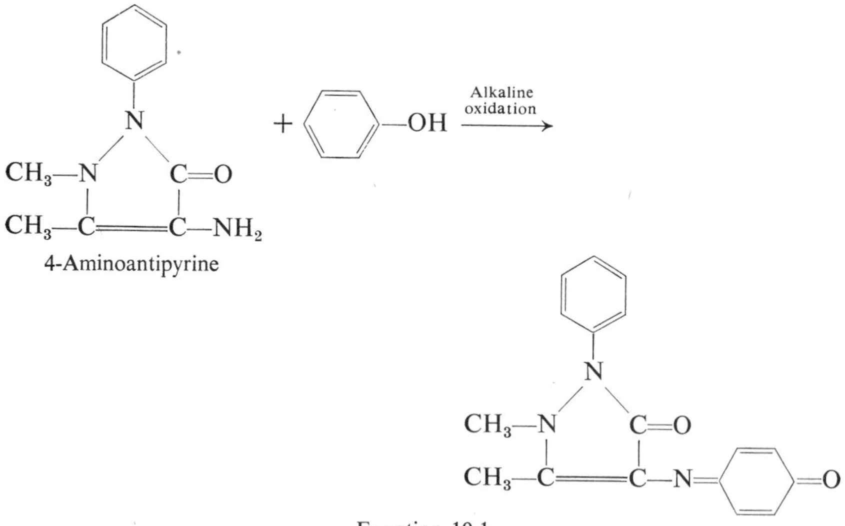

$$ \text{4-Aminoantipyrine} + \text{C}_6\text{H}_5\text{-OH} \xrightarrow{\text{Alkaline oxidation}} $$

4-Aminoantipyrine

Equation 10.1

hydroxyl. Some *para* substituents such as carbonyl, halogen, and methoxyl were found by Emerson to be expelled in the coupling and to produce color. Since *p*-cresol is a common phenolic material, its lack of reaction is a significant limitation of this technique, but despite its limitations, the simplicity and sensitivity of the method have given it wide use in industry (22–24) and it is from these sources that the recommended method given in this chapter is taken. The coupling agent is potassium ferricyanide and the reaction takes place in aqueous solution at pH 10. The colored coupled product is extracted with chloroform and the absorbance is measured at 4600 Å.

Thorough studies of the 4-aminoantipyrine method and its application to the examination of industrial waste waters have been published (4, 25) and it has been shown that the method can determine as little as 20 ppb of phenol in water (26). The color production was found to vary greatly among the

Table 10.3. Comparative Response to the 4-Aminoantipyrine Methods[a]

Phenol	1
o-Cresol	0.87
m-Cresol	0.76
p-Cresol	0.00
1-Naphthol	0.78
3,5-Xylenol	0.32

[a] Data from Ettinger, Ruchhoff, and Lishka (25).

reactive phenols, with the greatest response being for phenol. The relative absorbances (converted to an equivalent molar basis and compared to phenol) of some of the phenols is shown in Table 10.3. Although the absorptivity varies somewhat from day to day, under carefully controlled experimental conditions the molar absorptivity has been found to be approximately 1.2×10^4 liters/mole-cm for phenol.

DETERMINATION OF PHENOLIC COMPOUNDS IN WASTE WATERS

COLORIMETRIC 4-AMINOANTIPYRINE METHOD

Apparatus

Photometer: a spectrophotometer, suitable for use at 5100 Å, and accommodating a cell that gives a light path of 1.0–10 cm.
pH meter.

Reagents

4-Aminoantipyrine solution, 20 g/liter. Dissolve 2.0 g of 4-aminoantipyrine in water and dilute to 100 ml. Prepare this reagent fresh as used.

Ammonium chloride solution, 20 g/liter. Dissolve 20 g of ammonium chloride (NH_4Cl) in water and dilute to 1 liter.

Phenol standard solutions. Prepare as follows:

STOCK SOLUTION, 1.00 g/liter. Dissolve 1.00 g of phenol (C_6H_5OH) in freshly boiled and cooled water. Dilute to 1000 ml with freshly boiled and cooled water. Prepare a fresh stock solution within 30 days of use.

INTERMEDIATE SOLUTION, 1 ml = 0.01 mg phenol. Dilute 10.0 ml of the stock solution to 1000 ml with freshly boiled and cooled water. Prepare this solution fresh on day it is used.

PHENOL STANDARD SOLUTION, 1 ml = 0.001 mg phenol. Dilute 50 ml of the intermediate solution to 500 ml with freshly boiled and cooled water. Prepare this solution fresh within 2 hr of use.

Potassium ferricyanide solution, 80 g/liter. Dissolve 8.0 g of potassium ferricyanide ($K_3Fe(CN)_6$) in water and dilute to 100 ml. Filter if necessary.

Calibration

Prepare a series of 100-ml phenol standards in water containing 0, 10, 20, 30, 40, and 50 ml of intermediate standard phenol solution (1 ml = 0.01 mg phenol). All solutions used must be at room temperature. Develop color in the series of standards according to the procedure below.

Measure the absorbance of each standard at 5100 Å against the reagent blank as zero absorbance. Plot the absorbances against the corresponding weight in milligrams of phenol.

Determination of Phenolic Compounds

Transfer to a beaker 100 ml of sample, or a suitable aliquot diluted to 100 ml, containing no more than 0.50 mg of phenolic compounds. Also, prepare a blank consisting of 100 ml of water.

Add 5 ml of NH_4Cl solution to each. Adjust the pH to 9.8–10.2 with NH_4OH. Add 2.0 ml of 4-aminoantipyridine solution, mix immediately, then add 2.0 ml of $K_3Fe(CN)_6$ solution and again mix immediately.

After 15 min transfer the sample and blank solutions to absorption cells and measure the absorbance of the sample solution against the zero absorbance of the reagent blank at 5100 Å. By reference to the calibration curve and the absorbance obtained on the sample solution, determine the phenolic content of the sample.

Calculation

$$\text{Phenolic compounds, ppm} = \frac{(PA_s)}{A_p} \times \frac{1000}{S}$$

where P = mg of phenol in 100 ml of the standard solution
　　　A_s = absorbance of the sample solution
　　　A_p = absorbance of the standard
　　　S = ml of original sample present in 100 ml of the solution reacted with 4-aminoantipyrine

Another colorimetric method once widely used for the determination of phenols is based on their reaction with nitrous acid to form nitrosophenols, which are subsequently caused to rearrange to the highly colored quinoid salts on addition of an excess of alcoholic ammonium hydroxide to the reaction mixture (26). Lykken, Treseder, and Zahn (27) made a thorough study of this technique and its application to the determination of phenols in petroleum products and other materials. Rather large differences were found in the amounts of color formed from different phenols and, in contrast to the 4-aminoantipyrine method, p-cresol responds effectively, actually providing a greater absorbance than phenol itself. The relative responses of some of the common phenols in the colorimetric nitrosophenol method, compared to phenol, are shown in Table 10.4.

Table 10.4. Comparative Response to the Nitrosophenol Methods[a]

Phenol	1	2,4-Xylenol	1.20
m-Cresol	0.68	2,5-Xylenol	0.63
o-Cresol	1.74	2,6-Xylenol	0.31
p-Cresol	1.16	3,5-Xylenol	0.44
		Hydroquinone	0.51

[a] Data from Lykken, Treseder, and Zahn (27).

ULTRAVIOLET ABSORPTION METHODS
FOR DETERMINATION OF PHENOLS

The ultraviolet absorption spectra of simple phenols in aqueous solutions have a moderately strong absorption band between 2700 and 2800 Å. The conversion of the phenol to the phenoxide ion produces a shift in the absorption to a longer wavelength and increases the intensity of the absorption. These effects on a typical phenol, *p*-cresol, are shown in Figure 10.1, where it is seen that solution in 0.1*N* aqueous sodium hydroxide shifts the entire spectra. This spectral shift can be employed for determination of phenols by photometric titration or for the direct spectroscopic measurement of phenol content in basic solutions, using the absorption band in the vicinity of 3000 Å. This spectrophotometric method is capable of high sensitivity and has been used for the determination of phenols in waste and effluent waters (11, 28) and for the analysis of phenolic materials in rubber (29, 30), in polyoxyethylene ethers (31), and in gasolines (32).

A thorough investigation of the method variables was published by Martin, Orr, Kincannon, and Bishop (11), who developed a spectrophotometric apparatus for the continuous determination of phenols in an industrial aqueous waste stream. They examined the absorbance of a number of

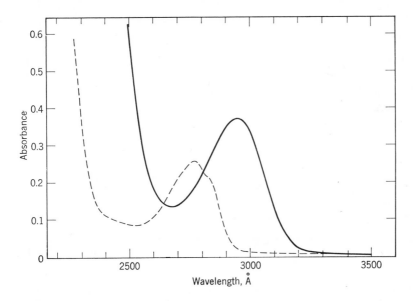

Figure 10.1   Ultraviolet absorption spectra of *p*-cresol in neutral and basic aqueous media. From Martin, Orr, Kincannon, and Bishop (11), from *J. Water Pollution Control Fed.*, **39**, 21 (1967). Reprinted with permission of copyright owner.

phenols and some other substances dissolved in 0.1N aqueous sodium hydroxide in the ultraviolet region between 2000 and 4000 Å. The positions of the absorption maxima were found to be in the vicinity of 2900 Å, as is shown in the data in Table 10.5. Taking 2925 Å as the average value for the absorption maxima, they measured molar absorptivities of the phenolates at this wavelength, finding an average value of 2.7 × 10³. Contrary to the results obtained with the colorimetric methods in which the sensitivity varies materially with the position of substitution, the differences in molar absorptivity among the alkyl phenols are not extremely great in the ultraviolet. The carboxylic acids examined produced essentially no interference at this wavelength. Since small concentrations of extraneous materials, such as mineral salts and colloidal particles, in waste waters limit the sensitivity of the direct spectroscopic determination, a differential absorbance technique was used. A measurement was made of the ultraviolet spectrum of an aqueous sample treated with sodium hydroxide to shift the absorption band and this was compared with a portion of the untreated sample in the reference beam. By this means it was possible to determine total phenols in aqueous feeds with a sensitivity of the order of 1 ppm using continuous instrumentation.

Since field samples may contain appreciable and varying amounts of interfering materials, the recommended method is based on the somewhat more laborious technique of Schmauch and Grubb (28), which calls for a preliminary extraction of the basic, aqueous solution with carbon tetrachloride to remove oils and grease. The aqueous solution is then adjusted

Table 10.5. Absorbance of Some Phenols and Acids in Basic Solution in the Ultraviolet Region Between 2000 and 4000 Å[a,b]

Compound	Absorption maxima, Å	Molar absorptivity at 2925 Å, liters/mole-cm
Phenol	2875	2.4 × 10³
o-Cresol	2895	2.9 × 10³
m-Cresol	2895	2.4 × 10³
p-Cresol	2950	2.6 × 10³
2,4-Xylenol	2960	2.9 × 10³
2,5-Xylenol	2925	3.5 × 10³
3,4-Xylenol	2950	2.8 × 10³
3,5-Xylenol	2900	2.5 × 10³
3-Ethylphenol	2890	2.5 × 10³
Resorcinol		3.5 × 10³
Benzoic acid		5
2-Ethylhexanoic acid		4

[a] Solvent: 0.1N aqueous sodium hydroxide.
[b] Data from Martin, Orr, Kincannon, and Bishop (11).

to a pH of 5 and extracted with tributyl phosphate to recover the phenols as a concentrate. The concentrate is then divided into two parts, one of which is made basic. Comparison of the absorbance of the two portions at 3010 Å is taken as a measure of the phenolic content of the sample. In the hands of the original investigators (28), the method was found to have a sensitivity in the ppm range. An indication of the behavior of phenols and other compounds in the method is shown in Table 10.6, from which it can be seen that the results are essentially approximate for alkyl phenols with the exception of those having bulky *ortho* substituents that do not respond at all. Highly variable results are obtained on aromatic phenols and no interference is found from carboxylic or sulfonic acids or pyridines. Despite the somewhat elaborate nature of this method and the less than ideal response from alkyl phenols, the extraction step allows removal of many impurities commonly

Table 10.6.   Extent of Recovery of Various Compounds in the Determination of Phenolic Compounds in Water by Ultraviolet Absorption[a]

Compound[b]	Response, % calculated as phenol
Phenol	100 (by calibration)
o-Cresol	140[c]
p-Cresol	124[c]
2,4-Dimethylphenol	145[c]
2-Ethylphenol	121[c]
2,6-Di-*tert*-butyl-4-methyl	0
1-Naphthol	27
2-Naphthol	138
Catechol	48
Hydroquinone	33
Thiophenol	5[c]
Pyridine	0
Quinoline	0.3
n-Heptanoic acid	0
Benzoic acid	0.1
2-Naphthoic acid	1.7
Phenol sulfonic acid	0
Phenol disulfonic acid	0
Sulfonated cresols	0

[a] Taken from results of Schmauch and Grub (28).

[b] Taken at 1 mg/liter in water.

[c] Calculated from distribution data and available molar absorptivities.

encountered in field samples, and consequently the technique of Schmauch and Grubb has found use for trace analysis of waste waters.

DETERMINATION OF PHENOLIC COMPOUNDS IN WASTE WATERS

ULTRAVIOLET ABSORPTION METHOD

Apparatus

Spectrophotometer, equipped with 1-cm cells.
Mechanical shaking machine.
pH meter.

Reagents

Potassium hydroxide, pellets.
Sodium chloride, crystals.
Carbon tetrachloride.
Hydrochloric acid, concentrated.
Tri-n-butyl phosphate.
Tetra-n-butylammonium hydroxide solution, 0.1M in methanol. Prepare according to the directions given in Chapter 23 except use absolute methanol in place of isopropyl alcohol and dilute to 0.1M.
Phenol stock solution, containing 1 mg/ml. Dissolve 1.0 g of phenol, weighed to the nearest 20 mg, in freshly boiled and cooled water. Dilute to 1 liter in a volumetric flask with freshly boiled and cooled water.
Standard phenol solution, containing 0.025 mg/ml. Dilute exactly 25.0 ml of the phenol stock solution to 1 liter with freshly boiled and cooled water. Prepare the solution fresh the day it is used.

Calibration of the Apparatus

Into each of three clean 1000-ml graduated cylinders, measure 400 ml of water and add 10 g of sodium chloride. Add to each 10.0, 20.0, and 40.0 ml of the standard phenol solution (1 ml = 0.025 mg of phenol) and adjust the volumes to exactly 500 ml. Mix and adjust the pH of each solution to 5 with concentrated hydrochloric as described under Procedure.

Obtain the net absorbance by subtracting the readings obtained on the acidic (methanol) solutions from the corresponding readings on the alkaline solutions. Prepare a calibration curve by plotting the net reading of each standard against the weight of phenol present in each solution.

Procedure

Add a measured 600 ml of sample to a 1-liter beaker and bring to pH 12 with potassium hydroxide pellets as required. Dissolve 10 g of sodium chloride in the solution and transfer to a quart bottle. Add 20 ml of carbon tetrachloride and shake mechanically for 30 min. Carefully pour the aqueous raffinate through a filter into a graduated cylinder and collect 500 ml. Discard the carbon tetrachloride extract.

Adjust the pH of the 500 ml of aqueous raffinate to 5 with concentrated hydrochloric acid and transfer to a clean quart bottle. Add, by pipet, 20 ml of tributyl phosphate and shake mechanically for 30 min. At the end of the shaking period, recover the concentrate of phenols in the tributyl phosphate by cautiously adding water until the upper layer can be removed from the neck with a pipet or hypodermic syringe.

Two solutions are prepared from the phenol concentrate for analysis. An alkaline solution is made by mixing 4 ml of the concentrate and 1 ml of quaternary hydroxide reagent in a 5-ml volumetric flask. A reference solution is obtained by mixing a second 4-ml portion of the concentrate with methanol in another 5-ml volumetric flask. An observed absorbance is measured on the spectrometer by comparison of the alkaline solution in the sample cell with the reference solution in the reference cell.

If the absorbance is above 0.8, both solutions are diluted equally to bring the absorbance between 0.8 and 0.2. To do so, the alkaline solution is diluted with a 4:1 mixture of tributyl phosphate and quaternary hydroxide reagent, and the reference solution is diluted with a 4:1 mixture of tributyl phosphate and methanol and the absorbance is measured.

Calculation

Obtain the net absorbance reading by subtracting the readings obtained on the acidic solution from the reading obtained on the alkaline portion of the sample. From the standardization curve determine the mg of phenol present:

$$\text{phenol, mg/liter} = \frac{(A)(B)(1000)}{500}$$

where A = mg phenol from standardized curve and B = dilution factor.

REFERENCES

1. F. P. Treadwell and W. T. Hall, *Analytical Chemistry*, 8th ed., Vol. II, Wiley, New York, 1935, p. 640.
2. W. F. Koppeschaar, *Z. Anal. Chem.*, **15,** 233 (1876).
3. A. W. Beshgetoor, L. M. Greene, and V. A. Stenger, *Ind. Eng. Chem., Anal. Ed.*, **16,** 694 (1944).
4. J. A. Shaw, *Anal. Chem.*, **23,** 1788 (1951).
5. W. Munday and A. Eaves, *Fifth World Petroleum Congress*, Section V, Paper 9, New York, 1959.
6. N. E. Skelly, *Anal. Chem.*, **33,** 271 (1961).
7. E. R. Adlard and G. W. Roberts, *J. Inst. Petroleum*, **51,** 376 (1965).
8. R. G. Buttery and B. N. Stuckey, *J. Agr. Food Chem.*, **9,** 283 (1961).
9. A. B. Van Haaften and S. T. Sie, *Am. Ind. Hyg. Assoc. J.*, **26,** 52 (1965).
10. F. K. Kawahara, *Anal. Chem.*, **40,** 1009 (1968).

11. J. M. Martin, Jr., C. R. Orr, C. B. Kincannon, and J. L. Bishop, *J. Water Pollution Control Fed.*, **39,** 21 (1967).
12. R. A. Baker, *J. Am. Water Works Assoc.*, **58,** 751 (1966).
13. R. A. Baker and B. A. Malo, *Environmental Sci. Technol.*, **1,** 997 (1967).
14. G. B. Crump, *J. Chromatog.*, **10,** 21 (1963).
15. W. N. Martin and R. M. Husband, *Anal. Chem.*, **33,** 840 (1961).
16. G. B. Crump, *ibid.*, **36,** 2447 (1964).
17. E. Stahl, *Arch. Pharmacol.*, **292,** 411 (1959).
18. L. R. Snyder and B. E. Buell, *Anal. Chem.*, **40,** 1295 (1968).
19. R. A. Baker, *J. Water Pollution Control Fed.* **37,** 1164 (1965).
20. E. Emerson, *J. Org. Chem.*, **8,** 417, 433 (1943).
21. E. Emerson and K. Kelley, *ibid.*, **13,** 532 (1948).
22. Method D-1783. American Society for Testing and Materials (ASTM), Part 23, 1969.
23. Method 716. American Petroleum Institute (API), "Manual on Disposal of Refinery Wastes," New York, 1957.
24. "Standard Methods for Water and Waste Water," American Public Health Association, New York, 1965.
25. M. E. Ettinger, C. C. Ruchhoft, and R. J. Lishka, *Anal. Chem.*, **23,** 1783 (1951).
26. R. W. Stoughton, *J. Biol. Chem.*, **115,** 293 (1936).
27. L. Lykken, R. S. Treseder, and V. Zahn, *Ind. Eng. Chem.*, *Anal. Ed.*, **18,** 103 (1946).
28. L. J. Schmauch and H. M. Grubb, *Anal. Chem.*, **26,** 308 (1954).
29. C. W. Wadelin, *ibid.*, **28,** 1530 (1956).
30. A. S. Wexler, *ibid.*, **35,** 1936 (1963).
31. C. F. Smullin and F. P. Wetterau, *ibid.*, **27,** 1836 (1955).
32. M. J. Murray, *ibid.*, **21,** 941 (1949).

DETERMINATION OF ETHERS

Satisfactory determination of alkoxyl groups, other than methoxyl and ethoxyl, is one of the more difficult organic functional problems. Because ethers are chemically rather inert, they require extremely active analytical reagents and consequently the methods generally lack that probing touch that produces specificity. The method most generally employed for the simpler alkoxyl determination is that of Zeisel, which is based on the hydroiodic acid destruction of the ether linkage.

$$R—O—R' + 2HI \rightarrow RI + R'I + H_2O$$

The method quantitatively determines the methoxyl and ethoxyl groups (1); however, the higher alkoxyls are only partially recovered because the method is dependent on the volatility of the alkyl iodide. Low molecular weight alcohols, esters, acetals, and other reactive compounds may interfere.

DETERMINATION OF THE OXYETHYLENE CONTENT OF POLYETHYLENE OXIDES

The reaction with hydroiodic acid can be used also to determine the composition of the polyalkylene oxides of all molecular weights by cleaving the polymer molecule between adjacent carbon and oxygen atoms by the following reaction:

$$HO—(CH_2—CH_2—O)_n—H + n(2 + x)HI \rightarrow$$
$$n(x)CH_3CH_2I + n(1 - x)CH_2{=}CH_2 + nI_2 + (n + 1)H_2O$$

where $n \geq 1$ and $x < 1$. Morgan (2) showed that the sum of the olefin and alkyl iodide produced was stoichiometrically equivalent to the polyethylene oxide reacted, although the ratio between olefin and iodide was not definite nor reproducible. That the production of iodine in the reaction, however, is stoichiometric was recognized by Siggia and his coworkers (3) and was made into a useful, quantitative method for the determination of oxyethylene content of polyethylene oxides. In this method the sample is heated with 55% hydrogen iodide under a blanket of carbon dioxide. After the reaction is completed, potassium iodide solution is added and the iodine is titrated with standard sodium thiosulfate solution. The recommended method is taken from their publication and data illustrating the results obtained in comparison with data from nuclear magnetic resonance and the expected compositions are shown in Table 11.1. Quite good precision and agreement were found in almost all cases.

DETERMINATION OF THE OXYETHYLENE DISTRIBUTION BY THIN-LAYER CHROMATOGRAPHY

A number of investigators have examined separation methods for the determination of the oxyethylene distribution of condensates by alkyl phenols or primary alcohols with ethylene oxide. Column chromatography was found to be slow and of limited resolution (4–7), whereas gas chromatography, either as the acetate esters (8) or the silyl ethers (9), could be used to quantitatively resolve individual homologs having only up to 10 or 12 oxyethylene units. One of the more useful techniques for this separation is that recently published by McCoy and Bullock (10), who employed thin-layer chromatography of the 3,5-dinitrobenzoate ester derivatives to separate the condensates into a series. Each group of the series contained all the homologs of the same number of oxyethylene units and its total amount was measured by a spectrophotometric procedure. An example of the use of this technique is illustrated in Figure 11.1, in the analysis of four samples in which the primary alcohols were mixtures in the range of 12–15 carbon numbers and ethoxylated to varying extents. Circular thin-layer chromatography was employed because it was found to provide a better resolution of this type of material than the usual linear method.

Table 11.1. Oxyethylene Content of Ethoxylated Alcohols, wt %

	Determined by	
As prepared	Recommended method (HI)	NMR
39.9	38.7	39.1 ± 1
	39.0	
38.8	39.4	38.7 ± 1
	39.7	
62.4	61.8	62.7 ± 2
	63.4	
59.8	59.7	59.8 ± 2
	59.9	
65.4	64.4	65.4 ± 2
	64.8	
71.8	71.4	71.6 ± 3
	71.6	

Figure 11.1. Circular thin-layer chromatographic separation of 3,5 dinitrobenzoate esters of primary alcohol polyoxyethylene condensates (10). Copyright 1969 by the American Oil Chemists' Society. Reprinted by permission of the copyright owner.

The samples were applied as 1 μl portions of benzene solutions containing, in each case, about 60–70 μg of the dinitrobenzoate esters. Chloroform, with 2% additional ethanol, was used as the migration solvent. The zones at the greatest distance from the center are the esters of the unreacted, original alcohols ($n = 0$), and the rings nearer the center have the largest number of oxyethylene units. Quantitative measurements are made by sectioning the adsorbent and developing a deep red color with 1,2-propanediamine. Distribution curves are obtained that cover the range of $n = 0$ to $n = 18$, as is shown in Figure 11.2 for two typical materials.

DETERMINATION OF OXYETHYLENE GROUPS
IN POLYETHYLENE OXIDES

HYDROGEN IODIDE METHOD

Apparatus

Erlenmeyer flask, 250-ml capacity.
Reflux condenser, with standard taper joint.
Adapter for purging, as is shown in Figure 24.3.

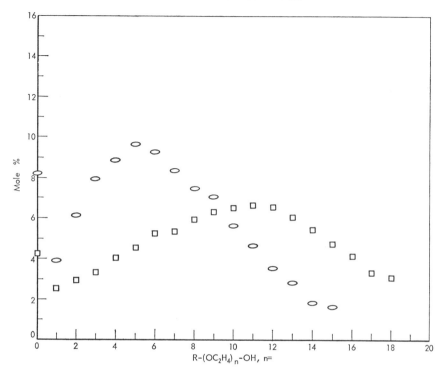

Figure 11.2. Oxyethylene distributions found for some primary alcohol condensates, R-(OC$_2$H$_4$)$_n$-OH. From McCoy and Bullock (10). Copyright 1969 by the American Oil Chemists' Society. Reprinted by permission of the copyright owner.

Reagents

Hydrogen iodide reagent, 56 wt % without stabilizer. Reagent grade material manufactured by Merck and Co., Rahway, New Jersey, is suitable as received. Destroy any free iodine by reaction with mercury. Add 1 ml of mercury for every 5 ml of reagent and shake vigorously until the iodine color is gone. Decant the reagent into a graduate containing a small piece of CO$_2$ and use before the CO$_2$ blanket is dissipated.

Sodium thiosulfate solution, 0.1N standard.

Starch indicator solution.

Potassium iodide solution, 20% aqueous.

Procedure

Weigh 80–100 mg of sample into a 250-ml Erlenmeyer flask. Drop in a small piece of CO$_2$ to displace air and add a boiling chip. Attach a reflux condenser to the flask. Pipet 5 ml of freshly prepared hydrogen iodide reagent through the condenser into the flask. Insert a tube in the top of the condenser and provide a gentle flow of N_2 to exclude air. Set the hot plate controls such that the solution boils gently and maintain this condition for 90 min.

Allow the flask and contents to cool. Wash the condenser with 20 ml of 20% potassium iodide solution and then wash with two 10-ml portions of water. Disconnect the flask and rinse the tip of the condenser with potassium iodide solution from a wash bottle to remove any remaining iodine and collect the washings in the flask. Immediately attach the purging adapter, connected to a CO_2 supply, to the flask and titrate with $0.1 N$ sodium thiosulfate solution using starch as an indicator.

Make a blank determination.

Calculation

$$\text{Oxyethylene content, wt \%} = \frac{(B - A)(N)}{W} \times \frac{22}{10}$$

where B = volume of sodium thiosulfate solution used for sample analysis, ml

A = volume of sodium thiosulfate solution used for blank determination, ml

N = normality of sodium thiosulfate

W = weight of sample, g

22 = equivalent weight of the oxyethylene groups in this determination

DETERMINATION OF THE ALKYL GROUP IN ETHERS AND POLYALKYLENE OXIDE CONDENSATES

The reaction with hydroiodic acid can also be used for the specific determination of the alkyl group from ethers and ether compounds if the alkyl iodides produced are trapped and analyzed by gas chromatography. This was shown to be feasible by Ehrenberger (11) and Merz (12), who described apparatus for treating with boiling hydroiodic acid and subsequent gas chromatographic analysis of the iodides and the olefins. The technique was applied to a series of products obtained from polyethylene oxides. A similar gas chromatographic technique had been used earlier by Mitsui and Kitamura (13) for determination of the alkyl groups (C_1–C_4) in a series of ethers and by Haslam, Hamilton, and Jeffs (14) for the determination of alkyl groups in polymeric esters after conversion to the corresponding iodides. This technique can be extended to higher molecular weight alkyl groups, including those in the detergent range (C_{14}–C_{18}), especially with derivatives of primary alcohols.

A method based on acid pyrolysis was published by Lew (15) for the determination of the alkyl chain length of polyalkylene oxide surfactants. In the method of Lew, the sample is mixed with P_2O_5 or 96% phosphoric acid and pyrolyzed at 400°C to produce olefinic hydrocarbons corresponding in chain length to the alcohols used to condense with the alkylene oxides with virtually no lower hydrocarbons being found. The olefins are a mixture of internal and α-olefins with the same carbon numbers of the alkyl group. From the relative areas of the olefin peaks, Lew calculates the carbon number distribution for alkyl chains and finds good agreement with the values expected from the alcohols used to prepare the ethoxylates. The technique was applied to condensates of C_{12}–C_{15} oxo-type alcohols with approximately 3 or 9 moles of ethylene oxide. The poly(ethylene oxide) portion of the molecule breaks into peaks one of which was identified as acetaldehyde and another as probably a C_4 aldehyde.

OTHER HALOGENATION TECHNIQUES
FOR DETERMINATION OF ETHERS

That aqueous bromine is an effective oxidizing agent for simple aliphatic ethers was pointed out by Deno and Potter (16). Some examples shown in their work are the quantitative oxidation of diethyl ether to acetic acid, dipropyl ether to propionic acid, and tetrahydrofuran to butyrolactone. Oxidations are conducted in aqueous solution in the dark, at 25°C and in the pH range of 1–6. Many reactions give yields of product above 80% and in several cases quantitative yields are observed. The reaction seems to be general for all ethers containing an α-hydrogen.

NUCLEAR MAGNETIC RESONANCE FOR THE ANALYSIS
OF POLYALKYLENE OXIDE CONDENSATES

A few years ago Flanagan, Greff, and Smith (17) illustrated the straight-forward applicability of the NMR technique for the analysis of the different types of polyalkylene oxide condensates. The materials examined included ethylene oxide–propylene oxide block copolymers, alkyl phenol–ethylene oxide condensates, long-chain alcohol–ethylene oxide condensates, as well as other somewhat similar materials. Generally well separated groups of peaks were obtained in the spectra, which made it possible to determine both qualitatively and quantitatively the types of protons in the molecules.

An essentially similar method has been employed by J. L. Jungnickel (18) to examine a series of alcohol ethoxylates of the general formula RCH_2—O—$(CH_2$—$CH_2O)_n$H, where R varied from C_6 to C_{17}. The value of n (degree of polymerization) was obtained from two sources of information, (1) the ratios of the proton intensities and (2) the weight of the reactants in the preparation of the condensates. The data (Table 11.2) show good agreement between the methods. Typical NMR spectra for a condensate with $n = 11$

Table 11.2. Values Obtained in Determination of Ratio of Ethylene Oxide to Alcohol Units in Condensates

General structure: $R-CH_2-O-(CH_2-CH_2-O)_n-H$

Sample	Carbon No. of R group	Value found for n By NMR	By weight[a]
A	10	0.97	0.89
B	12	1.07	1.01
C	12	3.15	3.00
D	12	3.25	3.04
E	12	4.8	4.8
F	13	5.0	5.1
G	17	8.8	8.8
H	12	9.4	9.05
I	16	9.5	8.7
J	12	11.5	11.0
K	12	12.9	13.1
L	11	14.9	15.0

[a] Based on weight of reactants consumed in the preparation.

are shown in Figure 11.3. Ludwig (19) reviewed the results obtained by NMR, gas chromatographic, and thin-layer chromatographic techniques in determining these materials.

ANALYSIS OF VINYL ETHERS

Alkyl vinyl ethers have an unusually high hydrolysis rate and can be readily determined by a preliminary acid-catalyzed hydrolysis to acetaldehyde, followed by determination of the aldehyde by reaction with hydroxylamine hydrochloride (20).

$$ROCH{=}CH_2 + H_2O \xrightarrow{H^+} CH_3CHO + ROH$$

Hydrolysis and oximation can be effected simultaneously in an acidic hydroxylamine hydrochloride solution. The acetal method described in Chapter 6 is recommended for this determination, and in addition, it is possible to determine the olefinic content of vinyl ethers by reaction with iodine and methanol to form the iodoacetal. Excess iodine is determined by titration with standard sodium thiosulfate solution in the method of Siggia and Edsberg (21).

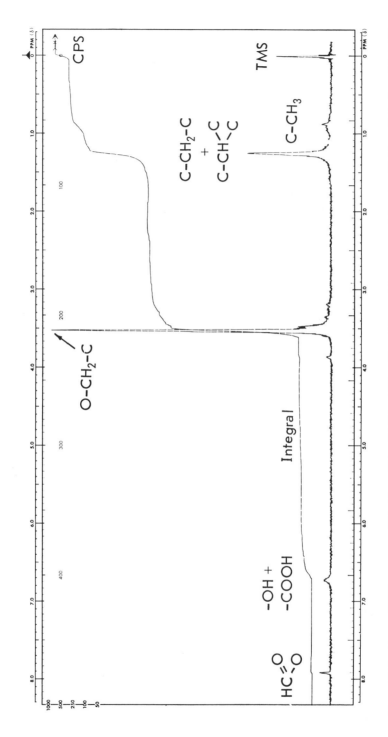

Figure 11.3. Proton NMR spectrum of $C_{12}H_{25}$—CH_2—$O(CH_2$—CH_2—$O)_{11}$—H containing a trace of formic acid. From J. L. Jungnickel (18).

DETERMINATION OF LOW CONCENTRATIONS OF POLYALKYLENE OXIDE DERIVATIVES IN WATER

Since the derivatives of polyethylene oxides find extensive use as industrial and household detergents, large amounts eventually find their way into waste waters and sewage systems and consequently it has become necessary to determine these polymeric ether derivatives at low concentrations in water. The preferred methods involve the reaction of an aqueous solution of an ionized reagent that is a complex metallic compound and the polyalkylene oxide to form either a precipitate, which can be separated and weighed, or a colored, hydrocarbon-soluble complex, which can be determined with a spectrophotometer. Some years ago Shaffer and Critchfield (22) described a gravimetric procedure for the determination of polyethylene oxides by precipitation with silicotungstic acid and barium chloride. The composition of the complex was not determined although evidence pointed to a ratio of 1 mole of polymer to 4 moles of mixed oxides ($2BaO \cdot SiO_2 \cdot 12WO_3$). In view of the empirical nature of this reaction it was necessary to obtain a gravimetric factor for each type of polyethylene oxide determined. Their work indicated a linear relationship between the amount of polymer and the weight of precipitate. The lower limit of sensitivity of this method appears to be equivalent to some 500 ppm of polyethylene oxides in water.

A considerably more sensitive method for the determination of polyethylene oxide derivatives results from their complex formation with a cobalt thiocyanate reagent, followed by measurement of the absorbance of the blue complex. This technique has been thoroughly studied with the nonionic detergents derived from condensation of ethylene oxide with alkyl phenols, acids, or long-chain alcohols. It has recently become significant for measuring the extent of biodegradation in concentrations at the ppm level. The development of this colorimetric method was originally described by Brown and Hayes (23), who made a thorough investigation of the method variables. They found that the complex formed between polyethylene glycol monooleate and the cobalt thiocyanate reagent was extractable into chloroform. The blue solution has absorption maxima at 6200 and 3185 Å, with the absorptivity being sixfold greater at the lower wavelength. They showed that polyethylene glycols with degrees of polymerization from 8.5 to 22 gave a positive reaction. Of the polyethylene glycol ethers and esters, only those prepared from glycols originally having a degree of polymerization greater than 6 gave a positive reaction. Table 11.3 gives a portion of the qualitative data obtained by Brown and Hayes (23) in the following test: To 5 ml of a 1 gram per liter solution of the compound, add 20 ml of ammonium cobaltothiocyanate reagent, shake for 1 minute and set aside for 5 minutes. Extract with 5 ml of chloroform into a dry test tube.

Table 11.3. Qualitative Results Obtained with the Ammonium Cobaltothiocyanate Reagent[a]

Materials are $R\text{—}O\text{—}(CH_2\text{—}CH_2\text{—}O)_nH$

Material		Observed reaction
R	n	
H—	6.3	Negative
	8.5	Slightly positive
	13	Positive
	22	Positive
	90	Negative
CH₃—	1	Negative
	7.5	Positive
	12	Positive
	16.5	Positive
$CH_3\text{—}(CH_2)_{16}\overset{\displaystyle O}{\overset{\|}{C}}\text{—}$	4	Negative
	6.3	Slightly positive
	8.5	Positive
	22	Positive

[a] Results from Brown and Hayes (23).

The application of the cobalt thiocyanate method to the study of the extent of biodegradation of the nonionic surfactants has been investigated in a number of laboratories (24–26). As is common with colorimetric methods, the extent of color absorptivity varies from compound to compound, making it necessary to calibrate with the nonionic being sought. This makes the colorimetric method difficult to employ for all biodegradation studies, as was shown by Huddleston and Allred (25), who also point out that there is not always a correlation between the colorimetric cobalt thiocyanate test and other measures of degradation.

The high sensitivity of the colorimetric cobalt thiocyanate method makes it useful for the determination of traces of nonionic surfactants in water and it is included in this chapter as a recommended method. The procedure is taken from earlier references (23–26), and involves a prior separation of the nonionics from an aqueous sample by extraction with diethyl ether. After removal of the ether the blue complex is formed and its absorbance measured with a spectrophotometer at 3185 Å. Table 11.4 presents some data obtained by the recommended method. The lack of any measurable effects from the unsubstituted polyethylene glycols (R = H) is due to their nonextractability by diethyl ether from the original aqueous solution. The low response of the

Table 11.4. Absorptivities of Ethoxylated Alcohols in
the Colorimetric Cobalt Thiocyanate Method

Preparations are $R-O(CH_2-CH_2-O)_nH$

Material		Absorptivity, liters/g-cm	
R	n	Direct calculation	Basis combined[a] ethylene oxide
C_{13}	3	0.5	1.25
C_{13}	5	4.0	7.7
$C_{10}-C_{12}$	6	5.0	8.2
$C_{12}-C_{15}$	7.5	6.1	9.9
$C_{12}-C_{15}$	9	7.8	11.8
$C_{14}-C_{18}$	9.5	6.9	10.9
$C_{12}-C_{15}$	12	8.9	12.5
$C_{12}-C_{15}$	15	10.2	13.5
H	9	<0.001	<0.001
H	17	0.002	0.002

[a] On the basis of amount of combined ethylene oxide in
the sample.

C_{13} ethoxylate with a degree of polymerization $n = 3$ is expected from the
work of Brown and Hayes. With the alkyl ethoxylates, as the degree of
polymerization increases there is a steady increase in the absorptivity,
calculated either on a direct weight basis or converted to the basis of combined ethylene oxide. With the higher molecular weight condensates, the
molar absorptivities range from 6 to 8 $\times$ 10³ liters/mole-cm, which would
put this measurement among the moderately sensitive techniques for trace
analysis. Since the ether extraction concentrates the surfactant and minimizes
interferences, it is possible to obtain useful analyses in the range of 1–20 ppm.
Certain cationic detergents interfere by forming a similar colored complex
but it should be possible to overcome this interference by removal of cationic
materials through use of an appropriate ion-exchange separation.

DETERMINATION OF LOW CONCENTRATIONS OF POLYALKYLENE OXIDE SURFACTANTS

COLORIMETRIC COBALT THIOCYANATE METHOD

Apparatus

Spectrophotometer, suitable for use at 3180 Å and equipped with 1- and 5-cm
cells.

Separatory funnels, equipped with Teflon stopcocks.

CAUTION! All glassware must be clean and free of surfactants.
Wash all glassware initially with an ionic-type detergent, rinse well

with water, then 5% alcoholic hydrochloric acid solution and then by additional water and methanol rinses. Allow to dry in a clean atmosphere. Segregate this glassware and use only for this purpose.

Reagents

Ethyl ether, anhydrous reagent grade.
Chloroform, spectral grade.
Sodium chloride, CP.
Sodium chloride, 30% aqueous solution.
Ammonium cobaltothiocyanate reagent. Prepare by dissolving 15 g of CP $Co(NO_3)_2 \cdot 6H_2O$, 100 g of CP NH_4SCN, and 80 g of NaCl in 500 ml of distilled water.

Procedure

Adjust the pH of the aqueous solution to be analyzed to 8 using either a pH meter or pHydrion paper. Place 100 ml of the solution in a 250-ml separatory funnel, add 30 g of NaCl and swirl to dissolve. Add 50 ml of ethyl ether and shake for 1 min, using occasional venting. Discard the lower aqueous layer and transfer the ether phase, which contains the nonionic surfactant, into a dry 125-ml separatory funnel, being careful not to transfer any droplets of water. Evaporate the ether extract to dryness by carefully mounting the unstoppered separatory funnel on a steam bath and directing a nitrogen stream into the top of the funnel to sweep out the ether vapors. Allow the funnel to cool to room temperature.

Prior to the analysis, cool the cobaltothiocyanate reagent to 10°C. Add 5 ml of the cooled reagent to the separatory funnel and swirl the contents to dissolve the dried surfactant. Complex formation should take place rapidly. Pipet 20 ml of chloroform, previously cooled to 10°C, into the separatory funnel and shake for 1 min. Withdraw the lower, chloroform, phase into a 1- or 5-ml cell and measure the absorbance reading at 3180 Å. Carry through a reagent blank using 100 ml of distilled water in place of sample.

While the sample analysis is being made, perform an identical analysis on a 100-ml aqueous standard solution containing a known, weighed amount of the pure nonionic surfactant. The standard solution should be chosen to approximate the concentration expected from the sample being analyzed.

Calculation

Subtract the absorbance found for the blank determination from that found for the sample. Calculate the nonionic surfactant content from the corrected absorbance as follows:

$$\text{Nonionic surfactant, ppm} = \frac{(A)(C)(100)}{(B)(V)}$$

where A = net absorbance of sample
        B = net absorbance of standard
        C = concentration of standard, ppm
        V = volume of sample, ml

REFERENCES

1. A. Elek, in *Organic Analysis*, Vol. I, Interscience, New York, 1953, pp. 67–127. Editorial Board J. Mitchell Jr., I. M. Kolfhoff, E. S. Proskauer, A. Weissberger.
2. P. W. Morgan, *Ind. Eng. Chem., Anal. Ed.*, **18**, 500 (1946).
3. S. Siggia, A. C. Starke, J. J. Garis, Jr., and C. R. Stahl, *Anal. Chem.*, **30**, 115 (1958).
4. J. Kelly and H. L. Greenwald, *J. Phys. Chem.*, **62**, 1096 (1958).
5. M. J. Rosen, *Anal. Chem.*, **35**, 2074 (1963).
6. K. Bürger, *Z. Anal. Chem.*, **224**, 425 (1967).
7. M. E. Puthoff and J. H. Benedict, *Anal. Chem.*, **33**, 1884 (1961).
8. L. Gildenberg and J. R. Trowbridge, *J. Am. Oil Chemists' Soc.*, **42**, 69 (1965).
9. J. Törnquist, *Acta Chem. Scand.*, **20**, 572 (1966).
10. R. N. McCoy and A. B. Bullock, *J. Am. Oil Chemists' Soc.*, **46**, 289 (1969).
11. F. Ehrenberger, *Z. Anal. Chem.*, **210**, 424 (1965).
12. W. Merz, *ibid.*, **232**, 82 (1967).
13. T. Mitsui and Y. Kitamura, *Microchem. J.*, **7**, 141 (1963).
14. J. Haslam, J. B. Hamilton, and A. R. Jeffs, *Analyst*, **83**, 66 (1958).
15. H. Y. Lew, *J. Am. Oil Chemists' Soc.*, **44**, 359 (1967).
16. N. C. Deno and N. H. Potter, *J. Am. Chem. Soc.*, **89**, 3550 (1967).
17. P. W. Flanagan, R. A. Greff, and H. F. Smith, *Anal. Chem.*, **35**, 1283 (1963).
18. J. L. Jungnickel, unpublished work from Shell Development Co.
19. F. J. Ludwig, Sr., *Anal. Chem.*, **40**, 1620 (1968).
20. S. Siggia, *Quantitative Organic Analysis via Functional Groups*, Wiley, New York, 1949, p. 59.
21. S. Siggia and R. L. Edsberg, *Anal. Chem.*, **20**, 762 (1948).
22. B. C. Shaffer and F. H. Critchfield, *Ind. Eng. Chem., Anal. Ed.*, **19**, 32 (1947).
23. E. G. Brown and T. J. Hayes, *Analyst*, **80**, 755 (1955).
24. N. T. Crabb and H. E. Persinger, *J. Am. Oil Chemists' Soc.*, **41**, 752 (1964); **45**, 611 (1968).
25. R. L. Huddleston and R. C. Allred, *ibid.*, **42**, 983 (1965).
26. R. A. Freff, E. A. Setzkorn, and W. D. Leslie, *ibid.*, **42**, 180 (1965).

DETERMINATION OF THE α-EPOXIDE GROUP

α-Epoxides are a group of cyclic ethers in which the oxygen atom forms a three-membered ring with two adjacent carbon atoms. In recent years,

α-epoxides have received increased attention because of their usefulness as reagents, intermediates, and end products. As a result of the strained three-membered ring, α-epoxides are the most reactive of the oxides and are far more reactive than ordinary ethers. Whereas open-chain ether linkages are characteristically inert to many reagents, the α-epoxides are attacked by almost all nucleophilic substances. Ring opening accompanied by formation of addition compounds occurs upon treatment with halogen acids, sulfonic acids, bisulfite, thiosulfate, carboxylic acids and anhydrides, hydrogen cyanide, water, alcohols, amines, and aldehydes. It is principally because of the reactivity of the α-epoxy group that these compounds have become important. They are seldom found in natural products but have found considerable use as chemical reagents in the manufacture of a wide variety of materials such as fine chemicals, surface-active agents, special solvents and plasticizers, dyes, cosmetics, synthetic resins, cements, and adhesives. Epoxy resins, which are polymers prepared by condensation of epichlorohydrin with polyhydric phenols or alcohols, contain unreacted α-epoxy groups at the ends of the chain.

The most specific and practical chemical methods for the determination of α-epoxides are those based upon the addition of halogen acids to form a halohydrin following which the acid consumed is taken as the measure of the epoxide. In the presence of large amounts of a solvent such as water or an alcohol, reactions other than the desired hydrochlorination can occur through acid-catalyzed hydration or alcoholation. These reactions, summarized in Table 12.1, make it difficult to use water or alcohol as solvents unless some means is undertaken to minimize their effect. Increasing the concentration of halide ion forces the opening of the ring, actually producing hydroxide ion, and is the basis of a qualitative test for the epoxide group.

Table 12.1. Reactions Involved in Determination of α-Epoxides

The most widely used methods for the determination of the α-epoxide group are based on the principles of these reactions. Early methods were based upon the use of HCl plus $MgCl_2$ as reagents in water or alcohol or of HCl in pyridine, diethyl ether, or dioxane (1). In each case the reaction mixture containing the sample was allowed to stand at room temperature, or in some cases with moderate heating, and the remaining acidity determined by titration. A number of the early methods have retained their utility and several are included as recommended methods in this chapter. A list of the principal features of the methods is given in Table 12.2, together with an indication of their utility and limitations. The Aqueous Magnesium Chloride–HCl method is a simple, easily applied method for the determination of the α-epoxy group in water-soluble epoxides, such as ethylene oxide and propylene oxide. The reagent has a high concentration of magnesium chloride in water and the reaction is carried out at room temperature. The Pyridinium Chloride method utilizes a reagent consisting of $1N$ dry HCl in pyridine and chloroform, and the reaction is conducted either at reflux temperature (ca. 60°C) or in a water bath at 60°C for 30 min. At the end of the reaction period the excess acid is titrated with alcoholic caustic to the phenolphthalein end point. The method has a wide applicability but suffers from a cumbersome preparation of reagent and relatively slow reaction. Consequently it is not generally used except for special cases involving α-epoxides unstable to acids. The HCl–Dioxane method involves the use of a reagent prepared by adding concentrated aqueous hydrochloric acid to dioxane. The effectiveness

Table 12.2. Principal Features of Methods for Determination of α-Epoxide Group

Method	Principal utilization	Applicability	Limitations
Aqueous magnesium chloride–HCl method	For water-soluble α-epoxides	Ethylene oxide, propylene oxide	Gives low results for isobutylene oxide, butadiene monoxide
Pyridinium chloride method	For α-epoxides unstable to acid such as isobutylene oxide	All range of α-epoxides	Method slow, reagent preparation cumbersome
HCl–dioxane method	For relatively rapid determination of α-epoxide group	All ranges of α-epoxides	Amines, buffering materials interfere. Styrene oxide, butadiene monoxide give low results
HBR–acetic acid method	For most rapid determination of α-epoxide group. Generally preferred method	All ranges of α-epoxides	Amines, buffering materials interfere. Styrene oxide, butadiene monoxide give low results
HCl–dioxane–argentimetric method	To be employed when amines or other buffering materials are present	All range of α-epoxides	Method slow
Infrared absorption spectroscopy	To be employed with resins undergoing "cure"	Polymeric α-epoxides and their products	Method needs calibration

of this reagent is high and the reaction with α-epoxides, in general, is complete in 15 min at room temperature. An even more rapid method, the HBr–Acetic Acid method originally published by Durbetaki (2), is based on the principle that the effective strength of acids is increased in glacial acetic acid. The reagent is a solution of hydrogen bromide in glacial acetic acid, which has such a high reactivity toward the α-epoxy group that it is possible to titrate the α-epoxy group directly with this reagent. The end point is determined by means of a color indicator. The method has found use in industry and has been accepted by the ASTM (3). The recommended method using Durbetaki's techniques (HBr–Acetic Acid method) is based on his original publication and, although useful, this method has some undesirable features such as the instability of the reagent, which requires careful handling and a daily standardization.

Several workers have published procedures in which a direct titration is conducted with a standard solution of perchloric acid in glacial acetic acid and the required halogen acid reagent produced in the reaction mixture by having either I^- or Br^- present initially as a salt. Jay (4) utilized tetraethylammonium iodide or bromide as the source of halide ion and titrated with

0.1N perchloric acid in glacial acetic acid. Satisfactory analyses were demon-strated on a series of epoxy resins and it was observed that HI provides for more energetic ring opening than HBr but that HBr is generally sufficiently rapid. Dijkstra and Dahmen (5) employed a commercial cetyltrimethyl-ammonium bromide as the source of halide ion and titrated with 0.1N perchloric acid in glacial acetic acid to the crystal violet end point and obtained quantitative results with ethylene oxide, propylene oxide, and epichlorohydrin.

Although the acidimetric methods are the most generally useful procedures for the determination of α-epoxides, basic components, such as amines, that may be present in occasional samples can interfere by consuming a portion of the titrant. This interference can be avoided by using a method with hydro-chloric acid in dioxane as the reagent and measuring the disappearance of the chloride ion by titration with standard silver nitrate. This procedure was published some years ago by Stenmark (6), who showed that glycidyl phenyl ether, glycidyl isopropyl ether, and epoxy resins were accurately determined even in the presence of considerable amounts of amines. The recommended method for this purpose, the HCl–Dioxane–Argentimetric method, is taken from the publication of Stenmark.

A particularly valuable, detailed review of methods for the determination of epoxide groups has been published by Dobinson, Hofmann, and Stark (7). Their monograph considers the applications of the methods to a wide variety of epoxy compounds. In their experience, the Durbetaki procedure, despite the instability of the reagent, has almost become a standard technique. They consider, however, that the techniques in which ionic bromide or iodide are first introduced and the titration made with perchloric acid are promising but more data are required on accuracy and interference with organic materials likely to be encountered.

DETERMINATION OF WATER-SOLUBLE α-EPOXIDES

AQUEOUS MAGNESIUM CHLORIDE–HCl METHOD

Reagents

Hydrochloric acid–magnesium chloride solution: prepare by shaking 1000 g of CP magnesium chloride hexahydrate with 300 ml of distilled water and 8.0 ml of concentrated (12N) hydrochloric acid until the solution is saturated. Allow the solution to settle for at least 2 hr. At the end of this time decant the supernatant liquid through glass wool and store in a glass-stoppered bottle.

Methyl orange indicator solution, 0.1%.

Sodium hydroxide solution, aqueous, standard 0.1N, carbonate free.

Bromocresol purple: Dissolve 0.1 g in 250 ml water and add 1.75 ml of 0.1N sodium hydroxide.

Procedure

Accurately pipet 50 ml of the hydrochloric acid–magnesium chloride reagent into a 250-ml glass-stoppered Erlenmeyer flask. Introduce into the flask a weighed quantity of sample as specified in Table 12.3, limiting the maximum amount of sample to 10 g. Stopper the flask, shake it vigorously, and allow the mixture to stand for 15 min. If the sample does not dissolve immediately, shake the flask at frequent intervals until the sample dissolves or until 30 min has elapsed.

For volatile samples, seal and weigh the sample in a thin-walled glass ampule and introduce a few small glass rods into the flask to break the ampule.

For samples that are aqueous solutions, sufficient magnesium chloride crystals to attain a saturated reaction mixture should be measured into the reaction flask and the reagent blank. An amount of water equal to the volume of water in the sample taken for analysis should be added to the reagent blank.

Rinse the stopper and neck of the flask with not more than 20 ml of distilled water. Add 2 to 3 drops of methyl orange indicator solution and titrate the mixture with $0.1N$ sodium hydroxide solution to the end point. Disregard any slow fading of the end-point color.

Make a blank determination according to the same procedure but omitting the sample.

Determine the acidity (or basicity) of the sample to the same end point, using 100 ml of neutralized distilled water as the solvent.

Table 12.3. Relationship Between α-Epoxy Value and Optimum Sample Size for the Aqueous Magnesium Chloride–HCl Method

α-Epoxy value, equiv/100 g	Approximate sample size, g
2.3	0.06–0.10
1.5	0.08–0.16
1.0	0.12–0.24
0.7	0.16–0.3
0.4	0.3–0.6
0.2	0.6–1.2
0.1	1.2–2.4
0.05	2–5
0.03 or less	8–10

Calculation

$$\alpha\text{-Epoxy, equiv/100 g} = \frac{(B - S)(N)}{10W} + A$$

where B = volume of sodium hydroxide solution, ml, used in titrating the blank
S = volume of sodium hydroxide solution, ml, used in titrating the sample
N = normality of sodium hydroxide solution
W = weight of sample, g
A = acidity of sample, equiv/100 g

DETERMINATION OF α-EPOXY GROUP

PYRIDINIUM CHLORIDE METHOD

Apparatus

Glass ampules.

Reaction bottles. Heavy-walled, 250–500-ml, with screw cap, crown cap, or spherical joint closure. The caps should be fitted with Teflon inserts 0.005 in. thick.

Reagents

Phenolphthalein indicator solution, 1.0% in 60% ethanol.

Pyridinium chloride–chloroform reagent, 1N. To prepare approximately 1 liter of solution: Weigh 75 g of CP anhydrous pyridine into a 2-liter graduated cylinder, add about 400 ml of anhydrous chloroform and weigh the cylinder and contents to the nearest gram. Place the cylinder in an ice-water bath and slowly bubble dry hydrogen chloride gas into the solution by means of a glass delivery tube fitted with two valves, the one closer to the gas source for turning the gas supply on or off and the other for regulating the rate of flow of the gas. At intervals of several minutes, shut off the hydrogen chloride supply (without changing the setting of the rate-regulating valve), remove the graduated cylinder from the bath, wipe dry, and weigh to establish the approximate rate of flow of hydrogen chloride. When approximately 35 g of hydrogen chloride has been introduced, allow the mixture to warm to room temperature and expel the hydrogen chloride vapors from the air space of the graduated cylinder with a stream of dry air. Add a 10-ml aliquot of the solution to 5 ml of water in a flask and titrate with standard 0.5N alcoholic sodium hydroxide solution to the phenolphthalein end point. Calculate the amount of pyridine to be added in order to neutralize the free hydrogen chloride, if any, and to attain a 5% excess, using the following equation:

$$\frac{(S)(N)(V)(79.1)(1.05)}{1000A} - W = \text{g of pyridine to be added}$$

where S = volume of sodium hydroxide solution, ml, used in titrating the aliquot
N = normality of sodium hydroxide solution
V = total volume of mixture after the aliquot has been taken
A = volume of aliquot, ml
W = weight of pyridine, g, added initially

Add the calculated amount of pyridine and dilute the solution with chloroform to a total volume of $(S)(N)(V)/A$ ml.

To verify that the reagent has been properly prepared, titrate 25 ml of the reagent with 0.5N alcoholic sodium hydroxide solution to the phenolphthalein end point and similarly titrate another 25-ml portion of the reagent that has been boiled gently in a hood for 15 min. The two titrations should agree within 0.1 ml of titrant.

Pyridinium chloride–chloroform reagent, 0.2N. Dilute 200 ml of the 1N pyridinium chloride–chloroform reagent to 1 liter with anhydrous chloroform.

Sodium hydroxide solution, standard 0.5N in methanol.

Procedure

Nonvolatile Liquids and Readily Soluble Solids.   Pipet 25 ml of the 1N pyridinium chloride–chloroform reagent into a 250-ml Erlenmeyer flask equipped with a standard taper joint. Add a quantity of sample containing 0.010–0.015 equiv of α-epoxide (see Table 12.4), and boil the mixture on a hot plate, under a reflux condenser, for 30 min. Cool the flask to ice temperature.

To the reaction vessel add 10 ml of distilled water and 0.2 ml of phenolphthalein indicator solution and titrate with standard 0.5N alcoholic sodium hydroxide solution to a definite pink color. Shake the mixture vigorously after each addition of titrant when near the end point. If the titration requires less than 15 ml of sodium hydroxide solution, repeat the determination using a smaller sample.

Make a blank determination on the reagent in an identical manner using the same amount of water and indicator and titrating, as above, to a definite pink color.

Determine the acidity or basicity of the sample by dissolving the amount of sample specified in Table 12.4 in 25 ml of chloroform, adding 25 ml of methanol and 10 ml of distilled water, and titrating with standard alcoholic hydroxide solution to the phenolphthalein end point.

Table 12.4.   Optimum Sample Size for 1N
Pyridinium Chloride Reagent

α-Epoxy value, equiv/100 g	Approximate sample size, g
2.3	0.4–0.6
2.0	0.5–0.8
1.5	0.7–1.0
1.0	1.0–1.5
0.8	1.3–1.8
0.6	1.8–2.5
0.4	2.5–3.5
≤0.3	5

Volatile Liquids.   Transfer a portion of the chilled sample into a cold 5-ml graduated cylinder; work in a well-ventilated hood. Introduce a quantity of sample containing 0.010–0.015 equiv of α-epoxide into a tared thin-walled glass bulb. Seal the bulb and weigh. Pipet 25 ml of the 1N pyridinium chloride–chloroform reagent into a crown-cap glass bottle, add the bulb containing the sample, and also add a few short sections of glass rod. Cap the bottle and shake to break the bulk. Heat the bottle for 30 min in a water bath at 60 ± 1°C, then allow it to cool to room temperature spontaneously. When cool, chill the bottle in ice water and remove the cap. Proceed as directed above.

Resins and Similar Solid Materials. Pipet 25 ml of the 0.2N pyridinium chloride–chloroform reagent into a 250-ml Erlenmeyer flask equipped with a standard taper joint. Add a quantity of sample containing 0.002–0.003 equiv of α-epoxide. Dissolve the sample by heating the mixture at about 40°C and boil the mixture on a hot plate, under a reflux condenser, for 2 hr. Cool the flask to room temperature. Proceed as directed above, except use standard 0.1N sodium hydroxide in methanol solution instead of 0.5N.

Calculation

$$\alpha\text{-Epoxy, equiv}/100 \text{ g} = \frac{(B - S)(N)}{10W} + A$$

where B = volume of sodium hydroxide solution, ml, used in titrating the blank
S = volume of sodium hydroxide solution, ml, used in titrating the sample
N = normality of sodium hydroxide solution
W = weight of sample, g
A = acidity of sample, equiv/100 g

DETERMINATION OF α-EPOXY GROUP

HCl-DIOXANE METHOD

Reagents

Cresol red indicator solution: dissolve 0.1 g of the sodium salt of cresol red in 100 ml of 50% ethanol.

Ethyl alcohol: add 1 ml of cresol red indicator solution to 100 ml of denatured alcohol 3A (anhydrous) and neutralize to the first violet color of the end point with standard 0.1N methanolic sodium hydroxide solution. Neutralize this solution immediately prior to use.

Hydrochloric acid in dioxane, approximately 0.2N. Prepare by pipeting exactly 1.6 ml of concentrated hydrochloric acid (sp gr 1.19) into 100 ml of purified dioxane contained in a dark bottle equipped with a Teflon-lined screw cap. Mix thoroughly and inspect to make certain that the reagent is homogeneous. Water in the dioxane tends to make dissolution slow or incomplete. Prepare only enough reagent for immediate use.

Purify the dioxane as follows: Reflux 2 liters of technical dioxane with 50 g of potassium hydroxide pellets for 3 hr while a slow stream of nitrogen is bubbling through the liquid. At the end of this time, distill off 1500–1600 ml of dioxane, at the rate of approximately 10 ml/min, using a simple water-jacketed condenser. (A fractionating column is not necessary.) Discard the portion of the distillate that boils below 98°C and collect the remainder in a can or dark bottle under nitrogen.

Add 0.1 g of IONOL* inhibitor for each 100 ml of purified dioxane. Replenish the nitrogen atmosphere each time the container is opened. Dioxane prepared and stored in this manner is usable for at least 2 months.

Sodium hydroxide solution, standard 0.1*N* in methanol.

Procedure

Pipet 25 ml of the hydrochloric acid–dioxane reagent into a 250-ml Erlenmeyer flask. Weigh a quantity of sample containing 0.002–0.004 equiv of α-epoxide (see Table 12.5) and swirl to effect solution.

Allow the reaction mixture to stand at room temperature for 15 min. At the end of this time add, by means of a graduate, 25 ml of the neutral ethyl alcohol and titrate the excess acid with standard 0.1*N* methanolic sodium hydroxide solution. If the titration requires less than 6 ml, repeat the determination, using a smaller sample.

Make at least one, and preferably two, blank tests on the reagents in an identical manner using the same amount of purified dioxane, if any, that was used to dissolve the sample and titrating as above to the first definite violet color.

Determine the acidity or basicity of the sample by dissolving a weight of sample similar to that taken above in 25 ml of purified dioxane, adding 25 ml of the neutral ethyl alcohol–cresol red indicator solution and titrating with standard methanolic base or acid to the yellow-violet end point color change.

Table 12.5. Optimum Sample Size for 0.2*N* HCl–Dioxane Method

α-Epoxy value, equiv/100 g	Approximate sample size, g
2.3	0.09–0.17
1.5	0.13–0.26
1.0	0.2–0.4
0.7	0.3–0.5
0.5	0.4–0.8
0.3	0.7–1.3
0.2	1.0–2.0
0.1	2–4
0.07 or less	3–5

Calculation

$$\alpha\text{-Epoxy, equiv/100 g} = \frac{(B - S)(N)}{10W} + A$$

* Registered Trademark, U.S. Patent Office (Shell Chemical Co.)

where B = volume of sodium hydroxide solution, ml, used in titrating the blank
    S = volume of sodium hydroxide solution, ml, used in titrating the sample
    N = normality of sodium hydroxide solution
    W = weight of sample, g
    A = acidity of sample, equiv/100 g

DETERMINATION OF α-EPOXY GROUP

HBr–ACETIC ACID METHOD

Reagents

Benzene.
Chlorobenzene.
Dioxane, purified.
Glacial acetic acid.
Hydrogen bromide in acetic acid, 0.1*N*. To make 4 liters: Cool 3590 ml of glacial acetic acid in ice until the acetic acid starts to freeze. Add 67 g of 48% aqueous hydrobromic acid and 200 g of acetic anhydride. Mix and adjust the solution to room temperature. Using a 10 ml sample determine the water content by Fischer titration, as g of water per liter, calculated from the equation:

$$\text{g } H_2O/\text{liter} = \frac{(\text{volume of titrant})(\text{reagent factor})}{10}$$

Add acetic anhydride calculated from the equation:

$$\text{ml of acetic anhydride} = 21(\text{g of } H_2O/\text{liter}) - 17$$

Determine the water content again. If the water content is larger than 1.5 g/liter, add more acetic anhydride and again determine the water content. The final value should be between 0.5 and 1.5 g/liter. Dispense this reagent from an all-glass buret assembly protected with a drying agent.
Methyl violet indicator solution, 0.1% in acetic acid.
Potassium acid phthalate, Mallinckrodt Analytical Reagent dried in a 120°C oven for 2 hr.

Apparatus

All-glass buret assembly, with 25-ml buret.
Magnetic stirrer.
Stirring bar, Teflon-coated.
Rubber stopper, to fit on the tip of the buret and in the mouth of a 50-ml Erlenmeyer flask. Notch the side of the stopper to allow air to escape from the flask.

Reagent Standardization

Weight 0.40–0.44 g of potassium acid phthalate into a 50-ml Erlenmeyer flask. Add 10 ml of acetic acid and 5 drops of methyl violet indicator solution. Stir at a slow speed and titrate to a blue-green end point. Note the room temperature and calculate the normality of the HBr reagent from the equation:

$$N = \frac{(\text{g of potassium phthalate})(1000)}{(\text{ml of reagent}) (204.23)}$$

Run the standardization in duplicate the same day the reagent is used.

Procedure

Weigh a sample containing 1–2.5 meq of α-epoxy (see Table 12.6) into a 50-ml Erlenmeyer flask. Dissolve epoxy resins in 10 ml of chlorobenzene or dioxane and other compounds in chlorobenzene, dioxane, or benzene. Add 5 drops of methyl violet indicator solution. Place a stirring bar in the flask, adjust the rubber stopper to close off the atmosphere, and titrate to a permanent blue-green end point while stirring at a slow speed with a magnetic stirrer.

Table 12.6.   Optimum Sample Size for $0.1N$
HBr–Acetic Acid Reagent

α-Epoxy, equiv/100 g	Sample size, g
2.0	0.05–0.13
1.5	0.08–0.20
1.0	0.10–0.25
0.7	0.14–0.35
0.5	0.2–0.5
0.3	0.3–0.6
0.2 or less	0.5–0.7

Calculation

$$\alpha\text{-Epoxy value, equiv/100 g} = \frac{(V)(N)}{10W}$$

where V = the volume of HBr reagent used, ml
       N = the normality of the HBr reagent
       W = the sample weight, g

DETERMINATION OF α-EPOXY GROUP

HCl-Dioxane–Argentimetric Method

Reagents

Hydrochloric acid in dioxane, approximately $0.2N$. Prepared as in the HCl–Dioxane Method.
Silver nitrate solution, $0.1N$, aqueous.
Ammonium thiocyanate solution, $0.05N$, aqueous.

Nitrobenzene, CP. The nitrobenzene used must not show a visible precipitate when tested with alcoholic silver nitrate solution.

Nitric acid, approximately 30 wt %. To prepare approximately 1 liter of solution, mix 345 ml of CP concentrated nitric acid with 690 ml of distilled water. Aerate to remove oxides of nitrogen carefully in an effective hood.

Ferric nitrate indicator solution. Dissolve 78 g of CP ferric nitrate crystals $(Fe(NO_3)_3 \cdot 9H_2O)$ in 250 ml of distilled water and add 50 ml of aerated 30% nitric acid.

Procedure

Pipet 25 ml of hydrochloric acid–dioxane reagent into a 500-ml Erlenmeyer flask. Weigh a quantity of sample containing a maximum of 0.004 equiv of α-epoxide plus amines and swirl to effect solution.

Allow the reaction mixture to stand at room temperature for 15 min. At the end of this time add 50 ml of water, 5 ml of 30% nitric acid, and 3 ml of ferric indicator.

From a buret add 0.5 ml of the ammonium thiocyanate solution. Swirl constantly and titrate with silver nitrate solution until the red color is discharged, then add 2–5 ml in excess. Add 10 ml of nitrobenzene. Stopper the flask tightly and shake it vigorously for 15 sec. Without refilling the buret, titrate slowly with thiocyanate solution until the end point is approached as indicated by a more slowly fading red color. Stopper the flask, shake vigorously for 20–30 sec, and continue the titration until one drop produces a distinct reddish coloration that does not fade upon swirling or vigorous shaking.

Make at least one, preferably two, blank tests on the reagents in an identical manner, omitting the sample.

Determine free halide in the sample in a manner identical with the epoxy determination except that the hydrochloric acid must be omitted from the dioxane.

Calculation

$$\alpha\text{-Epoxy content, equiv/100 g} = \frac{(V_b N - v_b n) - (V_s N - v_s n)}{10W} + A$$

where V_b = volume of silver nitrate, ml, used in titrating the blank
   V_s = volume of silver nitrate, ml, used in titrating the sample
   N = normality of the silver nitrate solution
   v_b = volume of ammonium thiocyanate, ml, used in titrating the blank
   v_s = volume of ammonium thiocyanate, ml, used in titrating the sample
   n = normality of the ammonium thiocyanate
   W = sample weight, g
   A = free halide in the sample, equiv/100 g

COMPARISON OF METHODS FOR DETERMINATION OF THE α-EPOXY GROUP

Since the ease of preparation of reagent and the speed of analysis are critical factors in the choice of an analytical method, there is a high order of preference for the direct titration methods. Consequently, the HBr–Acetic Acid method is widely used, either as published by Durbetaki or in other variations. For perhaps most α-epoxy compounds for which analysis is required, such a choice is satisfactory. However, it is important to point out that certain α-epoxides give quite low results with the more strongly acidic reagents. The α-epoxides for which recoveries are low are those that can undergo isomerization to carbonyl compounds under acid catalysis, such as styrene oxide (8), isobutylene oxide (9), and trimethylene oxide (9). Some diepoxides can give low results apparently due to cyclization reactions, which is particularly the case with the 1,2,5,6-diepoxy system, as indicated some years ago by the work of Wood and Wiggins (10), who found that hot water caused the following reaction to take place:

$$H_2C\overset{\diagdown}{\underset{O}{\diagup}}CH-CH_2-CH_2-CH\overset{\diagdown}{\underset{O}{\diagup}}CH_2 \xrightarrow{H_2O} HOH_2C\overset{\diagup\!\!\diagdown O\diagup}{}CH_2OH$$

Table 12.7. Extent of Recovery of Some α-Epoxy Compounds in the Recommended Methods

| Compound | Recovery in method,[a] wt % | | | | |
	Aqueous magnesium chloride–HCl	Pyridinium chloride	HCl–Dioxane	HBr–acetic acid	HCl–dioxane argentimetric
Ethylene oxide	98.9	99.2	99.4	99.7	
Propylene oxide	98.7	99.8	99.2		
Isobutylene oxide	ca. 30	98.2	92.9	92.4	
Butadiene monoxide	83	97.6	78–95	78–90	
Cyclohexene oxide			98.5	99.5	
Epichlorohydrin	97.8	98.9	99.3	99.0	99.1
1,2-Epoxydodecane				99.6[b]	
Styrene oxide		95.2	87	71.9	
Glycidyl acetate			97.5		100.4
Glycidyl allyl ether		99.7	99.5		99.6
Glycidyl isopropyl ether		99.9	99.5		99.5
Glycidyl phenyl ether		99.4	99.3	99.4[b]	99.4
				99.2	
Dimethyl-1,20-dicarboxy-7,8,11,12-diepoxy-eicosane			46		

[a] Values corrected for known impurities in samples.
[b] Data from Durbetaki (2).

Table 12.8.   Determination of the α-Epoxy Content of Resins by the Recommended Methods

α-Epoxy value, equiv/100 g

Method	Pyridinium chloride	HCl–dioxane	HBr–acetic acid
Reaction conditions	2 hr at reflux	15 min at room temp	Direct titration at room temp
Resin "A"	0.491, 0.494	0.488, 0.489	0.495, 0.495, 0.496, 0.497
Resin "B"	0.1038, 0.1039	0.1027	0.1037, 0.1045
Resin "C"	0.0556, 0.0561		0.0559, 0.0562, 0.0571

Presumably a corresponding monochlorohydrin would be produced from the reaction of 1 mole of HCl with the diepoxide.

A tabulation of results obtained in the determination of the α-epoxy function of some common epoxy compounds is shown in Table 12.7. For those compounds where side reactions are not a concern, a number of the methods listed provide essentially quantitative data. The three glycidyl ethers listed were highly purified compounds and the results (99.2–99.9% recovery) illustrate the high level of stoichiometry of the reaction. With those compounds that can isomerize to carbonyl compounds through acid catalysis, the results are most nearly correct in the weakest acid media, as would be expected. For example, styrene oxide of high purity gave an apparent α-epoxy content of 95.2% with the Pyridinium Chloride method and lower results in the HCl–Dioxane and the HBr–Acetic Acid methods. Some data are given in Table 12.8 for the determination of the α-epoxy function in epoxy resins by several of the methods. These epoxy resins are polymers whose structure is shown below:

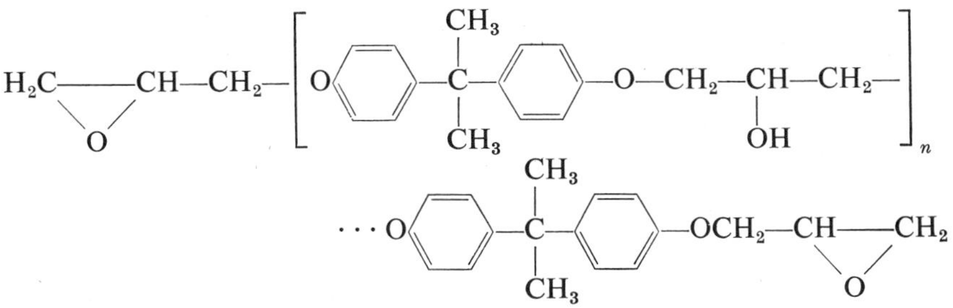

The three methods give essentially similar data on these polymers. A further comparison of the utilization of the methods is provided in Table 12.9, which is a summary of the extent of interference of other classes of compounds in methods for the determination of the α-epoxy group.

Table 12.9. Extent of Interference of Other Classes of Compounds in Methods for Determination of the α-Epoxide Group

Compound class	Extent of reaction in method, %				
	Aqueous magnesium chloride–HCl	Pyridinium chloride	HCl– dioxane	HBR–acetic acid	HCl–dioxane argentimetric
Hydrocarbons	None[a]	None	None	None	None
Chlorinated hydrocarbons	None[a]	None	None	None	None
Alcohols	None[a]	None	None	In large amount makes indistinct end point	None
Ethers	None[a]	None	None	None	None
Chlorohydrins	None[a]	None	None	None	None
Esters	In general, no interference, but formate esters may interfere by partial hydrolysis			None	None
Acids	None	None	None	None	None
Amines	Interference	Interference	Inter- ference	Interference	None
Saturated aldehydes	None	Slight	None	None	None

[a] With a two-phase system it will be necessary to extract the epoxy compound into the reagent phase by agitation.

In view of the speed of the HBr–Acetic Acid method, it is generally the preferable technique to use with α-epoxy compounds in general, of both low and high molecular weight. For the relatively unstable materials such as styrene oxide, isobutylene oxide, and butadiene monoxide, the nearest approach to accurate results would be the Pyridinium Chloride method. When amines or other buffering materials are present the HCl–Dioxane–Argentimetric method should be employed.

DETERMINATION OF THE α-EPOXY GROUP BY INFRARED ABSORPTION SPECTROSCOPY

It is possible to use infrared absorption spectroscopy for the determination of α-epoxy groups in epoxy resins by measuring the absorption band at 10.92 μ (11, 12). When the epoxy resin is "cured," the ring is opened through reaction and the 10.92-μ absorption band disappears as is shown in Figure 12.1, in which a series of spectra are given for increasing reaction time of the resin. To calculate the α-epoxy value from these spectra, the absorptivity per α-epoxy group was determined for the 10.92-μ band from the spectrum

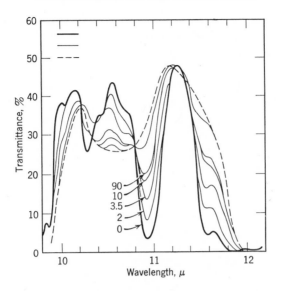

Figure 12.1. Infrared absorption of epoxy group in EPON resin. Heavy curve, uncured; light curves, partly cured; dashed curve, fully cured. Numerals indicate cure time at 65°C, in hours. Data from Dannenberg and Harp (11), courtesy of the American Chemical Society.

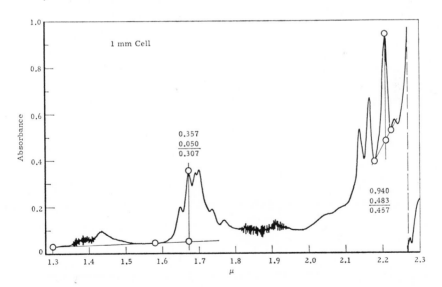

Figure 12.2. Near-infrared spectrum of a liquid epoxy resin showing evaluation of epoxy peak at 2.205 and reference peak at 1.668. Data from Dannenberg (13). Reprinted with permission from Transactions. Soc. Plastics Engineers, Vol. 3, No. 1, January, 1963.

of the uncured resin using the chemically determined α-epoxy value. This, of course, can be done since the uncured resins are soluble in the reagents used for chemical analysis. After "cure" has progressed, the resin gels and is no longer soluble. The infrared spectra of cured samples were obtained by use of the pressed plate technique, involving the embedding of the finely powdered resin in potassium bromide. The powdering of the cured resin to the required particle size was carried out by use of a vibratory ball mill.

DETERMINATION OF THE α-EPOXY GROUP BY NEAR-INFRARED ABSORPTION SPECTROSCOPY

Although the infrared method for the determination of α-epoxides is useful, its precision is not always high, especially for epoxy resins, since the absorption band of the terminal epoxy group at 10.92 μ has some interferences from another band that develops in the same region during condensation. For this reason, Dannenberg (13) developed a near-infrared technique for determination of the α-epoxy group and found it particularly useful in studying the chemical reactions during the curing process of epoxy resins.

The major absorption peak for the α-epoxy group in the near infrared is located at 2.205 μ. This band probably represents a combination of the C—H stretching with the CH$_2$ deformation fundamental. A typical spectrum of a liquid epoxy resin is shown in Figure 12.2. In the region shown the two distinct peaks are the α-epoxy absorption at 2.205 μ and a band at 1.668 μ, probably representing the first overture of a carbon–hydrogen stretching mode of the aromatic CH groups. Dannenberg found that the band at 1.668 μ was nonvariable during cure and that the ratio of the two bands gave the epoxy value relative to the amount of aromatic matter in the specimen. By using known materials, or by chemical analysis, he was able to set up calibrations and then use near-infrared spectroscopy to measure curing as the sample polymerized. Because the samples studied by Dannenberg hardened during the cure, disposable cells were made from commercially available rectangular glass tubing. Using a commercial near-infrared spectrophotometer, results were repeatable within 0.5 % when the height of the bands was calculated against a sketched background.

REFERENCES

1. J. L. Jungnickel, E. D. Peters, A. G. Polgár, and F. T. Weiss, in *Organic Analysis*, Vol. I, Interscience, New York, 1953, pp. 127–154.
2. A. J. Durbetaki, *Anal. Chem.*, **28**, 2000 (1956).
3. Method D1652, American Society for Testing and Materials, *Standards*, Part 20, 1969.

4. R. R. Jay, *Anal. Chem.*, **36,** 667 (1964).
5. R. Dijkstra and E. A. M. Dahmen, *Anal. Chim. Acta*, **31,** 38 (1964).
6. G. A. Stenmark, *Anal. Chem.*, **29,** 1367 (1957).
7. B. Dobinson, W. Hofmann, and B. P. Stark, *The Determination of Epoxide Groups*, Pergamon Press, London, 1969.
8. A. Klages, *Ber.*, **38,** 1969 (1905).
9. S. Winstein and R. B. Henderson, "Ethylene and Trimethylene Oxides," in *Heterocyclic Compounds*, Vol. I, R. C. Elderfield, Ed., Wiley, New York, 1950, pp. 47–52.
10. D. J. C. Wood and L. F. Wiggins, *Nature*, **164,** 402 (1949).
11. H. Dannenberg and W. R. Harp, Jr., *Anal. Chem.*, **28,** 86 (1956).
12. L. A. O'Neill and C. P. Cole, *J. Appl. Chem.*, **6,** 356 (1956).
13. H. Dannenberg, *Trans. Soc. Plastics Engineers*, **3,** 78 (1963).

DETERMINATION OF ORGANIC PEROXIDES

Organic peroxides can be considered as extended derivatives of hydrogen peroxide, HOOH, from which the peroxy compounds derive their oxidizing power. Structurally, the simplest peroxides are the alkyl hydroperoxides or peralcohols ROOH and the dialkyl peroxides R—OO—R. The chemistry of these materials has been studied for many years (1, 2). Under appropriate conditions organic peroxides can convert ferrous salts into ferric and hydrogen iodide into iodine and oxidize stannous and arsenite solutions. A listing of the principal types of organic peroxides is shown in Table 13.1 in the approximate order of their reactivity toward chemical reagents. The order of reactivity cannot be arbitrarily put into a firm classification, for rather large changes occur with a change in the R group and considerable overlapping occurs among the various classifications. The trioxides (3–5) represent one of the more reactive species, while the peracids are perhaps the next most reactive. The most stable peroxides are the dialkyl, of which di-*tert*-butyl peroxide is the commercially most important member. In fact, di-*tert*-butyl peroxide is unreactive in the analytical methods that are used to determine the more active classes quantitatively. Organic peroxides are so diverse in chemical properties as to preclude development of a single general method for determination of all types of peroxides.

Whereas the strong reducing agents are usually capable of determining more categories of peroxides than the weak reagents, the use of very strong reducing agents may lead to erroneous results through reduction of compounds other than peroxides and should be avoided. The approach that has been used in the analysis of slightly peroxidized materials is to measure only the more readily reducible peroxides. The reasonableness of this approach is supported by the fact that such peroxides are known to be the main initial product of peroxidation, and they also undoubtedly play a primary role in low-temperature explosion tendencies. Since the peroxides represent a variety of structures, it is not generally possible to express results in terms of a given assumed peroxide and results are ordinarily reported in terms of milliequivalents of active peroxide oxygen per weight or volume. In general, the determination of organic peroxides is made for one of the following purposes: (a) Determination of the purity of commercial organic peroxides

Table 13.1. Examples of Peroxide Types[a]

Dialkyl trioxides	$R—O—O—O—R$
Peracids	$\overset{\displaystyle O}{\overset{\|}{R}}C—OOH$
Hydroperoxides	$R—OOH$
Diacyl peroxides	$\overset{\displaystyle O}{\overset{\|}{R}}C—O—O—\overset{\displaystyle O}{\overset{\|}{C}}R$
Carbonyl peroxides	$RC\overset{\displaystyle OH}{\underset{\displaystyle OOH}{\Big\langle}}$
Peresters	$\overset{\displaystyle O}{\overset{\|}{R}}C—O—OR$
Dialkyl peroxides	$R—OO—R$

[a] Listed in order of decreasing reactivity.

that are used largely as initiators for polymerization reactions; (b) determination of trace amounts of peroxides remaining after polymerization has taken place; (c) determination of undesired peroxide formed during storage of ethers, ketones, and hydrocarbons because appreciable concentrations of peroxides are explosively unstable and represent hazards in distillation and storage.

Peroxides have been determined almost exclusively via chemical reduction, except for limited application of polarographic methods. The reductive reagents have included the iodide, ferrous, stannous, arsenite, or titanous ions, with most of the methods currently in use being either iodometric or ferrous ion methods. Numerous variations of the iodometric method exist, differing chiefly in the acidity, solvent, and time and temperature employed. Methods employing ferrous ion also generally involve the addition of an excess of thiocyanate ion as an indicator and are of two types: those in which the ferric thiocyanate formed is titrated with standard titanous solution and those in which it is measured colorimetrically. A summary of the principal features of methods for peroxide determinations is given in Table 13.2.

IODIDE ION METHODS

The reaction of iodide ion with a hydroperoxide may be represented as follows:

$$R—O—O—H + 2I^- + 2H^+ \rightarrow ROH + I_2 + H_2O$$

The free iodine (mainly as I_3^-) is titrated with standard sodium thiosulfate solution for the estimation of the peroxide content of the sample. Most investigators have employed acetic acid as the primary reaction solvent, with or without the addition of chloroform or isopropyl alcohol. This practice

Table 13.2. Principal Features of Methods for Determination of Organic Peroxides

Method	Determination	Applicability	Limitations
Sodium Iodide method	Peracids, hydroperoxides, diacyl peroxides, H_2O_2	Assay, determination of solutions	Dialkyl peroxides do not react
Hydrogen Iodide method	Dialkyl peroxides	Assay, concentrated solutions	Easily reduced compounds, such as aldehydes, interfere
Colorimetric Thiocyanate method	Hydroperoxides, peracids, diacyl peroxides	Rapid, sensitive method for peroxides in hydrocarbon solution	Results only approximate
Sodium Arsenite method	Diacyl peroxides, hydroperoxides	Low concentrations of peroxides in fuels	Dialkyl peroxides do not react
Polarographic methods	For examination of relatively well-defined systems	For simple, well-defined systems	Diffusion current variable. Needs close calibration. Method not quantitative for wide-range systems

is quite suitable for alkyl hydroperoxides and diacyl peroxides, which react with iodide ion under relatively mild conditions. However, when less reactive compounds, such as di-*tert*-butyl peroxide, are encountered, more rigorous reaction conditions are required for reduction of the peroxide group, as was shown by Dickey, Raley, Rust, Treseder, and Vaughan (6). In such cases the reaction mixture is mildly heated and strong mineral acids are used. The method originally recommended (6) for di-*tert*-butyl peroxide involved heating the sample at 60°C with a mixture of constant boiling (56%) hydrogen iodide and glacial acetic acid in an inert atmosphere. The mixture is diluted with oxygen-free water prior to the titration of the liberated iodine with sodium thiosulfate solution. The recommended Hydrogen Iodide method for determination of active oxygen in dialkyl peroxides is taken from the original publication (6). As can be seen from the data in Table 13.4, peroxides of lower reactivity are also determined by the Hydrogen Iodide method. Adams (7) has employed a solution of sodium iodide and concentrated hydrochloric acid in glacial acetic acid for the quantitative reduction of di-*tert*-butyl peroxide in a reaction conducted at 80°C for 15 min.

FERROUS ION METHODS

Although iodide ion is a stronger reducing agent than ferrous ion, the latter is nevertheless widely used as a reducing agent in methods for peroxide determination, but unfortunately the ferrous methods have a flaw in that they are not stoichiometric. The idealized equation for the reaction of peroxide with ferrous ion is:

$$ROOH + 2Fe^{2+} + 2H^+ \rightarrow ROH + 2Fe^{3+} + H_2O$$

The actual course of the series of reactions involved was elucidated by Kolthoff and Medalia (8) in a thorough investigation published some years ago. The true nature of the series of reactions involved with the ferrous ion methods was found to include several free-radical chains as is shown in Table 13.3. Both O_2, if present, and organic solvents can participate in the reaction. Oxygen gives high results and organic solvents tend to give low results, with the actual values being greatly dependent upon the structure of the solvent molecule. It has not been found possible to obtain a ferrous ion method as correct stoichiometrically as the iodide methods but some utility can be found because of the simplicity of the techniques using ferrous ion. The recommended ferrous method involves the colorimetric determination of the ferric thiocyanate product and is useful for approximate analysis, as is shown in the data in Table 13.4 in which results on some known reactive peroxides vary from some 80% to 112% of theory.

Table 13.3. Actual Reactions in Ferrous Ion Methods for Determination of Peroxide

$$ROOH + Fe^{2+} + H^+ \rightarrow RO\cdot + Fe^{3+} + H_2O$$

$$RO\cdot + Fe^{2+} + H^+ \rightarrow ROH + Fe^{3+}$$
$$RO\cdot + RH \rightarrow ROH + R\cdot$$

$$R\cdot + O_2 \rightarrow ROO\cdot$$
$$ROO\cdot + Fe^{3+} + H^+ \rightarrow ROOH + Fe^{3+}$$

$$\overset{\displaystyle H}{\underset{\displaystyle |}{CH_3COH}} + Fe^{3+} \rightarrow CH_3CHO + Fe^{2+} + H^+$$

DETERMINATION OF HYDROPEROXIDES

Sodium Iodide Method

Reagents

Acetic acid, glacial.

Isopropyl alcohol, 99.3 wt %.

Sodium iodide solution, saturated aqueous (approx. 200 g per 100 ml of water). Prepare in small quantities and keep in a dark bottle blanketed with carbon dioxide. When the blank titration exceeds 0.1 ml, the solution should be discarded and a fresh one prepared.

Sodium thiosulfate solution, 0.1N standard.

Procedure

Weigh a sample containing no more than 20 meq of peroxide into a 100-ml volumetric flask. Dilute to the mark with isopropyl alcohol and mix thoroughly. Use a 10-ml aliquot for test.

Into a 250-ml volumetric flask, drop a $\frac{1}{2}$-in. diameter piece of solid carbon dioxide and add 50 ml of isopropyl alcohol and 2 ml of glacial acetic acid.

After the carbon dioxide has completely sublimed, add by means of a pipet 10 ml of sample solution. Add the sample in such a manner that none adheres to the neck or the ground joint of the flask. Add 2 ml of saturated aqueous sodium iodide solution, stopper the flask, and swirl to mix. Place the flask in a water bath at $40 \pm 1°C$ for 1 hr.

Remove the flask from the bath and add from a graduated cylinder 75 ml of distilled water. Titrate to the disappearance of the yellow color with 0.1N sodium thiosulfate. Should the reaction mixture become sufficiently colored prior to titration to interfere with the end point, add 2–3 ml of chloroform and continue the titration with sodium thiosulfate, shaking thoroughly after each addition until no perceptible violet color remains in the chloroform.

Make a blank determination on the reagents exactly as described above but omitting the sample. The blank titration for this analysis is usually nil, but it cannot be assumed that the reagents are completely peroxide free unless tested.

Calculation

$$\text{Peroxide, wt \%} = \frac{(A - B)(N)(M)}{20W}$$

where A = volume of standard sodium thiosulfate solution, ml, used for the titration

B = volume of standard sodium thiosulfate solution, ml, used for the blank

N = normality of sodium thiosulfate solution

W = weight of sample, g, in aliquot taken for analysis

M = molecular weight of the peroxide

Calculate the active oxygen content by means of the following equation:

$$\text{Active oxygen, wt \%} = \frac{(A - B)(N)(8.0)}{10W}$$

DETERMINATION OF ACTIVE OXYGEN IN DI-ALKYL PEROXIDES

HYDROGEN IODIDE METHOD

Reagents

Acetic acid, glacial.

Hydrogen iodide reagent, 56 wt %, inhibitor-free. Reagent grade material manufactured by Merck and Co., Rahway, New Jersey, is suitable as received.

For each analysis withdraw slightly in excess of 5 ml, transfer to a test tube, and shake with a drop of mercury. Keep the contents of the bottle blanketed with carbon dioxide at all times during withdrawal of reagent.

Sodium thiosulfate solution, 0.1N standard.

Starch indicator solution.

Procedure

Weigh a sample containing 12–15 mmoles of peroxide into a 50-ml volumetric flask. Dilute to the mark with glacial acetic acid and mix thoroughly.

By means of a pipet, transfer 5 ± 0.01 ml of the sample solution to a second 50-ml volumetric flask that has been flushed with carbon dioxide for 2 min. Be careful not to touch the neck of the flask with the tip of the pipet. Add 5 ml of the 56 wt % hydrogen iodide reagent by placing the tip of the pipet near the bottom of the neck of the volumetric flask and allowing the reagent to run down the side of the flask. Any sample adhering to the neck of the flask may be washed down with the reagent. Do not touch the pipet to the ground surface or upper part of the neck of the flask. Stopper the flask firmly, swirl, and place in a 60 ± 1°C water bath for 45 ± 1 min.

At the end of the heating period, remove the flask from the water bath and allow to cool to room temperature. As rapidly as possible, transfer the contents of the flask to a 500-ml glass-stoppered conical flask that contains 150 ml of oxygen-free water. Allow a piece of solid carbon dioxide about the size of a marble to vaporize completely in the 150 ml of distilled water to free it of oxygen prior to the transfer. After the bulk of the liquid has been transferred, rinse the walls of both flasks with water.

The transfer of the sample from the volumetric to the conical flask must be made quickly because the iodide is rapidly oxidized, especially when a thin film is exposed to air.

Titrate the sample to a nearly colorless end point with standard $0.1N$ sodium thiosulfate solution. Add 2 ml of starch indicator solution and continue the titration to a colorless end point.

Make a blank determination on the reagents in the manner described above, substituting 5 ml of glacial acetic acid for the sample.

Calculation

$$\text{Peroxide, } \% = \frac{(A - B)(N)(M)}{20W}$$

where A = volume of standard sodium thiosulfate solution used for the titration of the sample, ml

B = volume of standard sodium thiosulfate solution used for the titration of the blank, ml

N = normality of the standard sodium thiosulfate solution

W = weight of sample, g, in the aliquot taken for analysis

DETERMINATION OF PEROXIDES IN HYDROCARBON MATERIALS

COLORIMETRIC THIOCYANATE METHOD

Apparatus

A spectrophotometer, equipped with 1-cm cells.

Reagents

Ferric alum solution, $0.003M$. Dissolve 2.89 g of ferric ammonium sulfate 24-hydrate in water and dilute to 100 ml. Pipet 10 ml of this solution into a 100-ml volumetric flask and dilute to the mark with water. Use this solution the same day it is prepared.

Ferrous thiocyanate reagent: dissolve 1.00 g of CP ammonium thiocyanate and 1.0 ml of 25 wt % sulfuric acid in 200 ml of CP methanol. Saturate the solution with CP ferrous ammonium sulfate by shaking for a few minutes with 0.2 g of the finely pulverized salt. Decant the supernatant solution into a brown glass-stoppered bottle.

The reagent has a faint pink color that gradually deepens. The usefulness of the reagent can be extended by keeping it in an inert atmosphere. Even so, it should be freshly prepared each day.

Methanol, CP, anhydrous.

Apparatus Standardization

Using a 1-ml graduated pipet, introduce volumes of 0.003M ferric alum solution and methanol as indicated into six 25-ml volumetric flasks.

Flask No.	Ferric alum solution, ml	Methanol, ml
1	0	1.0
2	0.1	0.9
3	0.3	0.7
4	0.5	0.5
5	0.7	0.3
6	0	1.0

Fill each flask to the mark with ferrous thiocyanate reagent and mix well. Immediately obtain the absorbances at 525 mμ relative to distilled water, using 1-cm cells. Correct the absorbance readings for flasks 2–5 by subtracting from each the average of the readings from flasks 1 and 6. Plot the corrected values against the corresponding volumes of 0.003M ferric alum added.

Procedure

Into a 25-ml volumetric flask introduce a volume of sample containing 0.0003–0.0015 meq of reactive peroxide. Add methanol sufficient to bring the volume to 1 ml. Fill the flask to the mark with ferrous thiocyanate reagent and mix well. After 10 ± 1 min obtain the absorbance at 525 mμ relative to water, using a 1-cm cell.

Make two blank determinations, substituting 1 ml of methanol for the sample.

Calculation

Correct the absorbance obtained for the sample by substituting the average blank absorbances. Convert the corrected absorbance to ml of 0.003M ferric alum solution by means of the standardization curve.

Calculate the peroxide value of the sample by means of the equation

$$\text{Peroxide value, meq/liter} = \frac{3V}{S}$$

where V = volume of ferric alum solution corresponding to the corrected sample absorbance, ml, and S = volume of sample taken, ml.

OTHER CHEMICAL TECHNIQUES FOR THE
DETERMINATION OF ORGANIC PEROXIDES

Since there are many reducing agents reactive with at least some of the organic peroxides, a number of other reagents have been used for the determination and differentiation of peroxides. Siggia (9) employed an aqueous 0.1N sodium arsenite solution to reduce reactive peroxides and this method, with some modifications, was later found applicable for the determination of hydroperoxides in petroleum products (10). A modified tetraethyllead extraction apparatus was used for both heating and extraction. The sample was refluxed with a measured quantity of standard aqueous sodium arsenite solution in a two-phase system containing sufficient ethyl alcohol to disperse the sample. At the end of the reaction period the aqueous phase containing the unreacted arsenite was separated quantitatively from the hydrocarbon phase and was titrated with standard iodine solution. Walker and Conway (10) reported that the method determined hydroperoxides accurately both in the analysis of peroxide concentrates and in the determination of low concentrations of peroxides in petroleum products. They compared the results obtained using the arsenite method and an iodometric method in the analysis of samples of gasoline, fuel oil, and a highly refined white oil containing increasing levels of added hydroperoxides. For gasoline and fuel oil the iodometric method gave very low and incorrect values for the hydroperoxide content, while the values obtained by the arsenite method were close to those expected. For white oil, however, the results obtained by both methods agreed closely with those calculated from the known amounts of added peroxide. It was suggested that the less refined gasoline and fuel oil contained components that reacted with the iodine and consequently produced low values in the iodometric method. In an examination of the arsenite method (11) with a number of pure peroxides dissolved in white oil, it was concluded that the method provides an accurate measure of reactive peroxides such as hydroperoxides, diacyl peroxides, and peresters. Some of these data are given in Table 13.4. The arsenite method was found particularly useful for the analysis of petroleum products because large samples can be used with consequent high sensitivity and because colored materials do not interfere since the color generally remains in the hydrocarbon phase during the extraction step. Consequently, the Sodium Arsenite method is included as a recommended method in this chapter.

Horner and his co-workers (12, 13) have shown that several unusual reagents can be helpful in distinguishing among the several types of peroxides. Tertiary phosphines and arsines reduce peracids, hydroperoxides, and diacyl peroxides but do not react with dialkyl peroxides. Diphenylsulfide will reduce peracids but, even with long reaction periods, reacts only partially

Table 13.4. Extent of Reaction of Peroxides in Several Methods

Material	Recovery, % in the indicated method			
	Sodium iodide method	Hydrogen iodide method	Colorimetric CNS method	Sodium arsenite method
tert-Butyl hydroperoxide	100.3, 100.5, 100.3, 100.3	100.4, 100.6, 100.9	105	
n-Butyl hydroperoxide	98.7, 98.4			
Cumene hydroperoxide	99.6, 99.6		112	99, 100
2,2-Bis(tert-butylperoxy)butane	2.5	99.2, 99.4		6
Di-tert-butyl peroxide	0.006	97.4	0.0	0.0, 0.0
Hydrogen peroxide	99.0		83	
Benzoyl peroxide	100.1			98, 99
Tetralin hydroperoxide	100.1		95	
tert-Butyl perbenzoate	65.4	96.7	88	98, 98
Cyclohexanone peroxide	—			98, 99

with hydroperoxides or diacyl peroxides and does not react with dialkyl peroxides.

Polymeric peroxides present somewhat unusual analytical problems. Many examples of polyperoxides are known, such as those from 1,3-butadiene (14), styrene (15, 16), and acrylonitrile and methacrylonitrile (17, 18). The peroxide polymer prepared from butadiene has been closely studied (14, 19). Handy and Rothrock (14) found the average degree of polymerization to be between 8 and 10 and concluded that the material was an alternating co-polymer of butadiene and oxygen. They noted that the concentrated peroxide can be detonated by ignition or severe shock. Braithwaite and Penketh (19) reported that a number of the usual analytical methods failed to give quantitative results for the peroxide content. They did, however, obtain satisfactory results with an iodometric method employing lithium iodide as a reagent of high solubility in isooctanol. Phosphoric acid was added to generate hydrogen iodide and the reaction carried on at reflux temperature in the absence of light.

SODIUM ARSENITE METHOD

DETERMINATION OF PEROXIDES

Apparatus

Extraction apparatus, conforming to the dimensions given in Figure 13.1 of ASTM D 526-66. Attach the condenser and sampling funnel to the flask by means of 24/40 standard taper joints. Wrap the stem of the flask with a 250-W

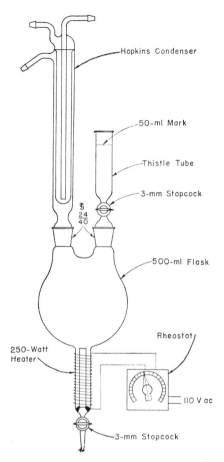

Figure 13.1. Extraction apparatus for determination of peroxides by the sodium arsenite method. Redrawn from ASTM D-526 (Standard Method for determination of lead alkyls in gasoline).

heating coil consisting of 9 ft of 30-gage nichrome wire and attach a service cord and plug to the coil. Fuse a small Carborundum boiling chip to the end of a 6-cm length of 2-mm glass rod and drop the rod, with the boiling chip up, into the annular space of the flask stem.

Variable autotransformer, 5-A minimum capacity for regulating the heating coil.
Erlenmeyer flasks, 500-ml capacity.

Reagents

Sodium arsenite solution, standard 0.1*N*. Weigh 4.945 grams of dry, reagent grade arsenic trioxide into a 25-ml beaker. With the aid of a large-stem funnel, transfer the reagent to a 1-liter volumetric flask. Rinse the beaker and funnel with 50 ml of $1N$ sodium hydroxide solution, followed with several water rinsings to ensure complete transfer of the reagent to the volumetric flask. Add about 500 ml of distilled water, heat the flask in a water bath at about 70°C, and swirl the liquid until all the arsenic trioxide is dissolved. Allow the solution to cool to room temperature, then add 51 ml of $1N$ sulfuric acid and dilute to exactly 1 liter with distilled water. Mix thoroughly.

Sodium hydroxide solution, $1N$.

Ethyl alcohol, formula 3A.

Phenolphthalein indicator solution, 1 % in ethyl alcohol.

Sodium bicarbonate, CP, powdered.

Starch indicator solution.

Iodine solution, standard $0.05N$. Prepare by dissolving 20 g of iodate-free potassium iodide in 25 ml of water. When completely dissolved add 6.35 g of reagent grade iodine. Dissolve by stirring and make up to 1 liter with distilled water. Store in a dark, glass-stoppered bottle. Standardize each day against the sodium arsenite solution.

Procedure

Remove the sampling funnel from the extraction apparatus and accurately pipet 25 ml of standard sodium arsenite solution directly into the flask. Add 25 ml of ethyl alcohol, 5 ml of $1N$ sodium hydroxide, a few drops of phenolphthalein indicator solution, and a quantity of sample as specified in the following table. Weigh the sample to the nearest 0.02 g.

Peroxide content, meq/100 g	Sample size, ml
0–1	100
1–2	50
2–4	25
4–8	10

When the peroxide content is above 8, adjust the sample size so that not more than one-third of the sodium arsenite is used.

It is convenient to pipet the appropriate volume of sample into a 50- or 100-ml volumetric flask; stopper the flask and obtain the total weight. Transfer the sample without rinsing to the extraction apparatus, and obtain the tare weight of the empty flask.

Replace the sampling funnel and place a 500-ml Erlenmeyer flask under the extractor drain to catch any reagent that may leak past the stopcock. Turn on the water to the condenser and apply line voltage to the heater coil until boiling begins, then regulate the voltage by means of the variable transformer so that the reflux is steady but slow. Continue the boiling for 1 hr and then turn off the heat, allow the phases to separate, and drain the lower phase as completely as possible into the Erlenmeyer flask. Add 5–10 ml of distilled water to the extraction flask and drain it into the Erlenmeyer flask to flush out any arsenite solution remaining in the stem.

Add 50 ml of distilled water to the extractor and again boil the mixture under reflux for 5 min. Allow the phases to separate and drain the water into the flask. Repeat the water extraction once again to ensure complete removal of the unused arsenite from the sample. Discard the upper layer.

To clean the extraction apparatus, add about 50 ml of distilled water and boil for approximately 5 min with the condenser water turned off. Drain the water, leave the reactor drain cock open, and add 50 ml of acetone to the sampling funnel. While the apparatus is still hot, open the stopcock on the sampling funnel and allow a small amount of acetone to enter the reactor. As soon as the vapors condense sufficiently to relieve the pressure, close the drain cock and add the remaining acetone as rapidly as it will flow in. Immediately drain the acetone and apply vacuum to the condenser vent tube to remove the acetone vapors.

Neutralize the combined extract and washing to the phenolphthalein end point by dropwise addition of $1N$ sulfuric acid; then add 2 ml in excess. Add one or two Carborundum boiling chips to the Erlenmeyer flask and boil the solution vigorously for 10 min to expel mercaptans.

Cool the extract to room temperature and add 2–3 g of sodium bicarbonate and 3–4 ml of starch solution. Titrate to the starch end point with $0.05N$ iodine solution.

Make a blank determination following the above procedure and using the same amounts of reagents but omit the sample.

Calculation

Calculate the peroxide content of the sample by means of the following equation:

$$\text{Peroxide value, meq}/100 \text{ g} = \frac{(B - S)(N)(100)}{W}$$

where S = volume of iodine solution consumed by the sample, ml
B = volume of iodine solution consumed by the blank, ml
N = normality of the iodine solution
W = weight of sample, g

DETERMINATION OF PEROXIDES BY POLAROGRAPHIC REDUCTION

Polarography is the principal instrumental method that has been applied to the determination of organic peroxides (20, 21). Data obtained by a number of investigators have shown that a large variation exists among the diffusion current constants even in homologous series of organic peroxides and, consequently, the accuracy of the method for general quantitative analysis is limited. The principal use of the method is for the examination of relatively well defined systems for determination of specific, reducible peroxides. For quantitative results, calibrations must be made with the peroxides actually known to be present. Since the width of the half-wave measurement is appreciable and other reducible materials, if present, may reduce in the measured range, it is important to make some tests to eliminate the possibilities of interference.

Skoog and Lauwzecha (22) determined the reduction characteristics of a homologous series of hydroperoxides in aqueous media and demonstrated that the half-wave potentials became less negative with increasing molecular weight. These data, shown in Table 13.5, were obtained at 25°C using a dropping mercury electrode in an aqueous–alcoholic system and with dilute sulfuric acid as the supporting electrolyte. In the aqueous system of Skoog and Lauwzecha the hydroperoxides reduced at potentials of −0.01 to −0.24 V (versus SCE). The measured diffusion current constants, I_d/C, show a regular change with the molecular weight of the hydroperoxides. Skoog and Lauwzecha concluded that the decrease observed with the larger molecules was the result of the decrease in diffusion rate expected with increased molecular size. A similar reduction in the diffusion current constant with increasing molecular weight was observed by Silbert, Witnauer, Swern, and Ricciuti (23) in examining diacyl peroxides. Their data, also shown in Table 13.5, were obtained in a nonaqueous system using $0.3M$ LiCl in benzene and methanol at 25°C. In a series of *tert*-butyl peresters, however, the diffusion current constants were relatively unchanged. The diffusion current constants are expressed as I_d/C, where I_d is the observed diffusion current in microamperes and C is the concentration of the peroxide in millimoles per liter. Measured diffusion currents are converted to concentration of peroxide in samples being examined by means of the appropriate constant. Consequently, variations among the diffusion current constants seriously limit the accuracy of the polarographic method for general quantitative determination of the peroxide functional group unless the system is defined and can be calibrated with the known peroxides actually present.

Since many other organic functions can be polarographically reduced, it is important to consider the interference of other functional groups as in any other method. The lack of procedural standardization in the published polarographic information makes it difficult to use much of the literature for a thorough inspection of this critical point. It is particularly difficult to compare half-wave potential data where the investigations have not chosen the same basic reference electrode. Fortunately, there are several publications reporting results with other types of compounds examined along with peroxides and under the same experimental conditions. Willits, Ricciuti, Knight, and Swern (21) examined a series of compounds in methanol–benzene solution using $0.3M$ LiCl as electrolyte. In their system hydroperoxides reduced at voltages of −0.61 to −0.96. Simple aliphatic ketones and aldehydes did not reduce in their system while aromatic or α,β-unsaturated carbonyl compounds reduced at voltages of −1.55 to −1.79. Those diketo-acids in which the carbonyl groups were adjacent reduced in the same range

Table 13.5.   Half-Wave Potentials and Diffusion Current Constants for Some Peroxides

	Half-wave potential ($E_{1/2}$), V vs. SCE	Diffusion current constant (I_d/C)
Hydroperoxides[a]		
1-Pentyl	−0.20	7.3
2-Pentyl	−0.24	7.0
3-Methyl-1-butyl	−0.23	7.0
1-Hexyl	−0.12	6.9
2-Hexyl	−0.16	6.7
3-Hexyl	−0.16	6.6
Cyclohexyl	−0.14	6.7
1-Heptyl	−0.03	
2-Heptyl	−0.12	6.3
1-Octyl	−0.02	
1-Nonyl	−0.01	5.8
Diacyl peroxides[b]		
Dipelargonyl	−0.10	9.1
Didecanoyl	−0.10	10.0
Dilauroyl	−0.09	9.6
Dimyristoyl	−0.12	8.2
Dipalmitoyl	−0.10	7.7
Distearoyl	−0.08	6.2
tert-Butyl peresters[b]		
Perpelargonate	−0.96	10.7
Percaprate	−0.90	10.9
Perlaurate	−0.87	10.0
Permyristate	−0.82	10.5

[a] Data from Skoog and Lauwzecha (22). Aqueous reduction system.
[b] Data of Silbert, Witnauer, Swern, and Ricciuti (23). Nonaqueous reduction system.

as the hydroperoxides and consequently would interfere in determination of hydroperoxides. Brüschweiler and Minkoff (24) examined the reductive behavior of methyl and ethyl hydroperoxides in both the presence and absence of formaldehyde and acetaldehyde and found no interference from the aldehydes.

Because of the limitations of the polarographic method for quantitative determination of the peroxide functional group in complex mixtures of materials, its application has been best utilized for examination of specific systems. For instance, it has been used to follow the disappearance of perlauric acid in the course of the epoxidation of unsaturated fatty esters (25), for the determination of the lower organic peroxides produced by combustion processes (24), and for following the rate of formation of tetralin hydroperoxide in the autoxidation reactions (26). The polarographic method has likewise been found useful in determination of the rate of peroxidation of fats both free of antioxidants and containing known added antioxidants (27).

DETERMINATION OF PEROXIDES BY NUCLEAR MAGNETIC RESONANCE

Until recently little use had been made of nuclear magnetic resonance in the analysis of organic peroxides principally because of the unavailability of pure reference peroxides. A number of investigators have been accumulating data on pure materials (28–32) and it is now possible to develop information based on proton shifts. In the detailed examination of the proton NMR spectra of 20 purified organic peroxides, Swern, Clements, and Luong (31) were able to make a series of comparisons. They divided the peroxides into two groups, those in which the proton was attached to the peroxy group and those in which it was not. Chemical shifts of the acidic, peroxy-linked protons were found to fall in order with acidity levels when compared to carboxylic acids and alcohols. For instance, peroxycarboxylic acids, which are somewhat stronger acids than the hydroperoxides, have chemical shifts in the range of 10.9–11.8 ppm (compared to tetramethylsilane) while the hydroperoxides fall between 7.6 and 9.2 ppm. The signal from the hydroperoxide proton shifts with dilution presumably from a decrease in intermolecular hydrogen bonding. The peroxycarboxylic acid proton shows little or no shift in dilution, which is in agreement with the intramolecular bonding proposed for these materials. In peroxides without acidic protons, chemical shifts are generally not much different from similar nonperoxy compounds.

REFERENCES

1. J. O. Edwards, Ed., *Peroxide Reaction Mechanisms*, Wiley, New York, 1962.
2. A. Rieche, *Alkylperoxyde und Ozonide*, Dresden, 1931.
3. P. D. Bartlett and P. Gunther, *J. Am. Chem. Soc.*, **88**, 3288 (1966).
4. L. R. Anderson and W. B. Fox, *ibid.*, **89**, 4313 (1967).
5. P. G. Thompson, *ibid.*, **89**, 4316 (1967).
6. F. H. Dickey, J. H. Raley, F. F. Rust, R. S. Treseder, and W. E. Vaughan, *Ind. Eng. Chem.*, **41**, 1673 (1949).
7. D. B. Adams, *Analyst*, **91**, 397 (1966).
8. I. M. Kolthoff and A. I. Medalia, *Anal. Chem.*, **23**, 595 (1951).
9. S. Siggia, *Anal. Chem.*, **19**, 872 (1947).
10. D. C. Walker and H. S. Conway, *ibid.*, **25**, 923 (1953).
11. G. C. Rounds and F. R. Brooks, unpublished work from Shell Development Co.

12. L. Horner and E. Jurgens, *Angew. Chem.*, **70**, 266 (1958).
13. L. Horner and W. Jurgeleit, *Liebigs Ann. Chem.*, **591**, 138 (1955).
14. C. T. Handy and H. S. Rothrock, *J. Am. Chem. Soc.*, **80**, 5306 (1958).
15. F. A. Bovey and I. M. Kolthoff, *ibid.*, **69**, 2143 (1947).
16. A. A. Miller and F. R. Mayo, *ibid.*, **78**, 1017 (1956).
17. K. C. Smeltz and E. Dyer, *ibid.*, **74**, 623 (1952).
18. S. G. Strause and E. Dyer, *ibid.*, **78**, 136 (1956).
19. B. Braithwaite and G. E. Penketh, *Anal. Chem.*, **39**, 1470 (1967).
20. P. Zuman, *Organic Polarographic Analysis*, Macmillan, New York, 1964.
21. C. O. Willits, C. Ricciuti, H. B. Knight, and D. Swern, *Anal. Chem.*, **24**, 785 (1952).
22. D. A. Skoog and A. B. H. Lauwzecha, *ibid.*, **28**, 825 (1956).
23. L. S. Silbert, L. P. Witnauer, D. Swern, and C. Ricciuti, *J. Am. Chem. Soc.*, **81**, 3244 (1959).
24. H. Brüschweiler and G. J. Minkoff, *Anal. Chim. Acta*, **12**, 186 (1955).
25. C. Ricciuti, L. S. Silbert, and W. S. Port, *J. Am. Oil Chemists' Soc.*, **34**, 134 (1957).
26. L. Dulong, *Makromol. Chem.*, **77**, 206 (1964).
27. J. W. Hamilton and A. L. Tappel, *J. Am. Oil Chemists' Soc.*, **40**, 52 (1963).
28. S. Fujiwara, M. Katayama, and S. Kamio, *Bull. Chem. Soc. Japan*, **32**, 657 (1959).
29. A. G. Davies, D. G. Hare, and R. F. M. White, *J. Chem. Soc.*, **1961**, 341.
30. W. F. Brill, *J. Am. Chem. Soc.*, **87**, 3286 (1965).
31. D. Swern, A. H. Clements, and T. M. Luong, *Anal. Chem.*, **41**, 412 (1969).
32. G. A. Ward and R. D. Mair, *ibid.*, **41**, 538 (1969).

DETERMINATION OF ORGANIC BASES

The category of organic bases covers essentially the basic derivatives of ammonia. These include the simple primary, secondary, and tertiary aliphatic and aromatic amines as well as the quaternary alkylammonium hydroxides and the amine oxides. The range in basic strength is large; the quaternary ammonium hydroxides have a basicity essentially equivalent to that of sodium or potassium hydroxide, while quinoline is an extremely weak base and yet can be quantitatively titrated with perchloric acid in nonaqueous solvents.

In recent years it has become the practice to express the aqueous dissociation constants of organic bases in terms of the equilibrium of the base and its conjugate acid with a solvated proton.

$$BH^+(aq) + H_2O \rightleftarrows B(aq) + H_3O^+(aq)$$

In dilute solutions the equilibria can be expressed by:

$$K_a = \frac{[B][H_3O^+]}{[BH^+]}$$

It is clear from this expression that a strong base will have a low value for K_a. To make comparisons more uniform with the pH scale, the values for K_a are generally given as the negative logarithm or pK_a. In this scale, of course, the strong base will have a high value for pK_a and a weak base, a low or even negative value for pK_a. Some values for the dissociation constants of organic nitrogen compounds and their comparative behavior in titration methods are given in Table 14.1. These data are taken from Perrin (1), who has issued a large compilation under the auspices of the International Union of Pure and Applied Chemistry. It should be understood that the values for those extremely weak bases whose pK_a is below 1 are quite uncertain and only to be regarded as approximate. Further data on ionization constants, and techniques for their determination, are given by Albert and Serjeant (2). It is clear from the data in Table 14.1 that organic nitrogen compounds fall into several classifications in regard to strength as bases. In the first class are the quaternary ammonium hydroxides, which are very strong bases. Since the equilibria of these bases are strongly on the side of reaction with

Table 14.1.   Dissociation Constants of Some Nitrogen Compounds and Behavior in the Titration Methods

Compound	pK_a[a]	Methyl red indicator method, % titrated	Perchloric acid–glacial acetic acid method, % titrated
Tetraalkylammonium hydroxides	(High)	100	100
Piperidine	11.1 ⎱		
Diethylamine	11.0 ⎟		
Triethylamine	10.8 ⎰ 100	100	
Ethylamine	10.7 ⎱		
2,4,6-Trimethylpyridine	7.4 ⎱		
3-Methylpyridine	5.6 ⎟		
2-Methylquinoline	5.5 ⎟		
Pyridine	5.2 ⎬ Poor end points	100	
Triethylamine-*N*-oxide	5.1 ⎟		
Quinoline	4.8 ⎟		
Aniline	4.6 ⎰		
2-Chloroaniline	2.7 ⎱		
Diphenylamine	0.8 ⎟		
Pyridine-*N*-oxide	0.8 ⎟		
Urea	0.2 ⎬ <0.1	<0.1	
Acetamide	−0.6 ⎟		
Indole	−2.4 ⎟		
Pyrrole	−3.8 ⎰		

[a] Values at 25°C in water, data from Perrin (1).

the proton, the pK_a's are very high. Next are the aliphatic or alicyclic bases with pK_a's in the range of 10–12, in which range ammonia also falls. Third are the aromatic nitrogen compounds with pK_a's in the range of 4–8 and generally classified as "weak bases." Last are the nitrogen compounds generally considered as "very weak bases," with pK_a's less than 1. Methods for their determination often involve reactions other than titration.

As in the analysis of acids, there are both aqueous and nonaqueous procedures available for the titration of these compounds. The aqueous procedures are limited in scope to those bases soluble in water and having higher pK_a values. It is possible to titrate an aqueous solution effectively with $0.1N$ aqueous standard sulfuric acid using an indicator changing at pH 5. A suitable indicator is methyl red and the recommended method for determination of water-soluble amines having the necessary basic strength employs this indicator.

DETERMINATION OF AMINES IN ORGANIC MATERIALS

METHYL RED INDICATOR METHOD

Reagents

Methyl red indicator solution, 1% in 60% alcohol.
Sulfuric acid solution, standard aqueous 0.1 and 0.5N.

Procedure

Add 25 ml of distilled water to a 250-ml glass-stoppered Erlenmeyer flask and neutralize to the methyl red end point. Weigh a quantity of sample into the flask, using a Lunge weighing bottle for liquid samples. Determine the amine present by titration to the methyl red end point with either 0.1 or 0.5N standard sulfuric acid solution, using the weaker acid when the amine content is low.

Calculation

$$\text{Base value, equiv/100 g} = \frac{(A)(N)}{10W}$$

where A = volume of acid used in the titration
N = normality of the acid
W = weight of sample, g

A number of methods are available for the determination of basic nitrogen compounds of which not all depend upon the titration of these materials as bases. Several recommended methods are given in this chapter to indicate the scope of the techniques available and this is also covered schematically in Table 14.2.

TITRATION OF WEAK BASES

The most generally useful method for the determination of the weakly basic amines is the recommended Perchloric Acid–Glacial Acetic Acid method. The glacial acetic acid solvent, unlike water, does not act as a competitive base. Perchloric acid is an extremely strong mineral acid and is able, in acetic acid, to cause the stoichiometric protonation of bases as weak as quinoline or aniline. Sharp end point inflections are obtained, as shown many years ago by Conant and Hall (3, 4); however, the acetic acid solvent exerts a leveling effect such that the titration curves for strong and weak bases are not differentiated. Basic nitrogen compounds in petroleum fractions titrate well by this technique and the method can be taken to quite low concentrations, as was shown some time ago (5). Since the extremely weak basic nitrogen compounds, such as the indoles and carbazoles, do not

Table 14.2. Principal Features of Methods for Determination of Basic Nitrogen Compounds

Method	Determination	Applicability	Limitations
Methyl red indicator	Total basicity for bases with $pK_a > 10$	Water-soluble bases of strong and moderate basicity	Aromatic bases not determined
Perchloric acid–glacial acetic acid	Total basicity of strong plus weak bases	Has wide range of basicity	Does not differentiate among bases
Azomethine titration	Secondary plus tertiary aliphatic amines	Aliphatic amines	Poor inflections sometimes encountered, especially with complex materials
Acetylation–perchloric acid	Tertiary amines	Generally useful method	Determines only tertiary amines
Titanous reduction	Amine oxides	Aliphatic and aromatic amine oxides	Other nitrogen–oxygen compounds reduced
Colorimetric bromphenol blue	Low centrations of long-chain amines in water	Higher molecular weight amines and amine oxides	Lower molecular weight materials do not respond

Table 14.3. Basic Nitrogen Content of Some Petroleum Materials[a]

Sample	Total nitrogen (Dumas), wt %	Total basic nitrogen (HClO$_4$) wt %	Total basic nitrogen (HClO$_4$) % of total N
Straight-run long residue	0.69	0.21	30
Straight-run distillate (lower boiling fraction of long residue)	0.34	0.095	28
Straight-run distillate (lower boiling fraction of long residue)	0.44	0.14	32
Straight-run distillate (hydrogenated)	0.12	0.052	45
Straight-run short residue (higher boiling fraction of long residue)	1.21	0.36	30
Catalytic cracked gas oil	0.20	0.042	21
Dubbs thermal residue	1.27	0.48	38
40–50 pen. asphalt A	0.94	0.21	21
40–50 pen. asphalt B	1.20	0.30	25
California crude A	0.34	0.104	31
California crude B	0.52	0.141	27
California crude C (heavy)	0.64	0.137	21
West Texas crude	0.12	0.027	23
Middle East crude	0.10	0.031	31

[a] Data from Deal, Weiss, and White (5). Copyright 1953 by the American Chemical Society Reprinted by permission of the Copyright owner.

238

titrate in this method, it is possible to obtain information on the types of nitrogen compounds present in petroleum fractions. The behavior of a number of nitrogen compounds in this method is given in Table 14.1. In the application of the Perchloric Acid method to petroleum samples, Deal, Weiss, and White (5) found it advantageous to dissolve the sample initially in chlorobenzene to a total volume of 50 ml and dilute the mixture with 50 ml of acetic acid. This provided good solvent power for many of the heavy samples, particularly asphalts, and yet gave satisfactory titration curves. A review of the titration behavior of a series of materials is shown in Figure 14.1, from which it can be seen that bases as widely different in pK_a values as piperidine (11.1) and quinoline (4.8) titrate in the same narrow region and that the midpoint of the inflection curve is not much different for these materials and potassium hydroxide. Crude petroleum, shale oils, and distillates and residues can be titrated in the same range and give values, as is shown in Table 14.3, indicating that 20–40% of the total nitrogen is present in titratable forms.

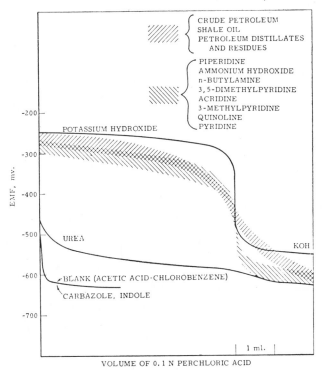

Figure 14.1. Illustrative titration curves in the Perchloric Acid Method. From Deal, Weiss, and White (5). Copyright 1953 by the American Chemical Society. Reprinted by permission of the copyright owner.

Some solvents other than acetic acid have been used for the titration medium. Chloro- and bromobenzene have been used by Burleigh, McKinney, and Barker (6) as solvents for vinylpyridine copolymers to bring them into solution for determination of basicity by titration with perchloric acid in the usual glacial acetic acid solvent. A significant contribution was made by Fritz (7) when he explored the use of acetonitrile for differential titration to distinguish between amines of different strengths. He pointed out that

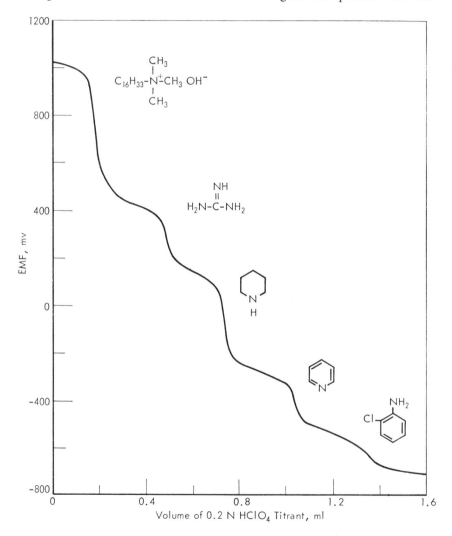

Figure 14.2. Titration of a mixture of bases using 3-methylsulfolane solvent. Copyright 1967 by the American Chemical Society. Reprinted by permission of the copyright owner.

acetic acid solvent cannot be used to differentiate aliphatic and aromatic amines of widely different base strength because both react nearly quantitatively with the solvent

$$B + HAc \rightarrow BH^+ + Ac^-$$

such that it is the acetate ion which is actually titrated. A solvent such as acetonitrile, that does not have basic properties, avoids this reaction and yet has a sufficiently high dielectric constant so that the titrations can be measured potentiometrically. A number of solvents were examined by Van Meurs, Van der Heijde, and Dahmen (8, 9) for the titration behavior of acids and bases and studies of acid–base equilibria in acetonitrile have been published by Kolthoff, Chantonni, and Bhowmik (10). Morman and Harlow (11) found that sulfolane, 3-methylsulfolane, and 2,4-dimethylsulfolane provided an extremely wide potential range for the differential titration of bases, as can be seen from the data in Figure 14.2.

DETERMINATION OF WEAK BASES

PERCHLORIC ACID-GLACIAL ACETIC ACID METHOD

Apparatus

Titrometer, fitted with glass and sleeve-type calomel electrodes.

Buret, 10-ml, graduated in 0.05-ml, with a tip that extends approximately 120 mm below the stopcock.

Buret, 25-ml, graduated in 0.1-ml, with a tip that extends approximately 120 mm below the stopcock.

Beaker, 250-ml, tall-form.

Reagents

Perchloric acid in acetic acid, standard 0.1N.

Glacial acetic acid, CP, containing less than 0.2% H$_2$O.

Crystal violet indicator, 0.1% in glacial acetic acid.

Malachite green indicator, 0.1% in glacial acetic acid.

Preparation of Apparatus

Glass Electrode. Before and after each titration, wipe the electrode with a soft cleansing tissue and rinse with distilled water. Between titrations, allow the glass electrode to soak in distilled water for at least 2 min. Clean the electrode weekly by immersing in cold chromic acid cleaning solution.

Calomel Electrode. Before and after each titration, wipe the calomel electrode with a soft cleansing tissue, carefully remove the ground glass sleeve, and thoroughly wipe both ground surfaces. Replace the sleeve, wetting the ground surfaces thoroughly with electrolyte, and rinse with distilled water. The calomel electrode should be drained once each week and refilled with fresh potassium chloride electrolyte.

Procedure

For Light-Colored Samples. Accurately weigh a sample containing 0.2–0.8 mg of base into a dry 250-ml flask. Add 125 ml of glacial acetic acid and 6–8 drops of crystal violet or malachite green indicator solution and add titrant until the indicator color change is apparent.

For Dark-Colored Samples. Accurately weigh a sample containing 0.2–0.8 meq of base into a dry 250-ml tall-form beaker. Add 125 ml of glacial acetic acid and place the beaker on the titration stand so that the electrodes are about half immersed. An initial cell potential of about -350 to -375 mV should be obtained. Record the initial buret and cell potential readings and the temperature of the titrant. Add titrant until the change in e.m.f. becomes greater than 5 mV per 0.1 ml, then take potential–volume readings every 0.05 ml. After each addition of titrant allow sufficient time for equilibration (1 min should suffice with good electrodes). Continue the titration until the meter reading is approximately -650 mV.

Plot the cumulative volumes of standard perchloric acid added against the corresponding cell potentials. Select the end point as the point of inflection.

Calculation

$$\text{Basicity, equiv/100 g} = \frac{(A)(N)}{10W}$$

where A = volume of the perchloric acid solution consumed by the sample, ml
$\quad\;\; N$ = normality of the perchloric acid
$\quad\;\; W$ = weight of the sample, g

TITRATION OF VERY WEAK BASES

The titration of the very weak bases that have pK_a's below 1 can be accomplished in certain solvents of which acetic anhydride has been most widely used. It was shown some time ago by Fritz and Fulda (12) that the addition of acetic anhydride to the titration solvents, acetic acid or nitromethane, gave considerably sharper end points in the titration of weak bases with $0.1N$ perchloric acid. They inferred from their experiments that the acetic anhydride functioned by removing the last traces of water from the mixture. Gremillion (13) found that by using acetic anhydride as the titration solvent he was able to titrate materials as weakly basic as urea and diphenylamine with sharp end points. Wimer (14, 15) extended the use of acetic anhydride as a solvent to the titration of amides and amine oxides with perchloric acid. Other solvents or mixtures can also be used, including a mixture of acetic anhydride and chloroform (16). Although acetic anhydride is a useful differentiating solvent for some very weak bases, the interpretation of the titration data is not always straightforward. Acetic anhydride is highly reactive and converts primary and secondary amides. Other functional groups, such as hydroxyl or aldehyde, and multifunctional compounds may undergo major changes due to the severe dehydrating property of this reagent. The solvent exerts a leveling effect on strong bases so that it is not possible to differentiate among the stronger bases present.

DETERMINATION OF PRIMARY, SECONDARY, AND TERTIARY AMINES

A great variety of nitrogen compounds may come to the attention of the analytical chemist, either from synthetic sources or in petroleum fractions. Those occurring in petroleum tend to be a complex admixture of basic nitrogen compounds (derivatives of pyridine, quinoline, and the like) and non-basic nitrogen compounds (derivatives of pyrrole and indole) (5, 17–20). In addition to the determination of a value for total basic nitrogen, it is often required to determine the content of primary, secondary, and tertiary amines in mixtures of synthetic materials. Techniques for the determination of classes of amines have been reviewed by Hillenbrand and Pentz (21).

The classical method for determination of *primary amines* is the Van Slyke method (22) in which the sample is reacted with sodium nitrite in acetic acid. The nitrogen oxides formed by the spontaneous decomposition of nitrous acid are removed by scrubbing with alkaline permanganate solution. The nitrogen formed from reaction with primary amine is measured in a gas buret. Secondary and tertiary amines do not produce nitrogen, and aromatic amines, such as aniline, react only to the extent of about 10%. The simple equation given in Table 14.4 is not always followed by the actual course of the reaction. In a thorough study of the Van Slyke method in application to the simple amino acid glycine (amino-acetic acid), Austin (23) found evidence for a much more complex reaction with the gaseous product including CO_2 and N_2O as well as N_2. Kainz, Huber, and Kasler (24) recommend the use of nitrosyl bromide reagent to overcome the anomalous results that have been found in the usual Van Slyke method.

Secondary plus *tertiary amines* can be determined in the presence of primary amines by the azomethine method, which was published some years ago by Wagner, Brown, and Peters (25) and involves treating the sample with an aldehyde, generally salicylaldehyde, which reacts with the primary amine to form the weakly basic azomethines. The treated mixture is then titrated with alcoholic hydrochloric acid, the first inflection corresponding to the titration of the unreacted secondary and tertiary amines. Some examples of the use of the technique are shown in Table 14.5, in which mixtures of

Table 14.4. Reactions in the Determination of Aliphatic Amines

Determination of primary amines by the Van Slyke method:

$$RNH_2 + HONO \rightarrow ROH + N_2 + H_2O$$
$$R_2NH + HONO \rightarrow R_2N{=}NO + H_2O$$
$$R_3N + HONO \rightarrow R_3N{\cdot}HONO$$

Determination of secondary plus tertiary amines by the azomethine method:

Determination of tertiary amines by acetylation:

$$2R_2NH + (CH_3CO)_2O \rightarrow 2R_2N{-}\overset{\overset{O}{\|}}{C}{-}CH_3 + H_2O$$

aliphatic amines were found (25) to respond essentially stoichiometrically by this reaction. The azomethine method, although useful for simple aliphatic amine mixtures, may give poor inflections with complex amine derivatives, which may contain other functions. Consequently its use should be carefully screened by examination of the titration curves. Fritz (7) showed

Table 14.5. Application of Azomethine Titration Method to Mixtures of Aliphatic Amines[a]

Primary	Secondary	Tertiary	Secondary plus tertiary amine determined, as percent added
$C_2H_5{-}NH_2$	$C_2H_5{-}\overset{H}{N}{-}C_2H_5$		99.2
$C_2H_5{-}NH_2$	$C_2H_5{-}\overset{H}{N}{-}C_2H_5$	$(C_2H_5)_3N$	100.9
$C_4H_9{-}NH_2$	$C_4H_9{-}\overset{H}{N}{-}C_4H_9$		99.5
$C_5H_{11}{-}NH_2$	$C_8H_{17}{-}\overset{H}{N}{-}C_8H_{17}$		98.5
cyclohexyl$-NH_2$	dicyclohexyl$-\overset{H}{N}-$		98.8
$-CH_2{-}CH_2{-}NH_2$	$C_3H_5{-}\overset{H}{N}{-}C_3H_5$		99.6
$C_2H_5{-}NH_2$	piperidine		99.7

[a] Data from Wagner, Brown, and Peters (25).

that the differentiation of secondary vs. primary amines could be made in acetonitrile solvent after treatment with salicylaldehyde and titration with perchloric acid. The basic strength of the secondary amine is unaltered, whereas the weakly basic azomethine, formed from the primary amine, is titrated subsequently at a higher potential. Values can be obtained directly for both the primary and secondary amine content using this technique.

Tertiary amines can be determined in the presence of the other functional types by acetylation of the groups other than tertiary with acetic anhydride, followed by titration of the unreacted tertiary amine with perchloric acid in glacial acetic acid solution. The recommended method for the determination of tertiary amines (Acetylation–Perchloric Acid method) is taken from the work of Wagner, Brown, and Peters (26) published some years ago and since widely used for this analysis. Some data obtained by this method are shown in Table 14.6, from which it can be seen that differentiation between tertiary and the primary and secondary amines is complete. The application of a similar acetylation titration technique for the characterization of nitrogen bases in petroleum products has been published by Nicksic and Judd (27), who provide data on the rates of acetylation for a considerable number of pure amines. They found that primary aromatic amines acetylated very rapidly, even at room temperature. A value for the combined primary and secondary amine content of a sample can be calculated from the difference between the total basic nitrogen and the tertiary amine content.

Table 14.6. Behavior of Amines in the Acetylation–Perchloric Acid Method[a]

Compound	Percentage unacetylated after 1 hr reflux
n-Butylamine	<0.1
Ethanolamine	<0.1
Allylamine	<0.1
Isopropylamine	<0.1
1,3-Dimethylbutylamine	<0.1
Diethylamine	<0.1
Di-*n*-butylamine	<0.1
Diethanolamine	<0.1
Dimethyallylamine	<0.1
Diisopropylamine	<0.1
Bis(1,3-dimethyl butyl)amine	<0.1
Triallylamine	95.3, 95.6
Tri-*n*-butylamine	97.5
Diisopropyl-*n*-propylamine	99.2
Triethanolamine	98.1

[a] Data from Wagner, Brown, and Peters (26).

DETERMINATION OF SECONDARY PLUS TERTIARY ALIPHATIC AMINES

AZOMETHINE TITRATION METHOD

Apparatus

Titrometer, fitted with glass and calomel electrodes.

Reagents

Salicylaldehyde, free of salicylic acid.

Hydrochloric acid in isopropyl alcohol, 0.5N. Mix 950 ml of CP isopropyl alcohol with 40 ml of concentrated CP hydrochloric acid, and standardize the solution against standard sodium hydroxide or a primary standard.

Methyl Cellosolve.

Procedure

Weigh a sample containing 1–4 meq of secondary plus tertiary amine and no more than 8 meq of primary amine, into a titration beaker containing 80 ml of methanol and 3 ml of salicylaldehyde. Cover with a watch glass, swirl gently to mix the solution, and allow to stand 30 min.

If the sample contains more than 10% of an amine having less than four carbon atoms, it should be weighed into a small glass bulb. The bulb may then be broken below the surface of the methanol solution.

Place the solution on the titrometer and titrate with 0.5N HCl in isopropyl alcohol to the first inflection point.

Calculation

Calculate the secondary plus tertiary amine content as follows:

$$\text{Secondary plus tertiary amines, equiv/100 g} = \frac{(V)(N)}{10W}$$

where V = volume of standard acid to first end point, ml
        N = normality of standard acid
        W = weight of sample, g

DETERMINATION OF TERTIARY AMINES

ACETYLATION–PERCHLORIC ACID METHOD

Apparatus

Erlenmeyer flasks, 250-ml, equipped with standard-taper ground glass 20/40 joints.

Reflux condensers, equipped with standard-taper glass joints to fit flasks.

Titrometer, fitted with glass and sleeve-type calomel electrodes.

Reagents and Solvents

Acetic anhydride, CP.
Glacial acetic acid, CP.
Perchloric acid in acetic acid, standard, 0.1*N*.
Crystal violet indicator, 0.1 % in glacial acetic acid.

Procedure

Into a 250-ml, glass-stoppered Erlenmeyer flask containing 20 ml of acetic anhydride and 2 ml of acetic acid introduce a sample weighing no more than 2 g, containing no more than 0.1 g of water but containing, if possible, 0.5–1 meq of tertiary amine. Connect the Erlenmeyer flask to a water-cooled condenser and reflux the sample for 1 hr. Quantitatively transfer the mixture to a titration beaker, washing the flask with portions of a total of 40 ml of acetic acid.

Titrate the contents of the beaker with standard 0.1*N* perchloric acid in acetic acid. Light-colored samples can usually be titrated with an indicator. Others should be done potentiometrically. Add 0.05-ml increments of the perchloric acid reagent when near the end point.

Make a blank determination carrying out the analysis in an identical manner but omitting the sample.

Calculation

$$\text{Tertiary amine content, equiv/100 g} = \frac{(V - B)(N)}{10W}$$

where V = volume of perchloric acid, ml, used in titration of sample
B = volume of perchloric acid, ml, used in titration of blank
N = normality of perchloric acid solution
W = weight of sample, g

DETERMINATION OF AMINE OXIDES

Amine oxides have the formula

$$R_1 - \overset{\overset{O}{\uparrow}}{\underset{R_3}{N}} - R_2$$

and are used in commercial formulations as detergents or fungicides. Analytically they offer a considerable choice of methods. Brooks and Sternglanz (28) showed that a reduction technique, using titanous (Ti^{3+}) chloride reagent, would provide a rapid and quantitative method for a wide range of practical samples. After reduction of the amine oxide with excess titanous chloride in acid solution, the remaining titanous ion was titrated with ferric ion in the presence of ammonium thiocyanate. At the end point a low concentration of ferric ion produces a red color due to the high molar absorptivity of ferric thiocyanate ($\varepsilon = 10^3$). The consumption of titanous ion, measured as the differences between the sample titration and the corresponding blank, is equivalent to the amine oxide present. The recommended method for amine oxides, given in this section, is taken from the procedure of Brooks and Sternglanz and some limited data on the application of this method to amine oxides are given in Table 14.7. The materials analyzed were all commercial products whose purity was expected to be of the order of 97–98%.

Both aliphatic and aromatic amine oxides have basic properties and can be titrated with perchloric acid, as was shown by Wimer (15), who used acetic anhydride as the solvent in the quantitative titration of a series of amine oxides. It should be noted that the aliphatic amine oxides have stronger basic properties than the aromatic amine oxides (Table 14.1). In an entirely different approach it has been observed (29, 30) that aliphatic amine oxides can be pyrolyzed in the injection port of a gas chromatographic apparatus

Table 14.7.   Extent of Recovery of Amine Oxides by Titanous
Reduction

Compound	Recovery, %
O↑N (pyridine N-oxide)	97.8, 98.3, 98.4, 98.5[a]
H₃C—N—CH₃ (lutidine N-oxide)	96.5, 97.3, 97.6, 98.1[a]
$C_{12}H_{25}$—N(CH₃)(CH₃) → O	97.3
(O↑N—S)₂ Zn	97.7, 98.1, 98.2, 98.2, 99.1[a]

[a] Data from Brooks and Sternglanz (28).

to the corresponding olefins, which can be separated and identified by chromatography.

DETERMINATION OF AMINE OXIDES

TITANOUS REDUCTION PROCEDURE

Apparatus

Adapter for purging with nitrogen (see Figure 24.3).

Reagents

Acetic acid, glacial.

Ammonium thiocyanate solution, 50%. Dissolve 50 g of CP ammonium thiocyanate in water and dilute to 100 ml.

Ferric alum, standard 0.1*N*. Dissolve 30 ml of conc. sulfuric acid and 48.22 g of ferric ammonium sulfate 12-hydrate in water and dilute to 1 liter. Standardize as follows: Pipet 25 ml of the reagent into a glass-stoppered flask. Add 3 g of CP potassium iodide, stopper, and swirl to dissolve the salt. Let the solution stand in the dark 15 min. Titrate with 0.1*N* standard thiosulfate solution to a starch end point.

Hydrochloric acid, 6*N*.

Potassium iodide, CP.

Sodium thiosulfate, 0.1*N*, standard.

Starch indicator solution.

Titanous chloride solution, 0.2*N*. Mix 100 ml of 6*N* hydrochloric acid and 75 ml of 20% titanous chloride solution and dilute to 1 liter.

Procedure

In a 250-ml glass-stoppered Erlenmeyer flask place a sample containing 0.5–1 mmole of amine oxide. Add 20 ml of 6*N* hydrochloric acid and 25 ml of acetic acid. Add a small piece of Dry Ice to displace oxygen from the flask. Place the stopper loosely in the joint with a strip of filter paper inserted to allow space for the gas to escape.

When the Dry Ice has evaporated, attach the purging device to a nitrogen line by rubber tubing and place it on the flask in place of the stopper. Continue a slow stream of nitrogen during this operation. Introduce 20 ml of 0.2*N* titanous chloride with a pipet and add 5 ml of 50% thiocyanate. Swirl the contents of the flask, replace the purging device with the glass stopper, and set the flask aside for 5–30 min. In the same way, add titanous chloride and thiocyanate to each sample and blank in turn.

Replace the stopper of the first flask with the purging device, with the nitrogen flowing, and titrate the contents with 0.1*N* ferric alum to a red end point. Proceed with the titration of each sample and blank.

Calculation

$$\text{Amine oxide, moles}/100 \text{ g} = \frac{(B - S)N}{20W}$$

where B = average volume of blank titrations, ml
  S = volume of sample titration, ml
  N = normality of ferric alum solution
  W = weight of sample, g

DETERMINATION OF LOW CONCENTRATIONS
OF LONG-CHAIN AMINES

Since long-chain tertiary alkylamine and quaternary ammonium salts are used as surface-active and germicidal agents at low concentrations in water, their determination is often of interest. Fortunately, a rapid and simple method is available for this purpose. The method is essentially the reverse of that used for the determination of anionic detergents (see Chapter 19) in that the reaction involves the formation of a complex between the amine (or quaternary ammonium salt) and an organic sulfonate.

$$R_3NH^+X^- + RSO_3^- \rightarrow (R_3NH \cdot RSO_3) + X^-$$

The reaction is carried on in aqueous solution but the complex has properties very different from the components from which it is made; in particular, it is only slightly water soluble but is soluble in organic solvents, particularly chlorinated materials. The published techniques involve the use of a sulfonate-carrying dye, extraction of the colored complex into a chlorinated solvent such as chloroform or dichloroethane, and spectrophotometric measurement of the product. In the recommended method given in this chapter for the determination of low concentrations of cation-active materials, the tetra-bromo sulfonphthalein indicator, bromophenol blue, is used as the complexing dye material. This method is designed for the determination of such cation-active materials as long-chain amines, amine oxides, or quaternary ammonium compounds in concentrations as low as 1 ppm.

The complexing reaction is conducted under acidic conditions, which converts long-chain amines into their cationic salts. Bromophenol blue is yellow in its acid form and the complex remains yellow. The recommended method is based on work of Mukerjee (31), who demonstrated the high sensitivity of the technique with typical surfactants and carefully outlined the significance of the variables of the method.

A number of variations of this method have been published, using other sulfonated indicators (32–35). Silverstein (35) describes an interesting technique for differentiation of primary, secondary, and tertiary amines in the ppm concentration in water using prior chemical treatments.

DETERMINATION OF LOW CONCENTRATIONS OF CATION-ACTIVE MATERIALS

COLORIMETRIC BROMOPHENOL BLUE METHOD

Apparatus

Spectrophotometer. Any spectrophotometer transmitting light at 416 mμ may be used.

Reagents

Bromophenol blue solution; dissolve 0.040 g of bromophenol blue in 0.6 ml of 0.1N/sodium hydroxide and 10 ml of water. Dilute to 250 ml.
Chloroform, CP.
Hydrochloric acid, 0.1N.
Sulfuric acid, 1N.

Procedure

Place 25 ml of water in a 125-ml separatory funnel. Add the sample containing 0.1–0.3 μeq of cation-active material and 5 ml of the bromophenol blue solution. Add dropwise 1N sulfuric acid until the mixture turns yellow. Add sufficient water to make the total volume approximately 50 ml. Add 10 ml of 0.1N hydrochloric acid and exactly 10 ml of chloroform. Shake the mixture and allow to settle. Drain the chloroform into a small stoppered flask and measure the absorbance of the chloroform solution at 416 mμ in a 1-cm cell.

Accompany the sample with two reagent blanks made up as above, but excluding the sample. Also prepare suitable known samples of the material being measured, and apply the method to these known samples.

Calculation

Subtract the average of the blank absorbances from each of the absorbances obtained from the samples and known standard samples. Prepare a calibration curve, plotting net absorbance vs. micrograms of material in the known standards. From this curve, read the μg of material in the unknowns.

Calculate the concentration of cation-active material in a sample as μg per ml of sample taken (approximately equivalent to parts per million).

DETERMINATION OF AMINES BY SPECTROSCOPY

In the same way that weak acids can be titrated spectrophotometrically, weak bases can be determined by the change in the ultraviolet absorption spectra that occurs as the two species are interconverted.

$$B + HA \rightleftharpoons BH^+ + A^-$$

Katchalsky and Miller have shown (36) that end points with simple and polymeric nitrogen compounds can be readily measured.

Bellamy (37) points out that tertiary amines are difficult to identify spectroscopically but that primary and secondary amines have distinctive absorption bands in the infrared. Energy is absorbed due to stretching of the N—H bonds in the region of 2.86–3.03 μ. Primary amines have two bands of medium intensity in this region and secondary amines have only one band, also of medium intensity. In the 6.0–6.4-μ region, energy is absorbed due to deformation of the N—H bond. Primary amines have a relatively sharp, strong band covering 6.0–6.3 μ, whereas that due to the secondary amines is weak and somewhat broader. Hydrogen-bonding effects may cause some shift in these positions. It is possible to distinguish between primary and secondary amines by measurements in the near infrared. In this spectral region, primary aromatic amines have an absorption band near 2.0 μ and there is also a band near 1.5 μ due to both primary and secondary amines. Illman (38) used these measurements, as well as those for hydroxyl and

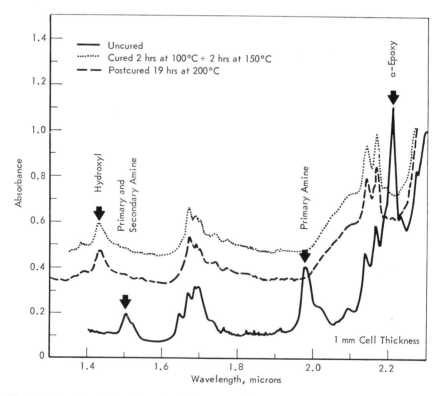

Figure 14.3. Near-infrared spectra during cure of an epoxy resin-amine system. From Illman (38).

α-epoxy groups, to study the chemical effects of curing an epoxy resin–amine system. The data, shown in Figure 14.3, indicate the value of this technique.

Aromatic nitrogen compounds can be identified and determined by visible and ultraviolet fluorescence spectroscopy. This technique, which has been widely used for polynuclear aromatic hydrocarbons, has only recently been more widely applied to other types of compounds in which fluorescence can be excited. Fluorescence spectroscopy has been recently put into effective use as a means of characterizing the microsize samples that were obtained in the gas chromatographic separation of aromatic nitrogen-, sulfur-, and oxygen-containing fractions from petroleum (39). By varying the excitation wavelength it was possible to observe a number of the principal types of the nitrogen compounds, anilines, quinolines, indoles, etc. By combining the luminescence data with values for retention time, it was possible to identify many of these materials. Sawicki, Stanley, and Elbert (40) found the fluorimetric method effective for determining the presence and the approximate amount of several polynuclear nitrogen heterocyclics in urban atmospheres.

DETERMINATION OF BASIC NITROGEN COMPOUNDS BY CHROMATOGRAPHY

The investigations of the heterocyclic compounds in petroleum have led to the development of valuable chromatographic methods for the separation and concentration of the basic nitrogen compounds (as well as the other members of the heterocyclic series). Jewell and Hartung (41) utilized adsorption on Al_2O_3, followed by elution with solvents of increasing polarity, to separate basic nitrogen compounds into a series of different base structures. Paper chromatography was then applied to the fractions to produce a finer separation. The separated fractions were characterized by mass spectrometry and by ultraviolet and infrared spectroscopy. Among the types of structures found were quinolines, benzoquinolines, and phenanthrolines. Nixon and Thorpe (20) used a commercial synthetic magnesium silicate (Florisil) to isolate the bulk of the nitrogen bases from a series of gas oil fractions of increasing boiling range and found that the ultraviolet absorption spectra of the nitrogen bases indicated the presence of pyridines, quinolines, and anilines. Anilines were generally found in catalytically cracked stocks and not in straight-run material. This designation was further explored by chemical analysis in which the aniline homologs were acetylated and the pyridines and quinolines then determined by titration with perchloric acid. Good agreement was found between the spectroscopic and chemical methods. Munday and Eaves (42) have used ion-exchange resins to separate nitrogen bases from petroleum fractions.

Gas chromatography has been widely used for the separation and analysis of the volatile nitrogen bases. Because of the high polarity of the amines, special packings may be employed to reduce tailing. In one of the early publications in gas chromatography, James, Martin, and Smith (43) observed that the diatomaceous earth used as support for the liquid phase was not inert and produced tailing of amines. This was partially overcome by pretreatment of the diatomaceous earth with alcoholic sodium hydroxide, although this treatment did not produce symmetrical peaks. Since that time a number of column packings have been investigated in the attempt to obtain better resolution and quantitative analysis of complex amine mixtures. Amell, Lamprey, and Schiek recommended (44) o-toluidine on C-22 firebrick in a column to be operated at room temperature. Häntzsch (45) found he could separate the lower amines effectively with packed columns prepared either from DC silicone oil on a treated diatomaceous earth or from hexaethyleneglycol dimethyl ether on Tide detergent. van der Meeren and Verhaar (46) separated pyridine bases on Celite or kieselguhr, which were coated with stationary phases containing glycols, esters, or silicones to which relatively nonvolatile amines had been added. Some years ago Knight (47) studied means to obtain symmetrical peaks with amino (and hydroxy) compounds and concluded that better resolutions of these materials could be obtained if the helium carrier gas was saturated with water and a volatile amine at 25°C. The water and amine saturated the active adsorption sites on the support, reducing peak tailing caused by adsorption. With thermal conductivity detection, the water and amine affect the baseline, reducing sensitivity; however, flame ionization detectors are insensitive to water and ammonia, and the latter can be substituted for the amine. Thus peak symmetry can be improved with little effect on the baseline. Using porous polyaromatic polymer beads of low polarity for a column packing, Hollis (48) was able to obtain a number of very useful GLC separations. When amines were chromatographed on the beads directly, excessive tailing was observed. However, when tetraethylenepentamine or polyethyleneimine was used as a modifier on the polymer beads, sharp and symmetrical peaks were obtained for the lower primary, secondary, and tertiary aliphatic amines. The wide application of this technique for the separation of aliphatic amines was shown by Smith and Waddington (49).

An alternative means of overcoming the unfavorable gas chromatographic behavior of the amines is the prior formation of derivatives. Van den Heuvel, Gardiner, and Horning (50) examined a large number of derivatives to improve separations and the quantitative aspects of determination of individual amines. Useful results were obtained with a number of simple and fluorinated esters. Morrissette and Link (51) pointed out the convenient separation of the trifluoroacetyl derivatives of fatty amines, amides, and hydroxyl compounds. This reagent was found by Dove (52) to be particularly useful for the quantitative analysis of mixtures of the aromatic amines since their trifluoroacetates are readily resolvable on conventional gas chromatographic equipment. Results obtained in the analysis of a commercial mixed xylidine sample are shown in Table 14.8. The commercial ethanolamines, which are mixtures of mono-, di-, and triethanolamine, as well as containing some impurities of similar structure, were quantitatively analyzed as the trifluoroacetyl derivatives by Brydia and Persinger (53). The acetylation reagent, trifluoroacetic anhydride, reacts with the active hydrogen of both the amino and hydroxyl groups. Pentafluoropropionic anhydride has likewise been employed as a reagent for amines (54).

Martin (55) developed a selective detection technique for nitrogen compounds that is sufficiently sensitive to follow separations of nitrogen compounds on a gas chromatographic column. The detection technique involves converting the nitrogen compounds, after their separation by gas chromatography, into ammonia by hydrogenation over a nickel catalyst at 440°C. The production of ammonia is quantitative and can be measured by titration with coulometrically generated hydrogen ions in the microcoulometer cell described in Chapter 21. Without using gas chromatography the technique was recommended as a rapid method to replace the Kjeldahl technique for determination of the nitrogen content of organic materials at concentrations as low as 1 ppm. With gas chromatography the detection technique can be used to determine the nitrogen compound distribution in complex petroleum

Table 14.8. Results Obtained in the Analysis of a Commercial Xylidine Sample by Gas Chromatography of the Trifluoroacetates[a]

Component	Wt % found[b]
o-Toluidine	2.8
o-Ethylaniline	1.8
2,5-Dimethylaniline	19.0
2,6-Dimethylaniline	7.7
2,4-Dimethylaniline	38.4
m-Toluidine	0.6
p-Toluidine	1.7
2,3-Dimethylaniline	14.0
3,5-Dimethylaniline	1.0
m-Ethylaniline	0.3
p-Ethylaniline	1.8
3,4-Dimethylaniline	11.6

[a] Data from Dove (52).
[b] Average of seven determinations.

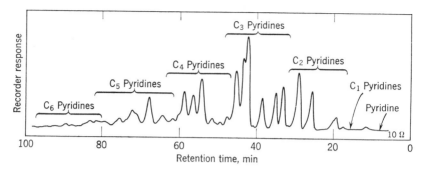

Figure 14.4. Chromatograph of nitrogen compounds in shale-oil naphtha using microcoulometer detector. Data from Martin (55), courtesy of the American Chemical Society.

and shale-oil fractions. A typical example of the results obtained on a shale-oil naphtha containing 1920 ppm of nitrogen is shown in Figure 14.4. Since the detector responds only to ammonia, there is no background from the carbon, hydrogen, or sulfur content of the sample; consequently, the components determined are solely those of the nitrogen compounds.

The ammonia titration cell contained two pairs of electrodes. One pair was used for generation of hydrogen ion. This pair consisted of a platinum anode generator and a platinum-coil cathode. The sensing pair of electrodes consisted of a platinum-blacked sensor (hydrogen electrode) paired with a silver–silver sulfate reference electrode. The sensor electrode was blacked with finely divided platinum by electrolytic reduction from chloroplatinic acid solution to make it more sensitive to the hydrogen ion concentration.

Albert (56) has continued the application of this gas chromatographic technique for the detailed examination of the nitrogen compounds in complex petroleum fractions. To categorize the components in some of the fractions, classical separation schemes, such as extraction with strong mineral acids, were also employed.

REFERENCES

1. D. D. Perrin, *Dissociation Constants of Organic Bases in Aqueous Solution*, Butterworth , London, 1965.
2. A. Albert and E. P. Serjeant, *Ionization Constants of Acids and Bases*, Methuen, London, 1962.
3. J. B. Conant and N. F. Hall, *J. Am. Chem. Soc.*, **49**, 3047 (1927).
4. N. F. Hall, *ibid.*, **52**, 5115 (1930).
5. V. Z. Deal, F. T. Weiss, and T. T. White, *Anal. Chem.*, **25**, 426 (1953).
6. J. E. Burleigh, O. F. McKinney, and M. G. Barker, *ibid.*, **31**, 1684 (1959).
7. J. S. Fritz, *ibid.*, **25**, 407 (1953).
8. N. Van Meurs and E. A. M. F. Dahmen, *Anal. Chim. Acta*, **21**, 193 (1959).

9. H. B. Van der Heijde and E. A. M. F. Dahmen, *ibid.*, **16**, 378 (1957).
10. I. M. Kolthoff, M. K. Chantooni, Jr., and S. Bhowmik, *Anal. Chem.*, **39**, 1627 (1967).
11. D. H. Morman and G. A. Harlow, *ibid.*, **39**, 1869 (1967).
12. J. S. Fritz and M. Fulda, *ibid.*, **25**, 1837 (1953).
13. A. F. Gremillion, *ibid.*, **27**, 133 (1955).
14. D. C. Wimer, *ibid.*, **30**, 77 (1958).
15. D. C. Wimer, *ibid.*, **34**, 873 (1962).
16. L. G. Chatten and C. K. Orbeck, *J. Pharm. Sci.*, **53**, 1306 (1964).
17. R. V. Helm, D. R. Latham, C. R. Ferrin, and J. S. Ball, *Anal. Chem.*, **32**, 1765 (1960).
18. H. L. Lochte and E. R. Littman, *The Petroleum Acids and Bases*, Chemical Publishing Co., New York, 1955.
19. F. P. Richter, P. D. Caesar, S. L. Meisel, and R. D. Offenhauer, *Ind. Eng. Chem.*, **44**, 2601 (1952).
20. A. C. Nixon and R. E. Thorpe, *J. Chem. Eng. Data*, **7**, 429 (1962).
21. E. F. Hillenbrand, Jr., and C. A. Pentz, *Organic Analysis*, Vol. III, Interscience, New York, 1956, pp. 129–201.
22. D. D. Van Slyke, *J. Biol. Chem.*, **9**, 185 (1911); **23**, 407 (1915).
23. A. T. Austin, *J. Chem. Soc.*, **1950**, 149.
24. G. Kainz, H. Huber, and F. Kasler, *Mikrochim. Acta*, **1957**, 744.
25. C. D. Wagner, R. D. Brown, and E. D. Peters, *J. Am. Chem. Soc.*, **69**, 2611 (1947).
26. C. D. Wagner, R. D. Brown, and E. D. Peters, *ibid.*, **69**, 2609 (1947).
27. S. W. Nicksic and S. H. Judd, *Anal. Chem.*, **32**, 998 (1960).
28. R. T. Brooks and P. D. Sternglanz, *ibid.*, **31**, 561 (1959).
29. G. L. K. Hoh, D. O. Barlow, A. F. Chadwick, D. B. Lake, and S. R. Sheenan, *J. Am. Oil Chemists' Soc*, **40**, 268 (1963).
30. H. Y. Lew, *ibid.*, **41**, 297 (1964).
31. P. Mukerjee, *Anal. Chem.*, **28**, 870 (1956).
32. A. M. N. Irving and J. J. Markham, *Anal. Chim. Acta*, **39**, 7 (1967).
33. G. Schill and M. Marsh, *Svensk. Farm. Tidskr.*, **67**, (14) 385–400 (1963).
34. R. A. Larrick, *Anal. Chem.*, **35**, 1760 (1963).
35. R. M. Silverstein, *ibid.*, **35**, 154 (1963).
36. A. Katchalsky and I. R. Miller, *J. Polymer Sci.*, **13**, 57 (1954).
37. L. J. Bellamy, *The Infrared Spectra of Complex Molecules*, 2nd ed., Wiley, New York, 1964, p. 248 ff.
38. J. C. Illman, *J. Appl. Polymer Sci.*, **10**, 1519 (1966).
39. H. V. Drushel and A. L. Sommers, *Anal. Chem.*, **38**, 10, 19 (1966).
40. E. Sawicki, T. W. Stanley, and W. C. Elbert, *J. Chromatog.* **26**, 72 (1967).
41. D. M. Jewell and G. K. Hartung, *J. Chem. Eng. Data*, **9**, 297 (1964).
42. W. Munday and A. Eaves, *Fifth World Petroleum Congress*, Section V, New York, 1959, paper 9.
43. A. T. James, A. J. P. Martin, and G. H. Smith, *Biochem. J.*, **52**, 238 (1952).
44. A. R. Amell, P. S. Lamprey, and R. C. Schiek, *Anal. Chem.*, **33**, 1805 (1961).
45. S. Häntzsch, *Talanta*, **13**, 1297 (1966).

46. A. A. F. van der Meeren and A. L. T. Verhaar, *Anal. Chim. Acta*, **40**, 343 (1968).
47. H. Knight, *Anal. Chem.*, **30**, 2030 (1958).
48. O. L. Hollis, *ibid.*, **38**, 309 (1966).
49. J. R. L. Smith and D. J. Waddington, *ibid.*, **40**, 522 (1968).
50. W. J. A. Van den Heuvel, W. L. Gardiner, and E. C. Horning, *ibid.*, **36**, 1550 (1964).
51. R. A. Morrissette and W. E. Link, *J. Gas Chromatog.*, **3**, 67 (1965).
52. R. A. Dove, *Anal. Chem.*, **39**, 1188 (1967).
53. L. E. Brydia and H. E. Persinger, *ibid.*, **39**, 1318 (1967).
54. Y. Masuda and D. Hoffman, *ibid.*, **41**, 650 (1969).
55. R. L. Martin, *ibid.*, **38**, 1209 (1966).
56. D. K. Albert, *ibid.*, **39**, 1113 (1967).

DETERMINATION OF NONBASIC NITROGEN COMPOUNDS

The nitrogen compounds that can be categorized as "nonbasic" or as "very weakly basic" cover a number of individual types of which those most commonly encountered will probably fall into the following functional classifications: nitriles, amides, diphenylamines, nitro compounds, and, in some petroleum fractions, pyrroles, indoles, and carbazoles. Although, as is discussed in Chapter 14, it is possible to titrate a limited group of these functions with perchloric acid using acetic anhydride as a solvent, it is generally preferable to employ other analytical methods because of the greater choice of selectivity and specificity. This chapter describes a number of the methods, other than those involving direct acidimetric titration, for the determination of these very weakly basic and nonbasic nitrogen compounds. An outline of this information is given in Table 15.1.

DETERMINATION OF AMIDES

Since amides are susceptible to quantitative acid hydrolysis, yielding both the acid and the amine, hydrolysis has been employed to analyze amides for the components, especially with those derived from complex amines. Rosen and Goldsmith (1) recommended analyzing diethanolamine–fatty acid amides (and esters) by refluxing the sample with a mixture of concentrated hydrochloric acid and glacial acetic acid, following which the product acids were separated by extraction. Gross and Jones (2) extensively investigated a

$$R-\overset{\overset{\displaystyle O}{\|}}{C}-N\overset{\displaystyle CH_2-CH_2-OH}{\underset{\displaystyle CH_2-CH_2-OH}{}} + CH_3OH \xrightarrow{HCl}$$

$$R-\overset{\overset{\displaystyle O}{\|}}{C}-OCH_3 + ClH_2N\overset{\displaystyle CH_2-CH_2-OH}{\underset{\displaystyle CH_2-CH_2-OH}{}}$$

Table 15.1.   Methods for the Determination of Nonbasic Nitrogen Compounds

Classification	Structure	Methods employed
Amides	$R-\overset{\overset{\displaystyle O}{\|}}{C}-NH_2$	Acid hydrolysis, reduction to amines
Nitriles	$R-C\equiv N$	Acid hydrolysis, reduction to amines, reaction with H_2O_2
Nitro compounds	⬡—NO_2	Reduction with titanous or chromous salts
Nitroso compounds	⬡—NO	Reduction with titanous salts or hydrogen iodide
Alkyl nitrates	$R-O-NO_2$	Gas chromatography, infrared
Pyrroles	(pyrrole ring, $\underset{H}{N}$)	Infrared, colorimetric with dimethyl-aminobenzaldehyde reagent
Indoles	(indole ring, $\underset{H}{N}$)	Infrared, ultraviolet, colorimetric
Carbazoles	(carbazole ring, $\underset{H}{N}$)	Ultraviolet, mass spectrometric

methanolysis technique for characterizing fatty acid alkanolamides in which the amides were converted to the amine and the methyl ester of the fatty acid by refluxing with hydrogen chloride in methanol. The products were neutralized and determined by gas chromatography. It was found that recoveries of the methyl esters were nearly quantitative but that recoveries of the amines were somewhat low although they were satisfactory for identification.

The recommended method for the determination of amides and nitriles involves hydrolysis with $10N$ hydrochloric to produce the corresponding carboxylic acid and ammonium chloride. The reaction is carried out in a

$$R-\overset{\overset{\displaystyle O}{\|}}{C}-NH_2 + H_2O + HCl \longrightarrow R\overset{\overset{\displaystyle O}{\|}}{C}-OH + NH_4Cl$$

$$R-C\equiv N + 2H_2O + HCl \longrightarrow R\overset{\overset{\displaystyle O}{\|}}{C}-OH + NH_4Cl$$

pressure bottle at 100°C; after completion of the reaction, excess alkali is added to the reaction mixture and the ammonia is distilled into dilute boric acid solution and titrated with standard acid. The recommended method is based on the publication by Krieble and Noll (3), who found that the hydrolysis rate increased rapidly with increasing concentration of hydrochloric acid and that aqueous sulfuric acid was considerably less effective than hydrochloric acid. They investigated the rate of hydrolysis of acetonitrile, propionitrile, cyanoacetic acid, and the α- and β-hydroxy propionitriles. Although the method was initially investigated for nitriles, it also applies to amides. Amine salts or other materials that hydrolyze to produce amines or ammonia will obviously interfere to give high results. Some typical data obtained with the recommended method are shown in Table 15.2.

Table 15.2. Results Obtained in the Analysis of Amides and Nitriles by the Acid Hydrolysis Method

Compound	Reactivity, %
Dimethylacetamide	97.7, 96.8
Methylacetamide	97.0, 96.2
Acetonitrile	98.0
Acrylonitrile	98.8, 98.8
β-Cyanobutylacetate	100.0, 100.1
Methacrylonitrile	99.7, 99.7, 99.9
Propionitrile	99.4

Hydrolysis under dilute basic conditions is not generally quantitative for amides or nitriles but the basic saponification technique has been used by Siggia, Hanna, and Serencha (4) to obtain differential reaction rates to analyze mixtures of amides and nitriles. Under more vigorous conditions it has been found possible to remove ammonia quantitatively from polyacrylonitrile. In the analysis of acrylonitrile–vinyl acetate copolymers, Gibson and Heidner found it necessary to use 50% aqueous KOH as the saponification medium (5). Lohman and Mulligan (6) point out that the rate of hydrolysis of lauric diethanolamide in alcoholic KOH is 70 times that of lauric monoethanolamide. They used these large differences in reaction rates to develop a differential analytical technique and applied it to mixtures of commercial products.

DETERMINATION OF AMIDES AND NITRILES

Acid Hydrolysis

Apparatus

Pressure bottles, 12-oz, designed to take crown caps.

Crown caps, fitted with Teflon inserts use DuPont Teflon 0.005-in. thick for gasket.

Bottle-capping machine.
Water bath, enclosed, for heating bottles at 100°C.
Distillation apparatus.

Reagents

Hydrochloric acid, 10*N*. Dilute 208 ml of 12*N* HCl to 250 ml.
Sodium hydroxide, 6*N*.
Standard sulfuric acid, 0.1*N*.
Methyl red indicator solution.
Boric acid solution, 1.5% neutralized to methyl red.

Procedure

Purge a pressure bottle with nitrogen to remove oxygen and weigh into the bottle a sample containing 2–4 mmoles of the nitrile or amide.

Introduce 20 ml of 10*N* hydrochloric acid and several small glass rods, 10–15 mm long. Cap the bottle with a crown cap having a Teflon gasket insert, break the ampule by vigorous shaking, and heat the mixture in the water bath at 100°C for 5 hr.

When the reaction mixture has cooled to room temperature, transfer it quantitatively to a 1-liter distilling flask provided with a side-arm buret and make up to 200 ml with water. Add boiling stones and connect the flask to the condensing apparatus. Place a 500-ml Erlenmeyer flask containing 100 ml of 1.5% boric acid solution neutralized to methyl red, so that the tip of the condenser extends beneath the surface of the liquid. Add through the side-arm buret of the distilling flask 50 ml of 6*N* sodium hydroxide and mix. Collect 150 ml of distillate (distilling slowly at first). Rinse the condenser with a few milliliters of distilled water, catching the washings in the distillate. Titrate the contents of each flask with 0.1*N* sulfuric acid to the methyl red end point color of 100 ml of the original boric acid solution diluted to 250 ml with water.

Calculation

$$\text{Amide or nitrile value, equiv/100 g} = \frac{(S - B)(N)}{10W}$$

where S = volume of standard acid consumed by the sample, ml
       B = volume of standard acid consumed by the blank, ml
       N = normality of standard acid
       W = weight of sample, g

In addition to the analysis of amides by acid hydrolysis, several other reactions have been employed for the determination of this functional group. Siggia and Stahl (7) developed a quantitative method based on the reduction of the amide to the corresponding amine with the vigorous reagent lithium aluminum hydride. After the reduction, the amines so produced are steam distilled from the reaction mixture and titrated. A considerable number of amides were examined by this method and its applicability was shown to be wide. It has been known for many years that amides react with hydroxylamine hydrochloride to give the hydroxamic acids

$$\underset{\substack{\| \\ R-C-NH_2}}{O} + NH_2OH \longrightarrow \underset{\substack{\| \quad | \\ R-C-N-OH}}{O \quad H} + NH_3$$

The hydroxamic acids produce a deep color with ferric ion and this permits a sensitive determination of amides. Other carboxylic acid derivatives, such as esters and anhydrides, also form hydroxamic acids, although far more rapidly than amides. The technique was thoroughly investigated by Bergmann (8), who showed its wide applicability. Bergmann recommended a heating period of several hours at 60°C for most amides. As with many colorimetric methods of analysis, the observed molar absorptivity varied widely (over a factor of 4) in the group of amides examined; consequently, it would be necessary to calibrate with the particular amide being sought.

DETERMINATION OF NITRILES

Although the recommended Acid Hydrolysis method is quite useful for the determination of nitriles, a number of other techniques have been published and should be of value for specific types of samples. Mitchell and Hawkins (9) published an aquametric method for the determination of nitriles in which the nitrile was hydrated to the amide using BF_3 as a catalyst. The reaction was conducted in acetic acid and the consumption of water, determined by titration with the Karl Fischer reagent, was taken as the measure of the nitrile content of the sample. The method is quite useful and is well described in their publication; however, the vigorous conditions required for the hydration reaction cause interference from other reactive functional groups, such as alcohols and aldehydes.

Reductive techniques in which nitriles are reduced to amines have been given some attention. Siggia and Stahl (7) were able to reduce amides and certain nitriles with lithium aluminum hydride to the corresponding amines, which were steam distilled and then titrated with standard acid. The method was generally satisfactory for a number of amides but had only limited utility for nitriles, since many could not be reduced completely. Huber (10) has shown that it is feasible to determine nitriles, as well as aromatic nitro compounds and pyrroles, by hydrogenation to the corresponding amines and titration with 0.2N perchloric acid. In this way these nonbasic nitrogen compounds can be determined quantitatively.

$$R—C{\equiv}N \rightarrow R—CH_2—NH_2$$
$$R—NO_2 \rightarrow R—NH_2$$

Huber found it best to employ a platinum oxide catalyst that had been previously treated with dilute nitric acid to remove basic contaminants and hydrogenated the sample in glacial acetic acid solvent in glass apparatus at a pressure of 1.5 atm and a temperature up to 80°C.

The glacial acetic acid solvent made it simple to titrate the hydrogenation product directly with perchloric acid in the usual way. Results on nitriles,

Table 15.3. Results Obtained in the Hydrogenation of Nitrogen Compounds and Subsequent Titration[a]

Compound	Reaction, %
Aromatic nitro compounds	
Nitrobenzene	99.7 ± 0.2
o-Dinitrobenzene	97.4 ± 0.2
o-Nitrophenol	99.8 ± 0.2
2,4-Dinitrophenol	99.8 ± 0.2
Picric acid	98.5 ± 1.0
p-Nitroaniline	100.1 ± 0.2
2,4-Dinitroaniline	96.0 ± 0.3
Methyl p-nitrobenzoate	99.5 ± 0.2
Aliphatic nitro compounds	
Nitroethane	85 to 89
Nitrocyclohexane	82 to 96
Pyrrole compounds	
Pyrrole	99.8 ± 0.1
Indole	100.7 ± 0.1
Methylindole	99.8 ± 0.1
Carbazole	99.5 ± 0.3
Nitriles	
Acetonitrile	99.3 ± 0.3
Benzonitrile	99.2 ± 0.2
Adiponitrile	98.4 ± 0.2
Succinonitrile	98.6 ± 0.4

[a] Hydrogenation in glacial acetic acid at low pressures. Titrant 0.2N perchloric acid in dioxane. Data from W. Huber (10).

shown in Table 15.3, indicate good precision and fair accuracy such that the procedure should be useful. The hydrogenation of aromatic nitro compounds in most cases leads smoothly and quantitatively to the cycloaliphatic amines, as was indicated by the consumption of hydrogen and the titration values. Picric acid and dinitroaniline were exceptions in that hydrogenation was sluggish and incomplete. Huber was unable to hydrogenate aliphatic nitro compounds quantitatively under these mild conditions. The hydrogenation of pyrrole derivatives went smoothly and quantitatively, giving good repeatability for the compounds examined. Amides did not hydrogenate under these mild conditions and, consequently, did not interfere.

Some years ago, Whitehurst and Johnson (11) published a procedure in which nitriles were converted to the corresponding amides by reaction with alkaline hydrogen peroxide. This reaction takes place rapidly at room temperature for a number of nitriles. According to McMaster and Langreck (12) this reaction takes place according to the following equation:

$$R{-}C{\equiv}N + 2H_2O_2 \xrightarrow{\text{(alkali)}} R\overset{\overset{\displaystyle O}{\|}}{C}NH_2 + H_2O + O_2$$

There is, however, some hydrolysis of the amide during the initial reaction. To obtain a stoichiometric reaction, the hydrolysis is made complete by concentrating the reaction mixture, thus converting all the amide to the salt of the corresponding acid. The remaining base is determined by titration with standard acid to the phenolphthalein end point. The difference between this value and the corresponding blank is a measure of the nitrile content of the sample since 1 mole of base is consumed in the overall reaction.

$$R{-}C{\equiv}N + 2H_2O_2 + KOH \longrightarrow R{-}\overset{\overset{\displaystyle O}{\|}}{C}{-}OK + NH_3 + H_2O + O_2$$

Good results were obtained with some of the simple nitriles such as acetonitrile, propionitrile, and succinonitrile, but high results were found with some others, including acrylonitrile and ethylene cyanohydrin, due apparently to further oxidation. Interferences were found from compounds or functional groups that oxidized under the reaction conditions. This interference was particularly severe with carbonyl compounds, but in some cases if the oxidation was quantitative a correction could be applied.

Some α,β-unsaturated nitriles can be determined, along with other similarly unsaturated compounds, by reaction with a mercaptan.

$$R{-}CH{=}CH{-}C{\equiv}N + R'SH \rightleftarrows RCH(SR'){-}CH_2{-}C{\equiv}N$$

The unconsumed mercaptan can be determined by titration with iodine to a visual end point or by electrometric titration with silver nitrate. The method was investigated some years ago with a number of pure α,β-unsaturated compounds (13) and it was found that acrylonitrile reacted rapidly and gave stoichiometric results. In general, α,β-unsaturated esters and aldehydes also reacted quantitatively in this method but the corresponding ketones only semiquantitatively. This reaction has been used by Haslam and Newlands to determine acrylonitrile in air (14).

DETERMINATION OF PYRROLES, INDOLES, AND CARBAZOLES IN PETROLEUM FRACTIONS

As part of the need to characterize the nonhydrocarbons in petroleum, extensive investigations have been made into methods for determining the nonbasic nitrogen compounds (15–17). The techniques involved followed the pattern for determination of the nitrogen bases in petroleum; for example, chromatography on alumina, silica gel, or Florisil has allowed the recovery of concentrates of indoles and carbazoles from petroleum. Since the pyrrolic proton in the $>$N—H in these materials has some acidic character, it can be replaced by a cation from an inorganic base. By reaction of the concentrate with powdered KOH in the temperature range of 140–175°C, Nixon and Thorpe (16) were able to isolate the pyrrolic potassium salts from the concentrates of a 480/540°F fraction of a catalytically cracked gas oil. The original nitrogen compounds could be recovered by hydrolysis and solution in isopentane. Examination of the infrared spectra showed a strong absorption band at 2.89 μ due to the NH structure. Ultraviolet absorption was also used to demonstrate that the pyrrolic nitrogen in this fraction was mainly in the form of indoles. The pyrrolic nitrogen content, determined by chromatography, isolation, and spectroscopy, agreed closely with the values determined directly by the colorimetric p-dimethylaminobenzaldehyde method, described in the next section and included as a recommended method.

In a thorough and detailed investigation of the composition of nonbasic nitrogen compounds in petroleum products, Hartung and Jewell (15) developed sophisticated methods for the separation and characterization of alkyl indoles, carbazoles, and phenazines in higher boiling fractions of petroleum. The concentrates, obtained by chromatography over alumina, were further purified and then analyzed by gas chromatography, ultraviolet absorption, and mass spectroscopy. The colorimetric method of Wanags (18, 19), which involves reaction with 2-bromo-2-nitroindandione-1,3, was found applicable to the carbazole fraction and in agreement with the other measurements made.

LaLau (20) examined concentrates obtained from petroleum distillates by mass spectrometry and was able to find multiring pyridines, quinolines, and carbazoles, as well as doubly heterocyclic compounds containing both S and N in the same molecule.

The catalytic hydrogenation technique developed by workers at the U.S. Bureau of Mines to simplify the gas chromatographic analysis of hetero compounds in petroleum has been employed also to good advantage by Thompson, Coleman, Ward, and Rall (21) in the determination of nitrogen compounds. By this technique, as an example, 2-methyl quinoline is converted to butylcyclohexane. This method greatly simplifies the chromatogram and provides information on the carbon skeleton of quite complex mixtures.

DETERMINATION OF PYRROLIC NITROGEN

A sensitive and relatively specific colorimetric method is available from the work of Thompson, Symon, and Wankat (22) and of Muhs and Weiss (23) for the determination of pyrrolic compounds based upon condensation with p-dimethylaminobenzaldehyde in the presence of acid to produce a red-violet dye. The reaction steps are as illustrated.

In the presence of acid the condensation product exists as a resonance hybrid (3 and 4) and the color formation is due to the contribution of the quinoidal form (4). The color present in dilute acid disappears in concentrated acid because of the formation of 5, which cannot exist in the color-producing quinoidal form.

This reaction was first reported by Ehrlich in 1901 (24) and has been used widely in biological analyses. The reaction is generally rapid for pyrroles and indoles in which an α or β position is unsubstituted. Carbazoles, of course, are not determined since no reactive sites are available. Molar absorptivities of the reaction products are high, which makes the method useful for trace analyses of these materials. Tetrasubstituted pyrroles react at a slower rate and carbazoles do not react at all. Some results on pure pyrrolic compounds by the recommended method, which is taken from the publication of Muhs and Weiss (23), are given in Table 15.4. In the application of this method to petroleum fractions it was found desirable to employ averaged adsorptivities for the calculation of pyrrole contents. The method is directly suitable for the analysis of straight-run and aromatic petroleum fractions but some interference was encountered with those products containing appreciable amounts of olefins. To overcome this interference, the pyrrolic compounds were separated from the olefins by adsorption chromatography prior to the color-forming reaction using the following separation procedure:

> Add the weighed sample directly to a 15 cm × 2 cm column of 60–200 mesh Florisil and elute with 50 ml of *n*-heptane, followed by 75 ml of benzene and finally with isopropyl alcohol to remove the benzene. Discard the heptane eluate (the border between the heptane and benzene zones is made apparent by a difference in shading of the zones) and collect the benzene eluate in three 25-ml portions. Using 50-ml volumetric flasks, dilute each fraction to the mark with benzene, pipet out 25.0 ml for the determination, and use the remainder for the blank. Make the determination on the first two benzene eluates and if the second has an absorbance greater than 25% of the first, run an additional analysis on the third eluate.

Table 15.4. Results of Reaction of Pyrrolic Compounds with *p*-Dimethylaminobenzaldehyde[a]

				Spectra	
Compound	mp., °C	bp, °C	n_D^{20}	λ_{max} mμ	Molar absorptivity, liters/mole-cm
Pyrrole		125–127	1.5090	545	55700
2-Methylpyrrole		80–82/80 mm	1.5015	545	66500
1-Butylpyrrole		92–95/90 mm	1.4741	555	75000
2,4-Dimethylpyrrole		51–52/7 mm	1.4970	536	59200
2,5-Dimethylpyrrole		60–61/13 mm	1.5060	522	91700
Indole	52–53			565	77300
2-Methylindole	60–61			540	81600
3-Methylindole	95–96			580	62100
Carbazole	240				0
9-Methylcarbazole	87–88				0
9-Ethylcarbazole	69–70				0

[a] Data from Muhs and Weiss (23). Copyright 1958 by the American Chemical Society. Reprinted by permission of the copyright owner.

Some results obtained by the colorimetric method on typical petroleum fractions are shown in Table 15.5, from which it can be seen that meaningful results can be obtained in the low ppm range. Where the olefin content of the samples was high, a prior separation using Florisil gave satisfactory results. An attempt to apply the separation procedure to a crude oil was not successful because the eluates gave turbid reaction mixtures with *p*-dimethylamino-benzaldehyde.

Table 15.5. Results Obtained for the Determination of Pyrrolic Nitrogen in Petroleum Fractions by the Colorimetric Method[a]

Description of sample	Pyrrolic N content, ppm
Aromatic solvent	0.7, 0.7
Straight-run gas oil	3.9, 3.1
Catalytically cracked gas oil	172, 185
Thermally cracked gas oil	64, 69
Aromatic solvent No. 1	7.7,[b] 7.8[b]
Aromatic solvent No. 2	1.3,[b] 2.0[b]
Thermally cracked gasoline	0.7,[b] 1.0[b]
Catalytically cracked gasoline	3.2[b], 3.3[b]

[a] Data from Muhs and Weiss (23).

[b] These samples were initially separated by chromatography to remove olefins prior to analysis.

DETERMINATION OF PYRROLIC NITROGEN

COLORIMETRIC *p*-DIMETHYLAMINOBENZALDEHYDE METHOD

Apparatus

Chromatographic tube with an inner diameter of 20 mm and a length of 200 mm.

Shaking machine; a Burrell wrist-action shaker, Model BB, is satisfactory, if it is adjusted for maximum agitation.

Spectrophotometer, equipped with 1-cm borosilicate glass cells.

Reagents

n-Heptane, free from pyrrole and olefin. Extract 2 liters of Phillips' pure grade *n*-heptane with five 100-ml portions of concentrated sulfuric acid and four 100-ml portions of distilled water. Dry the solvent over a mixture of anhydrous magnesium sulfate and potassium carbonate for 1 hr and filter. The solvent obtained should produce an absorbance of less than 0.015 at 550 mμ when subjected to the conditions of this method.

Benzene, CP.

Phosphoric acid, 85%, reagent grade.

p-Dimethylaminobenzaldehyde–phosphoric acid solution; dissolve 1.0 g of *p*-dimethylaminobenzaldehyde in 100 ml of reagent grade 85% phosphoric acid.

Acetic acid, CP, glacial.

Sampling

To obtain a readable absorbance, sample sizes should be chosen as listed below:

Pyrrolic nitrogen, ppm	Sample size, g
0.5–5.0	10
5–50	1
50–500	0.1
500–5000	0.01

Procedure

Make the determination on a solution of sample in 25–40 ml of *n*-heptane, using an equal amount of sample for the blank.

Place the solutions in a 125-ml separatory funnel and add 5 ml of the *p*-dimethylaminobenzaldehyde–phosphoric acid solution (for the blank use 5 ml of 85% phosphoric acid in place of the reagent sample). Shake the mixture for 10 min, using agitation equivalent to vigorous hand shaking (approximately equivalent to a setting of 7 on the Burrell shaker). Then add 50 ml of glacial acetic acid and continue shaking for 5 min. If the solution is homogeneous at this point, place in a 100-ml volumetric flask; if there are two phases, put only the lower layer in the flask. Wash the stopper, walls, and tip of the funnel with glacial acetic acid and add the washings to the volumetric flask. Dilute the solution to the mark with glacial acetic acid and measure the absorbance of the solution versus distilled water at 530, 540, 550, 560, and 570 mμ, using 1-cm cells. Because some samples produce unstable colors, make absorbance readings within 10 min of the completion of the procedure. If the absorbance of the solution is too high (above 1.0), dilute it and the corresponding blank suitably with a 5% solution of phosphoric acid in glacial acetic acid and divide the final results by the dilution factor.

Subtract the absorbance of the blank from that of the sample and add the corrected absorbances from each of the eluates that produced a violet color before making the calculation (generally only the first eluate produces any color due to pyrrolic nitrogen).

Calculation

Calculate the parts per million of pyrrolic nitrogen in the sample by means of the following equation:

$$\text{Pyrrolic nitrogen, ppm} = \frac{1.4 \times 10^6 (A)}{(W)(a)}$$

where A = total absorbance minus that of blank at a particular wavelength

W = weight of sample used in determination, g

a = molar absorptivity at a particular wavelength. Use the values below: for typical pyrrolic nitrogen compounds

mμ	liters/mole-cm	mμ	liters/mole-cm
530	49,500	550	57,100
540	54,000	560	50,000
545	57,000	570	38,000

Take the average of the values obtained at the six wavelengths as the value for the determination.

DETERMINATION OF NITROGEN COMPOUNDS OF THE HIGHER VALENCE STATE BY REDUCTIVE TECHNIQUES

Those organic compounds in which nitrogen is bonded to oxygen are often determined by a reductive technique. For instance, the recommended method for determination of amine oxides involves reduction of the oxides with a titanous chloride solution followed by back-titration of the remaining titanous chloride in the reaction mixture with a standard ferric ammonium sulfate reagent. A corresponding blank determination allows for the calculation of the amount of titanous chloride reduced by the amine oxide sample. Similar methods for the determination of other nitrogen functional groups in the oxidized state have been published by many investigators. An excellent review of many of these techniques was published some years ago by Becker and Shaefer (25). The use of chromous chloride solution and a potentiometric end point titration was described by Bottei and Furman (26). It is possible to reduce nitro groups with metallic tin according to the method of Vanderzee and Edgell (27) or with copper according to Juvet, Twicker, and Afremow (28) and measure the extent of reduction by loss in weight of the metal. The titanous chloride reagent can be stabilized with amalgamated zinc so that its normality remains essentially constant for several weeks. This reagent has been shown by Ma and Earley (29) to give a precision of about $\pm 0.3\%$ in the determination of aromatic nitro and nitroso compounds. Good accuracy was found by Tiwari and Sharma (30, 31) with a number of aromatic nitro compounds in a reduction technique using titanous sulfate. *N*-Nitroso compounds have been reduced by Gal, Stedronsky, and Miller (32) with iodide ion in the presence of acid to produce the corresponding amine and iodine following which the iodine is titrated with standard thiosulfate. A collection of data on the reductive determination of compounds in which nitrogen is bonded to oxygen by these techniques is in Table 15.6.

In addition to the chemical reductive methods, electrochemical procedures, principally polarography, have been widely investigated for the determination of the higher valent nitrogen compounds. Techniques for the reduction of hydroxyl-amines, azoxy, azo, nitroso, and nitro compounds have been reviewed (33, 34). The nitro group in aromatic compounds is one of the easiest to reduce and, depending upon the pH of the reduction solution and the system employed, a series of products can be obtained. In basic systems, electrochemical reduction of aromatic nitro compounds generally produces such bimolecular products as the azo, azoxy, and hydrazo derivatives, due to the base-catalyzed condensation of the initial reduction products. In neutral solutions, hydroxylamine and nitroso compounds may be produced, while in acidic solution amines are the principal product.

Polarographic analysis has been used for the determination of specific compounds in a number of examples. Some typical cases are the

Table 15.6. Results Obtained in the Determination of Nitrogen–Oxygen Compounds by Reductive Techniques

Compound	Reductant	Recovery, %	Ref.
Aromatic Nitro Compounds			
NO₂ (benzene ring)	$Ti_2(SO_4)_3$ $TiCl_3$ Sn	99.6 99.7, 100.2 99.1, 99.5, 100.4	a b c
NO₂ (benzene ring) NO₂	$Ti_2(SO_4)_3$ $TiCl_3$ Sn	100.0 100.2, 100.3 99.1, 99.9, 100.1	a b c
NH₂ (benzene ring) NO₂	$Ti_2(SO_4)_3$ $TiCl_3$ Sn	100.9 99.8, 100.1, 100.3 99.9, 100.3	a b c
COOH (benzene ring) NO₂	$Ti_2(SO_4)_3$ Sn	99.0 99.8, 100.8, 101.1	a c
COOH (benzene ring) NO₂	$CrCl_2$	99.6, 100.0, 100.1	d

Table 15.6 (*continued*)

Compound	Reductant	Recovery, %	Ref.
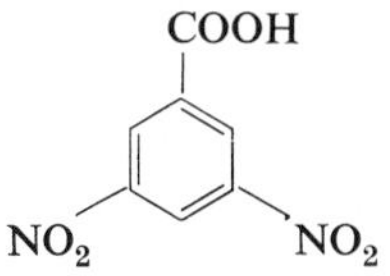 COOH with NO₂ groups (structure)	Ti₂(SO₄)₃ TiCl₃	100.7 100.2, 100.3	a b
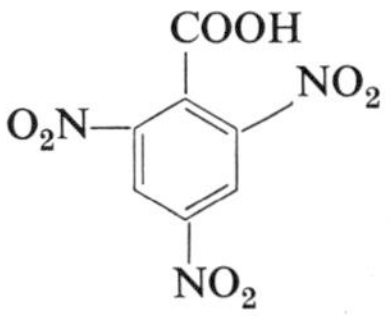 COOH with NO₂ groups (structure)	CrCl₂	99.8, 100.2	d
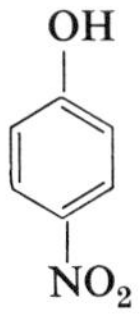 OH with NO₂ (structure)	TiCl₃ Sn	100.4, 100.7 100.2, 100.3, 100.4	b c
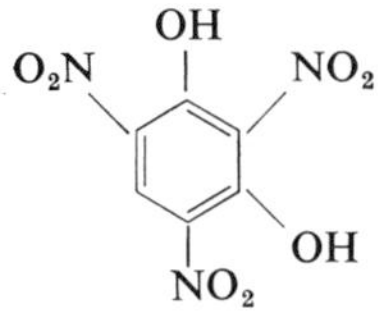 OH with NO₂ groups (structure)	CrCl₂	99.0, 99.0, 100.	d
Nitroso Compounds			
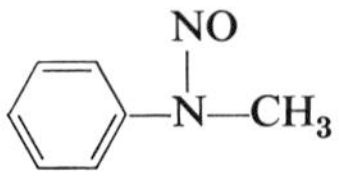 NO N—CH₃ (structure)	TiCl₃ HI	100.2, 101.2 98.9, 99.0, 99.3	b e
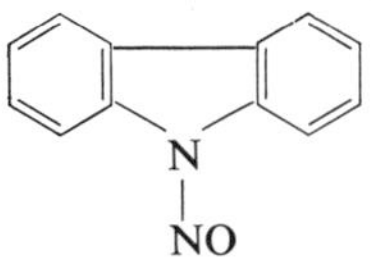 carbazole-NO (structure)	HI	99.2, 99.4	e
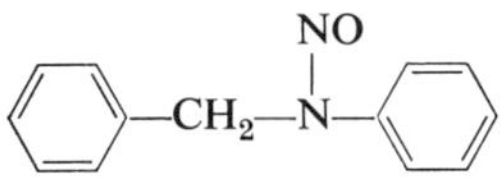 NO CH₂—N (structure)	TiCl₃ HI	100.5, 100.6 99.1, 100.0, 100.9	b e
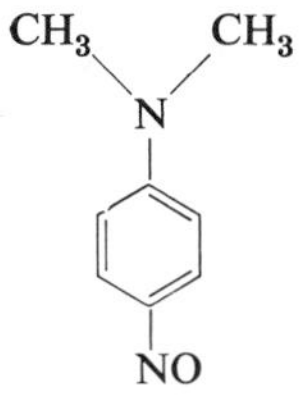 CH₃ N CH₃ NO (structure)	TiCl₃	99.6, 99.8	b

(*Continued overleaf*)

Table 15.6. (*continued*)

Compound	Reductant	Recovery, %	Ref.
OH NO	TiCl$_3$	100.3, 100.3	b
Amine Oxides			
O↑N (pyridine N-oxide)	TiCl$_3$	97.8, 98.3, 98.4, 98.5	
H$_3$C ⟶ O↑N ⟵ CH$_3$	TiCl$_3$	96.5, 97.3, 97.6, 98.1	
CH$_3$ C$_{12}$H$_{25}$—N→O CH$_3$	TiCl$_3$	97.3	
(O↑N—S)$_2$ Zn	TiCl$_3$	97.7, 98.1, 98.2, 98.2, 99.1	f

a Tiwari and Sharma (31).
b Ma and Earley (29).
c Vanderzee and Edgell (27).
d Bottei and Furman (26).
e Gal, Stedronsky, and Miller (32).
f Chapter 14.

determination of nitrofurazone (35) and 1,2-dimethyl-5-nitroimidazole (36) in medicated animal foods, and insecticides containing the nitro group (37). Polarography has also been employed in physical chemical studies such as in the measurement of the adsorption of aromatic nitro compounds (38).

DETERMINATION OF TRACE AMOUNTS OF ALKYL NITRATES IN AIR

Gas chromatography is a valuable technique for the determination of traces of alkyl nitrates since the electron-capture detector is extremely sensitive to the —ONO_2 group (39). This measurement was found particularly useful in studies of air pollution for the determination of peroxyacyl nitrates in part per billion concentrations by Darley, Kettner, and Stephens (39). The peroxyacyl nitrates have the general formula

$$R—\overset{\overset{\textstyle O}{\|}}{C}—O—ONO_2$$

and have been identified as important constituents of photochemical air pollution in that they cause serious plant damage as well as eye irritation at exposure levels of 10–20 ppb. The R groups can be C_1, C_2, C_3, or C_4; the toxic effects seem to be increasingly serious with the higher members of the homologous series.

Estimation of the minimum detectable quantity of peroxyacyl nitrate from the work of Darley, Kettner, and Stephens (39) is of the order of 10^{-11} g. In their work they employed a commercial gas chromatographic apparatus equipped with an electron detector and a 3 ft × 3 mm o.d. (1.5 mm i.d.) glass column packed with 5% Carbowax 400 on 100- to 120-mesh Chromosorb W and operated at 35°C. Dry N_2 was used as the carrier gas at a rate of 25 ml/min. A somewhat similar study was made by Camera and Pravisani (40) for the determination of low concentrations of alkyl polynitrates in air using an electron-capture detector and a 25-cm long glass column (2 mm i.d.) packed with 10% Igepal CO-880 on 80- to 120-mesh siliconized Chromosorb P and operated at 120°C. It was not possible to inject air samples directly because of adsorption of nitroesters on the walls and consequently they prepared their samples for analysis by bubbling air through tubes containing ethyl alcohol and then analyzing the alcohol solution. The sensitivities found for the several organic nitrates was the following:

Compound	Minimum detectable quantity, g
Propylene glycol dinitrate	5×10^{-11}
Ethylene glycol dinitrate	2×10^{-10}
Glycerol trinitrate	2×10^{-9}

It is possible to determine the peroxyacyl nitrates by their infrared absorption but this is not simple at the very low concentrations in which they are found in the atmosphere. However, these materials were first discovered during laboratory studies of reactions using a long-path infrared spectrophotometer (41). The peroxynitrates, when examined at dilute concentrations in air, are found to have a series of absorption bands between 5.4 and 12.6 μ that can be used for their determination at low levels (42).

REFERENCES

1. M. J. Rosen and H. A. Goldsmith, *Systematic Analysis of Surface Active Agents*, Interscience, New York, 1960, pp. 286, 287.
2. F. C. Gross and J. H. Jones, *J. Assoc. Official Agr. Chemists*, **49**, 1192 (1966).
3. V. K. Krieble and C. I. Noll, *J. Am. Chem. Soc.*, **61**, 560 (1939).
4. S. Siggia, J. G. Hanna, and N. M. Serencha, *Anal. Chem.*, **36**, 227 (1964).
5. M. E. Gibson, Jr., and R. H. Heidner, *ibid.*, **33**, 1825 (1961).
6. F. H. Lohman and T. F. Mulligan, *ibid.*, **41**, 243 (1969).
7. S. Siggia and C. R. Stahl, *ibid.*, **27**, 550 (1955).
8. F. Bergmann, *ibid.*, **24**, 1366 (1952).
9. J. Mitchell, Jr. and W. Hawkins, *J. Am. Chem. Soc.*, **67**, 777 (1954).
10. W. Huber, *Z. Anal. Chem.*, **197**, 236 (1963); **216**, 260 (1966).
11. D. H. Whitehurst and J. B. Johnson, *Anal. Chem.*, **30**, 1332 (1958).
12. L. McMaster and F. B. Langreck, *J. Am. Chem. Soc.*, **39**, 103 (1917).
13. D. W. Beesing, W. P. Tyler, D. M. Kurtz, and S. A. Harrison, *Anal. Chem.*, **21**, 1073 (1949).
14. J. Haslam and G. Newlands, *Analyst*, **80**, 50 (1955).
15. G. K. Hartung and D. M. Jewell, *Anal. Chim. Acta*, **26**, 514 (1962).
16. A. C. Nixon and R. E. Thorpe, *J. Chem. Eng. Data*, **7**, 429 (1962).
17. R. V. Helm, D. R. Latham, C. R. Ferrin, and J. S. Ball, *Anal. Chem.*, **32**, 1765 (1960).
18. G. Wanags, *Ber.*, **69**, 1066 (1936).
19. G. Wanags and A. Lode, *Ber.*, **71**, 1267 (1938).
20. C. LaLau, *Anal. Chim. Acta*, **22**, 239 (1960).
21. C. J. Thompson, H. J. Coleman, C. C. Ward, and H. T. Rall, *Anal. Chem.*, **34**, 151 (1962).
22. R. B. Thompson, T. Symon, and C. Wankat, *ibid.*, **24**, 1465 (1952).
23. M. A. Muhs and F. T. Weiss, *ibid.*, **30**, 259 (1958).
24. P. Ehrlich, *Med. Woche*, **1901**, 151.
25. W. W. Becker and W. E. Shaefer, in *Organic Analysis*, Vol. II, Interscience, New York, 1954, p. 71.
26. R. S. Bottei and N. H. Furman, *Anal. Chem.*, **27**, 1182 (1955).
27. C. E. Vanderzee and W. F. Edgell, *ibid.*, **22**, 572 (1950).
28. R. S. Juvet, Jr., M. C. Twicker, and L. C. Afremow, *Anal. Chim. Acta*, **22**, 87 (1960).
29. T. S. Ma and J. V. Earley, *Mikrochim. Acta*, **1**, 129 (1959).
30. R. D. Tiwari and J. P. Sharma, *Z. Anal. Chem.*, **191**, 329 (1962).
31. R. D. Tiwari and J. P. Sharma, *Anal. Chem.*, **35**, 1307 (1963).
32. J. Gal, E. R. Stedronsky and S. I. Miller, *ibid.*, **40**, 168 (1968).
33. F. D. Popp and H. P. Schultz, *Chem. Rev.*, **62**, 19 (1962).
34. P. Zuman, *Organic Polarographic Analysis*, Macmillan, New York, 1964.
35. F. L. Fricke, G. E. Keppel, and S. M. Hart, *J. Assoc. Offic. Agr. Chemists*, **47**, 788 (1964).
36. P. J. Cooper and R. A. Hoodless, *Analyst*, **92**, 520 (1967).

37. J. Kovac, *J. Chromatog.*, **11,** 412 (1963).
38. L. Holleck and B. Kastening, *Z. Anal. Chem.*, **173,** 100 (1960).
39. E. F. Darley, K. A. Kettner, and E. R. Stephens, *Anal. Chem.*, **35,** 589 (1963).
40. E. Camera and D. Pravisani, *ibid.*, **39,** 1645 (1967).
41. E. R. Stephens, P. L. Hanst, R. C. Doerr, and W. E. Scott, *Ind. Eng. Chem.*, **48,** 1498 (1956).
42. E. R. Stephens, *Anal. Chem.*, **36,** 928 (1964).

16

DETERMINATION OF SULFUR COMPOUNDS

"Group sulfur" analysis, as it is usually termed in the petroleum industry, is essentially the functional analysis of organic sulfur compounds in the reduced valence states. These functions include mercaptan, sulfide, disulfide, and polysulfide, each of which can be further subdivided into aromatic and nonaromatic structures. Analytical methods utilizing chemical reagents have been found particularly useful for determination of these sulfur functions.

The U.S. Bureau of Mines has done extensive work in the development of methods for the analysis of sulfur compounds (1, 2) in petroleum fractions and have published detailed procedures. Silver nitrate titration is used to determine the sum of the *hydrogen sulfide* and *mercaptans*. *Mercaptans* are specifically determined by extraction of hydrogen sulfide from a fresh sample with acidic cadmium chloride solution and titration with silver nitrate. *Disulfides* are determined from titration of the mercaptans produced by reduction with zinc and acid. *Aliphatic* plus *alicyclic sulfides* are measured by the change in sulfur content upon treatment with powdered mercurous nitrate. The same portion of the sample is then treated with powdered mercuric nitrate and the reduction in sulfur content is considered to be *aromatic sulfides* and *thiophenes*. Considerable data have been obtained with this series of procedures on a wide variety of petroleum fractions (1, 2). The method generally gives detailed analysis of gasolines and other light fractions, but there is often considerable undetermined residual sulfur, especially with heavy fractions. Some of this limitation was avoided in employing an entirely different approach for differentiating nonthiophenic from thiophenic sulfur (3) in which selective catalytic decomposition over alumina at 450–500°C was used to convert nonthiophenic sulfur compounds into hydrogen sulfide and, presumably, the corresponding olefin. Under these conditions, the thiophenic compounds are stable and titration of the hydrogen sulfide produced provided a rapid and relatively quantitative means of determining the content of nonthiophenic sulfur. Figure 16.1 illustrates, on pure sulfur compounds, the manner in which the following general categories respond:

Aliphatic plus alicyclic sulfur. All these compounds decompose to produce hydrogen.

Aromatic mercaptan precursors. These compounds are less completely

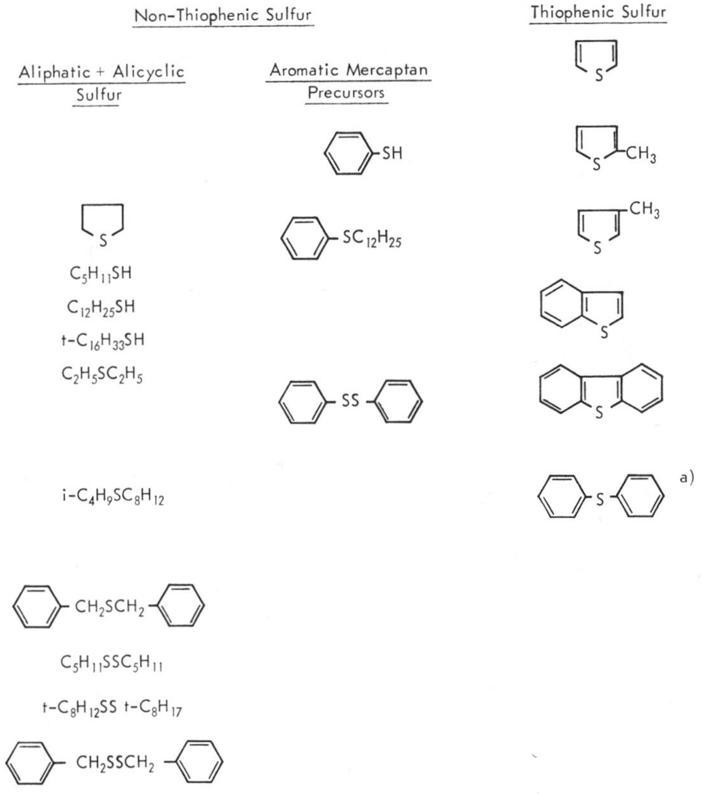

a) Considered as thiophenic sulfur for purposes of classification.

Figure 16.1. Classification of sulfur compounds by reaction over alumina at 450°C. From McCoy & Weiss (3). Copyright 1954 by the American Chemical Society. Reprinted by permission of the copyright owner.

decomposed to hydrogen sulfide, with some 20–90% of the sulfur remaining as aromatic mercaptans.

Thiophenic sulfur. This class includes the thiophenes and their analogs. The diphenyl sulfides are also resistant to decomposition and fall in this classification.

Actual data obtained in the catalytic decomposition of pure compounds, dissolved in white oil, are given in Table 16.1, which shows that the classification is not entirely quantitative but useful for the purpose of defining the general composition of sulfur compounds present in mixtures of petroleum and other fractions. At temperatures of 450–500°C the decomposition of thiophenes is of the order of 1–2% while the aliphatic and alicyclic sulfides generally produce more than 90% of the calculated amount of H_2S. Consequently, the alumina decomposition technique is useful to obtain definition of the types of sulfur compounds present. The "aromatic mercaptan precursors," which are generally present in very small amounts when detected at all, would be expected to be alkyl aryl sulfides or diaryl disulfides from the examples shown in Figure 16.1. It is interesting, in view of the low but significant data reported for this type of sulfur compound in Table 16.2, that a recent publication describes the positive identification of phenyl *sec*-butyl sulfide in a petroleum fraction and "establishes for the first time the presence of this class of sulfur compounds in petroleum" (4).

It was possible to apply the alumina decomposition method, together with available procedures for the determination of elemental sulfur, mercaptans, and disulfides to obtain the group sulfur analysis of a wide variety of petroleum products, including gasolines, gas oils, lubricating oil, residues, and crude oil. Some typical data are shown in Table 16.2. The ratio of nonthiophenic sulfur to total sulfur was highest in straight-run stocks and least in catalytically cracked products, as would be expected.

In this section, recommended methods are given for the determination of mercaptans, disulfides, free sulfur, and nonthiophenic sulfur. For a wider review of methods for the determination of functional sulfur groups, the publication of Karchmer is recommended (5). The method recommended for the determination of *mercaptans* uses potentiometric titration of the thiol group with standard silver nitrate solution, using a silver wire coated with silver sulfide as the indicating electrode. Sulfide ion (from H_2S) precipitates first at a high negative potential, as is shown in Figure 16.2, while the precipitation of silver mercaptide takes place subsequently. These precipitation reactions are quantitative and apply to wide-range mixtures of hydrogen sulfide and mercaptans. Free sulfur, if present, can interact and cause erroneous results but techniques for overcoming this interference are available (6). The development of this method for the titration of mercaptans is described in a series of publications by Tamele and his coworkers (6–8), and the recommended method for the determination of mercaptans is taken from these publications. Some data by this method or its earlier variations are given in Table 16.3; they show that the recovery of mercaptan is quantitative, in general, and that essentially no interference is produced with other types of sulfur compounds.

Disulfides are generally determined by a reduction technique in which mercaptans are produced. Several reagents have been investigated for this purpose, including a mixture of sodium borohydride and aluminum chloride dissolved in diethylene glycol dimethyl ether (9). The mercaptans produced were titrated potentiometrically with $0.1N$ silver nitrate solution. Kolthoff and his coworkers (10) employed a columnar reduction technique with granular

Table 16.1. Decomposition of Sulfur Compounds over Alumina[a,b]

Compound	Temp., °C	Recovery, % of sulfur added		
		as H₂S	as Mercaptan	Total
Sulfur[c]	450	83, 79	d	83, 79
Mercaptans				
n-Amyl	450	93, 94	d	93, 94
n-Dodecyl	400	90	d	90
	450	91	d	91
	500	93	d	93
	540	59	d	59
t-Hexadecyl	450	90, 92	d	90, 92
Benzyl	450	84, 87	d	84, 87
Phenyl	450	11	50	61
Sulfides				
Diethyl	450	95	d	95
Diisoamyl	450	93, 95, 96	d	93, 95, 96
Isobutyl-n-octyl	350	55	25	80
	400	86	d	86
	450	92, 94, 96	d	92, 94, 96
	500	97	d	97
	560	72, 85	d	72, 85
Dibenzyl	450	92, 94	d	92, 94
Phenyl decyl	450	73, 77	13, 11	86, 88
Thiophane	450	90, 94	d	90, 94
Diphenyl	450	2, 4	2, 3	4, 7
Disulfides				
Diamyl	450	85, 88	d	85, 88
Di-t-octyl	450	87, 91	d	87, 91
Dibenzyl	450	87, 89	d	87, 89
Diphenyl	450	55, 73	42, 26	97, 99
Thiophenes				
Thiophene	450	0.7, 0.1	d	0.7, 1.0
	500	1.5	d	1.5
	560	10.7	d	10.7
2-Methylthiophene	450	1.4	d	1.4
3-Methylthiophene	450	1.1	d	1.1
Benzothiophene	450	<0.5	d	<0.5
Dibenzothiophene	450	<0.5	d	<0.5
	500	1		1
	515	4		4
	540	22		22
Oxygenated compounds				
Thioglycolic acid	450	71, 80	d	71, 80
Diphenyl sulfoxide	450	5	4	9

[a] Data from McCoy and Weiss (3). Copyright 1954 by the American Chemical Society. Reproduced by permission of the copyright owner.

[b] Sulfur compounds dissolved in white oil to give approximately 1 % sulfur.

[c] Recoveries low because sulfur vapor partially crystallized in cooler top portion of reaction tube.

[d] None detected; generally less than 1 %.

Table 16.2. Typical Results Obtained for Group Sulfur Analyses[a]
No elemental sulfur or hydrogen sulfide were found in these materials.

Material	Sulfur, wt %, in						Nonthiophenic sulfur, % of total sulfur	Aromatic mercaptan precursor sulfur, wt %
	Mercaptan	Disulfide	Sulfide	Nonthiophenic	Thiophenic	Total		
Commercial gasoline	<0.001	0.007	0.01, 0.01	0.02, 0.02	0.09, 0.09	0.11	18, 18	n.d.[d]
Catalytically cracked gasoline	0.003	0.001	0.014	0.018	1.18	1.20	2	n.d.
Thermally cracked gasoline	0.12	0.03	0.39	0.54	1.52	2.06	26	0.018
Jet fuel	<0.001	<0.002	0.072	0.072	0.13	0.20	36	n.d.
Catalytic gas oil	<0.001	<0.001	0.002	0.002	0.10	0.10	2	n.d.
California lubricating oil	0.0025	<0.001	0.016, 0.017	0.18, 0.19	0.10, 0.09	0.28	64, 68	n.d.
Mid-Continent lubricating oil	0.025	0.012	0.050, 0.052	0.087, 0.089	0.053, 0.051	0.14	62, 64	ca. 0.003–0.004
Shale oil		0.04[b]	0.18	0.22	0.48	0.70	31	n.d.
Thermal distillate	0.004	0.005	0.47	0.48	0.85	1.33	36	ca. 0.01–0.02
Thermal distillate				0.78, 0.80	1.62, 1.60	2.40	32, 33	n.d.
Straight-run short residue[c]	0.01	0.01	1.0	1.0	1.1	2.08	49	n.d.
Asphalt[c]				0.16	1.42	1.58	10	n.d.
Straight-run long residue[c]	0.006	0.007	0.88, 0.89	0.89, 0.90	0.81, 0.80	1.70	52, 53	n.d.

[a] Data from McCoy and Weiss (3). Copyright 1954 by the American Chemical Society. Reproduced by permission of the copyright owner.
[b] Sum of mercaptan and disulfide sulfur.
[c] Sample admitted as pellet rolled with powdered alumina.
[d] n.d. = none detected.

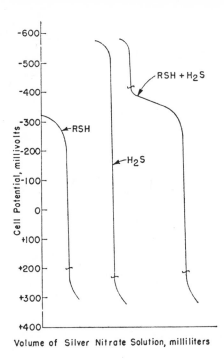

Figure 16.2. Titration of hydrogen sulfide and mercaptans with silver nitrate solution.

Table 16.3. Recovery of Sulfur Compounds in the Electrometric Titration of Mercaptans

Compounds	Recovery, % of theory
Mercaptans[a]	
Methyl mercaptan	100, 100
Ethyl mercaptan	100, 100
n-Butyl mercaptan	100, 100
tert-Butyl mercaptan	99, 100
n-Amyl mercaptan	99, 99
n-Heptyl mercaptan	98.5, 100
Isooctyl mercaptan	95, 97
Other sulfur compounds[b]	
Ethyl sulfide	0.1
Ethyl disulfide	0.1–0.2
Carbon disulfide	0.2
Thiophene	0.1–0.6
Ethyl sulfone	0.1
Butyl sulfone	0.1
Sodiumcymene sulfonate	0.1

[a] Data from Tamele, Ryland, and Irvine (8).
[b] Data from Tamele and Ryland (7).

Table 16.4. Results Obtained in the Determination of Organic Disulfides by Several Methods[a]

Compound	Structure	Sulfur added, wt %	Sulfur found by chemical reduction,[b] wt %		Polarographic data[c]	
			Reflux procedure	Room temperature stirring procedure	Half-wave potential ($E_{1/2}$) versus S.C.E.	Diffusion current constant (I_d/C)
2,3-Dithiabutane	C—S—S—C	0.032	0.012 0.012	0.032 0.032	−1.52	4.0
3,4-Dithiahexane	C_2—S—S—C_2	0.025	0.015 0.015	0.024 0.025	−1.65	3.6
4,5-Dithiaoctane	C_3—S—S—C_3	0.023	0.019 0.020	0.024 0.024	−1.72	3.4
5,6-Dithiadecane	C_4—S—S—C_4	0.024	0.023 0.023	0.024 0.024	−1.72	3.1
6,7-Dithiadodecane	C_5—S—S—C_5	0.023	0.022 0.022	0.022 0.023	−1.74	2.8
9,10-Dithiaoctadecane	C_8—S—S—C_8	0.028	0.029 0.028	0.029 0.029	−1.79	2.3
11,12-Dithiadocosane	C_{10}—S—S—C_{10}	0.024	0.024 0.025	0.025 0.026	−1.80	2.1
2,5-Dimethyl-3,4-dithiahexane	C—C—S—S—C—C (with C branches)	0.030	0.023 0.023	0.030 0.028	−1.84	0.7
3,6-Dimethyl-4,5-dithiaoctane	C—C—C—S—S—C—C—C (with C branches)	0.026	0.024 0.025	0.027 0.026	−1.81	0.5

Compound	Structure					
1,2-Dicyclopentyl-1,2-dithiaethane	(structure)	0.025	0.024 0.024	0.026 0.025	−1.90	0.5
2,2,5,5-Tetramethyl-3,4-dithiahexane	(structure)	0.024	0.020 0.019	0.003 0.003	−1.72	0.4
3,3,6,6-Tetramethyl-4,5-dithiaoctane	(structure)	0.024	0.017 0.015	0.004 0.004	−1.80	0.3
1,2-Diphenyl-1,2-dithiaethane	(structure)	0.025	0.023 0.023	0.022 0.022	−0.65	3.7
1,4-Diphenyl-2,3-dithiabutane[d]	(structure)	0.018	0.017 0.017	0.018 0.018	−1.4	3.1
1,2-Di(4-methylphenyl)-1,2-dithiaethane	(structure)	0.022	0.020 0.021	0.021 0.021	−0.68	3.5

[a] Data from Hubbard, Haines, and Ball (16).
[b] Chemical reduction procedures were applied to solutions of disulfides in isooctane.
[c] Polarographic data were obtained on solutions of disulfides in isooctane diluted 5 × with solvent electrolyte.
[d] Dissolved in benzene.

zinc that had been previously amalgamated with a low concentration of mercury, using a technique and apparatus similar to the Jones reductor method (11). In order to obtain quantitative results in the reduction of disulfides, it was necessary to operate the reduction column at 50°C. Many years ago, Faragher, Morrell, and Monroe (12) published a simple technique for the determination of disulfides involving reduction with zinc dust and glacial acetic acid. Variations of this method have been used by many workers some of whom have recommended heating under reflux (13, 14), heating at 100°C (15), or shaking at room temperature (14). The mercaptans produced are generally determined by titration with standard silver nitrate solution. A number of the published methods for the determination of disulfides were reviewed by Hubbard, Haines, and Ball (16), who examined the recovery of typical organic disulfides and concluded that the reflux procedure gave good recoveries for the various classes of disulfides but poor recovery of low molecular weight mercaptans, due to loss by volatility. The room-temperature stirring procedure was found to give good recoveries with all the primary and secondary disulfides but low results with tertiary disulfides. Because of the rapidity and ease of use of the room-temperature technique and its wide applicability to primary and secondary disulfides, they preferred it for routine work where tertiary disulfides are not significant. Hubbard, Haines, and Ball (16) also examined polarographic reduction as a means for the determination of disulfides and concluded that it was unsatisfactory for a wide range of materials because of the large variation observed for diffusion current constants. A summary of their data is given in Table 16.4. The polarographic studies were made with a standard polarograph using a dropping mercury electrode and with an electrolyte solvent prepared by mixing 404 ml of isopropanol, 83.5 ml of distilled water, and 12.5 ml of $1M$ tetra-n-butylammonium hydroxide. The diffusion current constant is expressed as I_d/C, where I_d is the observed diffusion current in microamperes and C is the concentration of the disulfide in millimoles per liter. The diffusion current constant was found to drop with increasing molecular weight and, more severely, with branching in the molecule.

Although polarographic reduction was not found suitable or applicable to a wide range of disulfides, the technique is useful for the determination and studies of the reactivity of sulfur compounds in simpler, better defined systems and, as such, receives considerable use, especially with biological materials. For instance, polarographic analysis has been used to examine the mechanism of reduction of bis(2-pyridyl)disulfide-di-N-oxide (17), the relative reactivities of the naphthalene disulfides (18) and the determination of methionine in aqueous hydrolysis (19). Polarographic studies have been made on proteins to determine the effect of pH and temperature on the reduction of disulfide bonds (20).

The recommended method included in this chapter for the determination of disulfides involves reduction at room temperature using zinc dust and glacial acetic acid and accomplishes agitation of the reaction mixture with a shaking machine. The method is taken from several earlier publications (3, 14) and is based on the original technique of Faragher, Morrell, and Monroe (12). It is recommended for general use but, as was shown by Hubbard, Haines, and Ball (16), it cannot be applied to tertiary disulfides.

It is occasionally necessary to determine *elemental sulfur* for the purpose of obtaining a more complete sulfur balance on a material. A particularly useful method for the determination of elemental sulfur, especially at trace levels, involves the reaction of sulfur with sodium cyanide to produce thiocyanate, which can be measured colorimetrically by addition of ferric salts.

$$S + NaCN \rightarrow NaCNS$$
$$3NaCNS + Fe(NO_3)_3 \rightarrow Fe(CNS)_3 + 3NaNO_3$$

A method based on this principle was published some years ago by Bartlett and Skoog (21), who provide detailed procedures for the application of the technique to the determination of sulfur in the range of 5–50 ppm in a number of petroleum products. Some interference was originally found from mercaptans but this can be easily overcome by pretreating the sample with aqueous mercuric chloride solution and with incorporation of this simple pretreatment step, the method can be applied, without interference, to samples containing sulfides, disulfides, and mercaptans. Bartlett and Skoog (21) found that an accurate determination of elemental sulfur could be made over a concentration range of 5–50 ppm and in the presence of organic sulfur compounds. Some of the data they obtained are shown in Table 16.5, which shows that known additions of sulfur were recovered with good accuracy.

Table 16.5. Determination of Elemental Sulfur in Solutions Containing Known Concentrations[a]

		Sulfur content, ppm	
Solvent	Other compounds present	Present	Found
Petroleum ether		5.0	5.2
		10.0	10.2
		15.0	15.4
		20.0	20.2
Benzene		25.0	24.9
Petroleum ether	n-Butyl mercaptan plus n-butyl sulfide	5.0	5.0
	n-Butyl mercaptan plus ethyl disulfide	10.0	9.9
	n-Butyl mercaptan plus H$_2$S	20.0	20.2

[a] Data of Bartlett and Skoog (21) using a spectrophotometric thiocyanate method.

The recommended method for the determination of elemental sulfur in petroleum fractions is taken directly from the work of Bartlett and Skoog. The reaction of elemental sulfur with cyanide has also been employed (22) as the basis for a volumetric method, the end point being detected by a sudden shift in the pH in the presence of excess cyanide. Since hydrocyanic acid is so weak ($K_a = 7.2 \times 10^{-10}$), the corresponding sodium salt is strongly hydrolyzed in an aqueous alcoholic solution, producing a high pH. The direct titration was rapid and results on solutions of sulfur in acetone were quite accurate.

DETERMINATION OF MERCAPTANS

ELECTROMETRIC TITRATION

Apparatus

Titration equipment, consisting of a cell system containing a glass reference electrode, a silver–silver sulfide indicating electrode, and a pH meter with integral titration stand and 10-ml buret.

Reagents

Diluents: sulfur-free toluene, "3A" denatured ethyl alcohol, and technical isooctane. To remove dissolved oxygen, purge these solvents with a rapid stream of nitrogen for 10–15 min each day prior to use; keep protected from atmospheric oxygen.

Silver nitrate solution, standard 0.1N alcoholic.

Silver nitrate solution, 0.01N alcoholic. Prepare daily by exact dilution of the standard 0.1N silver nitrate solution with 92% isopropyl alcohol.

Titration solvent. Dissolve 5 g of anhydrous sodium acetate in 75 ml of oxygen-free distilled water and pour into 925 ml of "3A" denatured ethyl alcohol. To remove dissolved oxygen, purge the solution with a rapid stream of nitrogen for 10–15 min each day prior to use; keep protected from atmospheric oxygen.

Titration

Accurately measure a quantity of sample containing 0.03–1 meq of mercaptan plus H_2S into a 250-ml tall-form beaker containing approximately 100 ml of the titration solvent. If the sample is not soluble in alcohol, dissolve it in 20–40 ml of toluene before adding the titration solvent. Immediately start the titration to avoid loss of low molecular weight components. Fill the buret with the silver nitrate solution using 0.01N for the lower amounts and 0.1N for the higher amounts of mercaptan. Titrate the solution potentiometrically. During some parts of the titration, especially when using 0.01N silver nitrate solution, electrode equilibration may be slow.

Curve Interpretation

Plot the cumulative volumes of silver nitrate solution added against the corresponding cell potentials, using the scale units indicated in Figure 16.2. Select end points at the most positive value of the steepest portion of each "break" in the titration curve as illustrated.

Calculation

Calculate the hydrogen sulfide and mercaptide content as weight percent sulfur by means of the following equations:

$$\text{sulfide, wt } \% \text{ as S} = \frac{(A)(N)(1.603)}{(D)(V)}$$

$$\text{mercaptide, wt } \% \text{ as S} = \frac{(B - A)(N)(3.206)}{(D)(V)}$$

where A = volume of standard silver nitrate solution, ml, used in titrating to the sulfide (first) end point

B = total volume of standard silver nitrate solution, ml, used in titrating to the mercaptide (second) end point

D = density of sample, g/ml

N = normality of the standard silver nitrate solution

V = volume of sample used, ml

DETERMINATION OF DISULFIDES

ZINC REDUCTION METHOD

Apparatus

Shaking machine.
Reaction bottles, heavy-walled, 250–500-ml, with crown cap or screw-cap closure. The caps should be lined with Teflon inserts.

Reagents

Glacial acetic acid, CP.
Ammonium hydroxide, concentrated (sp gr 0.90).
Disulfide solution, 0.05 wt % amyl disulfide in isooctane.
Titration solvent, from mercaptan method.
Zinc dust; check the reducing capacity of each batch of zinc dust by carrying out the procedure on the amyl disulfide solution. The mercaptan sulfur found should be within ±5% of the amount expected.
Silver nitrate solution, standard 0.1N aqueous.
Silver nitrate solution, 0.01N alcoholic.

Procedure

Determine the mercaptan content of the original sample by electrometric titration.

Accurately measure a quantity of sample containing no more than 2 meq of mercaptan plus disulfide into the pressure bottle. The total liquid volume should be 100 ± 0.2 ml. If dilution or solution is required, use isooctane or toluene. Then add 10 ± 0.1 ml of glacial acetic acid and 10 ± 0.2 g of zinc dust. Cap the bottle, place on a shaking machine, and shake for 20 min.

Remove the bottle from the shaking machine and filter the liquid through a fluted qualitative filter paper to remove the zinc dust. By means of a pipet, take an aliquot that would be expected to contain 0.02–1 meq of mercaptan. Transfer the aliquot, using a pipet, to a clean titration beaker containing 100 ml of titration solvent. Add 1.1 ml of concentrated ammonium hydroxide for each 10 ml of aliquot volume to neutralize the acetic acid. Choose either 0.1 or 0.01N standard silver nitrate solution so that the titration volume will fall between 2 and 10 ml, and determine the mercaptan content by potentiometric titration.

Calculation

$$\text{Disulfides, wt \% as S} = \frac{(V_2)(N)(3.207)}{(W_2)(A/110)} - \frac{(V_1)(N)(3.207)}{(W_1)}$$

where A = volume of aliquot, ml, of the reduced sample taken for analysis

N = normality of the standard silver nitrate solution

V_1, V_2 = volume of standard silver nitrate solution, ml, used in the titration before and after reduction, respectively

W_1, W_2 = weight of original and reduced samples, respectively, g

DETERMINATION OF ELEMENTAL SULFUR IN PETROLEUM FRACTIONS

SPECTROPHOTOMETRIC THIOCYANATE METHOD

Apparatus

Spectrophotometer, equipped with 1- and 5-cm cells.

Reagents

Petroleum ether.

Sodium cyanide, 0.1%. Dissolve 1 g of sodium cyanide in 1 liter of 95% isopropyl alcohol.

Isopropyl alcohol, 95%.

Mercuric chloride, 2%. Dissolve 20 g of mercuric chloride and 20 g of potassium chloride in 1 liter of water.

Ferric nitrate solution: dissolve 150 g of $Fe(NO_3)_3 \cdot 9H_2O$ in 8N nitric acid and dilute to 1 liter with 8N nitric acid.

Standard sulfur solution, 0.050 mg/ml. Dissolve 50.0 mg of elemental sulfur in 1 liter of petroleum ether and keep tightly stoppered.

Calibration

With pipets introduce exactly 0, 0.5, 1.0, 2.0, 4.0, and 10.0 ml of the standard sulfur solution (0.050 mg/ml, sulfur) into separate 60-ml separatory funnels, dilute to 10 ml with petroleum ether, and proceed as directed below. Read the absorbance of the solutions containing 0, 0.025, 0.050, and 0.100 mg of sulfur in 5-cm cells and those containing 0.100, 0.200, and 0.500 mg of sulfur in 1-cm cells. Correct each absorbance by subtracting the absorbance of the 0 ml standard and calculate each absorptivity as follows:

$$a = \frac{(A)(V)}{(b)(w)}$$

where a = absorptivity
A = absorbance
b = cell length, cm
V = volume of solution in which color is developed, ml
w = weight of component being determined in the colored solution, mg

Average the absorptivities and use the average in calculating elemental sulfur contents.

Procedure

Sample Solution. Pipet or weigh a sample containing 0.1–3.0 mg of elemental sulfur into a 100-ml volumetric flask. Dissolve the sample and bring to volume with petroleum ether. Pipet 50 ml of this solution into a 100-ml stoppered graduated cylinder. Add 50 ml of the mercuric chloride solution, shake well, and allow the phases to separate. With a pipet, withdraw 10 ml of the top layer and transfer it to a 60-ml separatory funnel.

Color Development

To the separatory funnel add 10 ml of the 0.1% sodium cyanide solution, mix, and let stand 2 or 3 min. Add 3 ml of water, shake the funnel for 30 sec, and let the phases separate. Draw off the aqueous phase into a 25-ml volumetric flask. Again add 3 ml of water to the separatory funnel, shake the funnel about 30 sec, and draw off the aqueous phase into the same volumetric flask. Dilute the solution in the volumetric flask to about 20 ml with isopropyl alcohol and add 1 ml of the ferric nitrate solution. Dilute to volume with isopropyl alcohol, mix, and store in the dark. Measure the absorbance within 30 min at 470 mμ relative to isopropyl alcohol.

Calculation

Subtract the absorbance found for a blank determination from that found for the sample. Calculate the elemental sulfur content of the sample directly from the corrected absorbance using the established absorptivity as follows:

$$\text{elemental sulfur content, wt } \% = \frac{(A)(D)}{(a)(b)(W)(10)}$$

where D = the sample dilution factor and W = weight of sample, g.

The sample dilution factor, D, as used in the above calculations is best illustrated by an example: a sample is diluted to 100 ml, and 10 ml of this solution is taken for color development which is finally diluted to 25 ml. The sample dilution factor is as follows:

$$D = \frac{(100)(25)}{(10)} = 250$$

DETERMINATION OF NONTHIOPHENIC SULFUR

ALUMINA DECOMPOSITION METHOD

Apparatus

Catalytic desulfurization apparatus; a schematic diagram of the apparatus is given in Figure 16.3. A description of the components is given in the following sections.

Reaction tube, made of Pyrex glass and equipped with a pyrometer accurate to $\pm 5°C$. The tube is 370 mm long and consists of a catalyst section, 18-mm i.d. and 220 mm long, filled to a depth of 100–120 mm with alumina pellets. A glass wool plug is placed at the bottom of the catalyst section. The upper end of the reaction tube is fitted with a 24/40 joint, a 3-mm i.d. thermocouple well is placed near the top of the catalyst and the exit end is provided with a 12/5 spherical joint for connection to the absorber system. A 24/40 joint, fitted with a side arm and a 10/30 joint placed concentric with the reaction tube is used for the cap.

Lunge pipet, fitted with a 10/30 joint to fit the reaction tube cap. To balance the pressure in the pipet, the top of the pipet is connected to the bypass by a joint.

Absorber system: the first absorber consists of a 16-mm i.d. tube, 200 mm long, jacketed for circulation of water and fitted with a coarse gas dispersion thimble. The second absorber is a 250-ml, tall-form beaker. Tap water, cooled by passage through an iced copper coil, is circulated through the jacket of the first absorber; the second absorber is cooled by placing it in a container of ice.

Nitrogen purification system, consisting of a tubular electric furnace capable of maintaining a Pyrex tube containing wire-form metallic copper at a temperature of 300–350°C.

Potentiometric titration apparatus and electrodes.

Reagents

Titration solvent, from mercaptan method.

Alumina, Harshaw Alumina Catalyst Al-0104T, pellet size $\frac{1}{8}$ in., has generally been found satisfactory.

Ammonium hydroxide, CP concentrated (sp gr 0.90).

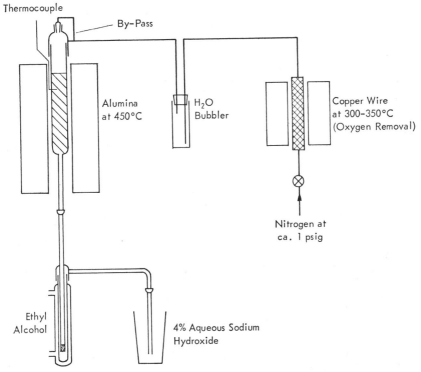

Figure 16.3. Schematic diagram of catalytic desulfurization apparatus. From McCoy & Weiss (3). Copyright 1954 by the American Chemical Society. Reprinted by permission of the copyright owner.

Ethyl alcohol, anhydrous. Formula 2B or 3A.
Isoamyl sulfide, 5% solution in sulfur-free white oil.
Silver nitrate solution, standard 0.1N.
Silver nitrate solution, standard 0.01N, alcoholic.
Sodium hydroxide solution, 4% aqueous.
Thiophene, 3% solution in sulfur-free white oil.

Apparatus Preparation

The reaction tube must be mounted vertically, the entire catalyst zone must be heated, and the pyrometer should be accurate to ±5°C. Other details are not considered critical. Pack the reaction tube to a depth of 10–12 cm with alumina catalyst and pass oxygen-free nitrogen through the system at a rate viewed in the bubbler of 3–5 bubbles/sec. Adjust the furnaces so that the reaction tube maintains a temperature of 450°C and the nitrogen purification system maintains a temperature of 300–350°C. Replace the catalyst with fresh catalyst daily and after each analysis of solid, highly viscous, or crude oil samples.

Catalyst Testing Procedure

Test each catalyst before use by passing a 3% solution of thiophene in white oil over the catalyst at 450°C and titrate the product as directed below. Make a second trial of the catalyst with a 5% solution of isoamyl sulfide in white oil. If the H_2S production is below 2% of the calculated sulfur content with thiophene and above 90% with isoamyl sulfide, accept the catalyst as satisfactory.

Procedure

Add 10 ml of ethyl alcohol to the first absorber, assemble the absorber, and attach it to the reaction tube. Place a 250-ml tall-form beaker containing 100 ml of 4% sodium hydroxide so that the exit tube from the first absorber dips nearly to the bottom of the beaker. Fill a Lunge pipet with sample, remove the plug from the reaction tube cap, place the plug in the ground joint provided on the top of the Lunge pipet, and place the weighed pipet in the reaction tube cap. Allow the system to purge for several minutes and add dropwise a quantity of sample, preferably containing 2–10 mg of nonthiophenic sulfur, dropping the sample directly onto the heated catalyst. Add the sample at such a rate that the catalyst temperature, measured near the top, does not drop over 10°C. Remove the pipet from the reaction tube and replace the plug.

Allow the system to purge for 30 min after addition of the last portion of sample, transfer the copper coil to a container of water at room temperature, and increase the nitrogen flow somewhat. Purge for an additional 5 min and remove the absorbers. Transfer the contents of the first absorber to a 250-ml tall-form beaker containing 100 ml of the titration solvent and rinse the absorber with a few milliliters of benzene. Potentiometrically titrate the contents of the first absorber with $0.01N$ alcoholic silver nitrate solution. Add 1 ml of ammonium hydroxide to the contents of the second absorber and potentiometrically titrate with $0.1N$ silver nitrate solution. Do not allow these solutions to stand more than a few minutes before titration.

Plot the cumulative volumes of silver nitrate solution added against the corresponding cell potentials and select the end points for mercaptans and hydrogen sulfide.

Calculation

Nonthiophenic Sulfur. Calculate the nonthiophenic sulfur content of the sample as follows:

$$\text{nonthiophenic sulfur, wt \%} = \frac{(V_1N_1 + V_2N_2)(1.6) + (V_3)(N_1)(3.2)}{W}$$

where V_1 = volume of silver nitrate solution, ml, required to titrate the hydrogen sulfide content of the first absorber

N_1 = normality of silver nitrate solution used to titrate the contents of the first absorber

V_2 = volume of silver nitrate solution, ml, required to titrate the hydrogen sulfide content of the second absorber

N_2 = normality of silver nitrate solution used to titrate the contents of the second absorber

V_3 = volume of silver nitrate solution, ml, required to titrate the mercaptan content of the first absorber

W = weight of sample, g

DETERMINATION OF SULFUR COMPOUNDS BY CHROMATOGRAPHY

Adsorption chromatography is used for the separation of sulfur compounds and to prepare concentrates for more detailed analysis by other techniques. In extensive studies, workers at the U.S. Bureau of Mines have found a preference for the use of alumina to obtain useful separations with petroleum fractions (1, 23). Earlier work involved a number of separation methods (24–26). Alumina was found (23) to be particularly useful since it accomplishes a resolution between aromatics and sulfur compounds and can be used to separate large amounts of materials from petroleum fractions for subsequent more detailed analyses.

The application of gas chromatography to the simple sulfur compounds of lower molecular weight is generally straightforward (27–30) and easily applied where the compounds are present in relatively high concentration in the sample and no serious interference is present. For more complex samples or compounds of higher molecular weight, a more intensive analytical concern may arise and, in these areas, some very interesting and useful methods have been developed that have wide areas of application.

The specific determination of sulfur compounds occurring either in very low concentrations or in complex materials has recently received considerable attention. Fredericks and Harlow (31) developed a technique for this purpose utilizing the automatic microcoulometer described in Chapter 21. Their application was for the separation and determination of the mercaptans present in sour natural gases and involved titration with silver ion using a silver–silver acetate electrode system. Hydrocarbons, of course, do not respond to this detection scheme and, since H_2S elutes early and can be vented, it is possible to determine the individual mercaptans in concentrations as low as 1 ppm in the presence of 30–50% H_2S. A thermal conductivity detector can be used in series with the microcoulometer and the results displayed on a two-pen recorder to provide a measure of both the hydrocarbons and the mercaptans. Such an example is shown in Figure 16.4, where the scale is 100:1 for the two recordings. Mercaptans being directly titratable with silver ion, it was not necessary in the work of Fredericks and Harlow (31) to subject the chromatographic effluent to further reaction and the gas stream was sent directly into the microcoulometer. Koppe and

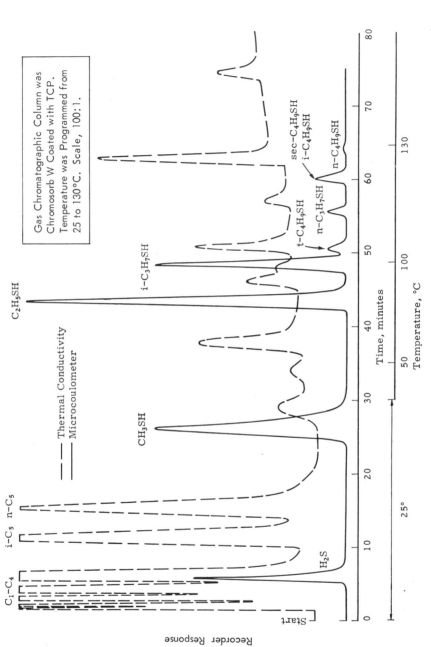

Figure 16.4. Chromatogram of condensate hydrocarbon–mercaptan mixture using two detectors. From Fredericks and Harlow (31). Copyright 1964 by the American Chemical Society. Reprinted by permission of the copyright owner.

Adams (32) used a bromine coulometric microtitration cell (33) to detect a larger variety of types of sulfur compounds and reported that this device allowed them to detect hydrogen sulfide, mercaptans, sulfur dioxide, organic sulfides, and disulfides since these compounds are all oxidized by bromine.

For application of the microcoulometric detector to the analysis of more complex sulfur compounds, Burchfield and his coworkers (34) have published a procedure in which the gas chromatographic effluent is hydrogenated at 950°C. In the drugs and pesticides with which they were concerned, combined chlorine and phosphorus were also occasionally present. Since the hydrogenation products, H_2S, HCl, and PH_3, all precipitate silver ion, it was recommended that specific adsorption tubes be introduced prior to the titration cell. For instance, a silica gel tube will remove HCl and an aluminum oxide tube will remove HCl plus H_2S. Examples are shown for specific determination of several complex materials.

It is also possible to measure sulfur selectively by oxidation to sulfur dioxide and titration by a modification of the microcoulometer in which iodine is generated for automatic conversion of the sulfur dioxide to sulfate ion. For this mode of operation the electrodes consist of a platinum anode sensor coupled with a platinum ‖ triiodide reference and a pair of platinum electrodes (anode and cathode) for generation. A typical cell reaction, using SO_2 as an example, is as follows:

$$I_3^- + SO_2 + H_2O \rightarrow SO_3 + 3I^- + 2H^+$$

The triiodide depletion in the electrolyte is detected by the reference/sensor electrodes and is replaced at the generator anode by current from the coulometer. The reaction is

$$3I^- \rightarrow I_3^- + 2e^-$$

Martin and Grant (35) obtained the sulfur compound distribution of a series of petroleum fractions by gas chromatography on a silicone rubber column. The eluent was oxidized and the sulfur dioxide determined by the microcoulometer. The sensitivity was such that individual sulfur compounds could be determined as low as 5 ppm. The strength of this measurement is illustrated by the data in Figure 16.5, where the sulfur compounds in gasoline are identified from elution times, which are correlated against known boiling points of pure compounds. In unrefined materials of higher boiling range and greater complexity of sulfur compounds, it is not possible to make specific assignments but some general assessments of the characteristics of the sulfur compounds could be made. Martin and Grant (35) and, later, Drushel (36) were able to obtain useful information in the characterization of aliphatic sulfides and thiophenes by passing the sample through a tube containing

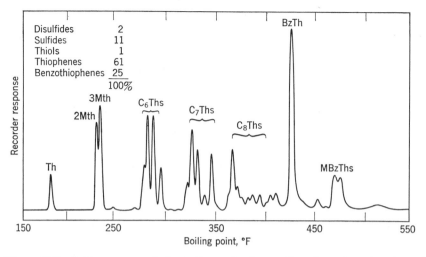

Figure 16.5. Sulfur compounds by boiling point in gasoline. Data from Martin and Grant (35), Copyright 1965 by the American Chemical Society. Reprinted by permission of the cogyright owner.

alumina at 600°C. As has been discussed earlier in this chapter, the aliphatic sulfides decompose to H_2S, although the thiophenes and condensed thiophenes do not lose sulfur under these conditions. Martin and Grant (35) found that thiophenic compounds are dealkylated and can then be separated according to the number of rings by gas chromatography.

Table 16.6. Products Obtained in the Hydrogenation of Pure Compounds by the Bureau of Mines Method[a].

Reactant	Temp., °C	Products
C_5H_7—S—⬡	215	n-Pentane, cyclohexane
H_5C_2—[thiophene]—C_2H_5	260	n-Octane
[benzothiophene]	155	Ethylcyclohexane
[benzothiophene]—CH_3	170	Isopropylcyclohexane

[a] Data from Thompson, Coleman, Ward and Rall (37).

SIMPLIFICATION OF ANALYSIS BY HYDROGENOLYSIS

The nonavailability of reference compounds above the C_8 range for any series of petroleum fractions except saturated and aromatic hydrocarbons severely limits the interpretation of gas chromatograms of higher boiling products containing atoms other than carbon and hydrogen. An important technique to reduce this limitation involves hydrogeneration to the corresponding hydrocarbons. This process, one of the more important aspects of "reaction gas chromatography" described in Chapter 21, provides a practical way in which the micro samples encountered in gas chromatography can be more readily identified after conversion to the carbon skeleton. An illustration of the application of this hydrogenation step to several pure sulfur compounds is shown in Table 16.6, taken from the work of Thompson, Coleman, Ward, and Rall (37). Further examples of this approach to the identification and determination of components in gas chromatographic separations are illustrated in Chapter 21.

REFERENCES

1. J. H. Hale, C. J. Thompson, M. G. Barker, H. M. Smith, and J. S. Ball, *Anal. Chem.* **23**, 287 (1951).
2. J. S. Ball, *U.S. Bur. Mines, Rept. Invest.*, 3591 (1941).
3. R. N. McCoy and F. T. Weiss, *Anal. Chem.*, **26**, 1928 (1954).
4. R. L. Hopkins, R. F. Kendall, C. J. Thompson, and H. J. Coleman, *ibid.*, **41**, 362 (1969).
5. J. H. Karchmer, in *Treatise on Analytical Chemistry*, Part II, Vol. 13, I. M. Kolthoff and P. J. Elving, Eds., Interscience, New York, 1966, pp. 337–517.
6. M. W. Tamele, L. B. Ryland, and R. N. McCoy, *Anal. Chem.*, **32**, 1007 (1960).
7. M. W. Tamele and L. R. Ryland, *Ind. Eng. Chem., Anal. Ed.*, **8**, 16 (1936).
8. M. W. Tamele, L. R. Ryland, and R. C. Irvine, *ibid.*, **13**, 618 (1941).
9. C. R. Stahl and S. Siggia, *Anal. Chem.*, **29**, 154 (1957).
10. I. M. Kolthoff, D. R. May, P. Morgan, H. A. Laitinen, and A. S. O'Brien, *Ind. Eng. Chem., Anal. Ed.*, **18**, 442 (1946).
11. F. P. Treadwell and W. T. Hall, *Analytical Chemistry*, Vol. II, Wiley, New York, 1935, p. 553.
12. W. F. Faragher, J. C. Morrell, and G. S. Monroe, *Ind. Eng. Chem.*, **19**, 1281 (1927).
13. J. H. Karchmer and M. T. Walker, *Anal. Chem.*, **30**, 85 (1958).
14. R. T. Bell and M. S. Agruss, *Ind. Eng. Chem., Anal. Ed.*, **13**, 297 (1941).
15. J. A. R. Coope and G. J. Maingot, *Anal. Chem.*, **27**, 1478 (1955).
16. R. L. Hubbard, W. E. Haines, and J. S. Ball, *ibid.*, **30**, 91 (1958).
17. I. El-Khiami and R. M. Johnson, *Talanta*, **14**, 745 (1967).
18. A. Zweig and A. K. Hoffman, *J. Org. Chem.*, **30**, 3997 (1965).
19. D. Kyriacou, *Nature*, **211**, 519 (1966).
20. R. Cecil and P. D. J. Weitzman, *Biochem. J.*, **93**, 1 (1964).

21. J. K. Bartlett and D. A. Skoog, *Anal. Chem.*, **26,** 1008 (1954).
22. D. A. Skoog and J. K. Bartlett, *ibid.*, **27,** 369 (1955).
23. H. J. Coleman, C. J. Thompson, R. L. Hopkins, and H. T. Rall, *J. Chromatog.*, **25,** 34 (1966).
24. O. L. Polly, A. C. Byrns, and W. E. Bradley, *Ind. Eng. Chem.*, **34,** 755 (1942).
25. D. Haresnape, F. A. Fidler, and R. A. Lowry, *ibid.*, **41,** 2691 (1949).
26. C. J. Thompson, H. J. Coleman, H. T. Rall, and H. M. Smith, *Anal. Chem.*, **27,** 175 (1955).
27. C. F. Spencer, F. Baumann, and J. F. Johnson, *ibid.*, **30,** 1473 (1958).
28. R. H. Bloembergen and C. Vermaak, *Erdol u. Kohle*, **18,** 185 (1965).
29. V. J. Farrugia and C. L. Jarreau, *Anal. Chem.*, **34,** 271 (1962).
30. D. Jenkins, L. L. Medsker, and J. F. Thomas, *Environmental Sci. Technol.*, **1,** 731 (1967).
31. E. M. Fredericks and G. A. Harlow, *Anal. Chem.*, **36,** 263 (1964).
32. R. K. Koppe and D. F. Adams, *Environmental Sci. Technol.*, **1,** 479 (1967).
33. D. F. Adams, G. A. Jensen, J. P. Steadman, R. K. Koppe, and T. J. Robertson, *Anal. Chem.*, **38,** 1094 (1966).
34. H. P. Burchfield, D. E. Johnson, J. W. Rhoades, and R. J. Wheeler, *J. Gas Chromatog.*, **3,** 28 (1965).
35. R. L. Martin and J. A. Grant, *Anal. Chem.*, **37,** 644, 649 (1965).
36. H. V. Drushel, *ibid.*, **41,** 569 (1969).
37. C. J. Thompson, H. J. Coleman, C. C. Ward, and H. T. Rall, *ibid.*, **32,** 424 (1960).

PART TWO

Analysis of Materials

APPLICATION OF ANALYTICAL
METHODS TO POLYMERS

The analytical chemist will encounter polymeric samples for examination as well as organic compounds of lower molecular weight. In the general application of functional methods, be they chemical or spectroscopic, there is little difference in principle between the two types of samples. The difference in the handling of polymers, due to a need for specific solvents in some cases, gives the appearance of complexity in analysis. This is, however, not the case and consequently, no differentiation is made in this text between the functional analysis of polymers and that of lower molecular weight materials except in the techniques for preparing the samples for analysis.

Several review texts are available that describe the techniques for analysis of polymers. These include works by Allen (1), Ke (2), and Kline (3). Good coverage is provided for such analytical topics as infrared absorption spectroscopy, electron diffraction, X-ray measurements, optical rotatory dispersion, column fractionation, and interpretation of nuclear magnetic resonance spectra. The three-volume set edited by Kline (3) is especially useful in that specific methods for the determination of functional groups and components are described under each of many classifications of polymers, and detailed information is given on the scope and applicability of the techniques themselves.

FUNCTIONAL ANALYSIS OF POLYMERS
WITH CHEMICAL REAGENTS

That chemical reagents may be employed with functional groups in polymer molecules is due to the small influence of molecular size on the kinetics in functional reactivity. In a review of the chemical reactivity of polymeric systems, Flory (4) showed that the intrinsic reactivity of a functional group is independent of molecular size except when the molecules are quite small. Rate constants are available for the esterification of a series of normal monobasic acids and for the saponification of some of the corresponding esters, which show (see Table 17.1) that, once the chain length exceeds three C atoms, no change in rate is observed even to quite large

Table 17.1. Effect of Molecular Size on Rates of Reaction Data for saturated straight-chain monocarboxylic acids. (Rate constants expressed as liters/mole-sec.)

Carbon No. of acid	Rate of esterification of acids[a]	Rate of saponification of esters[b]
2 (Acetic)	22.1	69.5
3	15.3	35.5
4	7.5	18.3
5	7.4	19.2
6	7.4	20.7
7		17.9
8		18.4
9	7.5	
10	7.5	
12	7.5	
14	7.5	
16	7.6	
18	7.6	
22	7.6	
22[c]	7.7	

[a] $K_s \times 10^4$ at 25°C, from P. J. Flory, *Principles of Polymer. Chemistry*, Cornell University Press, Ithaca, N.Y., 1953, p. 71 and B. V. Bhide and J. J. Sudborough, *J. Indian Inst. Sci.*, **8A**, 89 (1925).

[b] Rates at 25°C, from L. P. Hammett, *Physical Organic Chemistry*, McGraw-Hill, New York, 1940, p. 12.

[c] Data for erucic acid.

numbers of n. The data for esterification rate of erucic acid

$$[CH_3(CH_2)_7CH:CH(CH_2)_{11}CO_2H]$$

indicates that an olefinic linkage some distance from the carboxyl group has no effect on reaction rates. The data show that branching in the molecule greatly reduces the reaction rate; the more extensive the branching the greater the reduction in rate. In any regular series, when other variables are kept constant there is no effect of molecular weight on reaction rates.

From the practical analytical standpoint the result of these arguments is that many of the usual chemical reagents can be employed to determine functional groups in resinous and polymeric materials. It is the practical experience of many analysts that functional groups in polymers can often be readily determined by a number of the common methods. An illustration of the applicability of several of the methods discussed in this text is shown in Table 17.2 for the α-epoxy, hydroxyl, ester, and carbonyl functions. A comparison of the reaction conditions required for the determination of these functional groups in resins and polymers with the conditions used for compounds of low molecular weight indicates that the procedural differences are often quite small. The somewhat lower reactivity observed in some cases with polymers could be attributed to the higher viscosity of the polymer solutions.

It must be pointed out, however, that the simple relationship developed by Flory does not apply universally because in some reactions of polymers there are steric restraints that are not present in the simple molecules (5) and, also, polymers in solution are not necessarily in the fully extended form (6). Baines and Bevington (7) carried out a ^{14}C tracer study of the hydrolysis of methyl acrylate and methyl methacrylate under alkaline conditions. They found that methyl acrylate units were hydrolyzed rapidly and completely but that, under the same conditions, only about 9% of the ester groups in methyl methacrylate reacted. They concluded that the resistance of methyl methacrylate to hydrolysis depended upon steric factors and the environment within the polymer chain.

In the application of chemical methods to polymer analysis it is often important to avoid aqueous titration because many polymeric materials can be thrown out of solution by water. Consequently, nonaqueous methods of analysis may frequently be preferred as with the HBr–Acetic Acid method for the determination of the α-epoxy group, the $LiAlH_4$ method for the determination of the hydroxyl group, and the Fischer Carbonyl method.

Table 17.2. Reaction Conditions Required for Chemical Determination of Functional Groups in Polymers

		Reaction conditions	
Determination	Method	Low molecular weight compounds	Polymers
α-Epoxy	HBr–acetic acid method	Direct titration; room temp	Direct titration; room temp for epoxy resins with mol wt $\geq$ 3000
Hydroxyl	$LiAlH_4$ method	20–30 min at 0°C	30–150 min at 0°C for EPON resins with mol wt $\geq$ 3000
Ester	Saponification method	30 min to 3 hr at reflux	1–3 hr at reflux for allyl acetate and vinyl acetate copolymers of mol wt 6000–8000
Carbonyl	Fischer carbonyl method	2 hr at 60°C for most low mol wt compounds	4 hr at 60°C for polyacroleins of mol wt $\geq$ 100,000

Another illustration of the application of nonaqueous methods for polymer analysis is the work of Kirby and Baldwin (8) on the potentiometric determination of acid groups in acrylic polymers. The polymer was dissolved in a mixture of ethylene carbonate and propylene carbonate and the acidity titrated with $0.1N$ tetramethylammonium hydroxide reagent in the same solvent mixture. A platinum electrode system gave stable e.m.f. measurements and the system permitted the investigators to distinguish strong from weak acids at concentration levels of 20–50 μeq of acid per gram of polymer.

A particularly interesting review of the use of chemical reactions for the modification of polymer structures to aid in the analysis and characterization of polymers has been published by Harwood (9). Since derived structures may often be the more readily analyzed, both for low molecular weight and polymeric molecules, it is sometimes advantageous to employ chemical conversions prior to analysis. In fact, as Harwood clearly points out, this idea is not all new and some of his early references (10–12) are the work of many years ago in which polyvinyl acetate was saponified to polyvinyl alcohol and the latter characterized. Interconversions are valuable in the analysis of polymethacrylates, polymethacrylonitriles, and some of the polyhalocarbons, among others. The technique has a wide scope and Harwood provides over 160 references covering published work with many polymers.

ANALYSIS OF POLYMERS BY SPECTROSCOPIC METHODS

The two most useful spectroscopic methods for the analysis of polymers are infrared absorption and proton nuclear magnetic resonance (NMR) spectroscopy. In each of these areas of spectroscopy, the type of publications vary from those basically theoretical to those that are essentially practical. Particularly since the advent in the past decade of highly stereoregular polymers it is now possible to make valence force calculations of the vibrational frequencies and unambiguously assign infrared band locations to polymer molecular structures (13, 14). A number of practical texts are available providing directions for the spectroscopic (and other) analysis of polymeric materials. Haslam and Willis (15) cover the infrared techniques, measurements, and interpretations. Hummel (16) has assembled a considerable number of spectra of commercial polymers, and some plasticizers, in the usual and the far-infrared absorption regions. A discussion of the experimental techniques and the significance of spectroscopic data are also presented by Hummel. A volume entitled *Characterization of Macromolecular Structure* (17) describes work in determination of the molecular weight and size of high polymers by solution techniques.

The application of NMR spectroscopy to polymers is a more recent development but one that shows great promise. For instance, it is possible to show a quantitative difference between natural *cis-* and *trans*-1,4-polyisoprenes (18). The methyl group protons, adjacent to the double bond, have peaks at significantly different resonance positions in the *cis* and *trans* structures. A synthetic polyisoprene can be analyzed in regard to its *cis/trans* ratio by measuring the relative area of the two peaks. Kern and Schaefer (19) were able to determine monomer distributions in a series of copolymers prepared from propylene oxide and maleic anhydride by closely studying the high resolution NMR spectra. Ethylene copolymers with vinyl acetate or ethyl acrylate can be quantitatively analyzed by NMR since the proton peaks are well separated for the various structures (20).

NMR spectroscopy, especially with high resolution instruments, provides an extremely useful tool for determination of the stereochemistry of high molecular weight polymers. Bovey and Tiers (21) found that the spectra of various types of methyl methacrylate polymers, in chloroform solution, show three α-methyl proton peaks. These have been attributed to the three classifications in which the substituent groups can be oriented in space: isotactic, syndiotactic, and heterotactic. The isotactic configuration has been defined (22) to be that in which the successive carbon atoms in the chain are in the same repeating steric order while in the syndiotactic structure these have opposite steric configurations around the successive carbon atoms in the main chain. The heterotactic (or atactic) structure has a completely random order. The application of nuclear magnetic resonance to the differentiation of the stereochemical configuration of polymers has been reviewed by Bovey (23), Ramey and Brey (24), and Woodbrey (25).

Correlations between chemical and spectroscopic methods have been developed by a number of investigators for the determination of functional ·groups in polymers. The chemical methods are generally stoichiometric and can be used to calibrate the spectroscopic results. This approach is particularly useful where the polymer may undergo a "curing" process and become insoluble. Dannenberg and Harp (26) were able to measure the α-epoxy content of resins in the infrared by calibration against the HCl–Dioxane method (see Chapter 12) in a series of samples and then use the infrared absorptivities to determine the rate and extent of the "cure." It has been shown (27) that a useful correlation exists between an infrared method and a chemical method for the determination of the carboxyl group concentration in copolymers of butadiene and acrylic acid. The acid content of a series of these copolymers was determined by dissolving small pieces of the polymer in pyridine and titrating with $0.1N$ standard alcoholic potassium hydroxide. The chemical method was slow since solution in pyridine required a shaking period of 16 hr. On the other hand, the infrared method was rapid since thin films were found to be satisfactory for spectroscopic analysis. The C=O group has an absorption band at 5.88 μ that is easily observed. Since the amount of polymer in the light beam is variable, the most accurate measurement is by means of the ratio of this band to other distinct bands in the spectra. A linear relationship was found between absorbance ratio (5.88 μ/10.98 μ) and titration results for a series of polymers. It is possible, therefore, to prepare a calibration curve and employ the infrared method for determination of the carboxylic content.

An interesting comparison of results by chemical and spectroscopic measurements was reported by Forbes and Schissler (28) in the examination of polyacroleins of molecular weights above 100,000. Some polyacroleins can be in equilibrium with water, as shown in this typical reaction:

$$
\begin{array}{ccc}
\text{CH}_2 & & \text{CH}_2 \quad \text{CH}_2 \\
& \rightleftharpoons & \text{CH} \quad \text{CH} \quad + \text{H}_2\text{O} \\
\text{HO} \quad \text{O} \quad \text{OH} & & \text{CHO} \quad \text{CHO}
\end{array}
$$

When the Fischer–Carbonyl method (Chapter 6) is applied to these samples the equilibrium is shifted to the right and gives results that do not represent the actual sample. However, infrared absorption (at 5.83 μ) measures only the free carbonyl groups and consequently provides an accurate picture of sample composition. For the polyacroleins that were not soluble without structural change, the samples were suspended in Fluorolube and the absorptivity calibrated against a sample of poly-α-methylstyrene–acrolein copolymer whose carbonyl content had been established by the Fischer method.

DETERMINATION OF END GROUPS IN POLYMERS

An important aspect of the determination of functional groups in polymers has been for the purpose of "end group" analysis. If the functionality of the polymer is known, end group analysis can provide a value for the molecular weight, and, conversely, if the molecular weight is known from an independent physical measurement, end group analysis provides information on the functionality. Bonnar, Dimbat, and Stross (29) discuss in detail the physical methods for molecular weight determination and, in addition, discuss the application of functional methods to polymers that have characteristic end groups. For example, the free amino groups at the ends of a nylon chain were determined by titration with perchloric acid. It was assumed that one free primary amino group was present per molecule and a value of 11,000 was calculated for the molecular weight, which was close to the results obtained cryoscopically (10,000). Any procedure that obtains a measure of the distinctive end groups can be employed for this determination. For polymers with hydroxyl, carboxyl, or olefinic end groups, the general methods detailed in the functional chapters can often be used. For clean systems, infrared absorption spectroscopy is valuable because it is easily calibrated and is rapid and direct. The usual chemical methods are not well suited for the high molecular weight polymers because of the low concentration of the end groups in these materials. A much more sensitive approach is the use of a radiochemical determination. Trotman and Szwarc (30) determined the molecular weight of "living" polystyrene by terminating the polymerization reaction with $^{14}CO_2$. The polymer produced by this reaction thus contained radioactive carboxyl groups, which could be counted by the usual techniques. With the materials examined, molecular weights of the order of 17,000 were found, which agreed with other measurements. The general possibilities of the radiochemical method have been discussed by Bevington (31); an interesting suggestion is that hydroxyl end groups could be determined after esterification with ^{14}C-benzoyl chloride. Because of the high sensitivity available, the radiochemical approach has promise for obtaining precise results for the end group analysis of polymers of quite high molecular weight.

An interesting series of investigations has been conducted by Palit and his co-workers in which end groups are determined by dye partition. These techniques are simple and rapid and are sufficiently sensitive to be used for the characterization of the end groups in vinyl polymers of high molecular weight (32–35). The methods depend upon the reaction of ionizable groups in polymers with certain dyestuffs. The principle of the reaction is well known with surface-active agents and is described in detail in Chapter 19. An illustration can be given of its use for a polymer of methyl methacrylate prepared with persulfate as an initiator and thus containing the $ROSO_3^-$ end group. The end group can be made to react with methylene blue yielding a chloroform-soluble product of the polymer and dye.

$$R—OSO_3^-Na^+ + \text{methylene blue·Cl}^- \rightarrow$$
$$(R—OSO_3^-·\text{methylene blue}^+) + NaCl$$

The methylene blue complex partitions into the chloroform layer to an extent equivalent to the number of $R—O—SO_3^-$ groups present in the polymer. Variations using different dyes and changing the pH permit the determination of polymers carrying carboxylic acid end groups. Free hydroxyl end groups can be converted to strong acid groups by reaction with chlorosulfonic acid or by the partial esterification of a dibasic acid.

ANALYSIS OF POLYMERS BY DESTRUCTIVE MEANS

Some of the valuable aspects of gas chromatography in elucidation of the components of organic mixtures can be obtained with polymers by employing a decomposition reaction followed by determination of the products. A number of possible decomposition reactions can be considered to yield distinctive materials that can be used for the detailed characterization of a polymer by subsequent gas chromatography. To be useful the decomposition process must be easily controlled, repeatable, and capable of producing volatile compounds by direct breakdown without extensive isomerization or secondary reactions. Successful decomposition procedures have been published based either upon chemical reagents or upon pyrolysis of the polymers. For certain condensation polymers, chemical reactions provide a facile route to a directed decomposition and the production of simple and volatile structures. As is described in Chapter 7, it is possible to conduct transesterification on a polymer containing an ester function to yield volatile methyl esters. In this way Jankowski and Garner (36) were able to determine the combined acids, as their methyl esters, in commercial polyester fibers. Although the chemical methods are of value, their usefulness is limited to polymers bearing reactive groups. A much more general approach is that involving controlled thermal breakdown of the polymer.

Some years ago Davison, Slaney, and Wragg (37) of the Dunlop Research Center showed that it was possible to pyrolyze polymers at 650°C and analyze the volatile portion of the collected product by gas chromatography. By this pyrolysis technique, characteristic fingerprints were obtained from several important commercial polymers. A few years after this publication, Lehrle and Robb (38) showed that it was possible to pyrolyze a polymer directly in the inlet of the GC column and obtain useful chromatographic data. Since then a number of publications have appeared on the application of this direct technique, illustrating its usefulness for polymer identification and

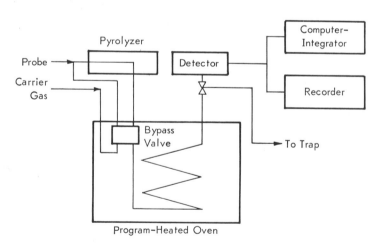

Figure 17.1. Schematic diagram of pyrolysis-GC instrument. Data from Dimbat and Eggertsen (4). Copyright 1965 by Academic Press. Reprinted by permission of the copyright owner.

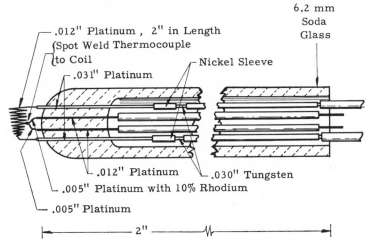

Figure 17.2.   Filament pyrolyzer. Data from Dimbat and Eggertsen (41). Copyright 1965 by Academic Press. Reprinted by permission of the copyright owner.

for quantitative determination of monomer contents. A general study covering a wide variety of applications of the technique has been published by Groten (39), who showed that a pyrolysis analysis could provide a quantitative determination of types and components in many polymers. Yasuda (40) employed a hydrogenation step following pyrolysis to simplify the analysis of the products from a number of commercial polymers including polymethyl methacrylate, natural rubber, neoprene, and polyethylene. Dimbat and Eggertsen (41) have published the description of a useful pyrolysis assembly, shown in Figure 17.1 as a schematic diagram. The filament pyrolyzer is shown in detail in Figure 17.2. Pyrolysis takes place in the conical platinum filament. In a typical experiment 0.1 mg of a solid polymer would be applied to the filament and the filament then placed in the pyrolysis inlet. Close temperature control can be achieved and it is possible to obtain heating rates from 1.6°C/min to 300°C/sec. Very repeatable pyrograms were obtained by Simon and his coworkers (42, 43) using the Curie point to obtain accurately controlled temperatures. The principle of this technique is that ferromagnetic properties are lost at an exact and definable temperature, the Curie point, for iron and nickel and their alloys. Above this temperature the wire cannot be heated by the absorption of electromagnetic radiation through an induction process, whereas below the Curie point induction heating is rapid. With this system, the surface temperature of the pyrolysis wire rises rapidly because the total induction energy is taken into the wire surface until it loses its ferromagnetic properties and thus rapidly achieves a high specific temperature. Willmott (44) found that a Curie point pyrolyzer provided the close temperature control to differentiate and identify a series of polyolefin homopolymers and copolymers having similar properties. The pyrolysis gases are usually swept by the carrier gas (generally H_2) into the gas chromatographic section. To simplify the characterization of the cracked products, it is preferable to hydrogenate olefins to saturates, which, of course, produces a single paraffin from all olefins with the same carbon skeleton. Dimbat and Eggertsen (41) made the hydrogenation catalyst an integral part of the column packing by mixing PtO_2 (3 wt %) with the column packing. The PtO_2 forms a uniform coating on the stationary phase and is reduced to Pt metal catalyst by the hydrogen carrier gas after the column is packed. When operated around 100°C, neither the column efficiency nor the order of elution is affected by the presence of Pt metal. Under these conditions, hydrogenation of olefin bonds is complete in the column but aromatics appear to be untouched. The hydrogen flame detector is recommended because of its high sensitivity; however, it does have a disadvantage in that it does not respond to nonhydrocarbons such as water and the carbon oxides. When these compounds are to be determined, the thermal conductivity detector is generally employed.

To determine the microstructure of polymers it is generally desirable to look for "index peaks" that can be determined as specific individual compounds. These can often be the original monomers used in preparing the polymer since monomer yields in a pyrogram may be appreciable. Yasuda (40) finds that rubber samples provide these characteristic products:

Type of rubber	Characteristic products
Polyisoprenes	2-Methyl-1,3-butadiene
Butyl rubber	Isobutylene, isobutane, 2,2-dimethylpropane
Neoprene	2-Chloro-1,3-butadiene

Thorough analysis of the hydrocarbon patterns obtained from the pyrolysis–hydrogenation of saturated hydrocarbon polymers has been made by van Schooten and Evenhuis (45) and Schatzki (46), who have been able to derive a mechanism for thermal pyrolysis. The decompositions involve initial thermal cracking to hydrocarbon radicals that can undergo a series of secondary reactions to eliminate olefins by a scission process. Radical transfer reactions can take place prior to the olefin decomposition process, or radicals can combine to give linear or branched hydrocarbons, either of low molecular weight or polymeric. To simplify the gas chromatographic analysis of the pyrolysate, the products were hydrogenated prior to chromatography. The pyrograms obtained were quite reproducible when apparatus conditions were held constant. Table 17.3 lists the principal peaks found for linear polyethylene and for polypropylene. As expected, the pyrolysis spectra

Table 17.3. Pyrolysis Spectra of Polyethylene and Polypropylene[a]
Pyrolysis conditions: 20°/sec heating to 550°C

Product,[b]	Linear polyethylene[c]	Isotactic polypropylene[d]
Methane} Ethane }	19.6	11.4
Propane	19.6	38.0
Isobutane		5.4
n-Butane	9.9	
n-Pentane	6.3	12.0
2-Methylpentane		7.9
n-Hexane	12.9	
2,4-Dimethylpentane		1.8
n-Heptane	7.6	
Methylcyclohexane	0.8	
4-Methylheptane		1.4
n-Octane	4.9	
2,4-Dimethylheptane		22.0
n-Nonane	3.9	
n-Decane	5.8	
n-Undecane	4.8	
n-Dodecane	3.7	

[a] Data from Schatzki (46).
[b] Saturates obtained after hydrogenation.
[c] Data normalize $C_1-C_{12} = 100\%$.
[d] Data normalize $C_1-C_9 = 100\%$.

consist of normal paraffins with a large preponderance of ethane and hexane. The polypropylene spectrum contains branched paraffins and the amounts of the various products can be predicted in at least an approximate fashion. These data indicate the analytical use of detailed pyrolysis spectra for distinguishing polymers in admixtures. An analysis of this nature has been reported by Bombaugh, Cook, and Clampitt (47), who studied the comonomer distribution in ethylene-acrylate and ethylene-methacrylate copolymers by pyrolysis and gas chromatography. With ethylene–methyl methacrylate copolymers, the fraction of methyl methacrylate that appeared as monomer in the pyrogram (based on the total methyl methacrylate polymerized) was found to decrease with increasing randomness of distribution of the methyl methacrylate in the polymer. This was attributed to the presumption that, wherever ethylene–methyl methacrylate junctions occur, new materials could be formed due to carbon–carbon bonds breaking other than at the original monomer units. Consequently, random copolymers produced a much lower yield of methyl methacrylate monomer than did mixtures of

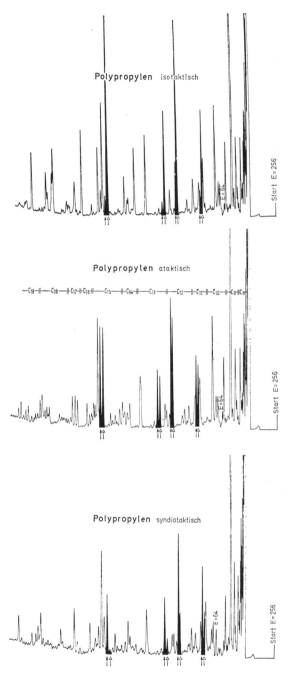

Figure 17.3. Pyrolysis-gas chromatography of polypropylenes of various tactic tacticities. From Noffz, Benz, and Pfab (49). Zeit. Anal. Chem., Volume 235, pages 121–137 (1968). Reprinted with permission of the copyright owner.

homopolymers or graft copolymers. A review of pyrolysis–gas chromatography and its application to many polymeric materials has been published by Groten (48).

A particularly interesting contribution was published by Noffz, Benz, and Pfab (49), who pyrolyzed a number of commercial polymers and noted that polypropylenes yielded chromatograms that differed according to the stereoclassification of the polymer. According to the definitions given earlier for the isotactic, syndiotactic, and heterotactic forms, different pyrolysis products could be expected for those molecules containing at least two asymmetric centers. Thus, isotactic polypropylene would give fragments having the same stereoconfiguration such that they would be *dd* or *ll* or *ddd* or *lll*. Syndiotactic polypropylene would give fragments in which the alternating configuration was present, such as *ld* or *ldl* or *dld*. With highly efficient gas chromatographic columns it is possible to separate a *dd* hydrocarbon from its *ld* isomer. Of course, *dd* and *ll* isomers have identical chemical properties and are not directly separable. The data obtained by Noffz, Benz, and Pfab, shown in Figure 17.3, illustrate that a polypropylene that was chiefly isotactic produced a series of C_{11}–C_{15} hydrocarbon pairs in the reverse ratio to the pairs found with a syndiotactic polypropylene, just as would be anticipated from the stereochemical argument. As would also be anticipated, the heterotactic polypropylene produced a scrambled series in which the ratio was nearly one.

REFERENCES

1. P. W. Allen, *Techniques of Polymer Characterization*, Butterworths, London, 1959.
2. B. Ke, Ed., *Newer Methods of Polymer Characterization*, Interscience, New York, 1964.
3. G. M. Kline, *Analytical Chemistry of Polymers*, Vol. 1–3, Interscience, New York, 1959–1962.
4. P. J. Flory, *Principles of Polymer Chemistry*, Cornell University Press, Ithaca, N.Y., 1953, p. 69.
5. H. Morawetz, *Macromolecules in Solution*, Interscience, New York, 1965, p. 425.
6. N. G. Gaylord, *J. Polymer Sci.*, C, **24**, 1 (1968).
7. F. C. Baines and J. C. Bevington, *J. Polymer Sci.*, A-1, **6**, 2433 (1968).
8. J. R. Kirby and A. J. Baldwin, *Anal. Chem.*, **40**, 689 (1968).
9. H. J. Harwood, *Angew. Makromol. Chem.*, **4/5**, 279 (1968).
10. H. Staudinger, R. Frey, and W. Stark, *Ber.*, **60**, 1782 (1927).
11. H. Staudinger and H. Warth, *J. Prakt. Chem.*, **155**, 261 (1940).
12. W. O. Hermans and W. Haehnel, *Ber.*, **60**, 1658 (1927).
13. R. G. Snyder and J. H. Schachtschneider, *Spectrochim. Acta*, **20**, 853 (1964).
14. J. H. Schachtschneider and R. G. Snyder, *ibid.*, **21**, 1527 (1965).

15. J. Haslam and A. A. Willis, *Identification and Analysis of Plastics*, Van Nostrand, Princeton, N.J., 1965.
16. D. O. Hummel, *Infrared Spectra of Polymers*, Interscience, New York, 1966.
17. Publication 1573, National Academy of Sciences, Washington, D.C., 1968.
18. M. A. Golub, S. A. Fuqua, and N. S. Bhacca, *J. Am. Chem. Soc.*, **84**, 4981 (1962).
19. R. J. Kern and J. Schaefer, *ibid.*, **89**, 6 (1967).
20. R. S. Porter, S. W. Nicksic, and J. F. Johnson, *Anal. Chem.*, **35**, 1948 (1963).
21. F. A. Bovey and G. V. D. Tiers, *J. Polymer Sci.*, **44**, 173 (1960).
22. M. L. Huggins, G. Natta, V. Desreux, and H. Mark, *ibid.*, **56**, 153 (1962).
23. F. A. Bovey, *Accounts Chem. Res.*, **1**, 175 (1968).
24. K. C. Ramey and W. J. Brey, *J. Macromol. Sci.—Rev. Macromol. Chem.*, C1(2), 263 (1967).
25. J. C. Woodbrey, in *The Stereochemistry of Macromolecules*, Vol. III, A. D. Ketley, Ed., Marcel Dekker, New York, 1968, pp. 61–147.
26. H. Dannenberg and W. R. Harp, Jr., *Anal. Chem.*, **28**, 86 (1956).
27. A. J. Scism, *Anal. Chim. Acta*, **42**, 177 (1968).
28. J. W. Forbes and D. O. Schissler, *J. Polymer Sci.*, C, **8**, 61 (1965).
29. R. U. Bonnar, M. Dimbat, and F. H. Stross, *Number-Average Molecular Weights*, Interscience, New York, 1958.
30. J. Trotman and M. Szwarc, *Makromol. Chem.*, **37**, 39 (1960).
31. J. C. Bevington, *ibid.*, **34**, 152 (1959).
32. S. R. Palit and B. H. Mandal, *J. Macromol. Sci.—Rev. Macromol. Chem.*, C2, 225 (1968).
33. S. R. Palit, *Makromol. Chem.*, **36**, 89 (1960).
34. S. R. Palit, *ibid.*, **38**, 96 (1960).
35. S. R. Palit and A. R. Mukherjee, *J. Polymer Sci.*, **58**, 1243 (1962).
36. S. J. Jankowski and P. Garner, *Anal. Chem.*, **37**, 1709 (1965).
37. W. H. T. Davison, S. Slaney, and A. L. Wragg, *Chem. Ind. (London)*, **44**, 1356 (1954).
38. R. S. Lehrle and J. C. Robb, *Nature*, **183**, 1671 (1959).
39. B. Groten, *Anal. Chem.*, **36**, 1206 (1964).
40. S. K. Yasuda, *J. Chromatog.*, **27**, 72 (1967).
41. M. Dimbat and F. T. Eggertsen, *Microchem. J.* **9**, 500 (1965).
42. W. Simon and H. Giacobbo, *Angew. Chem., Intern. Ed.*, **4**, 938 (1965).
43. W. Simon, P. Kriemler, J. A. Voellmin, and H. Steiner, *J. Gas Chromatog.*, **5**, 53 (1967).
44. F. W. Willmott, in *Advances in Chromatography*, A. Zlatkis, Ed., Preston Technical Abstracts Co., Evanston, Ill. 1969, p. 222.
45. J. van Schooten and J. K. Evenhuis, *Polymer*, **6**, 343, 561 (1965).
46. T. Schatzki, in press.
47. K. J. Bombaugh, C. E. Cook, and B. H. Clampitt, *Anal. Chem.*, **35**, 1834 (1963).
48. B. Groten, in *Gas Effluent Analysis*, W. Lodding, Ed., Marcel Dekker, New York, 1967, pp. 101–142.
49. D. Noffz, W. Benz, and W. Pfab, *Z. Anal. Chem.*, **235**, 121 (1968).

TRACE ANALYSIS

Trace analysis is considered to be the determination of a component or components in a sample vastly diluted by other materials. Many methods have been used for trace analysis; to put some of these methods into the proper perspective, the principal techniques used for the trace analysis of organic compounds have been listed in Table 18.1. To allow full consideration of a method of choice, comparisons are made on several critical points. The first comparison is based on the minimum number of grams of a component actually required for its firm and meaningful determination. The

Table 18.1. Characteristics of Principal Methods Used for Determination of Traces of Organic Compounds

Method	Selectivity factors		
	Sensitivity as minimum grams of component actually required for analysis[a]	Maximum sample weight, g	Selectivity, (component desired)/ (sample weight), ppm
Titration methods	10^{-4}	10	10
Spectroscopic techniques			
Proton NMR	10^{-4}	0.2	500
Mass spectrometric	10^{-9} to 10^{-10}	10^{-4}	10–100
Infrared	10^{-5}	0.1	100
Ultraviolet	10^{-6} to 10^{-7}	1	0.1–1
Biological methods	10^{-5} to 10^{-7}	10^{-2}	10
Colorimetric methods	10^{-6} to 10^{-7}	0.1	1–10
Chromatographic techniques			
Paper	10^{-7}	10^{-3}	100
Thin-layer	10^{-8}	10^{-3}	10
GLC	10^{-6} to 10^{-10}	10^{-3}	1
Electrochemical methods			
Polarographic	5×10^{-9}	10^{-2}	1
Coulometry	10^{-9}	10^{-1}	0.1
Radiotracer methods (^{14}C)	10^{-11} to 10^{-12}	1	parts per billion and less

[a] Calculated for determination of a material taken to be 100 molecular weight.

values in this column are often considered to be the *sensitivity* of the method. The next comparison is based on the mass of sample that can be handled effectively and with good resolution under normal procedures; this could also be called *loading capacity*. The final column is derived from the ratio of the previous two columns and is designated *selectivity*, perhaps the most critical feature of a trace method, since it indicates the ability of a method to provide a useful minimum value for the component in a real system. The development of the information in Table 18.1 is based on the characteristics of the methods in general application to organic samples and yields values that are necessarily approximate but should provide some assistance to the analyst in ordering the utility of the methods. The selectivity can often be increased, sometimes by several orders of magnitude, by the application of separating techniques to the sample prior to the determination of the desired component. However, these additional separating procedures require effort and add to the length of the determination. Other factors in the choice of a trace method will include a consideration of its applicability and limitations in actual systems, and this area of concern is dealt with in the functional chapters. The choice of the suitability of individual methods will vary with the availability of equipment to the laboratory. Fortunately, commercial gas chromatographic equipment, which provides high sensitivity and selectivity, is in use in many laboratories. A number of the colorimetric methods are quite selective and can be applied with equipment that is generally available and not particularly expensive. Some of the more sophisticated approaches, such as the combined use of gas chromatography and mass spectrometry, are quite expensive and will be available only to a limited number of laboratories.

The most sensitive and selective of the trace methods are techniques involving the use of radiotracers. The preparation of radioactive compounds with a high level of activity can be used to increase materially the sensitivity and selectivity of the trace methods. Other highly selective and sensitive methods are the gas chromatographic, ultraviolet, and colorimetric methods. The need for a sensitive technique in the final determination cannot be over-stressed. It is impossible to develop a truly successful method for trace analysis unless the final measurement is one of high sensitivity. For example, the high sensitivity of the GLC and the radiotracer methods make them eminently suitable for this purpose. In many cases, efficient separation methods can also add materially to the selectivity and success of any trace analysis. The general subject of trace analysis has received a great deal of attention from many investigators who have been concerned with inorganic materials, with organic compounds, and with determination of the elements. Specific references for the determination of traces of organic compounds in a number of systems are given in later sections of this chapter. Some useful general discussions have been published by Morrison (1) and by Meinke and Scribner (2), who review techniques and equipment for trace analysis. These volumes have particularly good coverage of the electrochemical methods as well as discussions of spectroscopic and microscopic techniques, although the applications for the latter tend to be principally for inorganic systems.

"Trace analysis" and "microanalysis" although often considered to be similar are in reality very much different. In each case a small amount of material is being sought. In trace analysis this small amount is diluted by a thousandfold to perhaps a millionfold with other components. In micro-analysis the small amount is present alone or at least in a high concentration. For trace analysis a number of the chemical methods are particularly useful, whereas for microanalysis the physical methods are generally preferred. The reason for the preference for the physical methods is quite apparent from consideration of the sample requirements given in Table 18.1. Of the methods listed, the mass spectrometer has the smallest sample requirement for nonradioactive compounds and is therefore particularly desirable for the truly micro samples that arise from gas–liquid chromatography. Commercial equipment is available for trapping fractions from gas chromatography and for their analysis by the several spectroscopic techniques. Particularly interesting is the direct coupling of a mass spectrometer to the outlet of a capillary GC column. Commercial mass spectrometers are now on the market that permit fast scanning rates up to mass 500 when operated in conjunction with a GLC unit. Single chromatographic peaks, containing no more than 10^{-6} to 10^{-7} g, can be examined for homogeneity and composition and the structure of the components determined from the mass spectra.

Evaluation of the data in Table 18.1 will assist in making an intelligent choice of methods for use in trace analysis. In general, if an individual component, or limited number of components, is to be determined at ex-tremely low concentrations, either gas chromatography or radiotracer anal-ysis should be given early consideration. For the few unusual materials that have high ultraviolet absorption, use of this technique may be of interest. If a functional group is to be determined at very low concentrations, the use of a colorimetric method is generally preferred over a titration method. However, the titration methods are simple and sometimes quite useful if the demands are not severe and the sample composition is not complex. These criteria have been used in arriving at the choice of the methods recommended here for the determination of trace components. For instance, colorimetric methods are recommended for the determination of trace concentrations of carbonyl (Chapter 6), phenols (Chapter 10), peroxides (Chapter 13), and pyrroles (Chapter 15), as well as for other functional groups. Gas chromato-graphic methods are widely used and are recommended in several sections.

The subsequent sections provide more detailed information on the choice of methods for trace analysis, their applicabilities and limitations. But first it is important to discuss some aspects of the most critical factor in trace analysis, that is, the proper collection of samples for analysis.

SAMPLING METHODS

The collection of representative and meaningful samples is the first and the most basic aspect of all practical analysis. It cannot be overstressed that samples must accurately represent the conditions existing at the point of sampling and that they must be properly preserved in that condition until the analysis is made. It is only when these conditions are met that the subsequent results can be valid. These points are even more important in the analysis of trace components, and if they are not properly observed the results obtained can be meaningless. The increasing availability of instrumental monitors or probes for the direct determination of components or properties is now making it possible to obtain data rapidly and accurately at the site without actually having to remove the sample physically. Such continuous monitors are available for measurement of pH, for dissolved oxygen in water, for a number of ions in aqueous systems, and for traces of water in gasous systems, as well as for many other measurements. Whenever possible, it is preferable to measure a component directly with an instrumental monitor *in situ*, or at least in the field, to avoid changes in composition. As is shown in Figure 22.1 (see Chapter 22, Determination of Water) significant values for determination of trace components can often only be achieved after steady conditions are reached.

TITRATION METHODS

A calculation of the ultimate sensitivity can be taken from the simple expression:

$$\frac{(V)(N)}{1000} \times 100 = \text{Ultimate sensitivity, g}$$

where V = the endpoint error, generally 0.1 ml
  N = the normality of the titrant, usually either $0.1N$ or $0.01N$ for titration of organic functional groups
  100 = the assumed molecular weight for comparative purposes

The sensitivity calculated from this expression, using $0.01N$ titrant, is 1×10^{-4} g. For a simple and straightforward determination, such as for a trace of acid or base in a neutral and stable material, a large sample can be taken, and consequently the selectivity can be in the region of 10 ppm. With less favorable determinations, or with complex systems, smaller samples probably would be used and a less favorable trace analysis would result.

SPECTROSCOPIC TECHNIQUES

The calculation of the sensitivity in the absorption spectroscopic methods for a compound can be made from a comparison of the measured *absorbance* (*A*) with the *absorptivity* (*a*). The definition of these terms follows.

Absorbance (*A*) is the $\log_{10}$ of the reciprocal of the transmittance and is a dimensionless number.

Absorptivity (*a*) is the absorbance divided by the product of the concentration of the substance in g/liter and the cell path length in cm.

Molar absorptivity (*ε*) is usually recorded in liters/mole-cm and is related by

$$a = \frac{\varepsilon}{\text{Mol wt}}$$

A sample calculation to illustrate this is taken with a compound of 100 mol wt and molar absorptivity of 2×10^5, thus having an absorptivity of 2×10^3.

$$a = \frac{A \text{ (liters)}}{(\text{g})(\text{cell length})}$$

If we assume a minimum readable value of 0.05 for *A*, which is already distinguished from the noise level, and use a 1-cm cell, we arrive at

$$2 \times 10^3 = \frac{0.05 \text{ (liters)}}{(\text{g})(1)}$$

or a concentration of 2.5×10^{-5} g/liter. Since a convenient volume of sample solution is generally of the order of 10 ml, the sensitivity as the least amount of the component required for analysis is of the order of 10^{-7} g. The molar absorptivity value chosen for this example is high but there are some classes of compounds, notably polynuclear aromatics, for which such high absorptivities occur. A similar calculation can be made for the other spectroscopic absorption techniques, infrared and colorimetric–spectrophotometric methods, and is useful for comparison of the suitability of trace methods. It is possible to make the spectrophotometric methods more sensitive in many cases by increasing the cell length.

Examination of the selectivity of the spectroscopic methods, as shown in Table 18.1, makes it apparent that the methods vary widely in their suitability for analysis in the ppm region. This is to be expected since the principles of the methods are actually quite different. With *proton NMR* the integrated absorption is strictly proportional to the concentration of protons of a given type giving rise to the absorption. Thus the sensitivity can vary greatly depending upon the number of protons being observed. For example, a single proton per large molecule is much more difficult to measure than a group containing a large number of equivalent protons, e.g., a *tert*-butyl group with nine equivalent hydrogens. *Ultraviolet absorption spectroscopy* has the possibility with favored compounds of being the most selective of the spectroscopic techniques. Polynuclear aromatics may have molar absorptivities as high as 2×10^5 liters/mole-cm; compounds with absorptivities so great can be determined at very low concentrations. The great variation in molar absorptivities of organic materials in the ultraviolet makes it essential that the system be clean for the measurement to be meaningful. Organic compounds have a generally low molar absorptivity in *infrared absorption spectroscopy*. Values will usually fall within the range of 1×10^2 to 8×10^2 liters/mole-cm. Because of these low absorptivity values, infrared is not particularly useful for direct trace analysis. For a typical system involving common organic functional groups, the lower limit of selectivity is in the range of 100–500 ppm. *Mass spectrometry* has the power to determine very small amounts of ions. Highest selectivity comes when analyzing materials that can provide unambiguous ion masses. For instance, aromatic hydrocarbons and some metal organic compounds can be determined as individual compounds at a ppm level. However, this high sensitivity cannot be commonly achieved without extensive instrumentation and very able specialists. As in all trace analysis, the selectivity of the spectroscopic methods can be improved by concentration or separation techniques to reject either specific or bulk impurities.

COLORIMETRIC METHODS

The use of chemistry to select a species with high light absorptivity offers quite sensitive methods of analysis for a number of functional groups. Some of the characteristics of the more widely used colorimetric methods are shown in Table 18.2. Molar absorptivities range from 10^3 to 10^4 liters/mole-cm, which allow for high sensitivity and good selectivity with modern spectrophotometric instruments. A rather significant limitation in the quantitative use of some of the colorimetric methods is the variation in the response factors for different compounds in several of the methods. This is particularly severe where a complex reaction may be involved in which the extent of reactivity to give the colored product varies with the type and degree of substitutions on the molecule. For example, in the methods for the determination of phenols, the variability in extent of reaction and consequent color formation is so great in the 4-aminoantipyrine method that the *para*-substituted phenols are not determined and some of the bisubstituted phenols have a response only about one-third that of phenol itself. This, however, is a particularly unsatisfactory case, and in general the determined molar absorptivities will not vary over such a wide range. The variation may be such that it is advisable to calibrate the method with the specific compounds to

Table 18.2. Characteristics of Some Colorimetric Methods

Functional group	Reagent	Molar absorptivity, liters/mole-cm	Absorption maxima, Å	Ref.
Acid	Pinacyanol	$2\text{–}5 \times 10^4$	6200	Chapter 5
Carbonyl	Dinitrophenylhydrazine	1×10^4	4800⎫	
	Chromotropic acid	1.9×10^4	5700⎬	Chapter 6
	3-Methyl-2-benzothiazolone	6.5×10^4	6350⎭	
	hydrazone		6700	
Ester	Hydroxamic acid	$0.8\text{–}1.2 \times 10^3$	5300	Chapter 7
Olefin (cyclic)	Phenyl azide	5.4×10^4	5150	[a]
Peroxide	Ferrous thiocyanate	5×10^3	5250	Chapter 13
Phenol	4-Aminoantipyrine	1.2×10^4	4600	Chapter 10
Pyrrole	Dimethylamino-benzaldehyde	$5\text{–}9 \times 10^4$	5200–5800	Chapter 15
Sulfonate	Methylene blue	8.5×10^4	6500	Chapter 19

[a] A. E. O'Donnell, M. M. Neal, F. T. Weiss, J. M. Bann, T. J. DeCino, and S. C. Lau, *Agr. Food Chem.*, **2**, 11 (1954).

be determined. This disadvantage must be traded off against the high sensitivity and ease of use of some of the colorimetric methods. Where colorimetric methods have been particularly useful, the methods are detailed in the appropriate functional chapters, generally with data indicating their application to known materials.

SEPARATION METHODS

Techniques for separating components are often used to simplify the mixtures being analyzed, to increase sensitivity, and to reduce the extent of interference. Practical separating procedures include chromatography, steam distillation, extraction with aqueous vs. nonaqueous solvents, and, in some cases, chemical removal of unwanted components. These separations are frequently important to reduce "background" interference from the matrix and may be called upon as a first step in colorimetric or spectroscopic methods. A number of examples of the use of these procedures is given in the functional chapters.

In the determination of traces of organic pollutants in waste waters, separation techniques have been employed to concentrate the organic impurities and to separate them from inorganic salts. The impurity concentrates are subsequently examined by chromatography and/or spectroscopic techniques for the determination of individual components. Practical procedures have been published in recent years that use such sample preconcentration methods for water pollution analysis. Some of these techniques should have a wide general applicability and may be worth considering for the determination of components in aqueous, and some nonaqueous, samples. For some years activated carbon has been employed to separate organic pollutants from waste waters (3, 4). Typical organic compounds that have been removed from water with activated carbon are phenols, cresols, organic cyanides, carboxylic acids, halogenated compounds, and pesticides. The water sample is generally pumped directly from the stream to activated carbon adsorbent maintained in a column. After sufficient sample has been treated, the carbon is drained of free water and the organics extracted with a suitable volatile solvent, often using a Soxhlet extractor. A common solvent is chloroform, although other low boiling halogenated solvents may be employed. Most of the solvent is evaporated from the sample and the residue can then be classified by specific methods. The freeze concentration technique (5–7) provides less exposure to chemical modification than distillation or extraction and is suitable for water with relatively low inorganic salt contents. Baker has published a procedure (5) in which the water sample is placed in a round-bottom flask connected to a rotating device. Ice crystals are added for seeding and the flask rotated in an ice–salt bath until the liquid volume is greatly reduced. A known amount of a pure organic compound can be added to estimate the efficiency of recovery by subsequent GC analysis. Recoveries in a number of cases were found to be in the vicinity of 90%.

CHROMATOGRAPHIC TECHNIQUES

The many chromatographic techniques depend upon the separation of components in a mixture through some process in which certain of the components travel more rapidly than others. Thus the mixture is either partially or more completely resolved into a number of component fractions that are usually chemically less complex than the original mixture. Consequently, it is then possible to apply relatively nonspecific and less sensitive methods to measure or determine the fractions or components. Of all the widely available methods, gas chromatography is the most suitable and generally used technique for the effective separation of organic materials. Since the degree of resolution obtainable is so large, gas chromatography can often be applied directly for trace analysis. By using one of the specific detectors, certain functional groups or types of compounds can be determined directly. The characteristics of gas chromatographic columns and detectors and their sensitivities are described in detail in Chapter 21. Other forms of chromatography have considerably less utility for trace analysis; adsorption chromatography offers lower resolution but can handle higher molecular weight or unstable components and, since the equipment required is so simple, it is used as an important technique for the prior concentration of the substance to be determined. Liquid–liquid chromatography has suffered from the lack of generally useful and sensitive detectors. Some new detectors are becoming available and the utility of this technique may improve. Neither paper nor thin-layer chromatography are uniformly suitable for trace analysis at the ppm level because the ratio of the detection sensitivity to the loading capacity is not as great as in certain other methods.

RADIOTRACER METHODS

The use of radiotracers, generally ^{14}C or ^{3}T, offers the highest level of chemical selectivity in the trace analysis of organic compounds. This technique is different from all the nthers listed in its requirement for the synthesis of the radioactive compound prior to any analysis. Although organic radiochemicals have been used for specific organic analysis for some time (8, 9), only in recent years has the significance of purity and validity of synthesis been fully appreciated (10). For the experimental results to be meaningful the labeled compounds must be pure, both chemically and radiochemically. This is, of course, a restatement of the fundamental axiom of analytical chemistry, stated many years ago by Berzelius, that the quality of the entire work depends upon the purity of the reagents. It was pointed out by Muhs, Bastin, and Gordon (10) that, although conventional methods of analysis are adequate to determine chemical purity, they may not be satisfactory for radiochemical purity. This is due to the high activity of the common radionuclei used for organic preparations (^{14}C, ^{3}T, ^{32}P, ^{35}S) for which radioactivity to the extent of millions of counts per minute may involve quantities of materials of the order of 10^{-7} to 10^{-9} g. The compound may be $>99.9\%$ chemically pure and yet have a low radiochemical purity. Consequently, it is necessary to determine, by proper analytical techniques, both the chemical and radiochemical purity. For compounds that are volatile or can be made so through derivatives, gas–liquid radiochromatography offers a useful technique. The combination of a conventional gas chromatographic apparatus with a dual detector system, one a thermal conductivity detector and the other an ionization detector, permits the simultaneous recording of chemical mass and radiochemical activity. By using this apparatus, Muhs, Bastin, and Gordon (10) found that impurities in some commercial labeled organic compounds arose from two sources. One group consisted of impurities that were of high specific activity and comparable in volatility to the compound itself. These impurities were usually formed during the synthesis step, especially when the synthesis was made with a very "hot" intermediate and

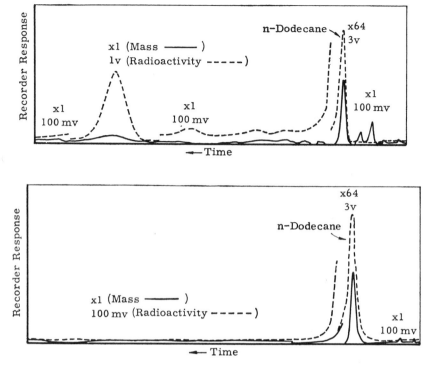

Figure 18.1. GLRC curves of impure (above) and purified (below) samples of *n*-dodecane-1-C^{14}. From Muhs, Bastin, and Gordon (3), courtesy of Pergamon Press.

the product then diluted with the nonradioactive chemical to the usual level of radioactivity before shipment. The second group were self-radiolysis products formed during storage. These are high-boiling materials, generally polymeric, and of an activity comparable to the parent compound. The self-radiolysis products are usually not recovered by gas chromatography, so that when this technique is used for purity measurements it is necessary to determine a total activity balance between the material injected into the gas chromatographic unit and that eluted into the ionization detector.

An example of the use of the radiochemical analysis of a sample of dodecane-1-^{14}C is given in Figure 18.1. The commercial material contained a highly radioactive impurity with a volatility considerably less than the dodecane. It was found possible to obtain dodecane-1-^{14}C pure and free of this component by use of a preparative gas chromatographic apparatus. When the purified material was subjected to the same analysis, the gas–liquid radiochromatographic curves showed a clean separation.

BIOLOGICAL TESTS

Biological tests have been used for many years to follow the separation and concentration of biologically active materials, such as hormones and vitamins, even before the composition of the material was known. The literature of this field is large and a number of good review volumes are available, including those of Dorfman (11) and Bliss (12).

A typical biological method for the determination of hormones could be illustrated by the Capon Comb Growth test discussed by Dorfman (11) as a technique for the determination of the androgens, which are substances whose biological activity affects the secondary sex characteristics of male animals. The Capon Comb test is employed on caponized Leghorn cockerels and involves measurement of the individual comb for the sum of length plus height. The animals are then treated with a daily dose of the sample dissolved in olive or corn oil and at the end of the fifth day, the combs are remeasured. Tests are generally made on groups of 8–10 animals and calibration curves are prepared from test series involving treatment with known weights of a chemically pure androgen. The results are such that a straight line can generally be drawn when comb growth (in millimeters) is plotted on a linear scale vs. the dose on a logarithmic scale. Less than milligram quantities of effective hormone can be measured by this technique. Many other natural biological phenomena are employed for bioassay, including measurements of the blood pressure of cats or rats for determination of adrenal extracts (11).

The methods mentioned above employ natural biological processes for the detection and determination of substances that may alter some specific process and often can be interpreted rather specifically. Another type of biological test is the measurement of the mortality when a toxic substance is tested on small groups of insects. For example, the analysis of the amount of insecticide present as residues on treated plant materials can be carried out by observing the mortality of the house fly, *musca Domestica*, or the vinegar fly, *Drosophila melanogaster*. In this bioassay the measurement is made by comparing the mortalities of the fly population exposed to the sample with a series of standards (13). Such bioassay methods have been used when a satisfactory chemical or spectroscopic analytical method was not yet available or to supplement the more specific methods to determine whether insecticide metabolites or decomposition products might possess appreciable toxicity. This technique is sensitive and it has been shown (13) that as little as 0.8×10^{-6} g of a common insecticide, dieldrin, will kill half the population of vinegar flies in a small jar. Due to the variation in the susceptibility of insects or to differences in the quantity and quality of plant extractives that may also be present, the mortality of insects for the same amount of insecticide may vary from test to test. Therefore it is necessary to prepare dosage–mortality curves under highly standardized conditions and make comparisons based on relative toxicities. The results must be evaluated by a careful statistical program (14). To overcome the interference of plant extractives in the bioassay, some separation procedure is often employed. The techniques used may involve partition between solvents or adsorption chromatography with alumina or activated carbon columns (15).

Another type of biological test useful for trace analysis is through the use of enzymes, which generally have rather specific reactions. An analytically important reaction has become available through the use of cholinesterase, which is a group of closely related enzymes whose function in nature is to hydrolyze acetylcholines to choline and acetic (or other) acid.

$$(CH_3)_3{}^+N—CH_2—CH_2—OC—CH_3 \xrightarrow[\text{enzyme}]{H_2O}$$
$$\underset{O}{\overset{||}{}}$$

$$(CH_3)_3{}^+N—CH_2—CH_2—OH + CH_3C—OH$$
$$\underset{O}{\overset{||}{}}$$

The organophosphorus insecticides that are now important commercially deactivate the cholinesterase to a degree dependent upon the quantity of the particular insecticides. The extent of the deactivation can be applied as an analytical method in a number of ways (16). In the general method, a standard cholinesterase preparation is reacted with plant extractives containing traces of organophosphorus insecticides to effect partial inhibition of the enzyme. The extent of inhibition can be measured by the addition of standard acetylcholine solution, which is allowed to react under closely controlled and specified conditions. Determination of the extent of deactivation of the enzyme is measured by the change in pH of the system, by titration of the liberated acetic acid, or by the determination of remaining acetylcholine through one of the colorimetric ferric hydroxamate methods (see Chapter 7). The sensitivity of the method is high and it has been shown by Giang and Hall (17) to be capable of measuring quantities of several organophosphorus insecticides in quantities as low as 2 or 3 × 10^{-8} g.

ANALYSIS OF GAS SAMPLES

The techniques described so far in this chapter have been applied to solid and liquid samples that can be handled directly with standard sampling procedures. It is for the analysis of gas samples, particularly air, that development of new procedures has been most marked because of the concern for the health hazards in urban areas caused by air pollution. Large sums of money are being spent in the development of methods and in the analysis for specific pollutants in the atmosphere. Highly sensitive techniques are now available through which concentrations of pollutants can be determined at concentrations as low as a few parts per billion.

SAMPLING EQUIPMENT FOR AIR ANALYSIS

Proper devices for reliable collection of materials from air have been reported by a number of investigators. Some of the most useful designs are the midget impingers and bubblers (18) used extensively by the U.S. Public Health Service Laboratories. Saltzman (18) points out that midget equipment can be used for practical gas sampling because it is inexpensive and economical of reagents and fits easily into portable equipment. Three midget sampling devices are shown in Figure 18.2. Device A is an impinger and B and C are bubblers with fritted glass end inlets. These devices are now commerically available, generally with a choice of porosity for the bubblers and with volumetric graduations. A growing number of methods are based on the use of absorbing reagents (19) that react with and remove air contaminants, generally for subsequent spectrophotometric analysis. These determinations

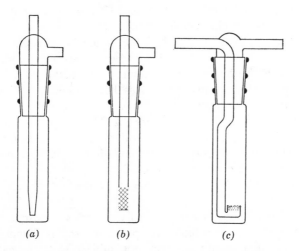

   (a)   (b)   (c)

Figure 18.2. Midget sampling equipment (a) Standard midget impinger. Nozzle about 1-mm diameter, passes 0.09–0.11 cfm at 12 in. H_2O vacuum. (b) Midget fritted tube end bubbler. (c) Midget fritted disk bubbler. Standard-taper 24/40 joints. Capacities of lower (outer) piece: 46 ml (A and B), 60 ml (C), when filled to brim. After Saltzman (18), Copyright 1961 by the American Chemical Society. Reprinted by permission of the copyright owner.

include methods for analysis of oxidants, aliphatic aldehydes, acrolein, and formaldehyde present in trace concentrations in polluted air samples. A number of the analytical methods are described in the functional sections of this volume.

DETERMINATION OF TRACES OF HYDROCARBONS IN THE ATMOSPHERE

A significant example of developments in this area is the work involving analysis of trace amounts of hydrocarbons in air. There are now two groups of techniques established for this purpose. Total hydrocarbon analyzers can be used to determine the sum of all hydrocarbons (generally plus other organic compounds) in the air. This group of techniques is nonchromatographic and utilizes either a nondispersive infrared instrument or a flame-ionization analyzer for the measurement of total hydrocarbons. Jackson (20) has examined several instruments used for this measurement and concluded that for analysis of automobile exhaust gases the flame-ionization analyzers provide a greater sensitivity and a better measure of the total hydrocarbon concentration than that indicated by the infrared instrument. The other group of techniques is specific for determination of individual hydrocarbons and utilizes sensitive gas chromatography. The first work of this nature reported was that of Eggertsen and Nelsen (21), who determined the C_2–C_5 hydrocarbons from engine exhaust and from the atmosphere. Their procedure involved trapping of these hydrocarbons in a short chromatographic column cooled in liquid oxygen followed by analysis by elution with helium through a longer chromatographic column. A thermal conductivity detector was employed and the sensitivity level was 0.05 ppm of the individual hydrocarbons. Advances in instrumentation and techniques have been used effectively by a number of investigators (22–29). The most sensitive of the published techniques combines a freezeout concentration step with a flame ionization detector to permit the determination of hydrocarbons at levels as low as 1 ppb in air samples.

From this set of intensive studies several specific facts arise:

1. Methane is a natural constituent of the earth's atmosphere and of the seas. It is formed by microbiological processes and is found generally at levels of 1–$1\frac{1}{2}$ ppm in atmospheres not subject to industrial pollution. Methane is the major hydrocarbon constituent of unpolluted air and of the gases extracted from waters in the open seas. In heavily polluted atmospheres, such as the Los Angeles basin, methane contents may rise to as much as 3 ppm, or even higher in the vicinity of a producing oil field.

2. Automotive exhaust produces a spectrum of hydrocarbons that, for

the most severe conditions (deceleration), may have the following approximate concentrations:

Methane	1800 ppm
Acetylene	1500 ppm
Ethylene	1400 ppm
Ethane	300 ppm
Propane	10 ppm

More complete data are shown in Table 18.3 from a detailed survey published some years ago.

3. The analysis of trace hydrocarbons in the Los Angeles basin atmosphere somewhat approximates an automotive exhaust diluted some 50,000-fold with air, containing, in addition, an overriding amount of methane due to natural sources plus that from exhaust pollution. Close comparison with exhaust gas analysis indicates, however, that Los Angeles basin air contains somewhat more propane and butane than would be anticipated from simple dilution of automotive exhaust, as well as perhaps more ethane and methane, as can be seen from typical data in Table 18.4.

Swinnerton and Linnenbom (27) of the Naval Research Laboratory in Washington, D.C., have determined the hydrocarbons present in ocean water and found methane, ethane plus ethylene, propane, propylene, and isobutane (Table 18.5). Their gas chromatographic apparatus did not readily

Table 18.3.   Analyses of Hydrocarbons in Engine Exhaust[a]

Hydrocarbon	Concentration, ppm			
	Idle	Acceleration	Cruise	Deceleration
Paraffins				
Methane	729	198	309	1890
Ethane	52	27	36	334
Propane		11	<1	
Isobutane		6		
n-Butane	b	b	b	b
Olefins				
Ethylene	287	165	248	1405
Propylene	b	b	b	b
C_4 olefins	62	15	38	143
Acetylene	483	140	121	1500

[a] Data from W. B. Heaton and J. T. Wentworth, *Anal. Chem.*, **31**, 349 (1959).

[b] n-Butane plus propylene values were 90, 41, 57, and 493 ppm.

Table 18.4.   Aliphatic Hydrocarbon Content of the Atmosphere in the Los Angeles Basin

	Concentrations in ppb (by volume)		
Compounds	Riverside heavy haze[a]	Los Angeles morning sample[b]	Huntington Beach (oil field)[c]
Methane	—[d]	1150–3690	4900
Ethane	66	85	138
Ethylene	59	75	30
Propane	30	35	81
Propylene	16	20	5
Isobutane	11	15	28
n-Butane	45	60	75
Acetylene	71	85	33
1-Butene	2		1
Isobutene	4		1
Isopentane	32		42
n-Pentane	22		31
2-Methyl pentane	10		12
3-Methyl pentane	8		8
n-Hexane	9		12

[a] Data of Stephens and Burleson (26).
[b] Data of Altshuller and Bellar (23).
[c] Data of Stephens, Darley, and Burleson (28).
[d] Not determined.

separate ethane from ethylene and consequently they are reported together. Samples of water were taken from the open North Atlantic ocean 500 km west of Ireland and from the Gulf of Mexico south of Mobile, Alabama. Since it may be expected that some approach to equilibrium exists between these hydrocarbons and the atmosphere, these hydrocarbons may be normal

Table 18.5.   Analysis of Ocean Waters for Hydrocarbons[a]

	Hydrocarbon concentration ($\times 10^{-7}$ ml/liter)			
	From North Atlantic		From Gulf of Mexico	
Hydrocarbon	Surface	30 m	Surface	30 m
Methane	474	600	676	2830
Ethane plus ethylene	99	51.3	45	102
Propane	1.9	3.4	2.4	6.6
Propylene	5.9	8.5	9.3	6.3
Isobutane	2.9	2.4	5.9	6.9

[a] Results of Swinnerton and Linnenbom (27).

constituents of the atmosphere. However, it is not possible to conclude at this time what their expected concentration may be.

Extensive investigations have also been conducted into the determination of traces of polynuclear aromatic hydrocarbons and heterocyclic compounds in polluted atmospheres since certain of these materials are suspected of being cancer producing. Preliminary concentrations are often made by means of column chromatography or by paper or thin-layer chromatography. The detection and final determination can be achieved by ultraviolet absorption spectroscopy or, more effectively in some cases, by fluorescence (30). A thorough study by investigators of the U.S. Public Health Service using these techniques showed that the airborne particulate matter from many cities contained trace quantities of pyrene, fluoranthrene, benzofluorene, benzanthracene, and several other polynuclear hydrocarbons (31). The exhaust from diesel engines has been examined by column chromatography and fluorescence spectroscopy (32) and shown to contain benzpyrene, anthracene, phenanthrene, and acenaphthene. Thin-layer chromatographic methods have been found valuable in determining the polynuclear hydrocarbon pollutants in the atmosphere over a number of American cities (33, 34).

REFERENCES

1. G. H. Morrison, Ed., *Trace Analysis: Physical Methods*, Wiley, New York, 1965.
2. W. W. Meinke and B. F. Scribner, Eds., *Trace Characterization: Chemical and Physical*, Nat. Bur. Std. Monograph 100, 1967.
3. R. W. Coughlin and F. S. Ezra, *Environmental Sci. Technol.*, **2**, 291 (1968).
4. *Standard Methods for the Examination of Water and Waste Water*, 12th ed., American Public Health Association, New York, 1965, pp. 214–218.
5. R. A. Baker, *J. Water Pollution Control Fed.*, **37**, 1164 (1965); "Micro-organic Matter in Water," ASTM Spec. Tech. Publ. No. 448, 1969, pp. 65–77.
6. P. A. Kammerer, Jr., and G. F. Lee, *Environmental Sci. Technol.*, **3**, 276 (1969).
7. J. Shapiro, *Science*, **133**, 2063 (1961).
8. S. Rothschild, ed., *Advances in Tracer Methodology*, Vol. I (1963) and 2 (1965), Plenum Press, New York.
9. L. R. Erwall, H. G. Forsberg, and K. Ljunggren, *Industrial Isotope Techniques*, Wiley, New York, 1964.
10. M. A. Muhs, E. L. Bastin, and B. E. Gordon, *Intern. J. Appl. Radiation Isotopes*, **16**, 537 (1965).
11. R. I. Dorfman, Ed., *Methods in Hormone Research*, Vol. II, *Bioassay*, Academic Press, New York, 1962.
12. C. I. Bliss, *The Statistics of Bioassay With Special Reference to the Vitamins*, Academic Press, New York, 1952.
13. Y.-P. Sun, E. R. Johnson, J. E. Pankaskie, N. W. Earle, and J.-Y. Sun, *J. Assoc. Offic. Agr. Chemists*, **46**, 530 (1963).

14. Y.-P. Sun and E. R. Johnson, *J. Econ. Entomology*, **58**, 838 (1965).
15. Y.-P. Sun and J. Sanjean, *ibid.*, **54**, 841 (1961).
16. J. C. Gage, in *Advances in Pest Control Research*, Vol. IV, R. L. Metcalf, Ed., Interscience, New York, 1961, pp. 183–210.
17. P. A. Giang and S. A. Hall, *Anal. Chem.*, **23**, 1830 (1951).
18. B. E. Saltzman, *ibid.*, **33**, 1100 (1961).
19. Public Health Service Publ. 999-AP-11, R. A. Taft Sanitary Engineering Center, Cincinnati, Ohio, 1965.
20. M. W. Jackson, *J. Air Pollution Control Assoc.*, **11**, 697 (1966).
21. F. T. Eggertsen and F. M. Nelsen, *Anal. Chem.*, **30**, 1040 (1958).
22. T. A. Bellar, J. E. Sigsby, C. A. Clemons, and A. P. Altshuller, *ibid.*, **34**, 763 (1962).
23. A. P. Altshuller and T. A. Bellar, *J. Air Pollution Control Assoc.*, **13**, 81 (1963).
24. M. Feldstein and S. Balestrieri, *ibid.*, **15**, 177 (1965).
25. R. E. Neligan, *Arch. Environ. Health*, **5**, 581 (1962).
26. E. R. Stephens and F. R. Burleson, *J. Air Pollution Control Assoc.*, **17**, 147 (1967).
27. J. W. Swinnerton and V. J. Linnenbom, *Science*, **156**, 1119 (May, 1967).
28. E. R. Stephens, E. F. Darley, and F. R. Burleson, paper presented at the API meeting, Los Angeles, California, May, 1967.
29. R. J. Gordon, H. Mayrsohn, and R. M. Ingels, *Environmental Sci. Technol.*, **2**, 1117 (1968).
30. E. Sawicki, T. W. Stanley, and W. C. Elbert, *J. Chromatog.*, **26**, 72 (1967).
31. E. Sawicki, W. C. Elbert, T. W. Stanley, T. R. Hauser, and F. T. Fox, *Anal. Chem.*, **32**, 810 (1960).
32. S. K. Ray and R. Long, *Combustion Flame*, **8**, 139 (1964).
33. D. F. Bender, *Environmental Sci. Technol.*, **2**, 204 (1968).
34. T. W. Stanley, M. J. Morgan, J. E. Meeker, *ibid.*, **3**, 1198 (1969).

ANALYSIS OF SURFACE-ACTIVE MATERIALS

Large amounts of commercial surface-active materials in use throughout the industrial nations are synthetic products derived from a petrochemical base. Several of the principal types of surface-active components used for detergent manufacture are shown in Table 19.1. These materials are the sodium alkylarylsulfonates, the alcohol and ethoxylate sulfates, the nonionic alcohol ethoxylates, and the sodium carboxylates. The first four materials constitute the major contribution to the present commercial market and are derived from synthetic operations. Sodium carboxylate, the classical "soap," is still used in large quantities, chiefly in hand soap. Most of the carboxylates in the detergent field are C_{16} and C_{18} and are derived from the saponification of natural fats. The alcohol ethoxylates are marketed with a range of average values for n. Formulated detergents also contain appreciable amounts of inorganic salts, principally phosphates, and certain other components in small concentrations to act as foam stabilizers or brighteners. Several comprehensive texts are available on the detailed analysis of surface-active materials (1–3).

A number of methods for the analysis of detergent mixtures containing these components have been published. The majority of the methods fall under the following two classifications:

1. The more absolute methods which require at least a minimal separation of components. The extent of separations depends upon the desired accuracy of the analysis. These methods require considerable time and care and are used chiefly for referee purposes.

2. Methods for the specific determination of the sulfate or sulfonate group, generally through color-forming reactions. These methods give a value only for the equivalents of surface-active component present and provide no information concerning the other components of the detergent mixtures. Because of their rapid and simple nature, these methods are used for process control but are not suited for complete analysis. It is essential to keep in mind that these methods are somewhat empirical, especially in the way the end points are selected. To obtain accurate results, the methods should be standardized with a known material of the type being determined.

Table 19.1. Principal Types of Surface-Active Materials in Common Detergents

$$R{-}\!\!\overset{\displaystyle R}{\diagdown}\!\!\left\langle \right\rangle \!\!-SO_3Na$$

$$R{-}CH_2{-}OSO_3Na$$

$$R{-}(OCH_2{-}CH_2)_n{-}O{-}SO_3Na$$

$$R{-}(O{-}CH_2{-}CH_2)_n{-}OH$$

$$\overset{\displaystyle O}{\underset{\displaystyle R{-}CONa}{\|}}$$

METHODS FOR THE SPECIFIC DETERMINATION OF THE ALKYL SULFATE OR SULFONATE GROUP

A number of methods have been published for the specific determination of alkyl sulfate or sulfonate groups in the corresponding surface-active materials. Generally, these methods depend upon reaction of the sulfonate of sulfate group with an amine salt (usually the hydrochloride or hydrobromide) to give a salt essentially according to the following equation:

$$RSO_3^-Na^+ + (R_1R_2R_3)NH^+X^- \rightarrow [RSO_3H{\cdot}N(R_1R_2R_3)] + Na^+X^-$$

In certain methods, the amine is chosen to yield a water-insoluble salt that is soluble, however, in organic media. The salt can be estimated turbidimetrically in aqueous suspension or, if the amine is a sufficiently weak base, this salt can be isolated by filtration or by extraction with an organic solvent and titrated with standard base. Other methods depend upon reaction of the sulfonate or sulfate with a water-soluble dye containing an amino group, yielding a colored complex salt extractable from water with chloroform. The amount of colored complex salt in the chloroform phase can be determined colorimetrically, or the end point of a titration of the sulfonate with an amine having cationic surface-active properties can be indicated by the removal of the colored salt from the chloroform phase.

The rapid methods for the determination of the sulfonate or sulfate group generally give a value only for the number of equivalents. To determine sulfonate or sulfate on a weight basis, it is necessary to know, from an independent source, the equivalent weight of the active material. Low-combining-weight sulfonates, such as sodium benzene sulfonate and sodium toluene sulfonate, do not react to an appreciable extent in these methods.

METHODS INVOLVING TITRATION OF AN AMINE-SULFONATE SALT WITH ALKALI

BENZIDINE HYDROCHLORIDE METHOD

One of the earlier methods applied to the rapid determination of sulfonates and alkyl sulfates involves the use of an aqueous benzidine hydrochloride reagent to form a water-insoluble salt with the surface-active material (4). The precipitated salt was isolated by filtration and dissolved in hot alcohol. Benzidine hydrochloride likewise reacts with inorganic sulfate ion to form the corresponding water-insoluble benzidine sulfate, which is insoluble, however, in hot alcohol. The alcohol extract, which therefore contains only the amine-sulfonate salt, can be titrated directly with standard alkali since benzidine is such a weak base that it is neutral to phenolphthalein. The reactions involved in this method are the following:

$$ClH \cdot H_2N-\underset{}{\bigcirc}-\underset{}{\bigcirc}-NH_2 \cdot HCl + 2RSO_3Na \longrightarrow$$

$$RSO_3H \cdot H_2N\underset{}{\bigcirc}-\underset{}{\bigcirc}-NH_2 \cdot HO_3SR + 2NaCl$$

$$RSO_3H \cdot H_2N\underset{}{\bigcirc}-\underset{}{\bigcirc}-NH_2 \cdot HO_3SR + 2NaOH \longrightarrow$$

$$H_2N\underset{}{\bigcirc}-\underset{}{\bigcirc}-NH_2 + 2RSO_3Na + 2H_2O$$

The benzidine hydrochloride method was originally developed by Kling and Püschel (4) for the determination of alkyl sulfates but the authors commented that sulfonated oils could be determined, at least partially, by the method. Jones (5) utilized the procedure of Kling and Püschel for the direct determination of the sulfonate content of surface-active materials and commented on the scope of the method. Shiraeff (6) modified the procedure of Kling and Püschel in several respects, using a more strongly acidic solution to reduce the extent of precipitation of benzidine sulfate and employing a higher concentration of benzidine hydrochloride.

Use of the method as a quantitative procedure is obviously limited to materials that are quantitatively precipitated by benzidine hydrochloride. Sodium diisopropylnaphthalene sulfonate and sodium ethylhexyl sulfate have been found to be precipitated only partially, and sodium diamylsulfosuccinate not at all, by aqueous solutions of benzidine hydrochloride.

Since the extent of recovery is somewhat low and the procedure lengthy, the method is no longer in much use.

p-TOLUIDINE HYDROCHLORIDE METHOD

Another method for the determination of the sulfonate and alkyl sulfate group by alkalimetric titration of the salt involves the use of *p*-toludine hydrochloride as the reagent. This depends upon the formation of a salt with *p*-toluidine hydrochloride in aqueous solution, following which the salt is extracted with carbon tetrachloride, the solution diluted with ethanol and titrated with standard base. The reactions involved are the following:

$$\text{RSO}_3\text{Na} + \text{CH}_3\!\!-\!\!\langle\bigcirc\rangle\!\!-\!\!\text{NH}_2\!\cdot\!\text{HCl} \longrightarrow \text{CH}_3\!\!-\!\!\langle\bigcirc\rangle\!\!-\!\!\text{NH}_2\!\cdot\!\text{HO}_3\text{SR} + \text{NaCl}$$

$$\text{CH}_3\!\!-\!\!\langle\bigcirc\rangle\!\!-\!\!\text{NH}_2\!\cdot\!\text{HO}_3\text{SR} + \text{NaOH} \longrightarrow \text{RSO}_3\text{Na} + \text{CH}_3\!\!-\!\!\langle\bigcirc\rangle\!\!-\!\!\text{NH}_2$$

Since *p*-toluidine is a very weak base, its salt with a strong acid, such as a sulfonic acid, can be titrated with alkali.

Marron and Schifferli (7) evaluated the *p*-Toluidine Hydrochloride method with several sodium alkyl aryl sulfonate detergents and, although the method was found to be empirical, the results were reproducible and the operations rapid. The method is included in this chapter as a recommended method.

METHODS INVOLVING PARTITION OF A COLOR BODY BETWEEN TWO PHASES

A colorimetric method for the determination of sulfonates and alkyl sulfates as described by Jones (5) involves reaction between the surface-active material and methylene blue chloride, in a water–chloroform mixture, to form a methylene blue–sulfonate salt soluble in chloroform. Methylene blue is a dye having two amine groups in the molecule. Jones (5) indicates that the reaction on which this determination depends is the following:

The reaction product has a color close to that of methylene blue and is completely extractable from aqueous solution with chloroform, while methylene blue chloride is not extractable from aqueous solution with chloroform. Consequently, the depth of color of the chloroform extract of an aqueous solution containing methylene blue and an anionic surface-active agent can be used to obtain a measure of the amount of surface-active material.

The basic principle of the methylene blue method of Jones was adapted into a rapid titration method for the analysis of sulfonates and alkyl sulfates by Barr and coworkers (8) and by Epton (9), independently but along similar lines. Epton's procedure and one procedure given by Barr are similar, both involving the titration of a water–chloroform mixture containing an anionic surface-active material and methylene blue (in approximately 200:1 molar ratio) with an aqueous solution of an amine salt having cationic surface-active properties, such as cetyl pyridinium bromide. The cetyl pyridinium bromide reacts with the sulfonate and with the methylene blue–sulfonate salt, giving first a cetyl pyridinium–sulfonate salt and then releasing methylene blue cation, which returns to the aqueous phase according to the following scheme (where [MB] is the methylene blue cation):

$$\left[\langle N\!-\!C_{16}H_{33} \right]\!\cdot Br + RSO_3Na \longrightarrow \left[\langle N\!-\!C_{16}H_{33} \right]\!\cdot RSO_3 + NaBr$$

$$\left[\langle N\!-\!C_{16}H_{33} \right]\!\cdot Br + [MB]\!\cdot RSO_3 \longrightarrow$$

$$\left[\langle N\!-\!C_{16}H_{33} \right]\!\cdot RSO_3 + [MB]\!\cdot Br$$

On the basis of these reactions, it would be expected that when one adds an amount of cetyl pyridinium bromide exactly equivalent to the sulfonate content plus the methylene blue content of the titration mixture, the blue color will have just returned completely to the aqueous phase. On the basis of the stoichiometry of the reaction, Barr selected as the end point the point at which the blue color had just returned completely to the aqueous phase. Epton, however, on the basis of the analysis of pure sodium alkyl sulfates, selected as the end point the point at which the depth of color of the two phases was identical.

A number of variations on these methods have been put into use. A particularly valuable contribution was published a few years ago by Lew (10) in which bromocresol green was employed as the indicator. This indicator is a sulfonate dyestuff and the titration is conducted under basic conditions such that amine oxides are not protonated and consequently do not interfere.

RECOMMENDED METHODS FOR SPECIFIC DETERMINATION OF THE SULFATE OR SULFONATE GROUPS

The four methods that, in the author's opinion, best illustrate the usefulness of these techniques are the *p*-Toluidine Hydrochloride method, the Colorimetric Methylene Blue method, the Methylene Blue Titration method, and the Bromocresol Green Titration method. A comparison of the principal features of these methods is shown in Table 19.2. The Toluidine Hydrochloride method is recommended for the assay of sulfated and sulfonated materials that may have a depth of color that could interfere in the color indicator titration methods. It finds its principal application in the analysis of petroleum sulfonates, sometimes called "mahogany" acids or soaps. The method is slow, requires a large sample, is not as precise as alternative methods and, consequently, is not generally recommended where other methods can be used. The Colorimetric Methylene Blue method is based on the earlier work of Jones (5) and has been investigated in more recent years by a number of workers for application to the determination of trace concentrations of detergent materials in polluted waters. Degens, Evans, Kommer, and Winsor (11) examined the application of the colorimetric methylene blue method for the determination of anionic detergents in sewage. It was found possible to overcome most of the interfering effects of naturally occurring materials and to determine surfactants as low as the ppm level. Longwell and Maniece (12) improved the application of the technique to sewage effluents and river waters by changing the conditions of the extraction and were able to eliminate interference from other components in these waste streams. The Colorimetric Methylene Blue method is quite sensitive; with sodium lauryl sulfate, the molar absorptivity has been found to be 85,000 liters/mole-cm, which allows for the determination of very low concentrations of surfactants. For the quantitative determination of the equivalents of sulfonate or alkyl sulfate functions in surfactants, the Methylene Blue Titration method is recommended as being more nearly stoichiometric than the corresponding colorimetric method. In this method the anionics are allowed to react with an aqueous solution of methylene blue and the resultant colored complex extracted with chloroform. The water–chloroform mixture is titrated with a standard aqueous solution of a quaternary ammonium chloride salt, Hyamine 1622, until the blue color is equally distributed between the two phases. The amount of Hyamine consumed is a measure of the content of anionic surfactant. Of the specific methods for determination of the alkyl sulfate or sulfonate group, this method has the highest precision and, if properly standardized with a known material of the type being analyzed, has the best accuracy in application to commercial detergents. Although it is generally the preferred method, it does have certain

Table 19.2. Comparison of Principal Features of Specific Methods for Determination of the Alkyl Sulfate or Sulfonate Group in Surfactants

Method	Extent of recoveries, %					Time for analysis, min	Sample requirement, g[a]	Principal use
	Na toluene sulfonate	Na xylene sulfonate	Sodium carboxylates	Amine oxides	Na C_{12}-benzene sulfonates			
p-Toluidine hydrochloride method	0.7		React	Interferes	95–105	45	1–1.5	Assay of petroleum sulfonates
Colorimetric methylene blue method	3		None	Interferes	95–105	45	1×10^{-4}	Trace analysis
Methylene blue titration method	3	27[b]	None	Approx. 100%	98–102	20	0.02	Usually preferred for formulated detergents
Bromocresol green titration method		1[b]	Partial[b] (Na laurate 26%)	None	97–103	20	0.02	For formulated detergents containing some interferences

[a] Calculated for a surface-active material of 300 equivalent weight.
[b] Data from Lew (10).

limitations that must be considered with some commercial formulated detergents. Toluene and xylene sulfonates and amine oxides interfere to the extents indicated in Table 19.2 and to avoid these interferences recourse is had to the Bromocresol Green Titration method. Since this method is conducted under basic conditions, the amine oxides are not protonated and do not interfere. Unfortunately, this method does suffer from partial interference by carboxylates. Also, the end point is not as cleanly differentiated as is that using methylene blue, which leads to a lower precision of the results.

METHODS FOR THE DETERMINATION OF OTHER SURFACTANTS

Further information on the determination of surfactants based on hydrophilic groups other than sulfate or sulfonate is given in Chapter 14 for cationic materials, in Chapter 5 for carboxylic acids and their salts, and in Chapter 11 for polyalkylene ethoxylates.

DETERMINATION OF SULFONATE CONTENT OF SODIUM SULFONATES

p-TOLUIDINE HYDROCHLORIDE METHOD

Reagents

Carbon tetrachloride, CP.
Hydrochloric acid solution, standard 0.5N.
Isopropyl alcohol, 99% and 50%.
Phenolphthalein indicator solution, 1% in 50% ethyl alcohol.
Sodium hydroxide solution, standard 0.5N, carbonate free.
p-Toluidine Hydrochloride Solution; prepare by dissolving 8.0 g of *p*-toluidine hydrochloride (at least 99% pure by titration) in sufficient water to make 100 ml of solution.

Procedure

Weigh a quantity of sample containing 4–5 meq of sulfonate into a 150-ml beaker. Add 30 ml of 50% isopropyl alcohol, warming and stirring to dissolve or disperse the sample.

Add 10 ml of water and 5–6 drops of phenolphthalein indicator solution. Neutralize the mixture with either 0.5N hydrochloric acid or 0.5N sodium hydroxide solution to the phenolphthalein end point.

Quantitatively transfer the neutral mixture to a 250-ml separatory funnel. Rinse the beaker and stirring rod with two 20-ml portions of water, two 5-ml portions of 99% isopropyl alcohol, and two 25-ml portions of carbon tetrachloride, in the order listed, adding these to the separatory funnel. Pipet 25 ml of *p*-toluidine hydrochloride solution into the funnel, stopper, and shake the contents vigorously for 2 min. Allow the funnel to stand until complete phase separation occurs, usually 10 or 15 min, then drain off and discard the lower carbon tetrachloride layer. Extract the aqueous phase a second time with 25 ml of carbon tetrachloride, allow the phases to separate, and discard the lower carbon tetrachloride phase as before.

Add 3 or 4 drops of phenolphthalein indicator solution to the funnel and titrate the contents with standard 0.5N sodium hydroxide solution to the first pink color of the end point.

Obtain at least one, and preferably two, blank determinations in an identical manner but omitting the sample.

Calculation

Calculate the sulfonate content of the sample as follows:

$$\text{sulfonate content, equiv/100 g} = \frac{(B - S)(N)}{10W}$$

where B = volume of sodium hydroxide solution required to titrate the blank determination, ml

S = volume of sodium hydroxide solution required to titrate the aqueous phase, ml

N = normality of the standard sodium hydroxide solution

W = weight of sample, g

DETERMINATION OF LOW CONCENTRATIONS OF ANIONIC DETERGENTS

COLORIMETRIC METHYLENE BLUE METHOD

Apparatus

Photoelectric colorimeter; Any spectrophotometer or photoelectric colorimeter equipped with an interference filter transmitting light at 650 mμ may be used. This procedure is written for a spectrophotometer equipped with 1-cm cells.

Reagents

Chloroform, CP.
Methylene blue solution. Dissolve 0.1 g of methylene blue chloride (USP) in 100 ml of distilled water.
Hydrochloric acid, CP, 6N.

Apparatus Standardization

Prepare four standards, using a material that contains a previously determined amount of the particular surfactant for which analysis is to be made, by accurately weighing out portions to contain approximately 0.0002, 0.0004, 0.0006, and 0.0008 meq (approximately 0.1–0.4 mg). Continue as directed below.

If the material is colored, weigh out another portion, to contain between 0.0002 and 0.0008 meq, for use as a color blank. Treat as below but omit the methylene blue solution.

Obtain a corrected absorbance for each standard. Plot the corrected absorbances against milliequivalents of surfactant.

Procedure

Weigh an amount of sample into distilled water or chloroform, whichever is more appropriate, so that after suitable dilution, an aliquot portion of 20 ml or less will contain between 0.0002 and 0.0008 meq.

Measure this portion into a 125-ml separatory funnel and add water and/or chloroform until approximately 20 ml of each is present. Neutralize the mixture by adding 6N hydrochloric acid dropwise, using an indicator paper, and add 3 or 4 drops in excess. Add 1 ml of the methylene blue solution, stopper the funnel, and shake gently for 1 min, venting the funnel occasionally. Allow the funnel to stand for 5 min and carefully drain the lower (chloroform) layer into a second 125-ml separatory funnel containing approximately 20 ml of distilled water. Stopper the second funnel, shake it for 1 min and allow it to stand for 5 min. Carefully drain the chloroform layer through a plug of cotton in the vortex of a filter funnel into a 100-ml volumetric flask. Make three additional extractions with 20-ml portions of chloroform. Each time, transfer the chloroform layer to the second funnel, wash with 20 ml of fresh distilled water as before and collect in the volumetric flask. Wash the filter funnel and cotton with chloroform and dilute to the mark.

Within 1 hr measure the absorbance relative to distilled water at 650 mμ.

Make a blank determination on the reagents by repeating the entire procedure but omitting the sample.

If the sample is colored, make a color blank determination by repeating the entire procedure on a similar-size portion of sample but omitting the methylene blue solution.

Calculation

Correct the absorbance obtained from the sample by subtracting the absorbance of the reagent blank and the absorbance of the color blank by means of the following expression:

$$\text{corrected absorbance} = A - \frac{(B)(D)}{C} - E$$

where A = absorbance obtained for the sample
  B = absorbance obtained for the color blank
  C = weight of sample taken for color blank, g
  D = weight of sample taken for analysis, g
  E = absorbance obtained for the reagent blank

Obtain the milliequivalents of surfactant present from the calibration curve. Calculate the surfactant content of the sample by means of the following expression:

$$\text{anionic surfactant content, meq/100 g} = \frac{100F}{W}$$

where F = surfactant present, obtained from calibration curve, meq, and W = weight of sample contained in portion extracted, g.

DETERMINATION OF ANIONIC SURFACTANT CONTENT OF DETERGENTS

METHYLENE BLUE TITRATION METHOD

Reagents

Chloroform, CP.
Sodium lauryl sulfate, recrystallized, 99$^+$% pure.
Sodium sulfate, CP, anhydrous.
Methylene blue indicator solution; dissolve 50 g of CP sodium sulfate in 120 ml of 2N sulfuric acid. Add 6.0 ml of a 0.5% aqueous solution of methylene blue chloride (USP) and dilute the mixture with sufficient distilled water to give a total volume of 1 liter.
Hyamine 1622 *Solution*, approximately 0.003M. Dissolve 1.4 g in distilled water and dilute to 1 liter. Standardize by titrating 10.0 ml of a 0.003M aqueous solution of the pure sodium lauryl sulfate. Hyamine 1622 is *p-tert*-octylphenoxyethoxy-ethyldimethyl-benzylammonium chloride and can be purchased from Rohm and Haas, Philadelphia, Pennsylvania.

Procedure

Prepare an approximately 0.003M solution of the sample in water. Some isopropyl alcohol can be used, but the concentration must not exceed 20 vol %.

Pipet 10 ml of this solution into a glass-stoppered mixing cylinder. Add 25 ml of methylene blue indicator solution and 15 ml of chloroform. Add from a buret an amount of Hyamine solution equal to approximately one-half of the expected titration, replace the stopper, and shake the mixture. Continue adding Hyamine solution in small quantities and shaking the mixture after each addition, until the color of the two phases becomes identical when viewed against a white background with the main source of light behind the operator.

Stable emulsions are sometimes formed during the early part of the titration. This difficulty is not encountered when reagent sufficient to react with at least half the sulfate present is added before the reaction mixture is shaken.

Calculation

$$\text{Sulfonate or sulfate ester content, equiv/100 g} = \frac{(V)(M)}{10W}$$

where V = volume of the standard Hyamine solution required to titrate a 10-ml portion of the solution, ml
M = molar concentration of the Hyamine solution
W = weight of sample in 10-ml portion of the sample solution, g

If the equivalent weight of the sulfate present in the sample is known, the results may be expressed as weight percent by multiplying the sulfate content in equivalents per 100 g by the equivalent weight.

DETERMINATION OF ANIONIC SURFACTANT CONTENT OF DETERGENTS

BROMOCRESOL GREEN TITRATION METHOD

Reagents

Bromocresol green indicator solution: dissolve 0.040 g of bromocresol green (3′,3″,5′,5″-tetrabromo-*m*-cresolsulfonphthalein, sodium salt), reagent grade, 70 g of anhydrous sodium sulfate, and 3.09 g of boric acid in approximately 800 ml of distilled water. Add 34.4 meq of sodium hydroxide (use 0.5 or 1N standard aqueous sodium hydroxide solution) and 0.055 meq of standard Hyamine solution and dilute to 1 liter with distilled water. Check the solution for the excess of bromocresol green over Hyamine by using 10 ml of distilled water in lieu of sample solution. Add additional Hyamine solution to the stock solution, calculating the amount to be added as follows: (975) × (titer)/25 ml. Mix the solution thoroughly and again check the solution in the manner indicated and make any further necessary additions to obtain a stock solution which gives zero titer.

The solution is buffered at pH 9.5 and should have the dye and Hyamine in equal molar amounts. A deficiency of dye would lead to low results for anionics, and, conversely, a deficiency of Hyamine would lead to high results. The presence of more dye in the chloroform phase than in the aqueous phase would indicate that too much Hyamine was added initially and the solution of bromocresol green should be discarded and a new one prepared using less Hyamine initially.

Chloroform, reagent grade.

Hyamine 1622 solution, standard, 0.003N. Dissolve 21 g of Hyamine 1622 in distilled water and dilute to 1 liter with additional distilled water. Standardize by titrating 10.0 ml of a 0.003M aqueous solution of pure sodium dodecyl sulfate. (Hyamine 1622, Rohm and Haas *p-tert*-octylphenoxyethoxyethyldimethylbenzyl-ammonium chloride, 366.1 g/equiv.)

Sodium lauryl sulfate, recrystallized, 99% pure.

Procedure

Prepare an approximately 0.003N anionic surfactant solution by dissolving the appropriate weight of sample in water and diluting to a definite volume in a volumetric flask.

Pipet a 10-ml portion of the solution into a 100-ml stoppered mixing cylinder and add 25 ml of the bromocresol green solution and 15 ml of chloroform. Titrate the mixture with the standard Hyamine solution, shaking the mixture vigorously after each addition of titrant. The end point is taken to be the point at which the intensities of the colors in the two phases are equal.

Calculation

Same as previous method.

SEPARATION AND ANALYSIS OF SURFACTANTS BY ION-EXCHANGE TECHNIQUES

As stated previously, more absolute methods of analysis of detergent and surfactant mixtures require a separation of components. Comprehensive methods were published some years ago (13) that illustrate the use of separation procedures to determine such components as neutral oil, sulfate or sulfonate, carboxylate, water, and inorganic salts as well as providing reliable values for the equivalent weight of the active material. Many of the separations were made by solvent partitioning, which is very time consuming and requires obtaining correction factors because of the equilibria in the partitioning of some components. During the course of the work on the comprehensive methods (13) it was realized that ion-exchange separations would provide for the improved and simplified determination of a number of components and an example was given of its use in the separation and determination of a nonionic detergent in admixture with an ionic detergent. Others who published practical ion-exchange separations of surface-active materials at that period of time were Winterscheidt (14) and Jenkins (15), but the present wide use of ion-exchange techniques in detergent analysis is due to the careful work of Voogt (16, 17), who realized their utility and carried on a thorough investigation, which led to the development of a number of valuable analytical methods from which the recommended methods in this chapter are derived. Primary separation of detergent components by ion exchange have a considerable advantage over separations by solvent partitioning in that components are generally separated more clearly on the basis of ionic type than on the basis of relative solubilities in immiscible or partially miscible solvents. The ion-exchange technique also permits the determination of anionic and cationic detergents in the presence of each other. These techniques have been used by O'Donnell as the basis for the development of procedures for the thorough analysis of household detergents (18).

The ion-exchange techniques given as recommended methods in this chapter are for the determination of the anion content, in equivalents, of anionic detergents and for the determination of nonvolatile nonionics in detergent mixtures. The anionic content can be determined, in equivalents per 100 g, by passing the sample, in water–alcohol solution, through an acid-form cation-exchange column. In this process the cations are exchanged for hydrogen ions. Any carbonic acid in the effluent is purged out with nitrogen and the acid then titrated with standard base. The procedure determines all anions other than hydroxide and carbonate in the sample. It is often desired to determine only surface-active ionics by the ion-exchange procedure and to do this it is necessary that the sample be initially free of inorganic salts (other than carbonates). An inorganic salt-free material can be obtained by leaching the original sample with 90% ethyl alcohol (19), or by an alternative desalting procedure (13), which is generally more complete, in which the sample is initially suspended in 50% isopropyl alcohol. The alcoholic solution is then saturated with anhydrous Na_2CO_3, which produces an aqueous phase containing inorganic salts and an alcoholic phase containing the organic components.

The determination of nonvolatile nonionics is achieved by passing an aqueous isopropyl alcohol solution of the sample through a cation exchanger in the acid form and an anion exchanger in the basic form. Ionic materials are removed and the nonionics in the effluent can be determined by evaporation of the solvent. The procedure given is satisfactory for the determination of the nonvolatile ethoxylates, but, due to steam distillation effects, may lose some C_{12}–C_{14} alcohols that are occasionally found in some commercial detergents. A slight change in procedure can avoid the loss of these partially volatile materials. To obtain an improved recovery of these materials, the effluent from the ion-exchange columns can be extracted with petroleum ether. The petroleum ether extract and the aqueous phase are evaporated separately and are blended near the end of the evaporation.

DETERMINATION OF ANION CONTENT OF ANIONIC DETERGENTS

ION-EXCHANGE ACIDIMETRIC METHOD

Apparatus

Ion-exchange columns, see Chapter 24.

Reagents

Cation-exchange resin AG50-X4, 50–100 mesh, acid form, obtainable from Bio-Rad Laboratories, Richmond, California.
Isopropyl alcohol–water solution, 1:1 by volume distilled water and 99% isopropyl alcohol.
Sodium hydroxide solution, 0.1N standard, alcoholic.
Phenolphthalein indicator solution, 1% in 60% ethanol.

Apparatus Preparation

Slurry 25 ml of resin with 100 ml of water, allow the resin to settle, and decant the water. Repeat this operation two additional times. Then slurry the resin with 100 ml of the alcohol–water solution and decant most of the liquid.

Close the stopcock on the column and add the slurry of resin to the transfer funnel attached to the column. Wash all the resin into the column with the alcohol–water solution and allow the liquid to pass through the column.

Remove the funnel, attach a rubber bulb to the outlet of the column, and draw out liquid until the level is at the top of the resin. Wash down the walls of the column above the resin while drawing liquid into the bulb.

Attach the clean connecting tube and feed funnel and pass 100 ml of the alcohol–water solution through the column and discard the effluent. Pass 50 ml of alcohol–water through the column and test for acidity using phenolphthalein. One drop of 0.1 N NaOH solution should give a pink color to phenolphthalein indicator in the solution. Continue washing if necessary to obtain a fraction free of acid.

Procedure

Dissolve a weighed amount of sample to contain 4–5 meq of anions, weighed to the nearest milligram, in 50 ml of alcohol–water solution. Transfer the solution quantitatively to the feed funnel and allow the liquid to pass through the column at the rate of 1–2 ml/min. Collect the effluent in a 250-ml flask. Wash the funnel several times with solvent to effect complete transfer of sample into the column. Temporarily remove the connecting tube and force the supernatant liquid to the top of the resin. Wash down the walls of the column above the resin several times with solvent. Attach the tube and pass 75–100 ml of solvent through the column. Purge the effluent solution with N_2 gas to remove CO_2 if carbonate or bicarbonate was present in the original sample.

Titrate the effluent solution with the standardized 0.1 N alcoholic sodium hydroxide solution using phenolphthalein indicator. Alternatively, titrate potentiometrically when it is desired to distinguish between strong and weak acidities.

Calculation

$$\text{Anion content} \begin{pmatrix} \text{minus any carbonate} \\ \text{and hydroxyl} \end{pmatrix}, \text{equiv/100 g} = \frac{(V)(N)}{10W}$$

where V = volume of titrant, ml
N = normality of the titrant
W = weight of sample used, g

DETERMINATION OF NON-VOLATILE NON-IONICS IN DETERGENT MIXTURES

ION-EXCHANGE GRAVIMETRIC PROCEDURE

Apparatus

Ion-exchange columns, see Chapter 24.
Steam bath.
Vacuum oven, capable of operation to 100°C.

Reagents

Anion-exchange resin AG1-X4, 50–100 mesh, chloride form (Bio-Rad Laboratories, Richmond, California).

Cation-exchange resin AG50W-X4, 50–100 mesh, acid form (Bio-Rad Laboratories, Richmond, California).

The resins are analytical grade products, which have the same numerical designations as those of Dowex resins made by the Dow Chemical Co. The AG1 resin is a strongly basis type and the AG50 resin is a strongly acidic material.

Isopropyl alcohol–water solution, 1:1 by volume distilled water and 99% grade isopropyl alcohol.

Apparatus Preparation

Anion-Exchange Resin Column. Close the stopcock on the column and add a slurry of 25 ml of resin in 25 ml of distilled water to the transfer funnel attached to the column. Wash all the resin into the column and allow the water to pass through the column. Replace the funnel with a connecting tube and feed funnel. Pass 300 ml of 1N aqueous sodium hydroxide solution through the column.

Remove the connecting tube and wash it and the funnel to remove all sodium hydroxide. Attach a rubber bulb to the outlet of the column and draw out liquid until the level is at the top of the resin. Wash down the walls of the column above the resin while drawing liquid into the bulb.

Attach the clean connecting tube and feed funnel and pass 100 ml of distilled water through the column. Pass 50 ml of alcohol–water through the column and test for basicity using phenolphthalein. Any pink color should be discharged by one drop of 0.1N acid.

Cation-Exchange Resin Column. Slurry 30 ml of resin in 25 ml of the alcohol–water solution and add to a column. Wash the prepared column with 100 ml of the alcohol–water and discard the effluent. Pass an additional 50 ml of solvent through the column and test it for acidity. One drop of 0.1N NaOH solution should give a pink color to phenolphthalein indicator in the solution.

Procedure

Dissolve 5 g of sample (less than 10 meq of cations), weighed to the nearest milligram, in 50 ml of the alcohol–water solution. Transfer the solution quantitatively to the feed funnel and allow the liquid to pass through the column at the rate of 1–2 ml/min. Collect the effluent in a 250-ml beaker. Wash the funnel several times with solvent to effect complete transfer of sample into the column. Temporarily remove the connecting tube and force the supernatant liquid to the top of the resin. Wash down the walls of the column above the resin level several times with solvent. Attach the tube and pass 25 ml of solvent through the column and then pass 50 ml of alcohol through the column.

Pass the effluent from the cation column through the anion column. Collect the effluent in a 500-ml beaker. When all the solution has been washed into the resin, pass 100 ml of alcohol through the column.

Evaporate most of the solvent on the steam bath. Add isopropyl alcohol during the evaporation to keep the nonionics in solution. Quantitatively transfer the remaining liquid to a tared 100-ml beaker and evaporate off all the water and isopropyl alcohol. Add several 5-ml portions of acetone to assist in dehydrating the residue.

Dry the residue for 4 hr in a vacuum oven (300 mm Hg) at 65°. Cool the beaker in a desiccator and weigh. Repeat the heating, cooling, and weighing until successive weighings agree to 1 mg.

Calculations

$$\text{Nonionics, non-volatiles, wt \%} = \frac{\text{Weight of residue} \times 100}{\text{Weight of sample}}$$

DETERMINATION OF ALKYL SULFATES

The distinction between organic sulfates and sulfonates is effectively made by acid hydrolysis of the sulfates and determination of the sulfuric acid liberated by hydrolysis. Sulfonates are completely stable under hydrolysis conditions. For alkyl sulfates, the hydrolysis procedure offers another means of determining equivalent weight in addition to the gravimetric ashing method. Hydrolysis is quantitatively effected by reflux with dilute aqueous sulfuric acid for 1 hr, as was shown many years ago by Hart (20). The recommended method is based on the work of Hart and has been found convenient and accurate. Either 0.5N sulfuric acid or 1N hydrochloric acid can be used to cause hydrolysis. If the sample contains a mixture of alkyl sulfates and sulfonates, the latter can be determined subsequent to hydrolysis by either the Methylene Blue or the Bromocresol Green Titration methods. These titration methods require only small weights of material, which makes convenient an evaluation of the composition of commercial mixed detergents. Some typical results on a group of pure sodium alkyl sulfate detergents are shown in Table 19.3, where theoretical combining weight values are compared with those obtained by acid hydrolysis and the conventional ashing procedure.

DETERMINATION OF ALKYL SULFATES

ACID HYDROLYSIS METHOD

Reagents

Methyl orange indicator solution, 0.1 % in water.
Sodium hydroxide solution, standard 1N, carbonate free.
Sulfuric acid solution, 5 vol %. Mix 1 vol of concentrated H_2SO_4 (sp gr 1.84) into 19 vol of water while stirring.

Table 19.3. Results Obtained in the Determination of Alkyl Sulfates by Acid Hydrolysis[a]

R—OSO$_3$Na, where R is	Combining weight, g/equiv		
	Theoretical	By ashing	By acid hydrolysis
n-C$_{10}$[b]	260	260	267
n-C$_{16}$[b]	344	344	351
n-C$_{18}$[b]	373	369	371
n-C$_{12}$[c]	288	286	288
n-C$_{14}$[c]	316	314	314
n-C$_{18}$[c]	373	371	373

[a] Data from Weiss, O'Donnell, Shreve, and Peters (13).
[b] Primary alcohol derivatives.
[c] Secondary alcohol, substituent in second carbon atom.

Procedure

Weigh a sample containing 10–15 meq of hydrolyzable acidity into a 250-ml Erlenmeyer flask. Add 50 ml of distilled water and then, by pipet, exactly 50 ml of the 5 vol % sulfuric acid solution. Introduce some glass beads to prevent bumping. Attach the flask to a reflux condenser, raise the solution to the boiling point, and heat carefully until foaming ceases; then heat gently for 1 hr. At the end of the heating period allow the contents to cool, wash down the condenser with water from a wash bottle, and disconnect the condenser. Add 5 drops of indicator solution and titrate the contents with $1N$ sodium hydroxide solution. Make a blank titration simultaneously with the sample including approximately the same weight of glass beads and heating as with the sample. Also determine the alkalinity of the sample by titrating with standard acid in the usual way.

Calculation

$$\text{Alkyl sulfate content equiv/100 g} = \frac{(V - B)(N)}{10W} - A$$

where V = volume of sodium hydroxide solution required to titrate the hydrolyzable solution, ml
B = volume of sodium hydroxide solution required for the blank, ml
N = normality of the sodium hydroxide solution
W = weight of sample, g
A = alkalinity of sample, expressed as equivalents per 100 g of sample

DETERMINATION OF ALKYLBENZENE SULFONATES

As is commonly the case with compounds containing aromatic structures, strong absorption in the ultraviolet region provides a useful means for determinations at low concentrations. Ultraviolet absorption spectroscopy was employed by Weber, Morris, and Stumm (21) for the quantitative determination of alkylbenzene sulfonates in dilute aqueous solutions. The absorption spectra for $10^{-5}M$ aqueous solutions of some alkylbenzene sulfonates are shown in Figure 19.1. These solutions were prepared in $10^{-2}M$ KH_2PO_4 to prevent adsorption of the surface-active materials on glassware and measurements were compared against a blank containing $10^{-2}M$ KH_2PO_4 in distilled water. The absorptivity of KH_2PO_4 is minor in this spectral range and the background is sufficiently low to allow sufficient energy to come through the cells for accurate measurements.

The molar absorptivity of benzene sulfonate is 7.9×10^3 liters/mole-cm, p-toluene sulfonate 10.9×10^3 liters/mole-cm, and all the long-chain alkylbenzene sulfonates (2-hexyl, 2-octyl, 2-decyl, 2-dodecyl, 3-dodecyl, 6-dodecyl, and 2-tetradecyl) have their maximum absorption at 2250 Å with molar absorptivities at 12.9×10^3 liters/mole-cm. The ultraviolet method is not well suited for the determination of these materials in complex waste streams because of many possible interferences. The technique is satisfactory for obtaining some basic data in closely defined systems and was

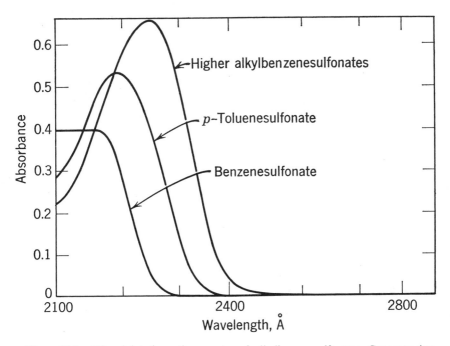

Figure 19.1. Ultraviolet absorption spectra of alkylbenzenesulfonates. Concentration $1 \times 10^{-5}M$. Data Weber, Morris, and Stumm (21), courtesy of the American Chemical Society. Copyright 1962 by the American Chemical Society. Reprinted by permission of the copyright owner.

used by Weber and Morris (22) to determine the kinetics of adsorption of alkylbenzene sulfonates from aqueous solutions.

REFERENCES

1. D. O. Hummel, *Identification and Analysis of Surface-Active Agents by Infrared and Chemical Methods*, Wiley, New York, 1962.
2. M. J. Rosen and H. A. Goldsmith, *Systematic Analysis of Surface-Active Agents*, Interscience, New York, 1960.
3. "Methods of Sampling and Testing Detergents," Brit. Std. 3762, British Standards House, 2 Park Street, London W.1, England, 1964.
4. W. Kling and F. Püschel, *Melliand Textilber.*, **15**, 21 (1934).
5. J. H. Jones, *J. Assoc. Offic. Anal. Chemists*, **28**, 398 (1945).
6. D. A. Shiraeff, *Am. Dyestuff Reporter*, **36**, 313 (1947); **37**, 411 (1948).
7. T. U. Marron and J. Schifferli, *Ind. Eng. Chem., Anal. Ed.*, **18**, 49 (1946).
8. T. Barr, J. Oliver, and W. V. Stubbings, *J. Soc. Chem. Ind.*, **67**, 45 (1948).
9. S. R. Epton, *Trans. Faraday Soc.*, **44**, 226 (1948).
10. H. Y. Lew, *J. Am. Oil Chemists' Soc.*, **41**, 297 (1964).
11. P. N. Degens, Jr., H. C. Evans, J. D. Kommer, and P. A. Winsor, *J. Appl. Chem.*, **3**, 54 (1953).
12. J. Longwell and W. D. Maniece, *Analyst*, **80**, 167 (1955).
13. F. T. Weiss, A. E. O'Donnell, R. J. Shreve, and E. D. Peters, *Anal. Chem.*, **27**, 198 (1955).
14. H. Winterscheidt, *Seifen-Öle-Fette-Wachse*, **81**, 408, 433 (1955).
15. J. W. Jenkins, *J. Am. Oil Chemists' Soc.*, **33**, 225 (1956).
16. P. Voogt, *Rec. Trav. Chim.*, **77**, 889 (1958).
17. P. Voogt, in *Analysis and Characterization of Oils, Fats and Fat Products*, Vol. 1, H. A. Boekenoogen, Ed., Interscience, New York, 1964, pp. 329-395.
18. A. E. O'Donnell, Paper presented at the 58th annual meeting of the American Oil Chemists' Society, May, 1967, New Orleans, Louisiana.
19. British Standards 3762, p. 22, Method B1, see ref. 3.
20. R. Hart, *Ind. Eng. Chem.*, **9**, 850 (1917).
21. W. J. Weber, J. C. Morris, and W. Stumm, *Anal. Chem.*, **34**, 1844 (1962).
22. W. J. Weber and J. C. Morris, *J. Sanit. Eng. Div., Proc. Am. Soc. Civil Eng.*, **90** (SA3), 79, (1964).

ANALYSIS OF PETROLEUM AND ITS PRODUCTS

There is a popular and erroneous belief that petroleum consists almost entirely of hydrocarbons and, consequently, that petroleum analysis is essentially an aspect of hydrocarbon analysis. Crude oil consists principally of hydrocarbons and their derivatives with appreciable amounts of combined sulfur, some nitrogen, and less oxygen; in addition, very small concentrations of metals including nickel, vanadium, and iron are complexed with natural organic chelates such as the porphyrins. The percentage of sulfur and nitrogen in the higher boiling fractions of crude petroleum is often so high that it is likely that the majority of the larger molecules contain some heteroatoms. An illustration of the complexity of crude oils examined in a recent survey of the distribution of sulfur, as shown in Figure 20.1, clearly indicates the wide spread of concentrations of sulfur in the various crude oils. Since petroleum is such a complex material, the analyst dealing with it will need a wide scope of techniques and procedures, of which some are covered in this text. Table 20.1 outlines the principal types of materials found either in crude oil or in the products of a petroleum refinery and the chapters in which their determinations are described. A thorough review of the composition of crude oil was published by Smith of the U.S. Bureau of Mines (1).

Table 20.1. Principal Materials Found in Crude Oil and Petroleum Products

Type of compound	Found in crude oil	Found in petroleum products	Chapter in which determination is described
Paraffinic hydrocarbons	Yes	Yes	1
Naphthenic hydrocarbons	Yes	Yes	1
Olefinic hydrocarbons	(very small)	Yes	3
Aromatic hydrocarbons	Yes	Yes	2
Sulfur compounds	Yes	Yes	16
Basic nitrogen compounds	Yes	Yes	14
Nonbasic nitrogen compounds	Yes	Yes	15
Phenols	Trace	Yes	10
Carboxylic acids	Yes	Yes	5

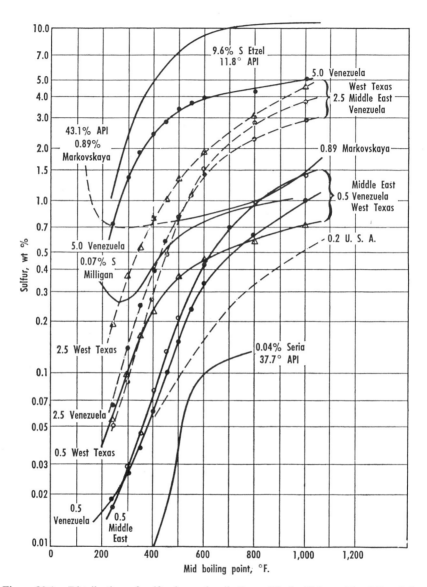

Figure 20.1. Distribution of sulfur in crude oil. From W. L. Nelson, *The Oil and Gas Journal*, Dec. 4, 1967, page 92. Reprinted by permission of the copyright owner.

Refinery processes are designed to manufacture products with closely defined specifications. In the United States the principal refinery product is automotive gasoline, which is produced by a number of processes involving distillation, cracking of crude oil, and some synthetic operations. Commercial gasolines contain saturated, olefinic, and aromatic hydrocarbons with an extremely low content of sulfur, nitrogen, or oxygen compounds since the heteroatoms are removed in processing. Because gasoline is such a major product and because of the close engine octane number requirement specified in its use, much attention has been given to the determination of the composition of this product. Higher boiling products have been extensively investigated but none in the great detail devoted to gasolines. Useful reviews of method development for hydrocarbon analysis have been published by the American Society for Testing and Materials (ASTM) (2, 3).

METHODS FOR HYDROCARBON TYPE ANALYSIS

Despite the vast strides that have been made in the field of hydrocarbon analysis in the past quarter-century, a thorough account of the individual hydrocarbons of which a petroleum distillate is composed does not extend beyond the gasoline range. For the higher boiling materials, considerable evidence is at hand concerning the types of compounds present, and, in some cases, specific compounds have been identified. However, such detailed knowledge, although useful, is not usually required to evaluate fuels or lubricants since the amount of any individual component is small. Rather, the performance of products is generally evaluated or the distribution of classes or groups of hydrocarbons determined. Consequently, "type" analysis is important. The principal classifications are paraffins, naphthenes, olefins, and aromatics, although further subdivision of types can occur in higher molecular weight fractions. With larger molecules it is possible to have mono-, di- and polycyclic aromatics and naphthenes or hydrocarbons with mixed functions and it is occasionally important to determine some of these specific subtypes. In general the most useful methods for determining classes of hydrocarbons involve selective adsorption.

The separation of hydrocarbon mixtures by selective adsorption generally involves their differential adsorption on silica gel, which decreases in the order: aromatics, olefins, saturates. When an appropriate mixture of these hydrocarbon types is passed into a column of silica gel and eluted with a polar solvent, the fractions collected appear in the following order: pure saturate, saturate–olefin mixture, pure olefin, olefin–aromatic mixture, and pure aromatic. Some years ago the Bureau of Standards developed analytical methods (4) based upon the use of a fine gel and a narrow column so that the volume of intermediate cuts was small compared to the total. The composition of the original gasoline was estimated from a plot of the volume collected vs. the refractive indexes of the cuts. These methods have found extensive use in the industry, being adopted by the American Society for Testing and Materials (5). Further developments in the adsorption technique for separation of hydrocarbons have gone in several directions. Fink, Lewis, and Weiss (6) were interested in obtaining large quantities of the separated gasoline fractions for further characterization and, for this purpose, investigated adsorbent characteristics and method variables. They concluded that the efficiency in this separation was directly proportional to the length of the column and inversely proportional to the square of its diameter (eff. $\sim L/D^2$). An example of an adsorptogram of a catalytically cracked gasoline fraction, shown in Figure 20.2, was obtained on a 1 × 230 cm column packed with 121 g of 100–200 mesh Davison silica gel. Twenty milliliters of sample was charged, the displacing agent was ethanol, and the separation was conducted at −40°C.

A particularly important technique to determine the position of the

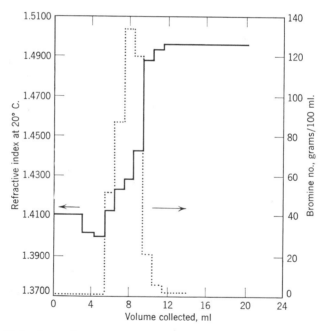

Figure 20.2. Separation of catalytically cracked gasoline fraction (200–250°F). (– – –) Bromine number. $\left(\dfrac{3}{M}\right)$ Refractive index. Data from Fink, Lewis, and Weiss (6). Copyright 1950 by the American Chemical Society. Reprinted by permission of the copyright owner.

hydrocarbon fractions on silica gel involves the addition of a mixture of indicating dyes to mark the position of the aromatics and the olefins (7, 8). Instead of eluting the sample from the column and examining the fractions collected, the determination of composition is made by measuring the length of the zones corresponding to the three hydrocarbon types. Fluorescent dyes have been found that make the boundaries visible under ultraviolet irradiation. Criddle and LeTourneau (8) applied the technique to petroleum products boiling below 500°F and found it possible to determine saturates, olefins, and aromatics with an accuracy of 1 %, which is an improvement on the bromination methods for olefin determination. Because of this, the fluorescent indicator adsorption (FIA) method has been taken into extensive use in the petroleum industry (9). The recommended method given in this chapter for the determination of hydrocarbon types in light petroleum distillates by fluorescent indicator adsorption is taken from earlier publications; this method is useful for the characterization of distillates that boil below 315°C. The classification "aromatics" will include also compounds containing S, N, or O as well as diolefins and aromatic olefins because of similar adsorption characteristics. The FIA method has been extended to the separation of heavier distillates by Knight and Groennings (10) and by work of the Hydrocarbon Analysis Panel of the Institute of Petroleum (11) and has also been utilized for the analysis of mixtures of oxygenated compounds with hydrocarbons in work published by Ellis and LeTourneau (12) and by Knight and Groennings (13). It has been found that olefins and monochloroparaffins of the same molecular weight range have similar adsorbabilities on silica gel and that polychloroparaffins behave like aromatics. Consequently it is possible to use the FIA method to analyze mixtures containing paraffins, monochloroparaffins, and polychloroparaffins (14).

DETERMINATION OF HYDROCARBON TYPES IN LIGHT PETROLEUM DISTILLATES

FLUORESCENT INDICATOR ADSORPTION (FIA) METHOD

Apparatus

Adsorption column for light distillates, made of glass, and consisting of a charger section, a separator section, and an analyzer section with tip, as shown in Figure 20.3. The analyzer section is made of true-bore capillary tubing of 1.60–1.65 mm i.d. The uniformity of the tubing must be such that an approximately 100-mm thread of mercury does not vary by more than 0.3 mm in length in any part of the analyzer section.

Column mounting, a manifold (air or nitrogen) pressure system convenient for multiple installations. The T-joints in the pressure line should be about 3–4 in. apart, and should have a shutoff valve and a stainless steel inner spherical joint to

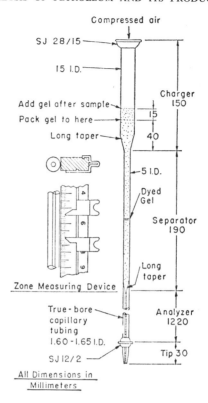

Figure 20.3. Adsorption column for light distillates. Reproduced by permission from the Shell Method Series.

fit the glass joints at the top of the columns. The line is fastened horizontally about $7\frac{1}{2}$ ft from the floor and 3–4 in. from the wall in a small darkroom.

Zone measuring device, grooved meter rules equipped with four movable metal clips. Very narrow zones are marked with a pair of clips, one of which is the mirror image of the other, and the tips of the clips may be painted with a luminous paint for better visibility. The rules are fastened adjacent to the analyzer sections of the columns.

Ultraviolet light source, with radiation predominantly at 3660 Å. A convenient arrangement consists of two 36-in. "black light" units, mounted vertically at each end and 8–10 in. in front of the bank of columns in the darkroom.

Dispensers for silica gel and for dyed silica gel, as illustrated in Figure 20.4. The dispenser for dyed silica gel delivers the prescribed amount, about 0.06 ml, with each turn of the handle.

Vibrator, for packing of the adsorbent.

Hypodermic tubing, for column cleaning; 19 gage (1.07 mm o.d.), about 90 cm long, with a 45° tip, and connected to tap water.

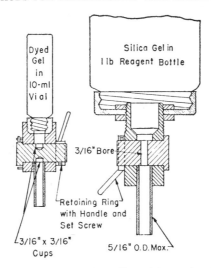

Figure 20.4.   Dispensers for silica gel and dyed silica gel. Reproduced by permission from the Shell Method Series.

Materials

Silica gel, Davison Chemical Co., Baltimore, Maryland. Grade 923, manufactured to insure minimum olefin polymerization. To be satisfactory, all the gel should pass through a 177 μ (No. 80) sieve, 95% (min) through a 149 μ (No. 100) sieve, and 15% (max) through a 74 μ (No. 200) sieve. Quickly transfer the dry gel as received to the 1-lb reagent bottle with a dispensing closure. It is important to keep the gel dry.

Dyed silica gel, silica gel impregnated with a dye mixture. This is available from Patent Chemicals, Inc., 335 McLean Blvd., Paterson, New Jersey. Store in a vial with a dispenser cap that will deliver the amount of gel required for a column.

Isopropyl alcohol, 99%.

Pressuring gas, air (or nitrogen), delivered to the top of the column at a regulated pressure up to 15 psi.

Procedure

Insert a piece of cotton in the tip of the column, and suspend the column freely from a loose-fitting clamp placed under the spherical joint. Introduce silica gel, in portions, from the 1-lb dispenser until the separator section is half-full, applying the vibrator in up-and-down motions as needed while supporting the fragile analyzer section with the palm of the hand and letting the column rotate slowly in its support. Add the measure of dyed silica gel (about a 4-mm layer) from its dispenser, followed by more silica gel, with a continual vibration, until the gel extends about 40 mm into the charger section; a 5-min vibration period may be required for satisfactory packing. If not used immediately close the column to protect the gel from atmospheric moisture.

From a pipet add slowly 0.75 ± 0.03 ml of sample to the top of the gel. Cover immediately with an approximately 15-mm layer of additional gel (to prevent intermixing with the eluting alcohol), and fill the charger section with isopropyl alcohol.

Samples containing a substantial amount of low-boiling material should be cooled and charged from a hypodermic syringe about 10 mm below the surface of the gel.

Apply sufficient pressure to move the liquid front at about 5 mm/min through the separator section. The pressure will vary with the nature of the sample; for gasolines it will be about 2 psi, a little higher for kerosine.

Observe the progress of the sample in ultraviolet light. When the red alcohol marker, which indicates the upper end of the sample, has advanced about 200 mm into the analyzer section, which should require about 1 hr, mark the zones by setting the clips on the meter rules. The saturate zone extends from the colorless liquid front to the lowest point of maximum greenish yellow fluorescence; the olefin zone extends from there to the lowest point of strong blue or whitish blue fluorescence; the aromatic zone extends from there to the highest point of strong red or reddish brown color, the latter being best observed in incandescent light. Quickly set the clips on the meter rule at these points; read and record the lengths of the zones.

Allow the sample to travel down the column another 100 mm, and again measure the zones as outlined above. Repeat until two consecutive sets of measurements are in good agreement.

Release the pressure, disconnect the column, and rinse out the gel with a jet of water from the long hypodermic tubing; then rinse with acetone or alcohol and dry.

Calculation and Reporting

$$\text{Aromatics, vol } \% = \frac{100L_a}{L}$$

$$\text{Olefins, vol } \% = \frac{100L_0}{L}$$

$$\text{Saturates, vol } \% = \frac{100L_s}{L}$$

where L_a, L_0, L_s = the lengths, in mm, of the aromatics, olefins, and saturates zones, and L = sum of the three zones, mm.

SEPARATION OF TYPE FRACTIONS FROM MIXTURES

For the more detailed analysis of components of each of the hydrocarbon types—saturates, olefins, and aromatics—it is most useful to examine a separated fraction. There are several procedures available for this purpose, including one used for many years that involves the reaction of olefins and aromatics with concentrated mineral acid and their removal by extraction with excess acid. Such a procedure is illustrated by Method A of ASTM D 2002 (15) in which the acid reagent is prepared from a mixture of concentrated sulfuric acid and phosphorus pentoxide. This technique has limitations and cannot be used, for example, on stocks containing appreciable concentrations of olefins, because olefins may react, under the influence of acid, with other components to produce higher molecular weight materials that are not extractable. A generally more useful method for isolation of the saturates is by adsorption chromatography over silica gel. The Fluorescent Indicator method is particularly useful, and its operation, illustrated by Method B of ASTM D 2002 (15) and by ASTM D 2003 (15), involves the use of a silica gel column. A fluorescent indicator is employed to locate the end of the saturates zone and the total effluent collected before the elution of this indicator is taken as the saturates fraction in the sample. The recommended method given in this chapter for the isolation of the saturates fraction from light petroleum distillates uses the apparatus of ASTM D 2003.

METHOD FOR ISOLATION OF SATURATES FRACTION FROM LIGHT PETROLEUM DISTILLATES

Apparatus

Adsorption column (Figure 20.5).
Receiver, graduated.
Vibrator.
Hypodermic syringe.
Ultraviolet light source, with radiation predominantly at 3660 Å.
Refrigerant circulation system, to circulate liquid cooled to 5–15°C through the adsorption column jacket.

Reagents

Isopropyl alcohol, 99%.
Silica gel and dyed silica gel, as specified in the Fluorescent Indication Adsorption method.

Procedure

Clean the adsorption column with chromic–sulfuric acid, water, and acetone and dry air.

Introduce a small glass pellet, approximately $\frac{1}{16}$ in. in diameter, to prevent the flow of silica gel from the bottom of the column, and sufficiently nonspherical to permit liquid elution.

Clamp the column in a vertical position and pack by adding silica gel slowly through a funnel while applying the vibrator. When the silica gel surface is within approximately 50 mm of the top of the 6-mm section, add approximately 0.5 ml of standard dyed gel. Continue adding silica gel and applying vibration until the

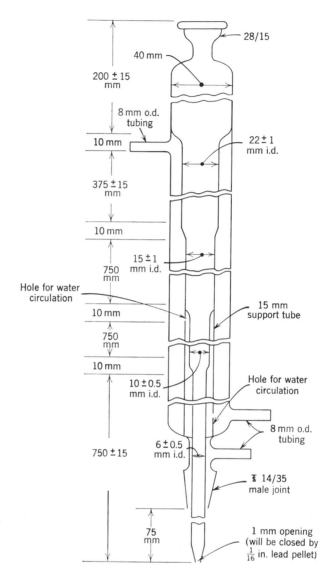

Figure 20.5. High-efficiency silica gel column. Copyright 1964 by the American Society for Testing and Materials. Reprinted by permission of the copyright owner.

surface reaches the top of the 22-mm section and does not drop noticeably with continued vibrating or tapping. The volume of aromatics plus olefins in the charge should not exceed 20 ml, which corresponds to 1 ml per 18 ml of silica gel. Chill the sample and a hypodermic syringe of sufficient size to 0–5°C. Draw the sample into the syringe and adjust the level to the volume desired. Discharge the total sample with the tip of the syringe needle inserted 20–30 mm below the surface of the silica gel. Add sufficient silica gel to raise the level 10 mm. Record the volume charged to the nearest 0.1 ml.

Fill the remaining portion of the column with isopropyl alcohol and apply N_2 at a pressure of no more than 10 psig to move the liquid down the column. Place the graduated receiver in a cooling bath filled with ice and water. Collect the saturates eluent in one fraction until the leading edge of the fluorescent yellow color reaches a point approximately $\frac{1}{4}$ in. above the column tip. Continue elution with alcohol to remove all the sample from the column. Discard and wash all the gel from the column with a jet of water.

REFERENCES

1. H. M. Smith, "Qualitative and Quantitative Aspects of Crude Oil Composition," Bull. 642, Bureau of Mines, U.S. Dept. of the Interior, 1968.
2. "Hydrocarbon Analysis," ASTM Spec. Publ. No. 389, 1965, Philadelphia, Pa.
3. *Manual on Hydrocarbon Analysis*, 2nd ed., 1968, ASTM Spec. Publ. No. 332 A, Philadelphia, Pa.
4. B. J. Mair and A. F. Forziati, *J. Res. Natl. Bur. Std*, **32**, 151 (1944).
5. ASTM Method D 936, *Standards*, Part 17, 1969.
6. D. R. Fink, R. W. Lewis, and F. T. Weiss, *Anal. Chem.*, **22**, 850, 858 (1950).
7. A. L. Conrad, *ibid.*, **20**, 725 (1948).
8. D. W. Criddle and R. L. LeTourneau, *ibid.*, **23**, 1620 (1951).
9. ASTM Method D 1319. ASTM *Standards*, Part 17, 1969.
10. H. S. Knight and S. Groennings, *Anal. Chem.*, **28**, 1949 (1956).
11. Hydrocarbon Analysis Panel, *J. Inst. Petroleum*, **51**, 138 (1965).
12. W. H. Ellis and R. L. LeTourneau, *Anal. Chem.*, **25**, 1269 (1953).
13. H. S. Knight and S. Groennings, *ibid.*, **26**, 1549 (1954).
14. T. A. Washall, *ibid.*, **41**, 971 (1969).
15. ASTM *Standards*, 1969, Part 17.

PART THREE

Laboratory Methodology and Practice

CHROMATOGRAPHY

This chapter will provide a review of the principal chromatographic methods employed in the analytical separation of organic compounds with concern for their applications and their limitations. No attempt will be made to cover all of this large and active area, nor is that necessary, since many excellent reviews and texts are available to which references will be made. Instead the goal will be, wherever possible, to describe and compare procedures and techniques so that the analyst will be able to make more precise decisions on the design of his analyses.

Chromatography is the name given to the process by which the components of a mixture are repeatedly partitioned between a stationary (solid or liquid) phase and a mobile (liquid or gas) phase. The four types of chromatography in use today can be readily characterized by the two phases involved: (*1*) liquid–solid, (*2*) liquid–liquid, (*3*) gas–liquid, and (*4*) gas–solid chromatography. In current analytical practice the mobile phase is applied either in elution or in displacement development. In elution chromatography the stationary phase is continually washed with a flow of the mobile phase to give rise to the familiar elution chromatogram of which gas chromatography provides a common example. In displacement development the mixture to be separated is put into contact with the stationary adsorbent phase and then forced to move in plug flow by a displacing agent which has a greater affinity for the stationary phase. The sample components are aligned in order of adsorbability with the more strongly adsorbed displacing those less strongly adsorbed. In displacement development there are no sample-free zones isolating the components of a sample. An important example of the use of displacement development is the FIA hydrocarbon type analysis described in Chapter 20. In practice, elution chromatography is more commonly employed for the determination of the individual components in a mixture because the eluting agent can be used to resolve and separate individual components. Chromatographic methods are further divided by reference to the actual physical conditions used, such as "column chromatography," "thin-layer" chromatography, or "paper" chromatography. Methods involving the use of ion exchangers and molecular sieves, although not usually considered a branch of chromatography, are also discussed in this chapter because they are closely linked in analytical practice to chromatography.

Methods of monitoring the separation of components are required in all chromatographic processes. In the separation of colored natural materials, the original observations were based on the natural colors of the separated components themselves. As utilization of the chromatographic technique spread into organic chemical analysis, optical, physical, spectroscopic, and chemical means have been used to follow separations. In much of the early work, fractions were taken and separately analyzed, but since this is so slow it has been supplanted largely by continuous monitors or "detectors." In those fields of separation that demand rapid monitoring of the column effluent, such as in gas chromatography, much thought has been given to detectors and a considerable discussion of this topic is presented later in this chapter.

LIQUID–SOLID CHROMATOGRAPHY

Liquid–solid chromatography, often called adsorption chromatography, is historically the earliest form of analytical chromatography and was used by Tswett in the early part of this century to analyze natural products. In the 1930's it was demonstrated that the technique could differentiate fine structural details in organic mixtures (1). Many workers soon entered the field and it developed rapidly. The most general value of liquid–solid chromatography is separation of mixtures on a type basis prior to the detailed determination of components or functional groups by a more specific method. Such a preliminary separation can reduce the background effect of interfering materials or permit the concentration of a component for more definitive analysis. Examples of the use of liquid–solid chromatography in the functional chapters are the removal of olefins prior to the determination of pyrroles (Chapter 15) and the separation of petroleum fractions into aromatics, olefins, and saturates (Chapter 20) for "type" analysis and also for the preparation of fractions for more complete analysis. In these chapters fully detailed procedures are given that illustrate typical applications of the techniques. The detection system in the FIA "type" analysis of petroleum fractions (Chapter 20) involves treating the silica gel by addition of fluorescent dyes that separate in such a way as to mark the boundaries between the hydrocarbon-type zones. The lengths of the zones are directly related to the concentration of the aromatics, olefins, and saturates in the original sample.

A listing of some of the common adsorbents is given in Table 21.1. An excellent review of the properties of the adsorbents and the principles and applications of the technique has been published by Snyder (2) and a useful compilation of information on solid adsorbents has been issued by Deitz (3). Adsorption chromatography is generally applied on an empirical basis because the isotherms are irregular and not always easily defined. The

Table 21.1. Examples of Some Common Adsorbents Employed in Chromatographic Separations

Adsorbent	Grade	Source	Composition	Typical uses
Alumina	Reagent, various mesh sizes, acidic, basic, neutral	Many suppliers	Al_2O_3	Separation of petroleum fractions, especially heterocyclics
	F-1, F-20, H-21	Aluminum Company of America	Activated aluminas	
	Porocel	Porocel Co.	Activated aluminas	
Attapulgus clay	Various mesh sizes	Attapulgus Clay Co., Philadelphia, Pa.	Hydrous magnesium aluminum silicate	Removal natural products prior to insecticide analysis
Calcium carbonate	Precipitated	Several suppliers	$CaCO_3$	Separation of carotenoids
Carbon	DARCO G-60	Matheson, Coleman and Bell	Activated wood charcoal	Can be used fairly widely; separations dependent upon surface activation
	Norit activated	American Norit Co.	Activated carbons	
	Nuchar	Westvaco Corp.	Carbonized cellulose	
Celite	Celite 545, various mesh sizes	Johns-Manville	Diatomaceous earth	Filter aid, diluent for adsorbents, gas chromatographic support
	Hyflosupercel	Johns-Manville	Diatomaceous earth	Filter aid, diluent for adsorbents, gas chromatographic support
Florisil	Various mesh sizes	Floridin Co., Pittsburgh, Pa.	Magnesium silicate	Separation of nitrogen compounds, insecticides, lipids, petroleum fractions
Magnesia		MgO	Powdered MgO	Separation of carotenes and similar natural products
Silica gel	Many mesh sizes available Code 923, 100–200 mesh	Many reagent suppliers Davison Chemical Co., Baltimore, Md.		Separation of petroleum fractions FIA determination of saturates, olefins, and aromatics
Silicic acid		Many reagent suppliers	$SiO_2 \cdot xH_2O$ Powdered, dry	
Sugar	Cane sugar	Sucrose, confectioners sugar		Separation of chlorophylls

choice of an adsorbent is generally based on the polarity of the adsorbent and the nature of the materials to be separated. Silica gel and alumina are typical polar adsorbents and are widely used to separate hydrocarbons of different types and heterocyclics. Both of these adsorbents are available from a number of suppliers in different levels of activity and mesh and pore sizes. Other polar adsorbents, used for certain separations, include Florisil and Attapulgus clay. Activated carbon is somewhat less polar, but the properties of commercial carbons vary greatly with the source. The diatomaceous earths are very weak adsorbents and find use as diluents in mixtures with other adsorbents, essentially as a filter aid. Other weak adsorbents, such as powdered sugar and calcium carbonate, have been used for the separation of the highly conjugated carotenoids. Many examples of applications of adsorbents are given in the texts of Snyder and Deitz.

MOLECULAR SIEVES

The "molecular sieves," which have become so useful as sorbents for small molecules such as H_2O or CO_2 (4) and for the long-chain regular structures such as the normal paraffins (5), are complex alumina silicates classified as zeolites. Detailed X-ray investigations of the structure of natural and synthetic zeolites (6) show that their framework encloses regular cavities as illustrated in Figure 21.1. When in contact with water vapor, the cavities are hydrated but lose this water when dried at elevated temperatures. In the dried molecular sieves, pores leading to the cavities permit molecules of small cross section to penetrate into the interior. A specific use for the determination of normal paraffins in petroleum fractions is described in Chapter 1 utilizing the facility with which the proper sieve can selectively sorb normal paraffins while rejecting branched paraffins, aromatics, and naphthenes.

A summary listing of the behavior of some common materials with two synthetic commercial molecular sieves is shown in Table 21.2. Molecular sieve Type 4A has an effective pore diameter of approximately 4 Å and rejects molecules larger than this. It is used principally for drying the light gases. Type 5A, with pore diameter in the range of 5 Å, is effective for the separation of the straight-chain organic molecules from their branched counterparts. In a study of the 5A sieve as a subtractor in gas chromatographic analysis (7), it was shown that columns operated at 100°C would completely remove normal paraffins (except CH_4), normal olefins, and normal alcohols, while allowing the following to pass: isoparaffins, aromatic hydrocarbons, naphthenes, branched olefins; branched alcohols, ketones, and ethers. It is interesting that isopropy alcohol, acetone, and methyl ethyl ketone were not retained while n-butanol and propionaldehyde were completely adsorbed.

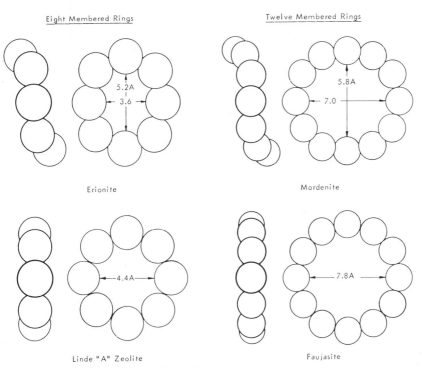

Figure 21.1. Zeolite pore openings.

Table 21.2. Behavior of Materials in Commercial Molecular Sieves[a]

Adsorbed in Type 5A and Type 4A	Adsorbed in Type 5A but not in Type 4A	Not adsorbed in either Type 4A or Type 5A
Water	n-Butanol and higher n-alcohols	Isobutane and all isoparaffins
Methanol	Butene and higher n-olefins	Benzene and all aromatics
Ammonia		
Hydrogen sulfide	Propane and higher n-paraffins	Cyclohexane and all cyclics with at least 4-membered rings
Carbon dioxide	Cyclopropane	Molecules larger than 5 Å
Propylene		
Ethylene		
Ethane		

[a] From Linde Co., Division Union Carbide Corp., "Octane Improvement," 1959, p. 8.

ION EXCHANGE

Ion-exchange separations are widely used both for the separation of inorganic materials of well-known ionic behavior and also for organic compounds whose ionic behavior may be somewhat less well defined. Because of the high degree of simplicity, utility, and directness of the ion-exchange techniques, they are becoming increasingly valuable in the analysis of organic compounds and their uses are discussed in several of the functional chapters, particularly for the analysis of surface-active materials (Chapter 19). Several excellent reviews are available on the properties and uses of ion exchangers (8–12).

The reviews of Samuelson (11, 12) are directed to analysis and gives a number of useful procedures for the separation and analysis of both inorganic and organic materials.

The commercially available ion-exchange resins developed for organic analytical use are based almost entirely upon crosslinked polymers that contain electrolyte functional groups. The cation exchangers may contain strongly acidic nuclear sulfonic groups on a polystyrene lattice, intermediately acidic phosphonic groups on polystyrene, or weakly acidic carboxylic groups on an acrylic lattice. Anion exchangers may be strongly basic quaternary ammonium groups on a polystyrene lattice, intermediately basic tertiary amines on an epoxy-polyamine lattice, or weakly basic polyamine groups on a polystyrene lattice.

For application to the separation of organic compounds the procedures involving ion exchange can be conveniently divided into the following classifications:

1. Separation of cations from anions, or vice versa.

2. Separation and removal of ionic materials from nonionics. This is employed in the analysis of commercial detergents (see Chapter 19).

3. Conversion of salts of organic compounds into acids or bases. An example of this would be the conversion of a salt of an organic acid into the free acid for a simplified determination of equivalent weight.

4. If an organic compound is not ionic, it may be converted into an ionic compound prior to separation. For instance, it has been demonstrated by Samuelson (11) that a basic resin can be reacted with sodium bisulfite, in which form it will retain some carbonyl compounds as their bisulfite addition compounds. Polyols, including the carbohydrates, can be separated on anion-exchange resins in the borate form since the polyol-borate complexes are ionic (13, 14).

5. Electrolytes can be separated from nonelectrolytes by the "ion-exclusion" technique of Wheaton and Bauman (15), who observed that ionic substances

are effectively excluded from the pores of an ion-exchange resin while the nonelectrolytes are admitted. The result is that the ionic substance elutes more rapidly from the column.

Systems for monitoring the separation of components are taken widely from available techniques. With surface-active materials the eluted components can be titrated as acids, determined colorimetrically, or simply taken to dryness and weighed. Considerably more sophisticated, continuous techniques have been employed, such as the continuous recording apparatus described by Harlow and Morman (16) in which the eluted acids are automatically titrated and the results measured by a recorder (see Chapter 5). Spectroscopic techniques are also useful and have been employed to follow separations.

ION-EXCHANGE SEPARATIONS IN NONAQUEOUS MEDIA

The rate of ion exchange is generally considerably lower in nonaqueous systems than in the corresponding aqueous system. With solvents that do not swell the resin, the ion-exchange rates may be particularly low. It is quite difficult to remove the last traces of water from an ion-exchange resin, and variations in the small remaining amounts of water that hydrate the ions supported on the resin have a large influence on the properties of the exchanger. Because of these quite practical problems, analytical chemistry has made only limited use of ion-exchange separations in completely nonaqueous media.

Some publications, however, have appeared that show that nonaqueous separations can be utilized under carefully specified conditions. Hale (17) gives information on procedures to be used in nonaqueous systems and points out that in many cases it is preferable to use moist resins rather than completely dry resins since the rates of exchange may be prohibitively slow with the dry resins. Munday and Eaves (18, 19) made an extensive study of the use of nonaqueous ion-exchange chromatography. They thoroughly studied the pretreatment of the resins with organic solvents, such as methanol, nitromethane, or amines, and were able to distinguish between physical adsorption and absorption due to ion exchange. Under closely defined experimental conditions they were able to separate small concentrations of organic acids and bases, as well as pyrrolic nitrogen compounds, from petroleum fractions. They found a considerable effect of molecular weight on exchangeability. As an example, naphthenic acids exchanged effectively with a commerical anion resin that had not been completely dried. To exchange the higher molecular weight naphthenic acids from gas oils, it was found preferable to use a resin with an expanded matrix structure that had been pretreated with methanol. Munday and Eaves (18) provide detailed information for the separation of naphthenic acids, alkyl phenols, nitrogen bases, such as quinoline and benzoquinoline, and pyrrolic compounds, such as indole and carbazoles. The pyrrolic compounds, which have an extremely low basicity, were all physically adsorbed by the resins and were readily eluted by methanol. Pyrrole itself polymerized on the resin and could not be recovered.

A number of specific applications were illustrated. *Alkyl phenols*, occurring at a concentration as low as 33.9 ppm in gasoline, were recovered by being passed through a commercial anion exchanger. The resin in the column had been converted to the basic form in the usual way with aqueous alkali and was washed with four bed volumes of hydrocarbon solvent prior to use. The resin column removed phenol equivalent to 60% of its exchange capacity prior to breakthrough. A flow rate of 40 ml of gasoline per minute was used. The phenols could be desorbed with an $0.2M$ aqueous solution of ammonium carbonate for a 98% recovery. *Nitrogen bases* in gasoline were removed by percolation over a cationic resin at a flow rate up to 75 ml/min. Desorption of the nitrogen bases was made after the column had been washed with petroleum ether and methanol. The bases were then removed with $2N$ aqueous hydrochloric acid.

Snyder and Buell have made important contributions in the application of ion exchange for the separation of petroleum fractions (20, 21). In their work a commercial cation-exchange resin is converted to the acid form with methanolic HCl and dried by being washed, consecutively, with methanol, benzene, and cyclohexane. When materials are introduced into the column, in cyclohexane solution, the aromatic hydrocarbons and most of the phenols are not adsorbed and pass through. The extremely weak bases, such as the carbazoles, are only held partially but the more strongly basic compounds, including the pyridines, are held and eluted with ethylamine in benzene–methanol. They find the separations on cation- and anion-exchange resins convenient and repeatable and have integrated them into a general separation scheme using also spectroscopic techniques for the determination of the nitrogen and oxygen compound types in petroleum fractions (22). Webster, Wilson, and Franks (23) have described the analytical application of ion-exchange resins of large pore size for nonaqueous separations of petroleum products.

LIQUID–LIQUID CHROMATOGRAPHY

Although liquid–liquid chromatography has been an available laboratory technique for a number of years, it had the reputation, until very recently, of being slow and cumbersome. The past limitations in obtaining satisfactory supports and liquid phases and the difficulties in finding suitable detectors seem to be in the process of being overcome. There appears to be the likelihood that current developments, especially those involving high pressure systems, may improve the speed of liquid–liquid chromatography so that it will find many practical uses. This is particularly true in areas in which gas chromatography is limited such as in handling materials of low volatility or of low thermal stability. The present surge of interest in liquid–liquid chromatography has brought forth a considerable group of publications but developments have not yet gone sufficiently far to enable a critical review or comparison of techniques to be made. Some of the principal developments, however, are discussed in this section and it is to be expected that further growth in this field will be rapid.

An early practical problem that must be faced in the development of any modern chromatographic apparatus is the design of a practical and sensitive continuous detector. In liquid chromatography the column effluent will contain the sample components vastly diluted by the eluant. Several types of detectors have been put into use: ultraviolet absorption detectors have been employed (24–27) and are commercially available but are obviously limited to those materials having strong absorption in the ultraviolet region of the spectrum and consequently are most usefully applied to aromatic compounds. Since the molar absorptivities vary, calibrations must be made for the individual components in a sample to relate recorder response to component concentration. Another detector is based on the differences in refractive index between the eluant and the components of the sample. Lambert and Porter (28, 29) have developed a useful liquid–liquid chromatographic apparatus using a commercial automatic recording differential refractometer as a detector. Another detection system has been described (30–32) in which the liquid effluent is allowed to drip onto a moving metal band or wire that takes it into a series of heated zones, first to evaporate the solvent and subsequently to pyrolyze the fractions being separated. The vapors from pyrolysis are swept into a detector by a current of inert gas. Several variations of this type of detector are now commercially available.

The resolution and speed of liquid chromatography can be materially increased by optimizing the packing materials and operating the system at high pressures. The efficiency of a column is increased by increasing diffusion rates. This can be accomplished by decreasing stationary phase thickness and particle size since thin layers allow more rapid diffusion. Horvath, Preiss, and Lipsky (33) developed a rapid liquid chromatographic separation based on the use of glass beads of 50 and 100 μ diameters coated with ion-exchange resins. Kirkland (25) has developed a coating for spherical siliceous particles that can be prepared with controlled surface porosity (CSP). An example of the effectiveness of this packing material in the separation of some aromatic herbicides is shown in Figure 21.2, where the elution times were under 6 min compared to more than 40 min with a conventional diatomaceous earth support (24). Some examples of the use of high pressures have been reviewed by Giddings and his coworkers, who have conducted separations at pressures up to 2000 atm (34). Sie and Rijnders have made separations with supercritical fluids as the moving phase (26, 27). Experiments with n-pentane and isopropyl alcohol as the mobile phases under supercritical conditions showed a marked increase in the rate of separation compared to that at normal operating pressures. An example of the effectiveness of their technique is shown in Figure 21.3, in which a mixture of four aromatic hydrocarbons containing from one to four rings per molecule is separated in 60 sec. The separation was carried out on an untreated alumina with n-pentane as the mobile phase at 213°C and a pressure of 50 kg/cm² (equivalent to 700 psi).

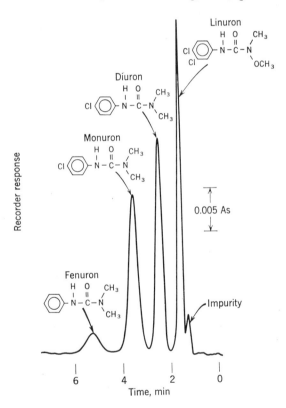

Figure 21.2. Example of separation of herbicides by liquid chromatography with controlled surface porosity support. Column: 500 mm × 2.1 mm i.d. Packing: 1.0% β,β'-oxydipropionitrile on 37–44 μ CSP support. Carrier: dibutyl ether. Flow rate: 1.14 cc/min. Sample: 1 μl of 67 ng/ml each in dibutyl ether. Data from Kirkland (25), Courtesy of the *Journal of Chromatographic Science.*

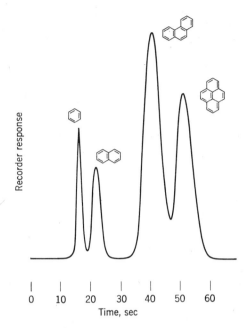

Figure 21.3. Example of a rapid separation by fluid-solid chromatography Column: 1 × 6 mm i.d. untreated alumina 120–140 mesh. Mobile fluid, *n*-pentane; temperature 213°C; pressure, 50 kg/cm². Data from Sie and Rijnders (26), courtesy of Elsevier Publishing Company.

They point out that the volatility gain of supercritical fluid chromatography over conventional gas chromatography is large for compounds boiling above 450°C and they predict that it should be possible to apply the technique to substances having very high boiling points and yet obtain separations in reasonable times.

SEPARATION BY PAPER CHROMATOGRAPHY AND THIN-LAYER CHROMATOGRAPHY

In paper and thin-layer chromatography the mobile phase flows over the stationary phase driven by capillary forces and perhaps also by gravity in the case of downward flow or descending development. It is possible to have the liquid flow upwards in ascending development or radially in a circular technique. These two techniques find a wide use for both qualitative and quantitative analysis of mixtures; a number of examples of their applications are given in the functional chapters. Excellent review texts are available, including those of Cassidy (35), Block, LeStrange, and Zweig (36), and Block, Durrum, and Zweig (37) on paper chromatography and those of Stahl (38),

Truter (39), Randerath (40), Bobbitt (41), and Kirchner (42) on thin-layer chromatography. Paper chromatography has certain advantages over column chromatography in that it requires (and is limited to) very small samples and can be used for two-dimensional separations. Thin-layer chromatography offers quite good resolution since the grain size of adsorbents for thin-layer work is very small (ranging from 1 to 60 μ). Typical adsorbents are such materials as silica gel, alumina, diatomaceous earth, the metallic phosphates or silicates, and other adsorbents commonly employed in column chromatography, including cellulose. With thin-layer chromatography the possibility exists of obtaining rapid separations with high resolution. An interesting example of the power of the technique is the work of McCoy and Bullock (43) in which a homologous series of polyoxyethylene condensates of primary alcohols were separated, as their 3,5-dinitrobenzoate esters, by circular thin-layer chromatography (Figure 11.1).

GAS CHROMATOGRAPHY

Gas chromatography is that form of elution chromatography in which the mobile phase is a gas. The stationary phase can be a solid, in which case the term gas solid chromatography applies or it can be a liquid and the technique is then termed gas liquid chromatography. The two techniques have had parallel developments except that gas solid chromatography was first limited to gases and light hydrocarbons. Early adsorbents produced nonlinear isotherms (peak-tailing effects) for polar materials and it was not until the introduction of several new types of stationary phases that the range of gas solid chromatography was extended to include the lower molecular weight polar materials and heavier hydrocarbons. An intermediate technique in which just enough stationary liquid was added to the adsorbent to produce a more linear isotherm was developed and found of value for certain hydrocarbon analyses (44). Gas liquid chromatography has the wider degree of application and is today used for the large majority of gas chromatographic analyses. The separation process requires that the sample be introduced into the sample injector port, either as a liquid or gas, where it is vaporized and swept into the chromatographic column by the carrier gas. The column can be operated either isothermally or by programmed increase in temperature. Each sample component emerges from the outlet of the column diluted with carrier gas. The detector senses the concentration of the component and translates this information into electrical impulses so that it can be recorded automatically.

Since the introduction of the technique of gas chromatography by James and Martin in 1952 (45) the rate of growth of this analytical tool has greatly outstripped that of any other in the field. Its utility for the reproducible analysis of organic materials covering a wide boiling range has made it indispensable. A vast literature has already become available on the theory and the applications of gas chromatography. Fortunately, a number of excellent general reviews is available to provide overall coverage of the field (46–49). Abstracts of the gas chromatographic literature are issued on a regular basis; those published by the Preston Abstracts Co. (50) are now available in a bound volume published monthly. This abstract service supplements their publication of abstracts on coded, punched cards, which Preston has issued since 1958. The abstracts are reported in a detailed and timely manner and have a wide coverage of the literature. The abstracts of the Institute of Petroleum (51) are issued quarterly and in a yearly cumulative volume with detailed indexes and a brief abstract of each reference. A considerable number of specialized publications are available, including compilations of retention data (52, 53) and proceedings of symposia (54–64). The series of reviews edited by Giddings and Keller (65) contains useful discussions of many aspects of the field.

A large variety of chromatographic instruments are commercially available. The two most significant areas of concern in the operation of the equipment lie in (*1*) the characteristics of the separating columns, and (*2*) the characteristics of the detectors. An understanding in these two areas is basic to the choice of equipment for any particular analytical problem.

CHARACTERISTICS OF SEPARATING COLUMNS

The column contains the essential part of the gas liquid chromatographic process; all else is required only for control and measurement of the separation. The column is physically the container for the partitioning medium, which in a *packed* column is a solid support consisting of an adsorbent for gas solid chromatography or a solid coated with a liquid stationary phase for gas liquid chromatography. In a *capillary* column the inside wall is used as the solid support for the stationary liquid. The solid supports used for gas liquid chromatography should possess no sorption properties and are most generally diatomaceous earths with an area of 1–5 m²/g and mesh size commonly in the range of 30–150. The variations of particle sizes should be restricted in practice, and ranges such as 60–80, 80–100, and 100–120 are commonly used. The gas liquid chromatographic column is prepared by adding several percent of some one of the liquid stationary phases, described in the next section, by a technique that can be typified by the following:

Add a solution of 20 g of silicone oil in about 200 ml of petroleum ether to 100 g of the 60–80 mesh solid support so as to wet all particles, using more solvent if necessary. Evaporate the ether on a steam bath while stirring, carrying off the vapors in a hood, until the mixture appears dry. Then continue drying in a steam bath for about 1 hr. Separate the fines with a 60-mesh sieve and discard.

The coated open tubular (capillary) column was originally described by Golay (66) and must be prepared very carefully to achieve the high efficiency of which these columns are capable. The recommended procedure included in this chapter for coating capillary gas liquid chromatographic columns is based on considerable experience and is taken from published reports of several sources (67, 68). The packed column and the open tubular column represent two extremes, and several intermediate types of column now exist, one of the more important being the support-coated open tubular column, sometimes represented by the acronym, S.C.O.T. column (69, 70).

PROCEDURE FOR COATING CAPILLARY GAS LIQUID CHROMATOGRAPHIC COLUMNS

Apparatus

The apparatus, shown in Figure 21.4, introduces either carrier gas or liquid into the capillary tubing that is being coated. It can be assembled from various pipe fittings. The volume of the reservoir should be about 25 ml.

Procedure

This procedure is satisfactory for the coating of a variety of columns. Measure the required length of capillary tubing to be coated for the GC column and coil the tubing to fit in the GC oven. If the column is to be used in a temperature-programmed air-stirred bath, it should be wound in loose spirals held apart with spacers.

Clean the inside of the reservoir by rinsing it with methylene chloride. Connect one end of the capillary tubing to the reservoir.

Add 20 ml of methylene chloride to the reservoir through the reservoir inlet. Force the liquid through the column by closing the upper toggle valve and opening the lower one and adjusting the nitrogen pressure to 100 psi.

Repeat the cleaning of the column with 10-ml portions of the following solvents in the order shown: isopropyl alcohol, water, N-methyl-2-pyrrolidone, acetone, and methylene chloride.

Connect the exit end of the column to a 20-ft length of 0.01-in. i.d. tubing. Dip the end of the tubing into a container of water. This 20-ft length of tubing is reused for coating other columns.

Prepare 20 ml of solution containing about 10 vol % of the liquid stationary phase selected dissolved in methylene chloride or other low-boiling solvent. Add the solution to the reservoir, close both toggle valves, and adjust the nitrogen pressure to 80 psig. Force a plug of the solution through the column at a linear flow of about 15 cm/sec as follows: Open the lower toggle valve for 1 min, then open the upper one and measure the time required for the liquid to pass through

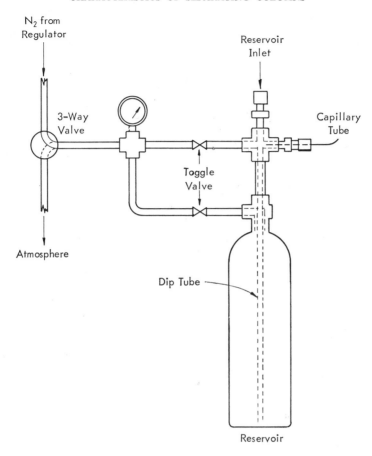

Figure 21.4. Apparatus for washing and coating capillary gas-liquid chromatographic columns.

the column and 20-ft capillary extension. The length of the column plus extension divided by the time from the last valve switching to reappearance of gas bubbles at the extension outlet (end of liquid plug leaving the extension) gives the average linear flow rate of the liquid passing through the column.

Inject a second plug of liquid as above but adjust the time interval (i.e., length of liquid plug) to give a linear flow of 17–20 cm/sec for the liquid. Repeat the procedure until a total of seven portions of coating solution have been forced through the column.

Purge the column overnight with the carrier gas at 80 psig.

The choice of packed versus capillary columns depends upon a number of factors, which are more completely elaborated in Table 21.3. If at all possible,

Table 21.3. Comparative Advantages and Disadvantages of Packed and Capillary Columns for Gas Chromatographic Separations

Comparison	Packed columns	Capillary (open-tubular) columns
Ease of preparation	Generally easy. Properties reproducible. Can use wider variety of stationary phases	Sometimes difficult especially with highly polar or polymeric liquids. Efficiency not always reproducible
Sample capacities	Samples range from 1 to 10 mg for $\frac{1}{4}$ in. o.d. column. Can be used for small-scale preparative fractions	Sample is approx. 0.01 mg for 0.01 in. i.d. column
Application to mixtures with low partition coefficients (C_1–C_5 hydrocarbons)	Suitable since V_L/V_g ratio is high. (V_L = liquid-phase volume; V_g = gas-phase volume)	Less suitable since V_L/V_g ratio is low
Application to simple and complex mixtures	Suitable for separation of simple mixtures of up to 20 easily resolved components	Suitable for separation of highly complex mixtures, especially hydrocarbons or esters
Application to trace analysis	Suitable for separation of trace components in 99% matrix provided traces are well resolved from matrix	Less suitable since sample capacity is small
Time required for chromatographic separation	5–60 min	5–60 min
Mechanics of operation	Relatively simple	Requires sample splitter at column entrance and sensitive detector

the analyst should have available gas chromatographic equipment both with packed and capillary columns so that he can take full advantage of the different capabilities offered by the two types of columns. Because of their ruggedness, ease of preparation and operation, and sample capacity, packed columns are more generally employed except with highly complex mixtures. In general, packed columns offer a more complete range of selectivities than do open tubular columns since some liquids do not coat the capillary wall efficiently. The open tubular columns can provide quite high resolution and efficiency and consequently find much use in the separation of highly complex mixtures with a large number of components, as is described in several of the functional chapters, especially those dealing with the analysis of hydrocarbons. Capillary columns have a limitation in some applications in that the ratio of the liquid phase volume (V_L) to the gas phase volume (V_g) is lower than that usually available from packed columns. The significance of this is that materials with low partition coefficients, such as the light hydrocarbons, do not dissolve extensively and thus are not efficiently separated in a capillary column. Sample capacity, but not V_L/V_g, can be improved by using wider bore open tubular columns. Columns of 0.030-in. i.d. can tolerate samples of the order of $\frac{1}{2}$–1 μl. Packed columns are used for trace determinations because of their large sample capacity but capillary columns can be adapted for this type of work (71).

EVALUATION OF STATIONARY PHASE FOR
GAS LIQUID CHROMATOGRAPHY*

Since the choice of the stationary phase in gas–liquid chromatography is one of the significant variables under the direct control of the analyst, it is important to have an understanding of the effect of structure of the liquid phase on the chromatographic results obtained. The most widely used stationary phases are usually pure compounds of medium molecular weight such as squalane or dinonylphthalate. Some petroleum fractions are employed, and some polymeric materials with molecular weight as high as 5×10^5 such as the silicones. A list of some materials that have been employed as stationary phases is given in Table 21.4, together with the symbol often used for identification and the approximate maximum temperature at which a column packed with the material is useful. The maximum temperature depends very much on the method of use and the sensitivity of the detector to "column bleed." This list is only an indication of the many materials that have been used as stationary phases but does illustrate the types of functional groups involved.

Selectivity is considered to be the property of providing different retention times for compounds having the same volatility but different chemical structures. A detailed investigation of the selectivity of a number of liquid substrates was made some years ago by Tenney (72), who examined a large number of components in test mixtures and plotted the boiling point of the test compound against its retention time relative to *n*-pentane. Figure 21.5 illustrates the relative selectivity of β,β'-oxydipropionitrile to a number of classes of compounds as determined by Tenney. Detailed classifications through such series of experiments have shown that stationary liquids containing a high proportion of cyano, hydroxyl, or amide groups have a high relative selectivity. Hydroxyethers, polyesters, and the fluorinated compounds exhibit a medium relative selectivity while ethers and ether

* Much of the basis for this section is from unpublished work of Dr. M. A. Muhs of the Shell Development Company, Emeryville, California.

Table 21.4. Structures of Some Materials Used as Gas Chromatographic Stationary Phases

Symbol	Name and structure	Maximum mp., °C
BCEF	*N,N*-Bis(2-cyanoethyl) formamide, $H-\overset{\displaystyle O}{\overset{\|}{C}}-N\begin{matrix}CH_2-CH_2-CN \\ CH_2-CH_2-CN\end{matrix}$	130
Bentone-34	Bentonite clay with added organic modifiers	
Carbowax 200–20,000	Polyethylene glycol, $HO-CH_2-CH_2-(O-CH_2-CH_2)_n-OH$	100–250
DC-200	Silicone oils, polydimethylsiloxanes	225
DC-710	Dow Corning Aromatic Silicone 710, $\left[\begin{matrix} \text{Ph} \\ -O-Si- \\ \text{Ph}\end{matrix}\right]_n$	250
DEGS	Diethylene glycol succinate, $(O-\overset{\displaystyle O}{\overset{\|}{C}}-CH_2-CH_2-\overset{\displaystyle O}{\overset{\|}{C}}-OCH_2-CH_2-O-CH_2-CH_2-O)_n$	200
DIG	Diglycerol, $HOCH_2-CH-CH_2-O-CH_2-CH-CH_2-OH$ with OH, OH	130
DNP	Dinonyl phthalate	100

FAE-E7	Zonyl (DuPont) fluoroalkyl ester, $ROOC$—[benzene ring]—$COOR$, $R = -CH_2-(CF_2)_nH$	220
FFAP	Carbowax 20,000 terminated with nitro terephthalic acid	250
FLEX-8N8	FLEXOL plasticizer, $R-\overset{O}{\overset{\|}{C}}-N(CH_2-CH_2-OOC-R)(CH_2-CH_2-OOC-R)$, $R = CH_3-(CH_2)_3-CH(CH_3)-CH_2-CH_3$	160
HAM-18	Hallcomid M-18, $CH_3-(CH_2)_n-\overset{O}{\overset{\|}{C}}-N(CH_3)(CH_3)$ $n = 14, 16$ in about equal amounts	130
HAM-OL	Hallcomid M-18-OL, $CH_3-(CH_2)_7-CH=CH-CH-(CH_2)_7-\overset{O}{\overset{\|}{C}}-N(CH_3)(CH_3)$	130
NPGAT	Neopentylglycol adipate (terminated)	240
NPGS	Neopentylglycol succinate	200–230
NPGSE	Neopentyl sebacate	240
ODPN	2,2'-oxydipropionitrile, $N\equiv C-CH_2-CH_2-O-CH_2-CH_2-C\equiv N$	100
OV-1	Methyl silicone, $-(Si(CH_3)(CH_3)-O)_n$	300
OV-7	20% Phenyl silicone	300
OV-17	50% Phenyl silicone	300

(continued overleaf)

Table 21.4 (continued)

Symbol	Name and structure	Maximum temp., °C
OV-210	Trifluoropropyl silicone	275
OV-225	Cyanopropyl phenyl silicone	275
PMPE	Poly-*m*-phenyl ether,	250
QF-1	Silicone polymer QF1-0065, a fluorinated alkylsilicone polymer	200–250
SE-30		300
SF-96	Polydimethylsiloxanes	250
Squalane	Hexamethyltetracosane, $C_{30}H_{62}$	70
TCEP	1,2,3-Tris(2-cyanoethoxy)propane,	160
TCP	Tricresyl phosphate	125
UCON-P	Polyglycol Ucon, a water-soluble substituted glycol polymer-copolymer of ethylene oxide and propylene oxide	200
XF-1105	Cyano-silicone fluids,[a]	200
XF-1150		200

For PMPE structure:

For TCEP:

$$CH_2-OR$$
$$CH-OR \qquad R = -CH_2-CH_2-CN$$
$$CH_2-OR$$

For Cyano-silicone fluids structure:

	x	y
[a] XF-1105	10	90
SF-1150	100	0

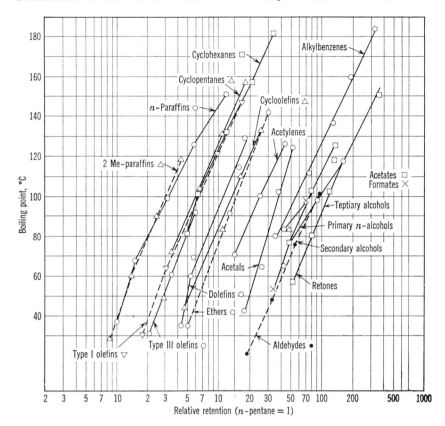

Figure 21.5. Selectivity of β,β'-oxydipropionitrile at 67°C. Data from Tenney (72), courtesy of the American Chemical Society. Reprinted by permission of the copyright owner. Copyright 1958.

esters are somewhat lower. Aromatic and alkyl silicones have little or no selectivity. Other relatively nonselective materials are alcohols, esters, and amides with long alkyl chains that counteract the effects of the polar groups. An interesting method for characterizing stationary phases has been published by Rohrschneider (73), who compares the retention differences of five compounds (benzene, ethanol, ethyl methyl ketone, nitromethane, and pyridine) to arrive at a basis for development of a column polarity index.

For specific systems it is possible to take advantage of known complexing reactions to provide very high specificities. For example, as is described in Chapter 3, olefins can be selectively retarded by use of a silver nitrate–glycol stationary phase. Aromatics form charge-transfer complexes with

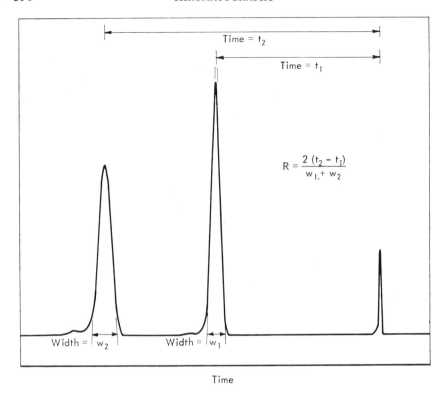

Figure 21.6. Calculation of resolution (R).

polynitro and polychloro compounds and this allows for their use as selective phases (Chapter 2). An interesting review of the design of selective stationary phases based on theoretical and experimental implications is given in a recent publication by Langer and Sheehan (74). They point out the desirability of high molal concentrations of selectively interacting groups and a preference for a single and strong selective interaction.

Resolution is related to the number of completely resolved peaks that can be placed between two arbitrary reference peaks, often two normal paraffin peaks. Figure 21.6 illustrates a method for the calculation of resolution. Good resolution is important in separating complex mixtures of isomers such as petroleum fractions, although really extensive resolution may not always be required for the problem at hand. Resolution is a function of a given column under given operating conditions and is, of course, affected by the conditions of the analytical separation. Open tubular columns come into their own when maximum resolution is required.

ADSORBENTS FOR GAS SOLID CHROMATOGRAPHY

As was discussed above, gas solid chromatography has had less use in the analysis of organic compounds than gas liquid chromatography since the early adsorbents produced nonlinear isotherms, especially with polar materials. In recent years efforts have been successful in the preparation of adsorbents with better characteristics and these are now being applied to many practical analyses. The application of the polymeric resins as a gas solid adsorbent by Hollis (75) was a particularly valuable and impressive development. These polymeric resins are synthesized in bead form by polymerizing styrene monomers together with divinylbenzene to produce a series of porous polymers of various properties. Resins of this type are commercially available and find extensive use since polar compounds have a low tendency to adsorb, the columns are easily stable up to 250°C and there is little of the column bleeding that is such a common concern with liquid stationary phases. The behavior of water provides a significant application since water is strongly adsorbed on most other materials. Hollis (75) reported that water eluted rapidly and cleanly, as is shown in the separation of a mixture with a number of organic compounds (Figure 21.7).

Considerable attention has also been given to modified inorganic materials for adsorbents in gas solid chromatography. Kirkland (76, 77) worked with a colloidal alumina, Baymal, whose surface was modified with acetate ions that could be removed or replaced with other ions. He found that Baymal exhibited unique adsorption properties, particularly when the acetate ion was removed or replaced with stearic acid. Scott and Phillips (78, 79) studied the effects of the deposition of inorganic salts on alumina and silica. Improved performance was found after the addition of several commonly available salts or sodium hydroxide. Graphitized carbon has also been reported to be an effective adsorbent in gas solid chromatography (80, 81).

CHARACTERISTICS OF THE DETECTORS

Although a considerable number of gas chromatographic detectors have been reported, only a limited group have found general use. A recent text (49) describes nearly 50 detectors but, of these, a much smaller group has survived the competition of application and is actually in common use. The present tendency in gas chromatography is to employ detectors of more or less universal response or detectors that have a specific response to certain classes of compounds. The thermal conductivity detector can be used for general response and, with many organic compounds, the flame ionization detector approximates this behavior. Some commonly used specific detectors

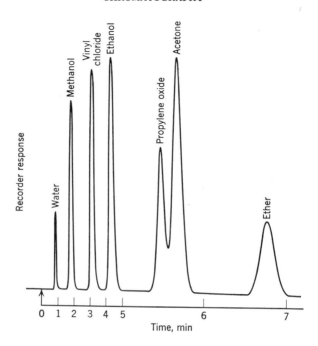

Figure 21.7. Separation of organic compounds from water. Conditions: 151°C, 60cc/minute H$_2$, column 6 ft × 3/16 in. Polymer No. 19. Data from Hollis (75), Copyright 1966 by the American Chemical Society. Reprinted by permission of the copyright owner.

are based on the principles of electron capture, coulometric titration, flame emission, or thermionic emission. The mass spectrometer is now often used in tandem with the gas chromatographic apparatus and a number of companies market rapid-scanning mass spectrometers for this purpose. Radiochemical detectors also form another area in which development work is actively progressing. The most generally significant characteristics of the principal detectors are listed in Table 21.5, and more detailed information on the individual properties are given in the subsequent sections. A useful reference for the characteristics of several commercial detectors is that published by McNair and Bonelli (82).

THE THERMAL CONDUCTIVITY DETECTOR

This is one of the detectors used early in the development of practical gas chromatographic equipment (83), and still finds wide use since it is rugged and provides a response closely equivalent to weight fraction of

Table 21.5. Principal Characteristics of Detectors for Gas Chromatography

Detector	Components detected	Components not detected	Uniformity of response	Linearity with concentration changes
Thermal conductivity	All		Generally within $\pm 10\%$ except for small molecules	Can be nonlinear with some low molecular compounds
Flame ionization	Organics with CH bonds	H_2O, CO, CO_2	Hydrocarbons $\pm 10\%$ others variable	Over wide range
Electron capture	Polyhalogenated compounds, conjugated organic structures with NO_2, $-C\equiv N$, $\diagup C=O$	Simple hydrocarbons, nonconjugated organics	Extremely variable	Only over narrow range
Microcoulometric	Combined halogen, nitrogen, or sulfur (after conversion)	Hydrocarbon and organics without reactive elements	Quantitative	Stoichiometric
Flame photometric	Phosphorus and/or sulfur compounds	Small response to hydrocarbon and organics in general	Apparently variable	Linear over restricted range
Thermionic emission	Phosphorus, halogen compounds	Small response to hydrocarbon and organics in general	Apparently variable	Linear over restricted range
Mass spectrometer	Mass units of all components		High	Linear
Radioactivity	Radiolabeled compounds	Nonradioactive materials	Quantitative	Quantitative

(continued overleaf)

Table 21.5 (*continued*)

Detector	Sensitivity, g	Carrier gas	Principal uses	Advantages	Limitations
Thermal conductivity	10^{-6}	H_2 He	To monitor packed columns	Rugged detector, response quite uniform	Not particularly sensitive
Flame ionization	10^{-12}	H_2 He	To monitor packed and capillary columns	Very sensitive and practical	Not sensitive to all compounds
Electron capture	For most sensitive 10^{-16}	N_2, Ar + CH_4	Traces of halogen-containing compounds	Very high sensitivity to polyhalogenates and conjugated structures	Response extremely variable from one type to another
Micro-coulometric	10^{-9}	He	Traces of organics with halogen, nitrogen, sulfur in molecules	Specific determination of certain components	Only limited number of components are determinable
Flame photometric	10^{-11} (P) to 10^{-9} (S)	N_2	Phosphorus pesticides	High specificity, high sensitivity	Limited linear range, limited operating temperature (240°C). Flame readily extinguished.
Thermionic emission	10^{-11} (P)	N_2	Pesticide residues	High specificity, high sensitivity	Limited linear range
Mass spectrometer	10^{-12} to 10^{-14}	He	Determination of empirical formulas	Can provide much information on organic structures	Equipment expensive and requires special care
Radioactivity	10^{-12} or less		^{14}C, ^{3}H-labeled organics	Very high specificity	Radioorganics must be specially prepared

organic and inorganic compounds in the H_2 or He carrier gas. The use of thermal conductivity for detection is based on the fact that heat is conducted away from a hot body at a rate which, other factors being controlled, is dependent upon the nature of the gas. Consequently the temperature and electrical resistance of the hot body (if it is an electrical resistor) are affected by the nature of the gas. The sensitive element in a thermal conductivity cell can be platinum or tungsten wire or a thermistor. Either two or four elements are made part of a Wheatstone bridge, as is shown in Figure 21.8. In this example two elements are in the measuring arm in the effluent from the column, and the other two are in the reference arm in a stream of pure carrier gas. Both arms are maintained at the same constant temperature by being mounted in the same block of metal of high heat capacity such that no change in electrical resistance occurs unless there is a change in gas composition. The nature of the carrier gas is of critical importance in the thermal conductivity cell. Helium and hydrogen are the most generally suitable since these light gases have much higher heat conductivities than other gases and vapors and, consequently, the imbalance that occurs when the measuring elements are surrounded by carrier plus sample is appreciable and relatively independent of the nature of the sample. Much useful work has been done, however, with other carrier gases such as nitrogen since helium is not everywhere available and hydrogen may be hazardous in some locations.

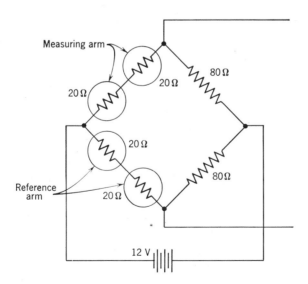

Figure 21.8. Typical four-element thermal conductivity bridge circuit. Data from Dimbat, Porter, and Stross (83), Copyright 1956 by the American Chemical Society. Reprinted by permission of the copyright owner.

The relative response for thermal conductivity detectors was thoroughly studied by Messner, Rosie, and Argabright (84), whose data have been placed on a relative weight basis, compared to n-heptane taken as 1.00. These data (see Table 21.6) show that, in general, most organic compounds fall within the values of 0.8–1.1 with the exception of lower molecular weight materials with somewhat higher values.

Table 21.6. Relative Response for the Thermal Conductivity Detector[a]

Compound	Relative response factor per gram of compound, n-heptane = 1.00
Methane	1.57
Ethane	1.19
Propane	1.03
Butane	1.03
Pentane	1.02
Hexane	1.00
Heptane	1.00
Octane	0.98
Nonane	0.97
Decane	0.98
3-Methylpentane	0.97
2,2-Dimethylpentane	0.93
2,4-Dimethylpentane	0.90
2-Methylhexane	0.94
3-Methylhexane	0.94
2,2,4-Trimethylpentane	0.90
Cyclopentane	0.97
Methylcyclopentane	0.95
Ethylcyclopentane	0.89
Cyclohexane	0.94
Methylcyclohexane	0.86
Ethylene	1.18
Propylene	1.05
Isobutylene	1.02
1-Butene	1.01
trans-2-Butene	1.04
cis-2-Butene	1.05
1,3-Butadiene	1.03
Benzene	0.89
Toluene	0.88
Ethylbenzene	0.86

(*continued overleaf*)

Table 21.6   (*continued*)

Compound	Relative response factor per gram of compound, *n*-heptane = 1.00
o-Xylene	0.86
m-Xylene	0.87
p-Xylene	0.87
n-Propylbenzene	0.86
p-Ethyltoluene	0.88
1,2,4-Trimethylbenzene	0.88
Acetone	1.03
Methyl ethyl ketone	0.96
Diethyl ketone	0.89
Methyl *n*-amyl ketone	0.81
Methyl *n*-hexyl ketone	0.80
Methanol	1.19
Ethanol	1.10
1-Propanol	0.97
1-Butanol	0.89
2-Butanol	0.90
1-Hexanol	0.80
Ethyl acetate	0.88
Isopropyl acetate	0.82
n-Butyl acetate	0.81
n-Amyl acetate	0.79
Diethyl ether	1.03
Di-*n*-propyl ether	0.89
Di-*n*-butyl ether	0.86
Di-*n*-amyl ether	0.81
Argon	0.77
Nitrogen	1.05
Oxygen	0.86
Carbon dioxide	0.76
Carbon monoxide	1.04
Water	0.81

[a] Data calculated from results of Messner, Rosie, and Argabright (84). Carrier gas was helium, temperature range 30–160°C, detectors were hot-wire and thermistor types.

THE FLAME IONIZATION DETECTOR

Extensive investigations have shown that the combustion of hydrocarbons generates measurable quantities of ions (85–87) by a series of reactions whose principal mechanism is suggested (85) to be

$$CH + O \rightarrow CHO^+ + e^-$$
$$CHO^+ + H_2O \rightarrow CO + H_3O^+$$
$$H_3O^+ + e^- \rightarrow H_2O + H$$

As a result of careful mass spectrometric studies of flames, Green and Sugden (85) concluded that the small concentrations of positive ions (presumably H_3O^+) observed in hydrogen flames originated from hydrocarbon impurities and that the intensity of the measured positive ions varied linearly with the concentration of added hydrocarbon, which in these experiments was acetylene.

The principle of the flame ionization detector is based on the linear relationship of ion formation to the concentration of organic material in the flame. In this detector the gaseous mixture containing hydrogen is burned at a small jet with air or oxygen and the change in electrical conductivity is measured. Early versions of this simple and useful detector were published, independently, by McWilliam and Dewar (88) and by Harley, Nel, and Pretorius (89) in 1958. The simplicity and high sensitivity has brought the flame ionization detector into extensive use for practical chromatography.

Relative responses for a number of hydrocarbons in the flame ionization detector, listed in Table 21.7, are taken from the data of Ettre (90), who determined the relative response of 52 paraffins, 33 cycloparaffins, and 20 aromatics. The data are given on a comparative weight basis with n-heptane taken as 1.00. In addition to data on the hydrocarbons, comparable values are also provided on some other materials taken chiefly from work of Sternberg, Gallaway, and Jones (91). In general, with the exception of the simple aromatics, hydrocarbons do not vary greatly in their response to the flame ionization detector. Considerably lower values are found for oxygenates and halogen-containing compounds.

THE ELECTRON-CAPTURE DETECTOR

This detector is essentially an ionization cell containing an electrode pair spaced about 1 cm apart. A radioactive isotope is employed to ionize the carrier gas that flows through the cell and the free electrons are collected at the anode, providing the base current. If some molecules that absorb electrons appear in the carrier gas the observed reduction in the current flowing to the anode is a function of the concentration of these molecules in the carrier gas. The detector was originally described by Lovelock and Lipsky (92) and since then has been used widely, especially for the determination of materials having high electron absorption cross sections such as the halogenated insecticides. A number of publications have been issued on the relative response of materials in this detector (93–95). The electron affinity of different molecular species varies over a range of at least 10^6 with the simple

Table 21.7. Relative Response for the Flame Ionization
Detector[a]

Compound	Relative response factor per gram (n-heptane $= 1.00$)
n-Pentane	1.04
2-Methylbutane	1.05
n-Hexane	1.03
2,2-Dimethylbutane	1.04
n-Octane	0.97
2,3,4-Trimethylpentane	0.99
2,2,3-Trimethylpentane	1.02
2,2,3,3-Tetramethylpentane	1.01
Cyclopentane	1.04
Cyclohexane	1.01
1,1-Dimethylcyclopentane	1.03
Isopropylcyclopentane	0.98
Ethylcyclohexane	1.01
1,1,2-Trimethylcyclohexane	1.01
Benzene	1.12
Toluene	1.07
p-Xylene	1.00
Ethylbenzene	1.03
Isopropylbenzene	0.97
n-Propylbenzene	1.01
$tert$-Butylbenzene	1.02
Diethyl ether	0.58[b]
n-Propyl alcohol	0.61[b]
n-Butyl alcohol	0.69[b]
sec-Butyl-alcohol	0.65[b]
n-Propyl acetate	0.53[b]
Chloroform	0.082[b]
Carbon tetrachloride	0.045[b]
1,3-Dichloropropane	0.37[b]
Trichloroethylene	0.23[b]
Tetrachloroethylene	0.19[b]
Argon Nitrogen Oxygen Carbon Dioxide Water	Essentially no response

[a] Data from Ettre (90) unless otherwise indicated.
[b] Data from Sternberg, Gallaway, and Jones (91).

hydrocarbons being essentially nonresponsive. Some of these data are collected in Table 21.8 and show that polyhalogenated or conjugated organic structures exhibit large effects. This phenomenon, of course, has made the detector an attractive means of following such materials as they emerge from a gas chromatographic column.

It is important to realize, however, that the electron-capture detector is by no means specific and that occasionally completely erroneous conclusions have been taken from peaks observed with this detector. For instance, Pearson, Aldrich, and Stone (96) found that elemental sulfur behaved identically to aldrin in a gas chromatographic electron-capture apparatus. Retention time on the column used was almost identical to that of aldrin and the response in the detector was high. No response for halogen was obtained, however, on the more specific microcoulometer halogen titration cell. The fact that the response of the electron-capture detector varies so greatly from one organic species to another makes it difficult to interpret results obtained on a system that has not been closely calibrated. With unknown systems it is

Table 21.8.   Relative Electron Absorption Coefficients for the Electron Capture Detector

Compound	Relative response factor per gram of compound (chlorobenzene $= 1.00$)
Saturated hydrocarbons Olefinic hydrocarbons Benzene Alkyl benzenes Styrene	<0.001
Alcohols Phenols Aliphatic amines Aromatic amines Aliphatic saturated aldehydes	0.001–0.05
Benzanthracene Cyclooctatetraene Azulene	30–300
Nitro aromatics Monoiodo, dibromo, trichloro compounds	100–1000
Diacetyl Dimethylfumarate Quinone	500–4000

Polyfluoro, tetrachloro,
   tribromo, and diiodo
   compounds
	500–10,000

particularly hazardous to interpret the data unless alternative means of obtaining information are also used. Goodwin, Goulden, and Reynolds (97) pointed out that a naturally occurring coextractive from some grain crops exhibited electron-capture interference with a retention time identical to that of aldrin. They overcame this uncertainty by use of multicolumn chromatography and by comparison using two detectors, one an electron-capture detector and the other a halogen-sensitive detector of the type used for locating refrigeration leaks (98).

THE MICROCOULOMETER DETECTOR

One of the few absolute detectors is the titration microcoulometer developed originally by Coulson and Cavanagh (99). This instrument employed the familiar coulometric principle in which the titration reagent is generated by electrical current. The current so generated is monitored on a recording potentiometer. The coulombs involved can be calculated directly from the recorder chart and converted into equivalents of titrant. Consequently, the measurement is absolute and only infrequent calibration is required to make certain the instrument is operating properly. The apparatus of Coulson and Cavanagh has a sensitivity at the nanogram level that allows its use as a detector for gas chromatography. The cell can be used to produce a number of titrants that, for example, allow the determination of halide ions, mercaptans, or H_2S with coulometrically generated Ag^+, the determination of SO_2 with coulometrically generated I_2, and the determination of bases with coulometrically generated H^+. The limitations of the cell are that there are only a limited number of reactions which have been employed and that the cell mixing and response time is finite (30–40 sec), which inevitably leads to some reduction in resolution.

The first application of the coulometric titration cell was for the specific determination of chlorinated insecticides, which, after being resolved into components by gas chromatography, were combusted with oxygen to produce water, carbon dioxide, and hydrogen chloride. The combustion products were swept into the titration cell with the carrier gas and the hydrogen chloride titrated with coulometrically generated Ag^+. Hydrogen sulfide and mercaptans can be determined directly, without a combustion step. If hydrogenation is used subsequent to gas chromatography, all sulfur-containing compounds can be converted to hydrogen sulfide for measurement in the microcoulometer. The operating basis of coulometry using the titration of Coulson and Cavanagh (99) is that of null balance. As is shown in Figure 21.9, the titration cell contains two pairs of electrodes, one pair of which function as an anode–cathode generator and the other as indicator or sensor electrodes. For the determination of halide, sulfide, or mercaptide ions, the generator pair is silver (anode) and platinum (cathode), the indicator pair

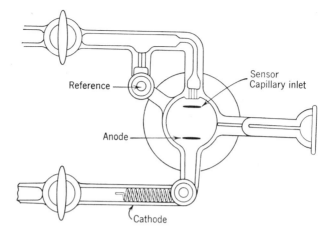

Figure 21.9. Design of microcoulometric titration cell. After McNulty (100).

being silver (sensor) and silver ‖ silver acetate (reference). The electrolyte is 70–85% acetic acid. When reactive ions enter the cell, silver ion is precipitated. As the silver ion concentration is lowered due to the titration, the indicator pair sends a signal to the amplifier that supplies current to the generator electrodes. Silver ion is then generated to such a level as to maintain an electrical balance. The current required for this generation of silver is recorded in the form of a peak. The principal reactions and types of titration cells presently available (100) are listed in Table 21.9. A number of the specific applications of these cells are described in the functional chapters for application to materials containing combined sulfur or nitrogen. The

Table 21.9. Principal Features of Microcoulometer Detectors[a]

Type	Silver cell	Iodine cell	Hydrogen cell
Electrolyte	70% acetic acid	0.04% acetic acid; 0.05% KI in water	0.04% Na_2SO_4 in water
Titration reaction	$Ag^+ + X^- \rightarrow AgX$	$I_3^- + SO_2 + H_2O \rightarrow SO_3 + 3I^- + 2H^+$	$H^+ + OH^- \rightarrow H_2O$
Generation reaction	$Ag^0 \rightarrow Ag^+ + e^-$	$3I^- \rightarrow I_3^- + 2e^-$	$\frac{1}{2}H_2 \rightarrow H^+ + e^-$
Electrodes			
Sensor	Ag	Pt	Pt black
Reference	Ag ‖ AgOAc	Pt ‖ I_3^-	Pb ‖ $PbSO_4$
Anode	Ag	Pt	Pt
Cathode	Pt	Pt	Pt

[a] From McNulty (100).

limits of sensitivity of the microcoulometer have been found in the order of 1–5 ng of S, halogen, or nitrogen in practical analyses.

FLAME-PHOTOMETRIC DETECTORS

Since a number of the elements can be caused to emit light at certain frequencies at flame temperatures, it is possible to design quite specific detectors based on this principle. Brody and Chaney (101) developed such a detector with interference filters to pass either the phosphorus emission at 526 mμ or sulfur at 394 mμ to a photomultiplier tube. By using two tubes, one with each filter, phosphorus and sulfur can be monitored simultaneously. Use of the single flame detector in pesticide residue analysis was reviewed by Bowman and Beroza (102), who pointed out that it can detect as little as 10^{-10} g of a phosphorus compound and somewhat more than 10^{-9} g of a sulfur compound, while a chlorinated insecticide had an equivalent response only at 10^{-5} g. Bowman and Beroza combined the separate detectors for phosphorus and sulfur into one unit and found they were able to obtain a more precise P/S ratio in the materials they examined.

THE THERMIONIC EMISSION DETECTOR

A modified flame ionization detector that provides a high response to the halogen and phosphorus compounds was reported by Karmen and Giuffrida (103) and was based on the selective increase in sensitivity of a hydrogen flame ionization detector by heating an alkali metal salt in the flame. This interesting effect has been further examined by Karmen (104), who developed a two-flame ionization detector that was highly responsive to low concentrations of combined halogens and phosphorus but not to organic compounds with other functional groups. Karmen's conclusion was that high sensitivity to halogen compounds arose since they increase the volatility of the alkali metal salt. Sensitivity to phosphorus is stated to be due to the fact that it increases the ionization of alkali metal salts. Commercial models of this type of detector are now available with alkali metal salts in such form that the detector is stable for several months.

THE MASS SPECTROMETER AS THE DETECTOR

Mass spectrometry has been used for the determination of components in petroleum fractions for over twenty years but it is only within the past few years that organic chemists generally have taken advantage of this powerful technique (105–108). The mass spectrometer provides the molecular weight of the material directly if a parent ion appears. Distinctive fragment ions yield considerable information concerning the structure, particularly when comparative reference spectra are available on the same instrument. An important use of this tool is in combination with gas chromatography (109) since component identification is facilitated by introducing a simpler mixture into the mass spectrometer. In several laboratories where mass spectrometers were in use in the 1950's, this technique was employed from almost the earliest days of gas chromatography to examine occasional fractions collected from a chromatographic column. In general, these techniques involved collecting the fractions manually by passing the effluent, at the time a peak arrived, into a chilled container and then subsequently examining the fractions by mass spectrometry or some other spectroscopic method. It was not until Gohlke (110) published a paper in 1959 on the combination of a gas chromatographic apparatus with a time-of-flight mass spectrometer that any advance in the fusion of the two techniques was made. This paper was published at a critical time when rapid advances were being made in the development of capillary columns where the sample sizes are so small that manual collection of fractions is either extremely difficult or well-nigh impossible. A number of firms now market gas chromatographic–mass spectrometer combinations or rapid-scanning mass spectrometers specifically designed for use with gas chromatographic columns.

A review of published work on the direct instrumental coupling of gas chromatographs with mass spectrometers is given by Völlmin, Simon, and Kaiser (111), who summarize the techniques and equipment employed by the many workers now using these combined techniques. The combination of capillary column separation with a Bendix Time-of-Flight mass spectrometer has been used effectively to identify and determine the components contained in fruits (112). McFadden has thoroughly described the utilization of this combined approach (113) and pointed to its high level of sensitivity. Applications to the solution of analytical problems of considerable complexity are now being frequently reported. These include the determination of steroids (114, 115), lipids (116), and, of course, odor and flavors (112), to indicate just a few examples of the use of the tandem techniques. To increase the volatility and stability of the compounds, advantage is often taken of the formation of derivatives prior to chromatography, including methylation of acids and silylation of hydroxyl groups. A particularly interesting use of the tandem techniques for the determination of preflame reaction products in a motored engine was reported by Maynard, Legate, and Graiff (117).

The technique for bringing an effluent sample from a gas chromatograph into the mass spectrometer must take into account the fact that the effluent is principally carrier gas and contains, even at the peak maxima, only a small concentration of the components. A generally satisfactory coupling technique is to pass the effluent stream through an enriching separator and thence, continuously, into the mass spectrometer. This direct-coupling process requires a specialized mass spectrometer (109, 118), but not necessarily one of the more expensive types. Several enriching devices have been described based on the principle that the effusion rate of gaseous molecules is inversely proportional to the square root of the molecular weight. Typical enrichers include that of Watson and Biemann (119), which uses a porous glass frit through which the carrier gas is preferentially pumped away, and that of Ryhage (120), in which the carrier gas flows through one capillary, directed at a second in such a way that the sample preferentially passes from one capillary to the other while a large fraction of the carrier gas is pumped away. Blumer (121) examined several of the enriching devices and suggested the use of a silver membrane. Both a Teflon membrane (122) and a silicone membrane (123) have been used for the selective removal of helium. Commercial apparatus is now available and is capable of giving an enrichment of sample to helium of a factor of 5 with materials of 100 molecular weight.

RADIOACTIVITY DETECTORS

The very high sensitivity offered by use of radioactive organic compounds in trace analysis has made gas–liquid radiochromatography (GLRC) an important tool (124–126). Radioactivity of the components emerging from the gas chromatographic column can be measured either discontinuously by trapping and subsequent counting or continuously by coupling a radio-activity detector to the column outlet. The radioisotopes most commonly used in tracer experiments involving organic compounds, tritium and carbon-14, are soft beta-emitters and are well counted by (a) scintillation counters, (b) proportional gas counters, and (c) ionization chambers. In general, the most effective continuous detectors have been found to be those in which the column effluent flows through the detector and produces an electrical effect which is taken as a measure of the radioactivity of the peaks as they pass. Past difficulties in obtaining satisfactory high temperature detectors have caused many investigators to combust the column effluent to CO_2 and H_2O and, since H_2O adsorbs strongly on many surfaces, the procedures generally call for the reduction of H_2O to H_2 before counting. There are advantages in using detectors that can count radioactivity directly in organic compounds containing tritium or carbon-14. The advantages include the development of a simpler apparatus than with the combustion process, better resolution, and a more rapid response to the gas chromatographic effluent.

Two of the most useful detectors for organic compounds containing tritium or carbon-14 are the proportional flow counter and the ionization chamber. The proportional flow counter consists of a center wire (anode) that is positively charged with respect to a coaxial cylindrical shell (cathode).

For direct and continuous measurement of radioactivity in the effluent the gas is introduced at one end of the cylinder and allowed to exit at the other. In order to prevent condensation of less volatile materials, the detector must be heated to a temperature similar to that commonly employed with other detectors in gas chromatography. A number of proportional flow detectors have been described, including those of Wolfgang and Rowland (127) and of Hawke and Stumpf (128), and some models are being offered commercially. In most effective use the potential impressed on the electrodes is of the order of 2000–4000 V. The radioactivity of the fractions can be calculated from the counts generated during passage of gas chromatographic fractions through the detector, the residence time of the fraction, and the counter efficiency. Proportional flow counters are now available that can operate satisfactorily in the vicinity of 250°C with limits of detection of the order of 10^{-3} to 10^{-4} μCi for tritium and 10^{-4} to 5×10^{-5} μCi for carbon-14. A drawback in the use of the proportional flow counter in the direct analysis of (uncombusted) organic compounds is the poisoning effect that is sometimes observed to cause variations in the counting efficiency. This effect is most apparent with compounds containing nitro or halogen groups but is generally not severe with most other compounds (127, 129, 130).

With the ion chamber the level of radioactivity is related to the current generated by ions produced by the radiation. The ion chamber generally consists of an inner electrode surrounded by a wall serving as the second electrode. A cutaway diagram of a typical high-temperature ionization chamber is shown in Figure 21.10, taken from the publication of Nelson, Ressler, and Hawes (131). The potential across the electrodes is generally of the order of 100 V. Ionization chambers of this design are reported to operate satisfactorily up to 300°C. The current produced by 1 μCi of carbon-14 in a

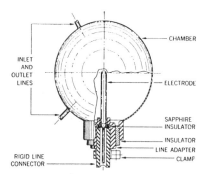

Figure 21.10. Cutaway of high-temperature ionization chamber construction. From Nelson, Ressler, and Hawes (131). Copyright 1963 by the American Chemical Society. Reprinted by permission of the copyright owners.

typical chamber is of the order of 10^{-12} A and must be measured with an electrometer amplifier. Beta emitters, such as tritium and carbon-14, produce electrons and positively charged molecules. The electrons attach themselves to gas molecules, giving them a negative charge. The charged particles move to the electrodes, producing a current that is a direct measure of the amount of radioactivity. The limits of detection for ion chambers have been found to be about 10^{-3} μCi for tritium and 3×10^{-4} μCi for carbon-14, which are sensitivities an order of magnitude less than those available with the proportional flow counters under ideal conditions.

Typical applications of GLRC include the determination of the purity of ^{14}C-labeled hydrocarbons (126), the composition of gaseous decomposition products from recoil tritium atoms (132), and the metabolism of steroids in animals (133), to indicate only a few examples of the many analyses made with this technique. In GLRC applications two detectors are commonly used in series, one a mass detector and the other a radiochemical detector, so that a relationship can be established between the chemical and radiochemical composition of the sample. An example of this technique is illustrated by Figure 18.1 for the determination of the purity of a labeled sample of n-dodecane.

CHEMICAL REACTIONS PLUS GAS CHROMATOGRAPHY

The wealth of knowledge available from classical organic functional group analysis has given the analyst a powerful guide to further the use of gas chromatography in application to materials not directly suitable for chromatography and also to assist in component identification. There are a number of techniques often referred to collectively as "reaction gas chromatography" that include such reactions as derivative preparation, pyrolysis and selective decomposition, complex formation, and catalytic conversion reactions. Beroza and Coad define reaction gas chromatography in the following way (134):

> Although in conventional gas chromatography the injected substances survive the chromatography unchanged, in reaction gas chromatography they are chemically altered or adsorbed. Somewhere within the closed system, between the introduction point and detector, the injected substances pass through a reaction zone; the products or unaffected substances continue to move with the carrier gas and eventually produce a chromatogram.

A somewhat wider scope, including also reactions completed before the products are injected, brings in a number of important practical examples some of which are included in the summary Table 21.10, wherein references are also made to sections of this text for more specific examples.

Table 21.10. Typical Techniques Employed Using Chemical Reactions with Gas Chromatography

Technique	Reaction or process	Point of application	Chapter: applications
Derivative preparation	R—C(=O)—OH → R—C(=O)—OCH$_3$ R—OH → R—O—Si(CH$_3$)$_3$	Prior to GC Prior to GC	5: Acids 8: Hydroxyl
Complex formation	C=C + AgNO$_3$ ⇌ complex	On GC column	3: Olefins
	R—⟨⟩ + nitrocompounds ⇌ charge transfer complex	On GC column	2: Aromatics
Subtracting	Removal of normal paraffins with molecular sieve	On GC column or precolumn	1: Saturates
Pyrolysis	Thermal decomposition	In chamber connected to GC	17: Polymers 11: Ethers
Selective decomposition	R—C(=O)—OR → R—C(=O)—OCH$_3$	Prior to GC	7: Esters
	C=C + O$_3$ → C=O	Prior to GC	3: Olefins
Catalytic conversion (hydrogenolysis)	C=C + H$_2$ $\xrightarrow{Pt}$ saturates	On GC column	17: Polymer pyrolysis
	[thiophene] + H$_2$ $\xrightarrow{Pt}$ C$_4$H$_{10}$ + H$_2$S	In chamber connected to GC	16: Sulfur compounds
	[furan] + H$_2$ $\xrightarrow{Pt}$ C$_4$H$_{10}$ + H$_2$S	In chamber connected to GC	—

The scope of reaction gas chromatography is vast since organic analysis provides many quantitative reactions for the functions that can readily be put into use by a gas chromatographer. Several reviews have described the possibilities in the field (135–137); no doubt, much more will be accomplished in the future.

The significance of the use of chemical reactions involves not only the specificity that can often be obtained in increasing the separation of one functional type from a mixture but also in the better definition of gas chromatographic fractions. For this purpose, hydrogenolysis is so important and so widely applicable that it is worthy of more discussion at this point.

Table 21.11. Products Obtained in Hydrogenolysis

Compound	Catalyst	Temp., °C	Products	Ref.
$CH_3-CH(NH_2)-C_5H_{11}$	5% Pt on glass	200	n-Heptane	141
2,5-dimethylpyrrole (H_3C—N(H)—CH_3 ring)	5% Pt on Glass	200	n-Hexane	141
indole (N—N)	5% Pt on glass	200	cyclohexyl—C_2H_5	141
carbazole (N—CH_3)	5% Pt on glass	200	cyclohexyl—cyclohexyl	141
$C_3H_7-N(H)-C_3H_7$	5% Pt on glass	210	Propane	139
$C_3H_7-C(O)-NH_2$	5% Pt on glass	210	Propane, butane	139
cyclohexyl—Cl	0.5% Pd on Al$_2$O$_3$	200	Cyclohexane	142
phenyl—Cl	0.5% Pd on Al$_2$O$_3$	200	Cyclohexane	142
naphthyl—F	0.5% Pd on Al$_2$O$_3$	200	tetralin + decalin	142
phenyl—$CH_2-CH_2-CH_2-Cl$	1% Pd on calcined diatomite	250	cyclohexyl—C_3H_7	139
$CH_3-CH(Br)-C_2H_5$	1% Pd on glass	187	n-Butane	139
$C_2H_5-CH(OH)-C_2H_5$	0.5% Pd on Al$_2$O$_3$	350	n-Pentane	143

(*continued overleaf*)

Table 21.11 (*continued*)

Compound	Catalyst	Temp., °C	Products	Ref.
⬡—OH	0.5% Pd on Al_2O_3	195	Cyclohexane	143
⬡—C(=O)—OH	0.5% Pd on Al_2O_3	200	Cyclohexane plus methylcyclohexane	143
	1% Pd on calcined diatomite	250	Cyclohexane	139
furan—CH=O	0.5% Pd on Al_2O_3	245	n-Pentane	143
CH_3—CH_2—CH_2—CHO	1% Pd on glass	265	Propane	139
$(CH_3$—$(CH_2)_5)_2O$	1% Pd on glass	260	n-Hexane	139
CH_3—CH_2—CH_2—CH_2—OH	1% Pd on glass	265	Propane	139
⬡—CH_2—CH_2—CH_2—OH	1% Pd on calcined diatomite	250	⬡—C_2H_5	139
$(C_2H_5)_2CH$—CH_2OH	0.5% Pd on Al_2O_3	175	n-Pentane plus (<10%) methylpentane	143
C_3H_7—CH(CH_3)—CH(H)=O	0.5% Pd on Al_2O_3	175	n-Pentane plus (<10%) methylpentane	143
CH_3—CH_2—CH_2—CH_2—SH	1% Pd on glass	260	n-Butane	139
⬡—S—⬡	1% Pd on glass	260	Cyclohexane	139
thiophene with C_2H_5 and C_2H_5	0.5% Pd on Al_2O_3	260	n-Octane	138
benzothiophene—CH_3	0.5% Pd on Al_2O_3	170	⬡—CH(CH_3)—CH_3	138

This technique was published by Thompson, Coleman, Ward, and Rall (138) of the U.S. Bureau of Mines, who developed a practical apparatus for the micro samples encountered in gas chromatography. The technique of the workers at the Bureau of Mines was designed for samples as small as 0.2 μl, which is the order of magnitude available from gas chromatographic fractions, at least with packed columns. The fractions were trapped in stainless steel tubes, prepared from hypodermic needle stock, and introduced into the desulfurization apparatus. The hydrocarbons produced in the reaction were trapped either in a liquid-nitrogen cooled U-tube or in a stainless steel tube cooled in Dry Ice and were then introduced into a gas chromatographic apparatus and analyzed in the usual way.

Beroza (139, 140) of the U.S. Department of Agriculture has developed a simpler apparatus based on the same principle but with increased sensitivity. In Beroza's apparatus the desulfurization tube, containing the catalyst, is directly connected to the gas chromatographic apparatus. Hydrogen is used as the carrier gas and the products are directly swept in the analyzing apparatus. This technique avoids the need for trapping and its inevitable requirement for an extra manipulation. Some information from the published reports, covering the application to a large number of organic compounds containing bound sulfur, oxygen, nitrogen, or halides and using platinum or palladium catalysts, is summarized in Table 21.11. Except for compounds containing oxygen, the course of reduction provides the intact carbon skeleton. With a number of materials containing an oxygen function in a terminal position, there is observed either a partial or complete loss of the end carbon atom in the resultant hydrocarbon product. Thus butyraldehyde yields propane, ethylbutanol-1 yields *n*-pentane and methyl pentane, and butyramide yields propane and butane.

REFERENCES

1. L. Zechmeister and L. Cholnoky, *Principles and Practice of Chromatography*, Wiley, New York, 1946.
2. L. R. Snyder, *Principles of Adsorption Chromatography*, Marcel Dekker, New York, 1968.
3. V. R. Deitz, "Bibliography of Solid Adsorbents," Nat. Bur. Std. Circ. 566, 1956.
4. C. K. Hersh, *Molecular Sieves*, Reinhold, New York, 1961.
5. R. M. Barrer and D. A. Ibbitson, *Trans. Faraday Soc.*, **40**, 195 (1944).
6. W. M. Meier, in *Molecular Sieves*, Society of Chemical Industry, London, 1968, pp. 10–27.
7. N. Brenner, E. Cieplinski, L. S. Ettre, and V. J. Coates, *J. Chromatog.*, **3**, 230 (1960).
8. F. G. Helfferich, *Ion Exchange*, McGraw-Hill, New York, 1962.
9. J. A. Marinsky, Ed., *Ion Exchange*, Vol. I, Marcel Dekker, New York, 1966.

10. R. Kunin, *Ann. Rev. Phys. Chem.*, **12**, 381 (1961).
11. O. Samuelson, *Ion Exchangers in Analytical Chemistry*, Wiley, New York, 1953.
12. O. Samuelson, *Ion Exchange Separations in Analytical Chemistry*, Wiley, New York, 1963.
13. J. X. Khym and W. E. Cohn, *J. Am. Chem. Soc.*, **76**, 1818 (1954).
14. R. B. Kesler, *Anal. Chem.*, **39**, 1416 (1967).
15. R. M. Wheaton and W. C. Bauman, *Ind. Eng. Chem.*, **45**, 228 (1953).
16. G. A. Harlow and D. H. Morman, *Anal. Chem.*, **36**, 2438 (1964).
17. D. K. Hale, in *Ion Exchangers in Organic and Biochemistry*, C. Calmon and T. R. E. Kressman, Eds., Interscience, New York, 1957, pp. 150 ff.
18. W. A. Munday and A. Eaves, Fifth World Petroleum Congress, Section V, New York, 1959, paper 9, published by Fifth World Petroleum Congress Inc., New York.
19. A. Eaves and W. A. Munday, *J. Appl. Chem.*, **9**, 145 (1959).
20. L. R. Snyder and B. E. Buell, *Anal. Chem.*, **34**, 689 (1962); **40**, 1295 (1968).
21. L. R. Snyder and B. E. Buell, *Anal. Chim. Acta*, **33**, 285 (1965).
22. L. R. Snyder, B. E. Buell, and H. E. Howard, *Anal. Chem.*, **40**, 1303 (1968).
23. P. V. Webster, J. N. Wilson, and M. C. Franks, *Anal. Chim. Acta*, **38**, 193 (1967).
24. J. J. Kirkland, *Anal. Chem.*, **40**, 391 (1968).
25. J. J. Kirkland, *J. Chromatog. Sci.*, **7**, 7 (1969).
26. S. T. Sie and G. W. A. Rijnders, *Anal. Chim. Acta*, **38**, 31 (1967).
27. S. T. Sie and G. W. A. Rijnders, *Separation Sci.*, **2**, 699 (1967).
28. S. M. Lambert and P. E. Porter, *Anal. Chem.*, **36**, 99 (1964).
29. S. M. Lambert, *ibid.*, **37**, 959 (1965).
30. A. T. James, J. R. Ravenhill, and R. P. W. Scott, *Chem. Ind. (London)*, **1964**, 746.
31. H. W. Johnson, Jr., E. E. Seibert, and F. H. Stross, *Anal. Chem.*, **40**, 403 (1968).
32. H. Coll, H. W. Johnson, Jr., A. G. Polgar, E. E. Seibert, and F. H. Stross, *J. Chromatograph. Sci.*, **7**, 30 (1969).
33. C. G. Horvath, B. A. Preiss, and S. R. Lipsky, *Anal. Chem.*, **39**, 1422 (1967).
34. J. C. Giddings, M. N. Meyers, and J. W. King, in *Advances in Chromatography*, A. Zlatkis, Ed., Preston Technical Abstracts Co., Evanston, Ill., 1969.
35. H. G. Cassidy, *Fundamentals of Chromatography*, Interscience, New York, 1957.
36. R. J. Block, N. LeStrange, and G. Zweig, *Paper Chromatography, A Laboratory Manual*, Academic Press, New York, 1952.
37. R. J. Block, E. L. Durrum, and G. Zweig, *A Manual of Paper Chromatography and Paper Electrophoresis*, Academic Press, New York, 1958.
38. E. Stahl, Ed., *Thin-Layer Chromatography, A Laboratory Handbook*, Springer, Berlin, 1965.
39. E. V. Truter, *Thin-Film Chromatography*, Interscience, New York, 1963.
40. K. Randerath, *Thin-Layer Chromatography*, 2nd ed., Academic Press, New York, 1966.

41. J. M. Bobbitt, *Thin-Layer Chromatography*, Reinhold, New York, 1963.
42. J. G. Kirchner, *Thin-Layer Chromatography* (Vol. 12 in *Technique of Organic Chemistry*), Interscience, New York, 1967.
43. R. N. McCoy and A. B. Bullock, *J. Am. Oil Chemists' Soc.*, **46**, 289 (1969).
44. F. T. Eggertsen, H. S. Knight, and S. Groennings, *Anal. Chem.*, **28**, 303 (1956).
45. A. T. James and A. J. P. Martin, *Biochem. J.*, **50**, 679 (1952).
46. S. Dal Nogare and R. S. Juvet, *Gas-Liquid Chromatography*, Wiley, New York, 1962.
47. A. B. Littlewood, *Gas Chromatography, Principles, Techniques and Application*, Academic Press, New York, 1962.
48. J. H. Purnell, *Gas Chromatography*, Wiley, New York, 1962.
49. L. S. Ettre and A. Zlatkis, Ed., *The Practice of Gas Chromatography*, Interscience, New York, 1967.
50. Preston Technical Abstract Co., Evanston, Ill. 60201.
51. "Gas Chromatographic Abstracts," Institute of Petroleum, London; Elsevier, Amsterdam.
52. W. O. McReynolds, *Gas Chromatographic Retention Data*, Preston Technical Abstracts Co., Evanston, Ill., 1966.
53. J. S. Lewis, "Compilation of Gas Chromatographic Data," ASTM Spec. Publ. No. 343.
54. D. H. Desty, Ed., *Gas Chromatography*, Academic Press, New York, 1958 (papers and discussion from Amsterdam Meeting, 1958).
55. R. P. W. Scott, Ed., *Gas Chromatography*, Butterworths, London, 1960 (papers and discussion from Edinburgh meeting, 1960).
56. M. van Swaay, Ed., *Gas Chromatography*, Butterworths, Washington, 1962 (papers and discussion from Hamburg meeting, 1962).
57. A. Goldup, Ed., *Gas Chromatography*, Institute of Petroleum, London, 1965 (papers and discussion from Brighton meeting, 1964).
58. A. B. Littlewood, Ed., *Gas Chromatography*, Elsevier, Amsterdam, 1967 (papers and discussion from Rome meeting, 1966).
59. C. L. A. Harbourn, Ed., *Gas Chromatography* (papers and discussion from Copenhagen meeting, 1968), The Institute of Petroleum, London, 1969.
60. A. Zlatkis and L. S. Ettre, Ed., *Advances in Gas Chromatography*, Preston Technical Abstracts Co., Evanston, Ill., 1966.
61. V. J. Coates, Ed., *Gas Chromatography*, Academic Press, New York, 1958 (Proceedings from Lansing, Mich. meeting, 1957).
62. Henry J. Noebels, Ed., *Gas Chromatography*, Academic Press, New York, 1961 (proceedings from Lansing, Mich. meeting, 1959).
63. N. Brenner, J. E. Callen and M. D. Weiss, Editors, *Gas Chromatography*, Academic Press, New York, 1962 (proceedings from Lansing, Mich. meeting, 1961).
64. Lewis Fowler, Ed., *Gas Chromatography*, Academic Press, New York, 1963 (proceedings from Lansing meeting, 1963).
65. J. C. Giddings and R. A. Keller, Eds., *Advances in Chromatography*, Vol. 1–6, Marcel Dekker, New York, 1965–1968.
66. M. J. E. Golay, in reference 54, pp. 36–53.

67. L. S. Ettre, *Open-Tubular Columns in Gas Chromatography*, Plenum Press, New York, 1965.
68. G. L. K. Hunter, *J. Chromatog.*, **11**, 124 (1963).
69. I. Halász and C. Horváth, *Anal. Chem.*, **35**, 499 (1963).
70. L. C. Ettre, J. E. Purcell, and K. Billeb, *Separation Sci.*, **1**, 777 (1966).
71. E. R. Adlard, P. Davies, and A. Evans, paper in press.
72. H. M. Tenney, *Anal. Chem.*, **30**, 2 (1958).
73. L. Rohrschneider, *J. Chromatog.*, **22**, 6 (1966); **17**, 1 (1965); **39**, 383 (1969).
74. S. H. Langer and R. J. Sheehan, in *Progress in Gas Chromatography*, J. H. Purnell, Ed., Interscience, New York, 1968, pp. 289–323.
75. O. L. Hollis, *Anal. Chem.*, **38**, 309 (1966).
76. J. J. Kirkland, *ibid.*, **35**, 1295 (1963).
77. J. J. Kirkland, reference 57, p. 285.
78. C. G. Scott and C. S. G. Phillips, *Nature*, **199**, 66 (1963).
79. C. G. Scott and C. S. G. Phillips, in reference 57, p. 266.
80. I. Halász and C. Horváth, *Anal. Chem.*, **36**, 1178 (1964).
81. A. V. Kiselev, reference 57, p. 238.
82. H. M. McNair and E. J. Bonelli, "Basic Gas Chromatography," Varian Aerograph, Walnut Creek, Calif., 1967.
83. M. Dimbat, P. E. Porter, and F. H. Stross, *Anal. Chem.*, **28**, 290 (1956).
84. A. E. Messner, D. M. Rosie, and P. A. Argabright, *ibid.*, **31**, 230 (1959).
85. J. A. Green and T. M. Sugden, *Ninth Symposium (International) on Combustion*, Academic Press, New York, 1963, p. 607.
86. H. F. Calcote, *ibid.*, p. 622.
87. M. E. Umsted, F. J. Woods, and J. E. Johnson, *J. Catalysis*, **5**, 293 (1966).
88. I. G. McWilliam and R. A. Dewar, in reference 54, pp. 142–147.
89. J. Harley, W. Nel, and V. Pretorius, *Nature*, **181**, 178 (1958).
90. L. Ettre, in *Gas Chromatography*, N. Brenner, J. E. Callen, and M. D. Weiss, Eds., Academic Press, New York, 1962, pp. 307–327.
91. J. C. Sternberg, W. S. Gallaway, and D. T. C. Jones, *ibid.*, pp. 231–267.
92. J. E. Lovelock and S. R. Lipsky, *J. Am. Chem. Soc.*, **82**, 431 (1960).
93. J. E. Lovelock, A. Zlatkis, and R. S. Becker, *Nature*, **193**, 540 (1962).
94. A. Zlatkis and J. E. Lovelock, *Clin. Chem.*, **11**, 259 (1965).
95. C. A. Clemons and A. P. Altshuller, *Anal. Chem.*, **38**, 133 (1966).
96. J. R. Pearson, F. D. Aldrich, and A. W. Stone, *J. Agr. Food Chem.*, **15**, 938 (1967).
97. E. S. Goodwin, R. Goulden, and J. G. Reynolds, *Analyst*, **86**, 697 (1961).
98. R. Goulden, E. S. Goodwin, and L. Davies, *ibid.*, **88**, 941, 951, (1963).
99. D. M. Coulson and L. A. Cavanagh, *Anal. Chem.*, **32**, 1245 (1960).
100. J. A. McNulty, "New Instrumental Methods of Analysis—Microcoulometric Titrating System," paper given at American Gas Association, Baltimore, Md., May 23, 1966.
101. S. S. Brody and J. E. Chaney, *J. Gas Chromatog.*, **4**, 42 (1966).
102. M. C. Bowman and M. Beroza, *Anal. Chem.*, **40**, 1448 (1968).
103. A. Karmen and L. Giuffrida, *Nature*, **201**, 1204 (1964).
104. A. Karmen, *Anal. Chem.*, **36**, 1416 (1964); and reference 60 (1969), pp. 91–99.

105. K. Biemann, *Mass Spectrometry. Organic Chemical Applications*, McGraw-Hill, New York, 1962.
106. J. H. Beynon, R. A. Saunders, and R. E. Williams, *The Mass Spectra of Organic Molecules*, Elsevier, Amsterdam, 1968.
107. F. W. McLafferty, *Mass Spectrometry of Organic Ions*, Academic Press, New York, 1963.
108. H. Budzikiewicz, C. Djerassi, and D. H. Williams, *Structural Elucidation of Natural Products by Mass Spectroscopy*, Vols. I and II, Holden-Day, San Francisco, 1964.
109. A. E. Banner, in *Modern Aspects of Mass Spectrometry*, R. I. Reed, Ed., Plenum Press, New York, 1968.
110. R. S. Gohlke, *Anal. Chem.*, **31**, 535 (1959).
111. J. A. Völlmin, W. Simon, and R. Kaiser, *Z. Anal. Chem.*, **229**, 1 (1967).
112. R. A. Flath, D. R. Black, D. G. Guadagni, W. H. McFadden, and T. H. Schultz, *J. Agr. Food Chem.*, **15**, 29 (1967).
113. W. H. McFadden, *Separation Sci.*, **1**, 723 (1966).
114. B. A. Knights, *J. Gas Chromatog.*, **5**, 273 (1967).
115. E. C. Horning, M. G. Horning, N. Ikekawa, E. M. Chambaz, P. I. Jaakonmaki, and C. J. W. Brooks, *ibid.*, **5**, 283 (1967).
116. F. A. Leemans and J. A. McCloskey, *J. Am. Oil Chemists' Soc.*, **44**, 11 (1967).
117. J. B. Maynard, C. E. Legate, and L. B. Graiff, *Combustion Flame*, **11**, 155 (1967).
118. A. B. Littlewood, *Chromatographia*, **1**, 37 (1968).
119. J. T. Watson and K. Biemann, *Anal. Chem.*, **36**, 1135 (1964); **37**, 844 (1965).
120. R. Ryhage, *ibid.*, **36**, 759 (1964).
121. M. Blumer, *ibid.*, **40**, 1590 (1968).
122. S. R. Lipsky, C. G. Horvath, and W. J. McMurray, *ibid.*, **38**, 1585 (1966).
123. P. M. Llewellyn and D. P. Littlejohn, Pittsburgh Conf. on Anal. Chem. and Appl. Spectry, February, 1966.
124. J. P. Adloff, *Chromatog. Rev.*, **4**, 19 (1962).
125. G. Popjak, *Biochem. J.*, **73**, 33 (1959).
126. M. A. Muhs, E. L. Bastin, and B. E. Gordon, *Intern. J. Appl. Radiation Isotopes*, **16**, 537 (1965).
127. R. Wolfgang and F. S. Rowland, *Anal. Chem.*, **30**, 903 (1958).
128. J. C. Hawke and P. K. Stumpf, *J. Biol. Chem.*, **240**, 4746 (1965).
129. J. K. Lee, E. K. C. Lee, B. Musgrave, Y-N Tung, J. W. Root, and F. S. Rowland, *Anal. Chem.*, **34**, 741 (1962).
130. L. Bruzzi, A. Castelli, and A. Cervellati, *Nucl. Instr. Methods*, **26**, 305 (1964).
131. D. C. Nelson, P. C. Ressler, Jr., and R. C. Hawes, *Anal. Chem.*, **35**, 1575 (1963).
132. E. Tachikawa and F. S. Rowland, *J. Am. Chem. Soc.*, **91**, 559 (1969).
133. N. Iritani and W. Wells, *J. Lipid Res.*, **7**, 372 (1966).
134. M. Beroza and R. A. Coad, *J. Gas Chromatog.*, **4**, 199 (1966).
135. S. G. Perry, *Chromatog. Rev.*, **9**, 1, (1967) particularly pp. 7–13.
136. V. G. Berezkin, *Analytical Reaction Gas Chromatography*, Plenum Press, New York, 1968.

137. A. B. Littlewood, *Chromatographia*, **1**, 133 (1968).
138. C. J. Thompson, H. J. Coleman, C. C. Ward, and H. T. Rall, *Anal. Chem.*, **32**, 424 (1960).
139. M. Beroza, *ibid.*, **34**, 1801 (1962).
140. M. Beroza and R. Sarmiento, *ibid.*, **35**, 1353 (1963).
141. C. J. Thompson, H. J. Coleman, C. C. Ward, and H. T. Rall, *ibid.*, **34**, 151 (1962).
142. C. J. Thompson, H. J. Coleman, C. C. Ward, and H. T. Rall, *ibid.*, **34**, 154 (1962).
143. C. J. Thompson, H. J. Coleman, R. L. Hopkins, C. C. Ward, and H. T. Rall, *ibid.*, **32**, 1762 (1960).

22

DETERMINATION OF WATER

The omnipresence of water and its influence on the properties and reactions of organic compounds make its quantitative determination necessary to the analyst. Of specific analytical importance is the need to determine the water content of certain analytical solvents and, especially, to follow the several valuable methods for determination of functional groups based on reactions leading to the quantitative production of water. For these reasons a procedure for the determination of water in organic materials is included here.

The specificity of the Karl Fischer reagent (1) for the determination of water has brought it into widespread use. The reagent is essentially an alcoholic solution of iodine, sulfur dioxide, and pyridine. The reaction involved can be written formally as

$$I_2 + SO_2 + H_2O + 3 \underset{}{\bigcirc} N + ROH \longrightarrow$$

$$2 \underset{}{\bigcirc} NH^+I^- + \underset{}{\bigcirc} N\overset{H}{\underset{SO_4R}{}}$$

Thorough investigations (2, 3) have been made into the nature of the reaction and from this have come many extremely useful applications, not only for the direct and specific determination of water but also for the determination of carbonyl, hydroxyl, anhydride, and other functional groups. In the wide use of the reagent, a number of improvements have been made including those introduced by Peters and Jungnickel (4), who prefer the use of methyl Cellosolve as the alcoholic component because it is more stable and produces a lower level of side reactions than methanol, used earlier. They describe practical equipment for dispensing the reagent and conducting the titration. The method given in this section is based on their publication. The recommended method can be applied to a large variety of compounds, including hydrocarbons, alcohols, phenols, ketones, acids, esters, amines, nitro compounds, halogenated compounds, and thioethers. It is not directly applicable to low molecular weight aldehydes since they condense partially

417

with the methyl Cellosolve reagent to produce acetals and water. Inorganic bases, carbonates, hydrogen sulfide, mercaptans, and hydroperoxides interfere. Some of the interferences can be overcome by modifying the procedure (3). For instance, inorganic bases and carbonates interfere by producing water from reaction with the HI in the reagent; however, if the basicity of the sample is determined, a straightforward correction can be applied to the water value determined by titration. The Fischer method has been extended to the micro range by Bastin, Siegel, and Bullock (5), who were able to titrate amounts of water as low as 0.01 mg with a cleverly designed, unified apparatus that has wide utility.

It is essential to avoid changes in the water content of the material during sampling. Errors of this nature are particularly significant in the analysis of substances having a low water content. To obtain quantitative results on materials of low water content it is necessary to limit contact with atmospheric moisture and, if possible, to equilibrate handling vessels, such as transfer pipets, by contacting them with a portion of the sample and discarding this prior to taking the analytical sample. When precautions of this type are used

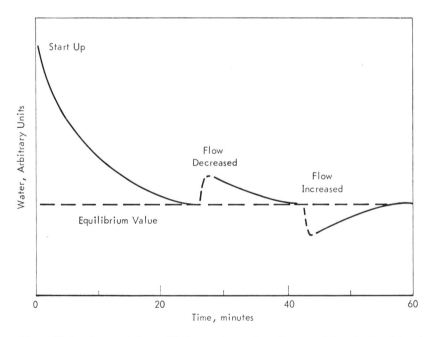

Figure 22.1. Approach to equilibrium under various flow conditions in the determination of water in hydrocarbons at the 0.1–5 ppm level. From Knight and Weiss (8). Copyright 1962 by the American Chemical Society. Reprinted by permission of the copyright owner.

and a sufficiently large sample taken, the Karl Fischer method can give meaningful results with samples containing as little as 5 ppm of water.

A number of other techniques find use in determination of water, especially in manufacturing facilities. Gas chromatography can be employed, such as with columns prepared from the porous polymer beads as described by Hollis, (6, 7), which provides quantitative results for water in many systems from levels of a few percent to as low as 100 ppm. An illustration of the gas chromatographic separation of water from a mixture of organic compounds is provided by Figure 21.7. Below this level of sensitivity it is possible to use gas chromatography in a method involving conversion of water to acetylene by reaction with CaC_2 and determination of the acetylene by gas chromatography (8, 9) or, alternatively, by infrared absorption (10). Another instrument type, especially valuable with a flowing gas system, is an electrolytic H_3PO_4 absorber (11). These highly sensitive methods are capable of determining water in the 0.1 ppm range and, since sampling is so critical in this concentration region, a flow system is generally recommended and data taken either continuously or intermittently until an equilibrium value is reached. It has been found that changes in the variables strongly affect the values obtained at low concentrations because of adsorption on the walls of the vessel or the lines. This is illustrated in Figure 22.1, showing the results of flow rate changes on the determined water content as measured by Knight and Weiss (8) employing the CaC_2–gas chromatographic techniques.

DETERMINATION OF WATER

FISCHER REAGENT METHOD

Apparatus

Buret assembly, an all-glass buret system. Protect all vents against atmospheric moisture with adequate drying tubes.
Volumetric flasks, 100-ml, glass-stoppered.
Side-well flask, 500-ml, as illustrated in Figure 22.2.

Reagents

Acetic acid, anhydrous.
Ethylene glycol–pyridine mixture.
Fischer reagent.
Methanol, CP, anhydrous.
Pyridine, CP, anhydrous.

Procedure

General Procedure. Introduce 10 ml of the ethylene glycol–pyridine mixture into each of two 100-ml glass-stoppered volumetric flasks and titrate until the

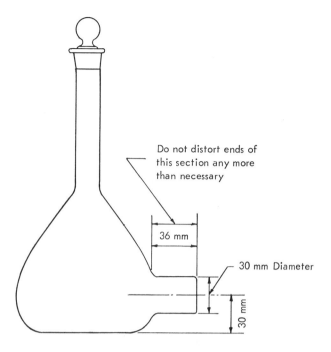

Do not distort ends of
this section any more
than necessary

36 mm

30 mm Diameter

30 mm

PYREX 500-ml. Volumetric Flask with Cylindrical Side-Well

Figure 22.2.   Side-well flask for determining water in hydrocarbons using Fischer reagent. From Peters and Jungnickel (4). Copyright 1955 by the American Chemical Society. Reprinted by permission of the copyright owner.

straw-yellow color changes to an orange-red that remains after vigorous swirling of the stoppered flask; view the color by transmitted light. Retain one flask as a color standard.

If the sample is known to be free of ketones, strong acids, and other interfering substances, methanol may be preferred to glycol–pyridine because of its better solvent properties and a more distinct color change at the end point.

Introduce into the flask a measured amount of the sample containing, preferably, between 0.1 and 0.2 g of water, but limit the maximum sample size to 10 ml. Mix well and titrate with Fischer reagent to the end-point color of the standard. This color should persist for at least 1 min upon vigorous swirling of the flask; normally, once the color persists for 1 min, it will remain for an indefinite time. Avoid wetting the stopper and the ground joint of the reaction flask with either the reagent or reaction mixture.

Ketones, Epoxides, and Organic Acids.   Introduce 10 ml of ethylene glycol–pyridine solution into each of two 100-ml glass-stoppered volumetric flasks, chill the bulb of the flasks to ice-water temperature, and titrate to the end-point color with Fischer reagent. Retain one flask as color standard and add a quantity of sample containing, preferably, between 0.1 and 0.2 g of water to the other. Titrate to the end-point color of the standard, keeping the reaction mixture near 0°C at all times.

> CAUTION! Pure epoxy compounds of low molecular weight sometimes react violently with Fischer reagent at room temperature; thus, ice temperature is specified. When analyzing these materials, wear a face shield and use samples of minimum size.

Nitrogen Bases. Introduce 10 ml of ethylene glycol–pyridine and 10 ml of anhydrous acetic acid into each of two 100-ml glass-stoppered volumetric flasks, mix, and chill to ice-water temperature. Titrate with Fischer reagent, retain one flask as color standard, and add a weighed quantity of sample containing not more than 0.09 equiv of nitrogen base nor more than 0.2 g of water. Limit the sample size to 10 g. Swirl the contents of the flask to ensure neutralization of the base and titrate the mixture to the end-point color of the standard, keeping the reaction mixture at ice-water temperature during the titration.

Inorganic Acids. Clean and dry two 100-ml glass-stoppered volumetric flasks and draw laboratory air through them at a brisk rate until equilibrium has been reached. Introduce 10 ml of anhydrous pyridine into each flask using dry pipets. Place one flask in a small Dewar flask containing solid carbon dioxide and chill the bulb of the flask until part of the pyridine freezes. Add cautiously an amount of sample containing, preferably, between 0.1 and 0.2 g of water, but limit the sample size to 3 g. Agitate vigorously to ensure complete conversion of the acid to the pyridinium salt. Allow the mixture to warm to room temperature, and add 10 ml of anhydrous methanol to each flask. Agitate until the pyridinium salt is dissolved and titrate both flasks with Fischer reagent.

Liquid Hydrocarbons. Introduce 15 ml of anhydrous ethylene glycol into each of two special side-well flasks and titrate to the orange-red end-point color with Fischer reagent; tilt the flasks and allow the mixture to flow into the side wells for comparison. Retain one flask as color standard. Introduce 100–300 g of sample, depending on the water content, into the other flask, shake vigorously to extract the water by the glycol phase, and titrate with Fischer reagent until the lower phase is near the end-point color. Stopper the flask, shake it vigorously, allow the phases to separate, and complete the titration, making comparisons with the standard in tilted position.

Calculation

From the standardization, calculate the equivalency factor, F, in milligrams of water equivalent to 1 ml of Fischer reagent, by means of the following equation:

$$F = \frac{1000 W_s}{V_s}$$

where W_s = weight of water, g, used for the standardization of Fischer reagent and V_s = volume of Fischer reagent, ml, consumed in the standardization.

Calculate the water content of the sample as follows:

$$\text{Water, wt \%} = \frac{(S - B)(F)}{10W}$$

where S = volume of Fischer reagent, ml, required by sample

B = volume of Fischer reagent, ml, required by blank determination

F = equivalency factor for Fischer reagent

W = weight of sample, g

REFERENCES

1. K. Fischer, *Z. Angew. Chem.*, **48,** 395 (1935).
2. D. M. Smith, W. M. D. Bryant, and J. Mitchell, Jr., *J. Am. Chem. Soc.*, **61,** 2407 (1939).
3. J. Mitchell, Jr., and D. M. Smith, *Aquametry*, Interscience, New York, 1948.
4. E. D. Peters and J. L. Jungnickel, *Anal. Chem.*, **27,** 450 (1955).
5. E. L. Bastin, H. Siegel, and A. B. Bullock, *ibid.*, **31,** 467 (1959).
6. O. L. Hollis, *ibid.*, **38,** 309 (1966).
7. O. L. Hollis and W. V. Hayes, *J. Gas Chromatog.*, **4,** 235 (1966).
8. H. S. Knight and F. T. Weiss, *Anal. Chem.*, **34,** 749 (1962).
9. A. Goldup and M. T. Westaway, *ibid.*, **38,** 1657 (1966).
10. J. W. Forbes, *ibid.*, **34,** 1125 (1962).
11. J. K. Crawshaw and F. G. Davidson, *J. Sci. Instr.*, **36,** 121 (1959).

CHAPTER

23

PREPARATION OF THE COMMON REAGENTS

Many of the reagents described in this volume, including those in this chapter, are now available commercially from a number of suppliers. It is the experience of the author's laboratory that it is quite possible to obtain good reagents from suppliers but it is important that the analyst be certain of the reagents he uses since the quality of the entire analysis depends upon the purity of the reagents. For this reason, specific directions are given for the preparation of the principal reagents to ensure that the analyst can prepare his own supply if he requires it. Since the quality of commercial reagents is continually improving and because of economy in time and money, it is advantageous for the analyst to purchase a number of reagents, which are well described in supplier's catalog.

> CAUTION! Many of the chemicals used in reagent preparation are hazardous and, consequently, a number of these operations should be conducted in an efficient fume hood. Do not breathe the vapors from pyridine, iodine, sulfur dioxide, bromine, or other toxic materials. Protect the face and hands during operations involving the halogens or the handling of sulfur dioxide and concentrated acids and bases by wearing rubber gloves and using a face mask. A buret system using all-glass components, recommended for hazardous and corrosive titrants, is shown in Figure 24.1 and consists of a 50-ml buret connected to a reservoir of resistant glass. The reservoir vent is protected against atmospheric moisture by a tube containing indicating Drierite.

PREPARATION OF SOLUTIONS FOR USE WITH THE FISCHER REAGENT METHODS

PREPARATION OF ETHYLENE GLYCOL-PYRIDINE MIXTURE

Reagents

Pyridine, CP, anhydrous.
Ethylene glycol, CP, anhydrous.

423

Preparation

Add 200 ml of CP anhydrous pyridine to 800 ml of CP anhydrous ethylene glycol. Mix thoroughly by shaking and store in a glass-stoppered Pyrex bottle.

PREPARATION OF SULFUR DIOXIDE AND PYRIDINE IN METHANOL (FOR CARBONYL DETERMINATION)

Reagents

Pyridine, CP, anhydrous.
Methanol, absolute. To ensure low blanks in the use of the solution for Fischer titration the water content should be less than 0.1 %.
Sulfur dioxide, commercial, anhydrous. Handle with caution!

Preparation

Using an efficient and large fume hood, place a cylinder of anhydrous liquid sulfur dioxide in a stable, substantial stand such that the cylinder is inverted with the outlet at the bottom. Put a metal pan under the stand of sufficient capacity to retain all the sulfur dioxide in case of spillage. Connect a needle valve to a 2–3-ft piece of aluminum tubing and attach the needle valve to the cylinder, *using proper fittings*.

For each liter of solution add 80 ml of pyridine to 875 ml of methanol in a clean dry Pyrex bottle. Cool the bottle and contents in a slurry of ice and water.

Stopper the mouth of a 100-ml graduated cylinder with a plug of cotton and cool the graduated cylinder in Dry Ice. When it is chilled, remove the cylinder from the Dry Ice bath and place it under the aluminum tube leading from the sulfur dioxide cylinder so that the tube extends 2–3 in. into the graduated cylinder. Close the opening between the graduated cylinder and the tube with cotton. Collect 45 ml of liquid sulfur dioxide. Add the sulfur dioxide slowly to the mixture of pyridine and methanol, keeping the bottle in the ice bath and swirling the bottle to prevent overheating.

PREPARATION OF FISCHER REAGENT

Reagents

Iodine, CP, resublimed.
Methyl Cellosolve (methyl ether of ethylene glycol), anhydrous.
Pyridine, CP, anhydrous.
Sulfur dioxide, commercial, anhydrous. Handle with caution!

Preparation

Conduct these operations in an efficient fume hood. Weigh 133 g of iodine into a 2-liter, dry glass-stoppered Pyrex bottle. Dissolve the iodine completely by adding

425 ml of pyridine. Remove the stopper occasionally to release the slight pressure but do not cool the solution. The temperature of the solution increases by about 4°C during the 10–15-min interval required for solution of the iodine. Add 425 ml of methyl Cellosolve and cool the resulting solution in an ice bath. Add 70 ml of liquid sulfur dioxide in small increments with occasional agitation of the solution.

Mix the solution thoroughly and test for sufficiency of sulfur dioxide by adding a few milliliters of water to a small portion of the reagent contained in a test tube. If the brown-red color of the reagent persists, add 5-ml increments of sulfur dioxide to the reagent being prepared, testing after each addition, until a straw-yellow color is obtained in the test.

Mix thoroughly and store in an automatic dispensing type of buret with all-glass connections and protected from atmospheric moisture.

The water equivalent of this reagent is approximately 6 mg of water per milliliter of reagent. Standardize the reagent in the following manner: Introduce 10 ml of anhydrous methanol into each of two 100-ml volumetric flasks and titrate each with Fischer reagent until the straw-yellow color changes to an orange-red that remains after vigorous swirling of the stoppered flask; view the color by transmitted light. Retain one flask as color standard and into the other weigh, from a Lunge weighing bottle, 0.15–0.18 g of water. Mix and titrate with Fischer reagent to the original orange-red end-point color. Calculate the equivalency factor as milligrams of water equivalent to 1 ml of the Fischer reagent.

Reference

E. D. Peters and J. L. Jungnickel, *Anal. Chem.*, **27**, 450 (1955).

J. Mitchell, Jr. and D. M. Smith, *Aquametry*, Interscience, New York, 1948.

PREPARATION OF SOLUTIONS OF THE STANDARD BASES

PREPARATION AND STANDARDIZATION OF SODIUM HYDROXIDE SOLUTIONS, 0.1*N*, 0.5*N*, AND 1.0*N* AQUEOUS (CARBONATE-FREE)

Reagents

Sodium hydroxide, saturated solution (see next preparation).
Potassium acid phthalate, primary standard.
Phenolphthalein, 1% in 60% ethanol.

Preparation

For each liter of solution of the desired normality, add the number of milliliters of saturated sodium hydroxide shown below to 500–600 ml of distilled water from which the carbon dioxide has been removed by bubbling with nitrogen. Mix by swirling and then dilute to 1 liter with carbon dioxide-free distilled water. Mix thoroughly by shaking. Store in a rubber-stoppered Pyrex bottle equipped with means for dispensing the solution and protected from carbon dioxide of the air by an Ascarite tube.

Normality	Saturated NaOH solution, ml
1.0N	53.9
0.5N	26.9
0.1N	5.4

Standardization

Accurately weigh the amount of potassium acid phthalate indicated on a tared watch glass. Transfer the salt to a 500-ml Erlenmeyer flask containing 100 ml of carbon dioxide-free distilled water. Add 4 or 5 drops of phenolphthalein indicator and then titrate to the first permanent pink color. Make all determinations in triplicate.

Normality	Potassium acid phthalate, g
1.0N	8.5–9.2
0.5N	4.3–4.6
0.1N	0.85–0.92

Calculate the normality of the sodium hydroxide solution from the equation:

$$N = \frac{(W)(1000)}{(V)(204.23)}$$

where W = g of potassium acid phthalate, and V = volume of standard sodium hydroxide required, ml.

PREPARATION OF SATURATED SODIUM HYDROXIDE SOLUTION

Apparatus

Funnels, Buchner type with fritted disk, 600-ml, Pyrex; one of porosity C, one of porosity M (Corning No. 36060).

Reagents

Sodium hydroxide, CP, 97–98%, pellets or sticks.

Preparation

Dissolve 1100 g of CP sodium hydroxide in 1 liter of carbon dioxide-free distilled water. Prepare the solution in an Erlenmeyer flask of suitable size immersed in an ice-water bath.

Add the sodium hydroxide to the water slowly while stirring with a mechanical stirrer so that the sodium hydroxide dissolves completely. Securely stopper the flask after solution is completed.

Filter the saturated solution through a coarse fritted glass funnel, using vacuum, into a Pyrex Erlenmeyer suction flask. Refilter the solution through a medium fritted glass funnel, using vacuum. Keep the exposed solution in filter funnel under an atmosphere of nitrogen at all times. Store in a rubber-stoppered Pyrex bottle.

Reference

W. F. Hillebrand, *Applied Inorganic Analysis* 2nd ed., Wiley, New York, 1953, pp. 178 and 180.

PREPARATION OF POTASSIUM HYDROXIDE IN ISOPROPYL ALCOHOL, 0.1N AND 0.2N

Apparatus

Funnels, Buchner type with fritter disk, 600-ml, Pyrex, porosity F (Corning No. 36060).

Water bath, steam heated.

Reflux condenser, fitted with standard-taper joint, water cooled.

Flask, Pyrex, of appropriate size and with a standard-taper joint to fit the reflux condenser.

Reagents

Potassium hydroxide, CP, 85–87%.

Isopropyl alcohol, refined caustic-treated isopropyl alcohol containing less than 0.9% water. The color developed on refluxing 100 ml of isopropyl alcohol with 10 g of CP potassium hydroxide pellets for 2 hr shall be no more than 100 when compared with platinum–cobalt color standards.

Preparation

For each liter of solution, add the amount of CP potassium hydroxide shown below to 200 ml of isopropyl alcohol and swirl to effect solution. Then dilute to 1 liter, add one or two boiling chips and gently reflux for 10 min.

Normality	Grams of CP KOH
0.1N	6.2
0.2N	12.4

Cool to room temperature and stopper the flask after mixing thoroughly. Let stand for at least 24 hr, then filter the clear, supernatant liquid through a fine fritted glass funnel using vacuum, if necessary. Mix thoroughly and store in a securely stoppered Pyrex bottle that has been purged with nitrogen. Protect the solution from the carbon dioxide of the air at all times.

Wash out the funnel as soon as time permits because the potassium hydroxide will attack the fritted glass disk if allowed to remain in contact with it for long. Scrape out the precipitate adhering to the disk with a spatula and then pour cleaning acid through it several times. Follow this with several washings with distilled water.

Preparation of Sodium Hydroxide in Methanol, 0.1 N

For each liter of solution, dissolve 4.0 g of CP sodium hydroxide in 200 ml of CP anhydrous methanol. Dilute to 1 liter with CP anhydrous methanol. Stopper the container and allow it to stand for 24 hr. Remove the clear liquid from the separated solid, by filtration, if necessary. Dispense the solution by means of a syphon-fed or automatic buret protected from the carbon dioxide of the air at all times. Standardize the reagent at the same temperature at which it is used, or correct for the change in normality with temperature by means of the equation:

$$N_2 = N_1[1 + 0.0013(t_1 - t_2)]$$

where N = normality and t = temperature, °C.

Preparation and Standardization of Tetra-n-Butyl Ammonium Hydroxide in Isopropyl Alcohol, 0.2 N

Apparatus

Ion-exchange column, Pyrex, 4.5 × 52 cm.

Reagents

Tetra-n-butylammonium iodide, CP.
Exchange resin, Amberlite IRA-400.
Isopropyl alcohol, CP, anhydrous (<0.1 % H_2O).
Potassium hydroxide, CP.
Potassium hydroxide, 1 N aqueous solution.
Benzoic acid, primary standard.

Preparation

Fill the narrow portion of the ion-exchange column with a slurry of Amberlite IRA-400 exchange resin in distilled water, making sure that all air bubbles are expelled. Prepare the resin by slowly passing 10 liters of 1 N KOH through the column. Follow this with 6 liters of distilled water and, finally, 5 liters of anhydrous isopropyl alcohol. Do not allow the column to run dry during the course of this procedure.

Dissolve 110 g of tetra-n-butylammonium iodide in 500 ml of anhydrous isopropyl alcohol by warming to about 40°C but not above 50°C. Pass this solution through the prepared resin at a rate not greater than 5 ml/min, collecting the effluent in a graduated cylinder or other suitable container. Then, at a slightly faster rate, pour through sufficient anhydrous isopropyl alcohol to bring the total volume of effluent to 1400 ml. Protect the effluent solution at all times from atmospheric CO_2.

Standardization

Accurately weigh 0.36 g of benzoic acid on a tared watch glass and transfer to a 250-ml tall-form beaker containing CO_2-free isopropyl alcohol. Titrate with the tetra-n-butylammonium hydroxide electrometrically to the end point as indicated by the inflection in the titration curve.

Calculate the normality of the tetra-n-butylammonium hydroxide solution from the equation:

$$N = \frac{(W)(1000)}{(V)(122.12)}$$

where W = weight of benzoic acid, g, and V = volume of tetra-n-butylammonium hydroxide required, ml.

Reference

G. A. Harlow, C. M. Noble, and G. E. A. Wyld, *Anal. Chem.*, **28**, 787 (1956).

PREPARATION OF SOLUTIONS OF THE STANDARD ACIDS

PREPARATION AND STANDARDIZATION OF AQUEOUS SULFURIC ACID SOLUTIONS, 0.1N, 0.5N, AND 1N

Apparatus

Weighing bottles, 15 × 50 mm, glass-stoppered.

Reagents

Sulfuric acid, CP, concentrated (95%).
Sodium carbonate, CP, anhydrous. See next preparation.
Sodium hydroxide, 0.1N. The exact normality need not be known.
Sodium hydroxide, standard, of the same approximate normality as the acid to be standardized.
Phenolphthalein, 1% in 60% ethanol.

Preparation

For each liter of solution use the following amount of sulfuric acid

Normality	ml of 95% H_2SO_4
1N	28.3
0.5N	14.2
0.1N	2.8

Add this amount of acid slowly to 500–600 ml of distilled water, and, after swirling the mixture, dilute to 1 liter. Mix well by shaking or by bubbling nitrogen through the solution and store in a glass-stoppered Pyrex bottle.

Standardization, primary (sodium carbonate)

First, determine the ratio of ml of the acid to be standardized to ml of 0.1N sodium hydroxide as follows. To a 250-ml Erlenmeyer flask containing 75–100 ml of distilled water, add the amount of acid as shown below. Titrate with 0.1N sodium hydroxide to the phenolphthalein end point.

Normality	ml of acid
1N	4.00
0.5N	8.00
0.1N	40.00

Next, weight the appropriate amount of sodium carbonate indicated into a tared, 15 × 50 cm, glass-stoppered weighing bottle.

Normality	Weight of sodium carbonate, g
1N	2.50
0.5N	1.25
0.1N	0.25

Transfer the sodium carbonate quantitatively to a 250-ml Erlenmeyer flask containing 75–100 ml of carbon dioxide-free distilled water. Calculate the volume of acid required to completely neutralize the sodium carbonate by the equation:

$$\text{ml of acid} = \frac{(\text{g of sodium carbonate})(1000)}{(\text{normality of acid})(53)}$$

Accurately measure this amount, plus a 2-ml excess, into the Erlenmeyer flask. Add one or two boiling chips and boil the contents of the flask for 5–10 min to drive off all carbon dioxide. After the flask has cooled, add 2 or 3 drops of phenolphthalein and titrate the excess acid with 0.1N sodium hydroxide to the first, faint pink color. If the end-point color fades or is not sharp, make another determination and boil for a longer period of time. Make at least three determinations.

Calculate the normality of the acid from the equation:

$$\text{Normality} = \frac{(W)(1000)(2)}{[V - (v \times R)](105.99)}$$

where W = weight of sodium carbonate, g
V = total volume of acid used, ml
v = volume of 0.1N sodium hydroxide, ml
R = ratio between ml of acid and ml of 0.1N sodium hydroxide.

Standardization, secondary (sodium hydroxide solution)

From a buret run 40–45 ml of the acid into a 250-ml Erlenmeyer flask containing 75–100 ml of carbon dioxide-free distilled water. Add 2 or 3 drops of phenolphthalein and titrate with standard sodium hydroxide solution of approximately the same normality to the first faint pink color. Make at least three determinations. Calculate the normality of the acid from the equation:

$$\text{Normality} = \frac{(V)(N)}{v}$$

where V = volume of standard sodium hydroxide, ml
      N = normality of the standard sodium hydroxide
      v = volume of acid used, ml

PREPARATION OF SODIUM CARBONATE, ANHYDROUS, PRIMARY STANDARD

Apparatus

Muffle, electric.
Desiccator, with indicating Drierite.
Weighing bottle, 40 × 50 mm, glass-stoppered.

Reagents

Sodium carbonate, CP, anhydrous.

Preparation

Grind the anhydrous sodium carbonate to a fine powder. Place it in an evaporating dish, taking care not to fill the dish more than half-full. Press the sodium carbonate against the wall of the dish with a clean spatula, forming a uniformly thick layer. Place the evaporating dish and contents in the muffle, which has been preheated to 450°C, and maintain it at that temperature for 3–4 hr. Mix the sodium carbonate several times during the course of the heating. Remove the dish from the muffle, place it in a desiccator charged with Drierite, and allow it to cool, then transfer the sodium carbonate to a weighing bottle and store it in a desiccator.

PREPARATION AND STANDARDIZATION OF PERCHLORIC ACID IN GLACIAL ACETIC ACID, 0.1N

Apparatus

Meter, glass electrode, calomel reference electrode, stirrer, buret, and stand.

Reagents

Acetic acid, glacial. Determine the water content of the acetic acid by the Fischer method. Acid containing more than 0.5% water must not be used.
Acetic anhydride, reagent.
Perchloric acid, "Baker's Analyzed" reagent, 70–72%.
Potassium acid phthalate, primary standard.

Preparation

For each liter of solution add 21 g (20 ml) of acetic anhydride to 1000 ml of glacial acetic acid to react with the water in the 70% perchloric acid to be added subsequently.

> **CAUTION!** Conduct the operations in a well-ventilated hood. Wear rubber apron, gloves, and a face shield for protection against corrosive action of the reagents. Any spillage must be promptly flushed with water. The exterior of the reagent bottles should be flushed with water before replacing them on the shelf to prevent adhering droplets of the reagents from coming in contact with the skin during subsequent handling.

Also add 4.2 g (4 ml) of acetic anhydride for each 0.1% water in the acetic acid used. Add slowly with stirring 14.5 g (8.9 ml) of 70% perchloric acid.

> **CAUTION!** Perchloric acid can cause explosive hazard when used improperly.

Mix the solution thoroughly and store in a glass-stoppered bottle. Attach a label indicating the corrosive nature of the reagent.

Standardization

Standardize against an accurately weighed amount of potassium acid phthalate dissolved in glacial acetic acid, containing no more than 0.2% of water. To hasten the solution of the phthalate it may be desirable to warm the solution, but allow it to cool before titrating potentiometrically. Perform also a blank determination omitting the potassium acid phthalate.

The thermal expansion of acetic acid is about 0.1%/°C. Therefore, in the most accurate work it is necessary to introduce a correction. For $0.1000N$ solution, 0.0001 is added to the normality for each degree the standardization temperature exceeds the temperature of the acid at the time of titration in any subsequent determination. Conversely, if the latter temperature exceeds the standardization temperature, 0.0001 is subtracted from the normality for each centigrade degree difference.

PREPARATION OF SOLUTIONS FOR USE WITH THE HALOGENATION METHODS

PREPARATION AND STANDARDIZATION OF SODIUM THIOSULFATE SOLUTION, $0.1N$

Reagents

Sodium thiosulfate pentahydrate, CP.
Sodium carbonate, CP.
Chloroform, CP.
Iodine, CP (Mallinckrodt A.R.).

Potassium iodide, CP, granular, neutral.
Starch, 1%.

Preparation

For each liter of solution, dissolve 25 g of sodium thiosulfate pentahydrate in 500–600 ml of distilled water and then dilute to 1 liter. Add 0.01 g of sodium carbonate and 0.4 ml of chloroform as a preservative. Mix thoroughly by shaking or by bubbling nitrogen through it for approximately 15 min and store in a glass-stoppered Pyrex bottle.

Standardization

Place 2.5–3.0 g of potassium iodide in a 15 × 50 mm weighing bottle (about one-third full), and add enough distilled water with an eyedropper to completely wet it with no excess. Replace the glass stopper and gently tap the weighing bottle so that a layer of saturated potassium iodide appears above the potassium iodide crystals, being careful that no water adheres to the walls or stopper of the weighing bottle.

Let the bottle stand in a dark place for 15 min, then wipe it dry and weigh to the nearest 0.1 mg. Remove the stopper and add 0.3–0.5 g of iodine, being careful that no iodine crystals are left on the walls of the flask above the saturated potassium iodide. Replace the stopper and again weigh as before.

Remove the stopper and drop both it and the weighing bottle into a 500-ml glass-stoppered Erlenmeyer flask containing 150–200 ml of distilled water. Swirl the flask to dissolve the contents of the weighing bottle and titrate the iodine with the sodium thiosulfate solution to the starch end point. Make all determinations in triplicate.

Calculate the normality of the sodium thiosulfate solution from the equation

$$\text{normality} = \frac{(W)(1000)}{(V)(126.92)}$$

where W = weight of the iodine, g, and V = volume of sodium thiosulfate solution, ml.

PREPARATION OF STARCH SOLUTION, 1%

Reagents

Starch, CP, soluble, powdered.
Potassium hydroxide, CP, pellets.
Litmus paper, neutral.

Preparation

For each liter of solution, suspend 10 g of powdered starch in 1 liter of distilled water. While stirring vigorously, slowly add 30 g of potassium hydroxide pellets and continue stirring until all the potassium hydroxide has been dissolved. Allow the solution to stand for 1 hr and then neutralize with concentrated hydrochloric acid using litmus paper. Add 5 ml of glacial acetic acid as a preservative. Store in a glass-stoppered Pyrex bottle.

PREPARATION OF BROMINE IN POTASSIUM BROMIDE SOLUTION, $0.1N$ AND $0.2N$

Apparatus

Bottle, Pyrex, glass-stoppered, of appropriate size.

Reagents

Liquid bromine, CP. Handle with care.
Potassium bromide, CP.

Preparation

To prepare 1 liter of solution, dissolve the quantity of potassium bromide specified in 100 ml of water. Without further dilution, add the quantities of liquid bromine specified below. Mix thoroughly until all the bromine is in solution. Dilute to volume and again mix thoroughly.

Normality	Weight of KBr, g	Volume of Liquid Bromine, ml
$0.1N$	17.9	2.83
$0.2N$	35.8	5.7

CAUTION!   Liquid bromine must be handled with great care since it produces painful burns on contact with the skin. Bromine vapor attacks the membranes of the eyes, nose, and lungs. Prepare the above solution in a well-ventilated hood. Rubber gloves and a face mask must be worn while handling the liquid bromine.

PREPARATION OF BROMINE IN CARBON TETRACHLORIDE, STANDARD $0.2N$

For each liter of solution dissolve 5.5 ml of CP bromine in CP carbon tetrachloride.

Standardize daily as follows: to a 500-ml glass-stoppered Erlenmeyer flask, add 25 ml of carbon tetrachloride and approximately 100 ml of distilled water. Allow the mixture to cool in an ice bath for 10 min. Then, with a rubber light-shielding cover in place around the neck of the flask to exclude light, add 15 ml of the bromination reagent, measured to 0.01 ml, from the buret, stopper the flask, swirl it gently for a few seconds, and place the bath containing the flask in a dark cabinet. At 10 min ± 10 sec after the addition of the bromination reagent (without removing the flask from under the light-shielding cover), add 15 ml of potassium iodide solution, then remove the light shield from the flask, remove the flask from the ice bath, immediately stopper the flask, and shake it vigorously. Titrate the liberated iodine to the starch end point with standard thiosulfate solution, shaking vigorously at frequent intervals as the end point is approached. Repeat the standardization using 20 ml of the bromination reagent. Calculate the normality of the bromination reagent from the equation:

$$\text{normality} = \frac{(\text{Vol of thiosulfate soln, ml})(\text{Normality of thiosulfate soln})}{(\text{Vol of bromination reagent, ml})}$$

PREPARATION OF POTASSIUM IODIDE SOLUTION, 20% AQUEOUS

The solution must not contain iodate or free iodine. Prepare by dissolving 20 g of CP potassium iodide in water and diluting to a volume of 100 ml. Any yellow color that develops on standing (due to free iodine) should be removed by dropwise addition of $0.1N$ sodium thiosulfate solution.

PREPARATION AND STANDARDIZATION OF BROMIDE-BROMATE SOLUTION, $0.2N$

Apparatus

Bromination bottle, Pyrex, 300 ml, with 20/40 Standard taper joint.
Stopcock, 2 mm with angle bore; fitted with 20/40 standard taper joint.

Reagents

Starch solution, 1%.
Potassium bromide, CP.
Potassium bromate, CP.
Sulfuric acid, 2N.
Sodium thiosulfate, standard $0.1N$.
Potassium iodide solution, 10%. The solution must be free from iodate or free iodine. If a yellow color develops on standing, dispel by the dropwise addition of sodium thiosulfate solution.

Preparation

For each liter of solution, dissolve 20 g of KBr and 5.6 g of $KBrO_3$ in 500–600 ml of distilled water and then dilute to 1 liter. Mix thoroughly by shaking or by bubbling nitrogen through the solution and store in a glass-stoppered Pyrex bottle.

Standardization

From a buret, draw into an evacuated bromination bottle a measured amount (about 20 ml) of the $0.2N$ bromide–bromate solution. Rinse the connecting rubber tubing three times with distilled water. Next draw 20 ml of $2N$ sulfuric acid into the bottle. Shake for 30 sec, then draw into the bottle 15 ml of 10% potassium iodide solution, shake for 30 sec, and then draw into the bottle about 50 ml of distilled water. Remove the stopper and wash the inside of it and the ground joints with distilled water and immediately titrate the liberated iodine with standard $0.1N$ sodium thiosulfate to the starch end point. Make all determinations in triplicate and vary slightly the volume of bromide–bromate solution taken.

Calculate the normality of the bromide–bromate solution from the equation

$$\text{normality} = \frac{(V)(N)}{v}$$

where V = volume of sodium thiosulfate, ml
$\quad\ N$ = normality of the sodium thiosulfate
$\quad\ v$ = volume of bromide–bromate taken, ml

PREPARATION OF SOLUTIONS FOR ARGENTIMETRIC TITRATIONS

PREPARATION AND STANDARDIZATION OF AMMONIUM THIOCYANATE SOLUTION, $0.05N$

Reagents

Ammonium thiocyanate, CP.
Ferric ammonium sulfate, 28%, in $1N$ nitric acid.
Nitric acid, 30%.
Silver nitrate, $0.1N$, standard.

Preparation

For each liter of solution, dissolve 3.80 g of CP ammonium thiocyanate in 500–600 ml of distilled water and then dilute to 1 liter. Mix thoroughly by shaking or by bubbling nitrogen through it, then store in a glass-stoppered Pyrex bottle.

Standardization

Measure 40 ml of the thiocyanate solution from a buret into a 250-ml Erlenmeyer flask containing 50–60 ml of distilled water and 5 ml of 30% nitric acid. Swirling the flask constantly, add 22–24 ml of standard $0.1N$ silver nitrate solution from a buret, then stopper the flask and shake it for 30 sec. Add 2–3 ml of ferric ammonium sulfate and back-titrate with thiocyanate solution to the red ferric thiocyanate end point. Make all determinations in triplicate.

Calculate the normality of the ammonium thiocyanate solution from the equation

$$\text{normality} = \frac{(V)(N)}{v}$$

where V = volume of silver nitrate solution, ml
$\quad\ N$ = normality of the silver nitrate solution
$\quad\ v$ = volume of ammonium thiocyanate solution, ml

PREPARATION OF FERRIC AMMONIUM SULFATE SOLUTION, 28%, IN NITRIC ACID

Reagents

Ferric ammonium sulfate, CP, $(Fe_2(SO_4)_3 \cdot (NH_4)_2SO_4 \cdot 24H_2O)$.
Nitric acid, 30%.

Preparation

Dissolve 350 g of CP ferric ammonium sulfate in 1 liter of distilled water, then add 200 ml of 30% nitric acid that has been aerated to remove oxides of nitrogen. Mix thoroughly and store in a glass-stoppered Pyrex bottle.

PREPARATION OF NITRIC ACID, 30% SOLUTION

Reagents

Nitric acid, CP, concentrated.

Preparation

For each liter of solution, mix 335 ml of CP concentrated nitric acid with 670 ml of distilled water. Mix thoroughly by bubbling nitrogen through it for about 15 min, which also removes oxides of nitrogen from the solution. Store in a glass-stoppered Pyrex bottle, securely stoppered.

PREPARATION AND STANDARDIZATION OF SILVER NITRATE SOLUTION, 0.1N

Apparatus

Bottle, Pyrex, of appropriate size and painted black.
Drying oven.

Reagents

Silver nitrate, CP.
Ferric ammonium sulfate, 28%, in 1N nitric acid;
Nitric acid, 30%.
Nitrobenzene. The nitrobenzene must not show a visible precipitate when tested with alcoholic silver nitrate.
Ammonium thiocyanate.
Sodium chloride, Analytical Reagent (cryst). Dry in an oven for 4 hr at 120°C before using.

Preparation

For each liter of solution, dissolve 17.0 g of CP silver nitrate in 500–600 ml of distilled water and then dilute to 1 liter. Store in a dark Pyrex bottle. Stopper the bottle securely and mix thoroughly by shaking.

Standardization

Transfer 15–20 g of AR sodium chloride to a glass-stoppered weighing bottle and heat it in a drying oven at 120°C for 3–4 hr. Place the weighing bottle and contents in a desiccator to cool.

Determine the ratio of ml of silver nitrate to ml of 0.05N ammonium thiocyanate by accurately measuring 40 ml of 0.05N ammonium thiocyanate from a buret into a 500-ml glass-stoppered Erlenmeyer flask containing 50–60 ml of distilled water and 5 ml of 30% nitric acid. Swirling the flask constantly add 22–24 ml of the 0.1N silver nitrate from a buret, then stopper the flask and shake it for 20–30 sec. Add 2–3 ml of ferric ammonium sulfate and back-titrate with thiocyanate solution to the red ferric thiocyanate end point. Calculate the ratio

$$\frac{\text{ml of } 0.1N \text{ silver nitrate}}{\text{ml of } 0.05N \text{ ammonium thiocyanate}}$$

to four significant figures.

Weigh 0.24–0.30 g of sodium chloride into a 500-ml Erlenmeyer flask containing 100–150 ml of distilled water. Add 5 ml of 30% nitric acid, 10 ml of nitrobenzene, 3 ml of ferric ammonium sulfate, and, from a buret, 0.04–0.6 ml of 0.05N ammonium thiocyanate solution. Swirling constantly, titrate with the silver nitrate solution until the red color of the ferric thiocyanate is discharged, then add 2–5 ml in excess. Stopper the flask tightly and shake it vigorously for 15 sec to coagulate and remove the precipitate from the aqueous phase. Without refilling the buret, titrate slowly with 0.05N thiocyanate solution until the end point is approached as indicated by a more slowly fading red color. Stopper the flask, shake it vigorously for 30 sec, and continue the titration until one drop produces a distinct reddish coloration that does not fade upon swirling or vigorous shaking. Make all determinations in triplicate.

CAUTION! Nitrobenzene in a toxic substance. Avoid contact with the liquid or breathing of the vapor. The reagent should be stored in a hood when not in use.

Calculate the normality of the silver nitrate by means of the following equation:

$$\text{normality} = \frac{(W)(1000)}{[V - (v \times R)]58.45}$$

where W = weight of sodium chloride, g
 V = volume of silver nitrate, ml
 v = volume of ammonium thiocyanate, ml
 R = ratio of ml of silver nitrate to ml of ammonium thiocyanate.

ANALYTICAL EQUIPMENT

Equipment for conducting most of the methods is generally listed in the text unless the requirements are so simple that it is to be expected that no specific designation is required. In most cases satisfactory equipment can be purchased from a number of supply houses, but some apparatus may need to be put together for the purpose, which can be done with simple glass-blowing or instrument shop facilities. The methods contain information on most of the equipment needed; this chapter presents some illustrations of equipment used more widely in a number of the methods. In some methods or tabulations specific manufacturers are mentioned, since the data were obtained with the particular designated piece of equipment, but in no case is this to be considered a recommendation, since alternate equipment may likewise be suitable.

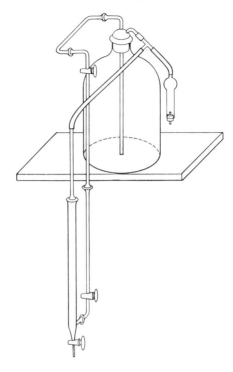

Figure 24.1. All glass siphon-type buret assembly. After E.D.Peters and J. L. Jungnickel, *Anal. Chem.*, **27**, 450 (1955). Reprinted by permission of the American Chemical Society.

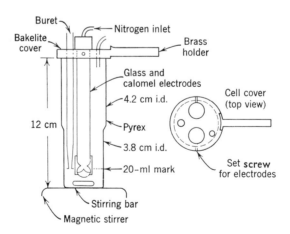

Figure 24.2. Reduced-scale titration cell. After V. Z. Deal, and G. E. A. Wyld, *Anal. Chem.*, **27**, 47 (1955), reprinted by permission of the American Chemical Society.

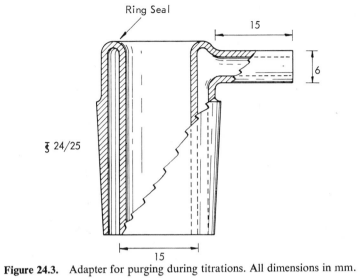

Figure 24.3. Adapter for purging during titrations. All dimensions in mm.

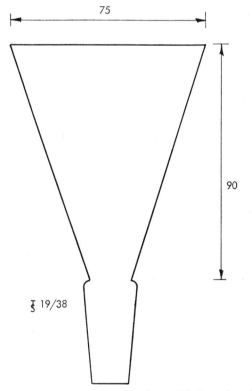

Figure 24.4. Funnel for ion-exchange column. All dimensions in mm.

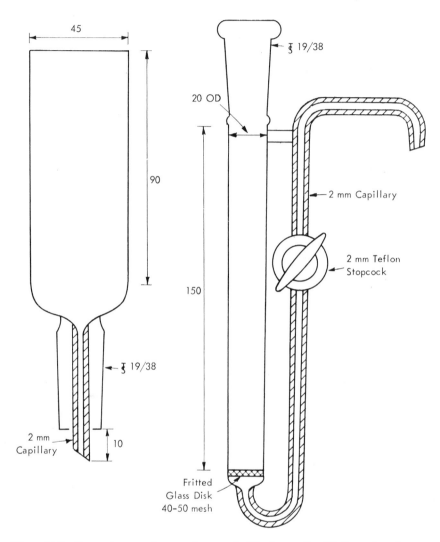

Figure 24.5. Ion-exchange column and reservoir, 35 ml capacity. All dimensions in mm.

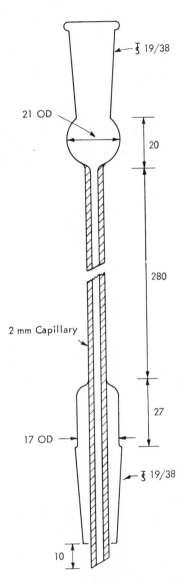

Figure 24.6. Connecting tube for ion-exchange column. All dimensions in mm.

SAFETY IN THE LABORATORY

Although the analytical laboratory does not have a number of severe hazards, there are sufficient areas of danger to require close attention to safety. Safe and careful working habits allow the analyst to protect himself and his coworkers while directing his attention to the proper course of his work. Close attention to safe handling of toxic materials used in the preparation of reagents is essential. The directions given for preparation of reagents include information on hazards and the necessary precautions to be undertaken for safe working conditions. Some more general concerns are given in this section in regard to toxicity and air contamination.

TOXICITY

Most chemicals are harmful to the body although the response may vary considerably from one person to another. Effects can be acute, sometimes almost immediate, with rapid recovery provided the amount ingested is not above the critical level, or they can be chronic due to slow and cumulative poisoning. Some of the aromatic solvents, such as benzene and pyridine, constitute a long-term chronic hazard and should always be handled with great care. In the analytical laboratory, chemical hazards can arise not only from reagents and solvents but also from the samples received for analysis. If the sample originates elsewhere, the analyst should require that it be labeled with both a descriptive chemical name and a statement of any possible hazard. Chemicals whose toxicity have not yet been established should always be handled with the greatest care.

The following rules are the results of many years experience and it is recommended they be followed by all laboratory workers.

1. To protect the eyes, safety spectacles should always be worn in the laboratory. These provide the minimum protection against chemical splashes and flying particles. They are commercially available in a hardened lens either with nonprescription lenses or prescription-ground.

2. A full face shield should be worn when larger amounts of concentrated mineral acids, strong caustic, or other corrosive materials are being handled.

When taking samples from reactors or lines containing hazardous chemicals, a face shield should be used.

3. Use rubber gloves whenever required to prevent gross accidental exposure to the hands.

4. Remove chemicals spilled on the skin by washing immediately with a great excess of water. If the chemical is corrosive or toxic, obtain first aid or medical care at once.

5. Never take the chance of ingesting chemicals by mouth. *Never* pipet by mouth. Use a vacuum line or aspirator bulb. Wash hands before eating and never store food in the vicinity of chemicals.

AIR CONTAMINATION

Every analytical laboratory must have an effective hood because many of the reagents and solvents required in the course of a normal working day are toxic. As a partial guide for the control of health hazards in the air, the threshold limits for toxicity of some of the common chemicals are listed in Table 25.1. These data are taken from the work of the American Conference of Governmental Industrial Hygienists. The data cannot be used in an exact fashion to compare hazards since there is a wide variation in individual susceptibility. Proper laboratory practice requires the control of chemicals in air at the lowest possible level. The data in Table 25.1 are best used as a warning and offer information leading to choices among reagents. For example, toluene is less toxic than benzene and consequently toluene is the preferred solvent to use in the laboratory wherever it can be utilized in place of benzene. Another common reagent, pyridine, is very toxic and since it is used as a solvent and a reagent in the Karl Fischer titration methods, large volumes may be employed in organic analytical laboratories. The Karl Fischer reagents must be prepared in an effective hood and any spillage must be immediately cleaned up with damp towels or rags.

GENERAL INFORMATION ON LABORATORY SAFETY

Because of concern for the safe handling of many chemicals that are now in common industrial use, several important reference textbooks have been written. These include the classic work of Jacobs on the toxicology of industrial chemicals and solvents (1) and the two-volume set by Patty on industrial hygiene and toxicology (2). The review volume of Sax (3) is particularly valuable for a rapid reference of toxicity of various materials. Manufacturing Chemists Association publish data sheets for the safe handling of many commercial organic chemicals (4). The documentation of the threshold limit values given in Table 25.1 are available in a bound

Table 25.1.   Threshold Limit Values of Some Chemicals as Air Contaminants[a]

Substance	Threshold limit, ppm	Substance	Threshold limit, ppm
Acetaldehyde	200	Ethylene oxide	50
Acetic anhydride	5	Ethyl mercaptan	0.5[b]
Acetone	1000	Furfural	5
Acetylene tetrabromide	1	Hydrogen bromide	3
Acrolein	0.1	Hydrogen cyanide	10
Ammonia	50	Hydrogen fluoride	3
Arsine	0.05	Hydrogen sulfide	10
Benzene	25	Methyl bromide	20
Boron trifluoride	1	Nickel carbonyl	0.001
Bromine	0.1	Nitrobenzene	1
Carbon tetrachloride	10	Ozone	0.1
Chlorine	1	Phosgene	0.1
Chloroform	50	Phosphine	0.3
Diborane	0.1	Pyridine	5
Diethylamine	25	Sulfur dioxide	5
Diethyl ether	400	Tetrahydrofuran	200
Dioxane	100	Tetranitromethane	1
Ethyl acrylate	25	Toluene	200
Ethyl amine	10	Xylene	100
Ethylene diamine	10		

[a] Source of data: American Conference of Governmental Industrial Hygienists (1969).
[b] Proposed value.

volume (5) with much detailed information on the toxicology of the specific compounds.

REFERENCES

1. M. B. Jacobs, *The Analytical Chemistry of Industrial Poisons, Hazards and Solvents*, 2nd ed., Interscience, New York, 1949.
2. F. A. Patty, Ed., *Industrial Hygiene and Toxicology*, Interscience, New York; Vol. 1, 1958; Vol. 2, 1963.
3. N. I. Sax, Ed., *Dangerous Properties of Industrial Materials*, 3rd ed., Reinhold, New York, 1968.
4. "Chemical Safety Data Sheets," Manufacturing Chemists Association, 1825 Connecticut Ave., N.W., Washington, D.C.
5. "Documentation of Threshold Limit Values," Secretary-Treasurer, American Conference of Governmental Industrial Hygienists, 1014 Broadway, Cincinnati, Ohio.

AUTHOR INDEX

Abrams, S. T., 25, 26, 27, 28
Adams, D. B., 233
Adams, D. F., 297, 300
Adams, E. W., 113
Adkins, H., 113
Adlard, E. R., 185, 414
Adloff, J. P., 415
Afremow, L. C., 271, 276
Agruss, M. S., 299
Ahlberg, D. L., 23, 28
Albert, A., 63, 64, 82, 235, 256
Albert, D. K., 256, 258
Aldrich, F. D., 400, 414
Allen, D. S., Jr., 55
Allen, P. W., 303, 315
Allred, R. C., 196, 199
Alsop, W. G., 173
Altshuller, A. P., 23, 28, 103, 106,
        114, 332, 334, 414
Alway, C. D., 107, 114
Amell, A. R., 254, 257
Anders, M. W., 163
Anderson, L. R., 233
Andrussow, K., 63, 64, 83
Anger, V., 120, 123
Antener, I., 114
Argabright, P. A., 396, 398, 414
Austin, A. T., 243, 257

Babiec, J. S., Jr., 162, 164
Bacon, F. S., 83
Bailey, J. J., 75, 83
Baines, F. C., 305, 315
Baker, M. O., 34, 35, 36, 37, 55
Baker, R. A., 177, 186, 324, 333
Baldwin, A. J., 306, 315
Balestrieri, S., 334
Ball, J. S., 257, 276, 284, 285, 287,
        299
Bann, J. M., 323

Banner, A. E., 415
Barghoorn, E. S., 18
Barker, M. G., 240, 256, 299
Barlow, D. O., 257
Barnes, D., 113, 115
Barnes, L., 57, 62
Barnes, R. B., 155, 164
Barr, T., 339, 354
Barrante, J. R., 162, 164
Barrer, R. M., 18, 411
Bartlett, J. K., 285, 288, 300
Bartlett, P. D., 233
Bastin, E., 325, 333, 415, 418, 422
Bauer, R. H., 55
Bauman, W. C., 374, 412
Baumann, F., 300
Becker, R. S., 23, 25, 28, 414
Becker, W. W., 271, 276
Beesing, D. W., 276
Begemann, P. H., 55
Belcher, R., 152, 163
Belchetz, L., 18
Belisle, J., 133, 163
Bell, R. T., 299
Bellamy, L. J., 107, 114, 163, 252,
        257
Bellar, T. A., 332, 334
Belsky, T., 18
Bender, D. F., 334
Bendoraitis, J. G., 15, 18
Benedict, J. H., 199
Bentley, R., 163
Benz, W., 314, 315, 316
Berezkin, V. G., 415
Bergmann, F., 263, 276
Berkowitz, L. M., 55
Beroza, M., 18, 49, 56, 403, 407,
        411, 414, 415, 416
Beshgetoor, A. W., 185
Bevilacqua, E. M., 49, 55

447

Bevington, J. C., 305, 309, 315, 316
Beynon, J. H., 415
Bhacca, N. S., 49, 55, 316
Bhide, B. V., 304
Bhowmik, S., 241, 257
Bieber, M., 163
Biemann, K., 405, 415
Bierl, B. A., 49, 56
Billeb, K., 414
Bishop, J. L., 181, 182, 186
Bjork, R. C., 59, 62
Black, D. R., 415
Blair, C. M., 3, 4, 17
Bliss, C. I., 327, 333
Block, R. J., 379, 412
Bloemberger, R. H., 300
Blumer, M., 405, 415
Blytas, G. C., 10, 18
Bobbitt, J. M., 380, 413
Boekenoogen, H. A., 55, 354
Boer, H., 56
Bölsing, F., 124, 163
Bombaugh, K. J., 114, 313, 316
Bonelli, E. J., 392, 414
Bonhoeffer, K. F., 164
Bonnar, R. U., 308, 316
Boruff, C. S., 114
Bottei, R. S., 271, 276
Bovey, F. A., 234, 307, 316
Bowman, M. C., 403, 414
Bradley, W. E., 300
Braithwaite, B., 227, 234
Brasseaux, D. J., 3, 5, 6, 7, 17, 28
Breck, D. W., 10, 18
Brenner, N., 10, 18, 411, 413, 414
Brey, W. J., 307, 316
Bricker, C. E., 103, 114
Briegleb, G., 27
Brill, W. F., 234
Brody, S. S., 403, 414
Brooks, C. J. W., 415
Brooks, F. R., 233
Brooks, R. T., 248, 257
Brown, B. L., 15, 18
Brown, C. A., 34, 35, 55
Brown, E. G., 195, 196, 197, 199

Brown, G. W., 164
Brown, H. C., 34, 35, 55
Brown, R. D., 243, 244, 245, 257
Bruckenstein, S., 68, 83
Bruening, C. F., 173
Brunnock, J. V., 10, 16, 18
Brüschweiler, H., 232, 234
Bruss, D. B., 83
Bruzzi, L., 415
Bryant, W. M. D., 81, 83, 84, 86, 113,
    125, 128, 131, 163, 422
Brydia, L. E., 255, 258
Budzikiewicz, H., 415
Buell, B. E., 177, 186, 376, 412
Buist, G. J., 165, 172
Bull, W. C., 114
Bullock, A. B., 172, 173, 188, 189,
    190, 199, 380, 413, 418, 422
Bunton, C. A., 172
Burchfield, H. P., 297, 300
Burdett, R. A., 27
Burger, K., 199
Burleigh, J. E., 240, 256
Burleson, F. R., 332, 334
Burlingame, A. L., 18
Burnham, H. D., 113
Buttery, R. G., 185
Byrns, A. C., 300

Caesar, P. D., 257
Calcote, H. F., 414
Callen, J. E., 413, 414
Calmon, C., 412
Calvin, M., 18
Camera, E., 275, 277
Carnes, W. J., 23, 28
Carter, G. B., 172, 173
Caruso, J. A., 83
Cassidy, H. G., 379, 412
Castelli, A., 415
Castiglioni, A., 113
Cavanagh, L. A., 401, 414
Cecil, R., 299
Cervellati, A., 415
Chadha, R. K., 173
Chadwick, A. F., 257

Chakaravarty, S. N., 55
Chambaz, E. M., 415
Chamberlain, N. F., 28
Chaney, J. E., 403, 414
Chantonni, M. K., Jr., 241, 257
Chapman, O. L., 162, 164
Chatten, L. G., 257
Chaudet, J. H., 28
Chen, H. Y., 49, 55
Cholnoky, L., 411
Chumachenko, M. N., 126, 163
Chung, Y. H., 115
Cieplinski, E. W., 28, 411
Circle, S., J., 114
Clampitt, B. H., 313, 316
Clar, E., 27
Clements, A. H., 233, 234
Clemons, C. A., 23, 28, 334, 414
Coad, R. A., 407, 415
Coates, V. J., 10, 18, 411, 413
Cohen, A. I., 115
Cohen, I. R., 106, 114
Cole, C. P., 217
Cohn, W. E., 412
Coleman, H. J., 267, 276, 298, 299,
    300, 411, 416
Coll, H., 412
Colson, A. F., 34
Colson, R., 173
Comendant, F., 25, 26, 27, 28
Comisarow, M. B., 163
Conant, J. B., 237, 256
Conrad, A. L., 365
Conway, H. S., 226, 233
Cook, C. E., 313, 316
Cooke, W. D., 161, 164
Coope, J. A. R., 299
Cooper, A. R., 28
Cooper, P. J., 276
Coughlin, R. W., 333
Coulson, S. M., 401, 414
Crabb, N. T., 199
Craig, B. M., 55
Crawshaw, J. K., 422
Criddle, D. W., 359, 365
Criegee, R., 49, 55, 56

Critchfield, F. E., 163, 195, 199
Crowe, P. F., 122, 123
Crowne, C. W. P., 28
Crump, G. B., 186
Culmo, R., 163
Cummins, R. L., 114
Cundiff, R. H., 68, 83
Curtis, J. L. S., 34, 35, 36, 37, 55

Dahmen, E. A. M. F., 68, 83, 203,
    217, 241, 256, 257
Dalgliesh, C. E., 83
Dallas, M. S. J., 172, 173
Dal Nogare, S., 413
Dannenberg, H., 215, 216, 217, 307,
    316
Darley, E. F., 275, 277, 332, 334
Davidson, F. G., 422
Davies, A. G., 234
Davies, L., 414
Davison, V. L., 55
Davison, W. H. T., 316
Dawson, G., 163
Dawson, H. J., Jr., 23, 24, 28
Day, A. R., 176
Deal, V. Z., 71, 83, 238, 239, 256,
    440
DeCino, T. J., 323
Deeley, E. L., 122, 123
Degens, P. N., Jr., 340, 354
Deitz, V. T., 370, 372, 411
De Jongh, D. C., 163
de Kok, W. J. C., 34
Dellow, G. B., 11, 12, 13, 18
Deno, N. C., 192, 199
Desreux, V., 316
Desty, D. H., 413
Dewar, R. A., 396, 414
Dickey, F. H., 221, 233
Dijkstra, R., 203, 217
Dimbat, M., 308, 310, 311, 312,
    316, 395, 414
Djerassi, C., 415
Dobinson, B., 203, 217
Doerr, R. C., 277
Dollear, F. G., 34

Domsky, I., 28
Dorfman, R. I., 327, 333
Douglas, A. G., 28
Dove, R. A., 255, 258
Downing, D. T., 83
Drushel, H. V., 257, 297, 300
Dryhurst, G., 152, 163
Duke, F. R., 163
Dulong, L., 234
Durbetaki, A. J., 202, 203, 212, 216
Durrum, E. L., 379, 412
Dyer, E., 234
Dyer, J. R., 166, 173

Earle, N. W., 333
Earley, J. V., 271, 274, 276
Eaves, A., 177, 185, 253, 257, 375,
    376, 412
Edgell, W. F., 271, 274, 276
Edsberg, R. L., 193, 199
Edwards, J. O., 233
Eegrive, E., 114
Eger, H. H., 114
Eggertsen, F. T., 10, 18, 310, 311,
    312, 316, 330, 334, 413
Eglinton, G., 18
Ehrenberger, F., 191, 199
Ehrlich, P., 267, 276
Eiffert, R., 155, 157, 164
Elbert, W. C., 28, 101, 114, 253,
    257, 334
Elderfield, R. C., 217
Elek, A., 199
El-Khiami, I., 299
Ellis, W. H., 359, 365
Elving, P. J., 82, 113, 163, 299
Emerson, E., 177, 178, 186
Engelhardt, E. D., 18
Epton, S. R., 339, 354
Erskine, J. W. B., 170, 173
Erwall, L. R., 333
Ettinger, M. E., 178, 186
Ettre, L. S., 28, 396, 399, 411, 413,
    414
Evans, A., 414
Evans, H. C., 340, 354

Evenhuis, J. K., 312, 316
Eversole, W. G., 10, 18
Ezra, F. S., 333

Faragher, W. F., 284, 285, 299
Farrell, P. G., 28
Farrugia, V. J., 300
Fedoronko, M., 115
Feigl, F., 120, 123
Feinland, R., 62
Feldstein, M., 334
Ferrin, C. R., 257, 276
Fiddler, F. A., 300
Fink, D. R., 358, 365
Fischer, K., 422
Flanagan, P. W., 192, 199
Flath, R. A., 415
Flory, P. J., 304, 305, 315
Forbes, J. W., 44, 46, 55, 107, 109,
    114, 158, 159, 160, 161, 164,
    308, 316, 422
Forsberg, H. G., 333
Forziati, A. F., 365
Fowler, L., 413
Fox, F. T., 28, 334
Fox, W. B., 233
Francis, A. W., 55
Franks, M. C., 376, 412
Fredericks, E. M., 295, 296, 300
Freedman, B., 163
Freff, R. A., 199
Frehden, O., 120, 123
Freitas, E. R., 11, 12, 13, 18
Freudenberg, W., 164
Frey, R., 315
Fricke, F. L., 276
Friedel, R. A., 163
Fritz, J. S., 68, 83, 118, 123, 133,
    163, 240, 242, 244, 256, 257
Fugua, S. A., 49, 55, 316
Fujiwara, S., 234
Fulda, M., 242, 257
Furman, N. H., 271, 276

Gaffney, G. W., 113
Gage, J. C., 334

Gal, J., 271, 274, 276
Gallaway, W. S., 396, 399, 414
Gallegos, E. J., 8, 9, 17
Gardiner, W. L., 254, 258
Garey, J. J., 163
Garis, J. J., Jr., 199
Garner, P., 122, 123, 310, 316
Garrett, E. R., 107, 114
Gaylord, N. G., 315
Gellerman, J. L., 83
Gent, P. L., 28
Giang, P. A., 328, 334
Gibson, M. E., Jr., 261, 276
Giddings, J. C., 378, 381, 412, 413
Gildenberg, L., 199
Gillam, A. E., 27
Giuffrida, L., 403, 414
Goddu, R. F., 74, 83, 120, 121, 123
Gohlke, R. S., 404, 415
Göhring, K. E. H., 18
Golay, M. J. E., 3, 17, 382, 413
Goldsmith, H. A., 259, 276, 354
Goldstein, T., 59, 62
Goldup, A., 413, 422
Golub, M. A., 49, 55, 316
Goodwin, E. S., 401, 414
Gordon, B. E., 113, 325, 333, 415
Gordon, R. J., 334
Gore, R. C., 155, 164
Goulden, R., 401, 414
Gouw, T. H., 26, 28
Graiff, L. B., 404, 415
Grant, J. A., 297, 298, 300
Green, J. A., 396, 414
Green, J. W., 8, 9, 17
Greene, L. M., 185
Greene, R. S., 83
Greenwald, H. L., 199
Greff, R. A., 192, 199
Gregeley, G., 56
Gremillion, A. F., 242, 257
Grimes, M. D., 10, 18
Groennings, S., 3, 10, 17, 18 , 28,
    51, 56, 359, 365, 413
Gross, F. C., 259, 276
Groten, B., 311, 315, 316

Grubb, H. M., 182, 183, 186
Guadagni, D. G., 415
Gunther, P., 233
Gutnikov, G., 153, 163
Gyenes, I., 83

Haehnel, W., 315
Hafliger, O., 114
Hahn, K. W., 114
Hähnel, S., 114
Haines, W. E., 284, 285, 287, 299
Halász, I., 414
Hale, D. K., 375, 412
Hale, J. H., 299
Hall, M. E., 114
Hall, N. F., 237, 256
Hall, R. T., 123
Hall, S. A., 328, 334
Hall, W. T., 185, 299
Halpern, G. D., 18
Hamill, W. H., 164
Hamilton, J. B., 191, 199
Hamilton, J. W., 234
Hammett, L. P., 118, 119, 123, 304
Handy, C. T., 227, 234
Hanessian, S., 163
Hanna, J. G., 113, 163, 164, 261,
    276
Hanst, P. L., 277
Häntzsch, S., 254, 257
Harbourn, C. L. A., 413
Hare, D. G., 234
Haresnape, D., 300
Harley, J., 396, 414
Harlow, G. A., 68, 69, 70, 71, 78,
    79, 83, 240, 241, 257, 295,
    296, 300, 375, 412, 429
Harp, W. R., Jr., 155, 157, 164, 215,
    217, 307, 316
Harper, R., 163
Harries, C. D., 55
Harrison, S. A., 276
Hart, R., 351, 354
Hart, S. M., 276
Hartung, G. K., 253, 257, 266, 276
Harwood, H. J., 306, 315

Haslam, J., 191, 199, 266, 276, 306,
    316
Hatton, J. V., 61, 62
Hauser, T. R., 28, 101, 114, 334
Hawes, R. C., 406, 415
Hawke, J. C., 406, 415
Hawkins, W., 263, 276
Hayes, T. J., 195, 196, 197, 199
Hayes, W. V., 422
Heath, F. W., 83
Heaton, W. B., 331
Heidner, R. H., 261, 276
Heinrich, B. J., 10, 18
Helfferich, F. G., 411
Hellwigh, W. B., 163
Helm, R. V., 257, 276
Henderson, R. B., 217
Hendrickson, J. G., 162, 164
Henze, H. R., 3, 4, 17
Hepner, L. S., 15, 18
Hermans, W. O., 315
Herrmann, R., 113
Hersh, C. K., 411
Hill, A. J., 57, 62
Hill, D. W., 163
Hillebrand, W. F., 427
Hillenbrand, E. F., Jr., 243, 257
Hobart, E. W., 59, 62
Hoffman, A. K., 299
Hoffman, D., 258
Hofmann, W., 203, 217
Hoh, G. L. K., 257
Holleck, L., 277
Hollis, O. L., 75, 83, 150, 163, 254,
    257, 391, 392, 414, 422
Holst, J. J., 3, 17, 51, 56
Hoodless, R. A., 276
Hopkins, R. L., 299, 300, 416
Horner, L., 226, 234
Horning, E. C., 83, 254, 258, 415
Horning, M. G., 83, 415
Hornstein, I., 122, 123
Horváth, C. G., 377, 412, 414, 415
Howard, H. E., 412
Hribar, J. D., 163
Hubbard, R. L., 284, 285, 287, 299

Huber, H., 243, 257
Huber, W., 83, 263, 264, 276
Huddleston, R. L., 196, 199
Hugetz, A. M., 119
Huggins, C. M., 164
Huggins, M. L., 316
Hume, D. N., 74, 83
Hummel, D. O., 306, 316, 354
Hummerlstedt, L. E. I., 74, 83
Hunter, G. L. K., 414
Husband, R. M., 186
Hyne, J. B., 164

Ibbitson, D. A., 18, 411
Ikekawa, N., 415
Illman, J. C., 252, 257
Ingels, R. M., 334
Iritani, N., 415
Irvine, R. C., 283, 299
Irving, A. M. N., 257
Iskhakova, E. K., 18

Jaakonmaki, P. I., 415
Jackson, M. W., 330, 334
Jacobs, M. B., 445, 446
James, A. T., 83, 254, 257, 380,
    412, 413
Jamieson, D. R., 114
Jankowski, S. J., 122, 123, 310, 316
Jarreau, C. L., 300
Jay, R. R., 217
Jeffs, A. R., 191, 199
Jenkins, D., 300
Jenkins, J. W., 347, 354
Jensen, G. A., 300
Jentoft, R. E., 26, 28
Jewell, D. M., 253, 257, 266, 276
Johns, R. B., 18
Johnson, D. E., 300
Johnson, D. P., 163
Johnson, E. R., 333, 334
Johnson, H. R., 114
Johnson, H. W., Jr., 412
Johnson, J. B., 265, 276
Johnson, J. F., 300, 316
Johnson, J. L., 107, 114
Johnson, L. D., 176

Johnson, R. M., 299
Johnson, W. S., 55
Johnstone, R. A. W., 28
Jones, D. T. C., 396, 399, 414
Jones, E. P., 55
Jones, G. G., 83
Jones, J. H., 259, 276, 337, 354
Jones, L. C., Jr., 27, 47, 55, 113
Jordan, D. E., 91, 113, 117, 123
Judd, S. H., 245, 257
Jungnickel, J. L., 29, 44, 46, 55, 61,
    62, 83, 158, 159, 160, 161,
    164, 192, 194, 199, 216, 417,
    420, 422, 425, 440
Jurgeleit, W., 234
Jurgens, E., 234
Juvet, R. S., 271, 276, 413

Kabasakalian, P., 115
Kabot, F. J., 28
Kainz, G., 243, 257
Kaiser, R., 404, 415
Kamio, S., 234
Kammerer, P. A., Jr., 333
Karchmer, J. H., 279, 299
Karmen, A., 403, 414
Kasler, F., 243, 257
Kastening, B., 277
Katayama, M., 234
Katchalsky, A., 252, 257
Katz, R., 59, 62
Kawahara, F. K., 185
Kaye, W. I., 25, 28
Ke, B., 303, 315
Keeling, J., 28
Keller, R. A., 381, 413
Kelley, K., 186, 199
Kendall, R. F., 299
Keppel, G. E., 276
Keppler, J. G., 55
Kern, R. J., 307, 316
Kester, R. B., 412
Ketley, A. D., 316
Kettner, K. A., 275, 277
Khym, J. X., 412
Kincannon, C. B., 181, 182, 186

Kindler, K., 119
King, J. W., 412
King, R. W., 162, 164
Kingsbury, C. A., 118, 123
Kingston, B. H. M., 163
Kirby, J. R., 306, 315
Kirchner, J. G., 380, 413
Kirkland, J. J., 26, 28, 377, 378,
    391, 412, 414
Kiselev, A., 414
Kislinsky, A. N., 18
Kitamura, Y., 191, 199
Klages, A., 217
Kleber, C., 113
Kline, G. M., 303, 315
Kling, W., 337, 354
Knight, H. B., 231, 234
Knight, H. S., 10, 11, 18, 28, 62, 254,
    258, 359, 365, 413, 418, 419
    422
Knights, B. A., 415
Knox, K. L., 83
Kolthoff, I. M., 49, 55, 63, 68, 82,
    83, 113, 199, 221, 233, 234,
    241, 257, 280, 299
Kommer, J. D., 340, 354
Königstein, J., 115
Kooyman, E. C., 56
Koppe, R. K., 295, 300
Koppeschaar, W. F., 176, 185
Kortüm, G., 63, 64, 83
Kovac, J., 277
Kressman, T. R. E., 412
Kresze, G., 173
Krieble, V. K., 261, 276
Kriemler, P., 316
Kunin, R., 412
Kurtz, D. M., 276
Kyriacov, D., 299

Laitinen, H. A., 299
Lake, D. B., 257
Lalau, C., 266, 276
Lambert, S. M., 377, 412
Lamprey, P. S., 254, 257
Lange, N. A., 64

Langer, S. H., 28, 163, 390, 414
Langrech, F. B., 265, 276
Larrick, R. A., 257
Latham, D. R., 257, 276
Lau, S. C., 323
Lauwzecha, A. B. H., 231, 232, 234
Lazarus, W., 170, 173
Leach, P. W., 23, 28
Le Blanc, N. F., 120, 121, 123
Lee, D. F., 55
Lee, E. K. C., 415
Lee, F. A., 83
Lee, G. F., 333
Lee, J. K., 415
Lee, T. S., 49, 55
Lee, W., 114
Leemans, F. A., 415
Leenson, F. G., 126, 163
Legate, C. E., 404, 415
Lehmann, G., 121, 123
Lehrle, R. S., 310, 316
Lemieux, R. V., 55
Lennerstrand, M., 114
Leslie, W. D., 199
LeStrange, N., 379, 412
Le Tourneau, R. L., 8, 9, 17, 359,
    365
Lew, H. Y., 191, 199, 257, 339, 341,
    354
Lewis, J. D., 172
Lewis, J. S., 413
Lewis, R. W., 358, 365
Lijinsky, W., 22, 28
Lindeman, L. P., 8, 9, 17
Linek, K., 115
Link, W. E., 163, 254, 258
Linnenbom, V. J., 331, 332, 334
Lipsky, S. R., 377, 398, 412, 414,
    415
Lishka, R. J., 178, 186
Littlejohn, D. P., 415
Littlewood, A. B., 413, 415, 416
Littman, E. R., 257
Ljunggren, K., 333
Llewellyn, P. M., 415
Lochte, H. L., 257

Lodding, W., 316
Lohaus, G., 56
Lohman, F. H., 261, 276
Lomas, J., 172
Long, R., 334
Longwell, J., 340, 354
Lovelock, J. E., 23, 25, 28, 398, 414
Lowry, R. A., 300
Lucas, H. J., 117, 123
Ludwig, F. J., Sr., 193, 199
Luke, L. A., 10, 16, 18
Luong, T. M., 233, 234
Lykken, L., 68, 83, 180, 186

Ma, T. S., 271, 274, 276
MacDonald, A. M. G., 152, 163
Mack, F., 113
Maczek, A. O. S., 28
Mahadevan, V., 75, 83
Maingot, G. J., 299
Mair, B. J., 22, 28, 365
Mair, R. D., 234
Mairs, M. A., 49, 55
Makita, M., 150, 163
Malaprade, L., 165, 172
Malo, B. A., 186
Manatt, S. L., 162, 164
Mandal, B. H., 316
Maniece, W. D., 340, 354
Mann, R. S., 114
Mannering, G. J., 163
Marinsky, J. A., 411
Mark, H., 316
Mark, H. B., Jr., 118, 123
Marketos, D. G., 20, 27
Markham, J. J., 257
Markunas, P. C., 68, 83
Marquart, J. R., 11, 12, 13, 18
Marron, T. U., 338, 354
Marsh, M., 257
Martin, A. J. P., 83, 254, 257, 380
    413
Martin, J. M., Jr., 181, 182, 186
Martin, R., 146, 163
Martin, R. L., 255, 256, 258, 297,
    298, 300

Martin, W. M., 186
Mason, G., 28
Masuda, Y., 258
Mathews, R. G., 28
Mathias, A., 164
Matsumato, T., 28
Mattick, L. R., 83
Maxcy, W., 113
May, D. R., 299
Mayer, T. J., 22, 28
Maynard, J. B., 4, 17, 404, 415
Mayo, F. R., 234
Mayrsohn, H., 334
McCarthy, E. D., 18
McCloskey, J. A., 415
McConnell, H. M., 20, 27
McCoy, R. N., 188, 189, 190, 199,
 280, 281, 282, 293, 299,
 380, 413
McFadden, W. H., 404, 415
McGlotten, J., 115
McIlhiney, P. C., 31, 55
McKennis, H., Jr., 113
McKinney, O. F., 240, 256
McKinnis, A. C., 56
McLafferty, F. W., 415
McMaster, L., 265, 276
McMurray, W. J., 415
McNabb, W. M., 176
McNair, H. M., 392, 414
McNulty, J. A., 402, 414
McPherson, S. P., 114
McReynolds, W. O., 413
McWilliam, I. G., 396, 414
Medalia, A. I., 221, 233
Medsker, L. L., 300
Meeker, J. E., 334
Meier, W. M., 411
Meinke, W. W., 319, 333
Meinschein, W. G., 18
Meisel, S. L., 257
Merritt, J., 25, 26, 27, 28
Merz, W., 60, 62, 191, 199
Messner, A. E., 396, 398, 414
Meyer, M. E., 114
Meyers, M. N., 412

Miller, A. A., 234
Miller, D. L., 103, 114
Miller, I. R., 252, 257
Miller, S. I., 271, 274, 276
Milton, R. M., 10, 18
Minkoff, G. J., 232, 234
Mitchell, J., Jr., 81, 83, 86, 113, 114,
 125, 128, 131, 163, 199,
 263, 276, 422, 425
Mitooka, M., 28
Mitsui, T., 191, 199
Miyake, M., 28
Monroe, G. S., 284, 285, 299
Morawetz, H., 315
Morgan, M. J., 334
Morgan, P., 299
Morgan, P. W., 187, 199
Morman, D. H., 70, 71, 78, 79, 83,
 240, 241, 257, 375, 412
Morrell, J. C., 284, 285, 299
Morris, J. C., 353, 354
Morrison, G. H., 319, 333
Morrissette, R. A., 163, 254, 258
Mortimer, J. V., 10, 18, 28
Muhs, M. A., 53, 56, 267, 268, 276,
 325, 333, 385, 415
Mukerjee, P., 79, 83, 250, 257
Mukherjee, A. R., 316
Müller, K., 60, 62
Mulligan, T. F., 261, 276
Munday, W. A., 177, 185, 253, 257,
 375, 376, 412
Murray, M. J., 186
Musayev, I. A., 18
Musgrave, B., 415

Nadeau, H. G., 173
Natta, G., 316
Neal, M. M., 323
Nel, W., 396, 414
Neligan, R. E., 334
Nelsen, F. M., 330, 334
Nelson, D. C., 406, 415
Nelson, K. H., 10, 18
Nelson, W. L., 356
Nestler, F. H. M., 122, 123

Newberger, S. H., 173
Newlands, G., 266, 276
Nickell, E. C., 49, 56
Nicksic, S. W., 245, 257, 316
Nicolaides, H., 56
Nixon, A. C., 253, 257, 266, 276
Noble, C. M., 71, 83, 429
Noebels, H. J., 413
Noffz, D., 314, 315, 316
Noll, C. I., 261, 276

Oaks, D. M., 173
O'Brien, A. S., 299
O'Donnell, A. E., 323, 347, 352, 354
Offenhauer, R. D., 257
Olah, G. A., 163
Oliver, J., 354
O'Neal, M. J., Jr., 8, 17
O'Neill, L. A., 217
Orbeck, C. K., 257
Orr, C. R., 181, 182, 186

Pack, V. C., 34
Pailer, M., 56
Palit, S. R., 309, 316
Pankaskie, J. E., 333
Pantages, P., 163
Pantazoplos, G., 28
Pappo, R., 55
Pasciak, J., 114
Pathy, M. S. V., 114
Patty, F. A., 445, 446
Paulsen, P. J., 161, 164
Paylor, R. A. L., 62
Pearson, J. R., 400, 414
Pederson, C. S., 83
Penketh, G. E., 227, 234
Pentz, C. A., 243, 257
Percival, D. F., 122, 123
Perrin, D. D., 235, 236, 256
Perry, S. G., 415
Persinger, H. E., 199, 255, 258
Pesez, M., 163
Peters, E. D., 59, 62, 83, 114, 216,
    243, 244, 245, 257, 352, 354,
    417, 420, 422, 425, 440

Petersen, E., 155, 164
Peterson, D. L., 10, 18
Pettitt, B. C., 83
Pfab, W., 314, 315, 316
Phillips, C. S. G., 28, 391, 414
Pietrzyk, D. J., 133, 163
Pimentel, G. C., 164
Planck, R. W., 34
Polgár, A. G., 3, 11, 17, 18, 29, 51,
    55, 56, 114, 216, 412
Pollard, S. A., 60, 62
Polly, O. L., 300
Ponndorf, W., 95, 96, 113
Popjak, G., 415
Popov, A. I., 83
Popp, F. D., 276
Port, W. S., 234
Porter, P. E., 68, 83, 377, 395, 412,
    414
Porter, R. S., 316
Potter, N. H., 192, 199
Pravisani, D., 275, 277
Preiss, B. A., 377, 412
Prelog, V., 114
Pretorius, V., 414
Price, H. A., 59, 62
Privett, O. S., 49, 56
Proskauer, E. S., 199
Purcell, J. E., 414
Purnell, J. H., 413, 414
Püschel, F., 337, 354
Puthoff, M. E., 199

Rader, C. P., 164
Radford, T., 163
Raha, C. R., 28
Raley, J. H., 221, 233
Rall, H. T., 267, 276, 298, 300, 411,
    416
Ramahi, H. Y., 28
Ramey, K. C., 307, 316
Rampton, H. C., 18
Randerath, K., 380, 412
Ravenhill, J. R., 412
Rawlinson, J., 122, 123
Ray, S. K., 334

Rechnitz, G. A., 118, 123
Redemann, C. E., 117, 123
Reed, R. I., 415
Reed, T. B., 10, 18
Reid, L. C., 113
Reid, V. W., 163
Ressler, P. C., 406, 415
Reynolds, J. G., 401, 414
Rhoades, J. W., 300
Ricciuti, C., 231, 232, 234
Richards, R. E., 61, 62
Richter, F. P., 257
Richter, W., 18
Rieche, A., 233
Rijnders, G. W. A., 26, 28, 378, 379, 412
Ripper, M., 113
Robb, E. W., 83
Robb, J. C., 310, 316
Roberts, G. W., 185
Roberts, J. D., 56
Roberts, K. H., 114
Robertson, T. J., 300
Rogers, H. R., 113
Rohrschneider, L., 389, 414
Root, J. W., 415
Rosen, M. J., 199, 259, 276, 354
Rosenthaler, L., 114
Rosie, D. M., 396, 398, 414
Rothrock, H. S., 227, 234
Rothschild, S., 333
Rounds, G. C., 233
Rouve, A., 56
Rowan, R., Jr., 16, 18
Rowland, F. S., 406, 415
Ruchhoff, C. C., 178, 186
Ruliffson, H. D., 68, 83
Rust, F. F., 221, 233
Ryhage, R., 405, 415
Ryland, L. B., 283, 299
Rylander, P. N., 55

Safavi, T., 28
Sahasrabudhe, M. R., 172, 173
Saito, A., 83
Saltzman, B. E., 329, 334

Samuelson, O., 374, 412
Sanders, W. N., 4, 17
Sandler, S., 115
Sanjean, J., 334
Sarmiento, R., 18, 416
Saunders, M., 164
Saunders, R. A., 415
Sawicki, E., 22, 28, 101, 114, 253, 257, 334
Sax, N. I., 445, 446
Scanlan, J., 55
Schachtschneider, J. H., 315
Schaefer, J., 307, 316
Schatzki, T., 312, 313, 316
Schäuffelhut, F., 173
Schenck, P. A., 18
Schenk, G. H., 153, 163
Schenk, G. S., 133
Schiek, R. C., 254, 257
Schifferli, J., 338, 354
Schill, G., 257
Schissler, D. O., 107, 109, 114, 308, 316
Schlenk, H., 83
Schmauch, L. J., 182, 183, 186
Schopf, J. W., 18
Schultz, H. P., 276
Schultz, T. H., 415
Schwartz, R. D., 3, 5, 6, 7, 17, 28
Scism, A. J., 316
Scoggins, M. W., 59, 62
Scott, C. G., 391, 414
Scott, P. M., 18
Scott, R. P. W., 412, 413
Scott, W. E., 277
Scribner, B. F., 319, 333
Seibert, E. E., 412
Sen, B., 114
Serencha, N. M., 261, 276
Serjeant, E. P., 63, 64, 82, 235, 256
Sethi, S. C., 34, 55
Setzkorn, E. A., 199
Shaefer, W. E., 123, 271, 276
Shaffer, B. C., 195, 199
Shakunthala, A. P., 114
Shapiro, J., 333

Sharkey, A. G., Jr., 163
Sharma, J. P., 271, 274, 276
Shaw, J. A., 185
Sheehan, R. J., 390, 414
Sheenan, S. R., 257
Shiraeff, D. A., 337, 354
Shoolery, J. N., 164
Shreve, R. J., 352, 354
Sie, S. T., 26, 28, 185, 378, 379, 412
Siegel, H., 95, 96, 97, 98, 113, 172,
    173, 418, 422
Siggia, S., 59, 62, 113, 114, 163, 164,
    187, 193, 199, 226, 233, 261,
    262, 263, 276, 299
Sigsby, J. E., 334
Silbert, L. S., 231, 232, 234
Silverstein, R. M., 250, 257
Simmonds, P. G., 83
Simon, W., 311, 316, 404, 415
Sircar, A. K., 55
Sivasankaran, K., 34, 35, 55
Skelly, N. E., 185
Skoog, D. A., 231, 232, 234, 285,
    288, 300
Skrabal, A., 110, 114, 119
Slaney, S., 310, 316
Sleva, S. F., 103, 114
Smeltz, K. C., 234
Smith, D. M., 81, 83, 84, 86, 113,
    114, 125, 128, 131, 163,
    422, 425
Smith, G. F., 163
Smith, G. H., 254, 257
Smith, H. F., 192, 199
Smith, H. M., 299, 300, 365
Smith, J. R. L., 254, 258
Smith, V. N., 25, 26, 27, 28
Smullin, C. F., 133, 163, 186
Snyder, L. R., 177, 186, 370, 372,
    376, 411, 412
Snyder, R. G., 315
Sommers, A. L., 257
Spath, E., 56
Spencer, C. F., 300
Spencer, S. F., 28
Sprung, M. M., 176

Stahl, C. R., 59, 62, 199, 262, 263,
    276, 299
Stahl, E., 186, 379, 412
Stanley, T. W., 28, 101, 114, 253,
    257, 334
Stark, B. P., 203, 217
Stark, W., 315
Starke, A. C., 199
Staudinger, H., 315
Steadman, J. P., 300
Stedronsky, E. R., 271, 274, 276
Stein, R. A., 56
Steiner, H., 316
Stenger, V. A., 64, 83, 113, 185
Stenmark, G. A., 146, 163, 166,
    172, 203, 217
Stenroos, L., 75, 83
Stephens, E. R., 275, 277, 332, 334
Stern, E. S., 27
Sternberg, J. C., 396, 399, 414
Sternglanz, P. D., 248, 257
Stetzler, R. S., 133, 163
Stevenson, D. P., 11, 18, 20, 27
Stewart, M. F., 172, 173
Stoll, M., 56
Stone, A. W., 400, 414
Stone, L., 114
Stoughton, R. W., 186
Strause, S. G., 234
Streuli, C. A., 68, 83
Stross, F. H., 308, 316, 395, 412, 414
Strouts, C. R. N., 170, 173
Stubbings, W. V., 354
Stuckey, B. N., 185
Stumm, W., 353, 354
Stumpf, P. K., 406, 415
Suatoni, J. C., 28
Sudborough, J. J., 304
Sugden, T. M., 396, 414
Sun, Y.-P., 333, 334
Sun, J.-Y., 333
Sweeley, C. C., 163
Swern, D., 231, 232, 233, 234
Swinehart, B. A., 173
Swinnerton, J. W., 331, 332, 334
Symon, T., 267, 276

Szwarc, M., 309, 316

Tachikawa, E., 415
Taggart, W. T., 176
Tamele, M. W., 279, 283, 299
Tappel, A. L., 234
Taüfel, K., 113
Taylor, L. W., 27, 47, 55
Teeter, R. M., 8, 9, 17
Tenney, H. M., 385, 389, 414
Thomas, J. F., 300
Thomas, T. L., 10, 18
Thompson, C. J., 267, 276, 298, 299,
      300, 411, 416
Thompson, P. G., 233
Thompson, R. B., 267, 276
Thorpe, R. E., 253, 257, 266, 276
Tiers, G. V. D., 307, 316
Tiwari, R. D., 271, 274, 276
Tollens, B., 95, 113
Topchiev, A. V., 18
Törnquist, J., 199
Treadwell, F. P., 185, 299
Treseder, R. S., 180, 186, 221, 233
Trotman, J., 309, 316
Trowbridge, J. R., 199
Troy, A., 173
Truelove, R. K., 163
Truter, E. V., 380, 412
Tuemmler, F. D., 68, 83
Tullock, A. P., 55
Tung, Y. -N., 415
Turowa-Pollak, M. B., 18
Tverdyukova, L. B., 126, 163
Twickler, M. C., 271, 276
Tyler, W. P., 276
Tyson, F., 57, 62

Umsted, M. E., 414
Uzdina, I. L., 114

Vail, A. H., 114
Van Atta, R. E., 114
van der Heijde, H. B., 68, 83, 241,
      257
Van den Heuvel, W. J. A., 254, 258

van der Meeren, A. A. F., 254, 258
Van Der Stricht, M., 28
Vanderzee, C. E., 271, 274, 276
Van Duuren, B. L., 21, 28
Van Haaften, A. B., 185
Van Meurs, N., 241, 265
Van Rysselberge, J., 28
van Schooten, J., 312, 316
Van Slyke, D. D., 243, 257
van Swaay, M., 413
van Westen, H. A., 34
Vaubel, W., 55
Vaughan, W. E., 221, 233
Veatch, F. C., 91, 113
Vegezzi, G., 114
Veibel, S., 82
Verhaar, A. L. T., 254, 258
Verley, A., 124, 163
Vermaak, C., 300
Vickers, G. D., 162, 164
Vinson, J. A., 118, 123
Völlmin, J. A., 316, 404, 415
Vogel, W., 63, 64, 83
Von Rudloff, E., 55
Voogt, P., 347, 354
Vorbeck, M. L., 83
Vorländer, D., 113

Waddington, D. J., 254, 258
Wadelin, C. W., 186
Wadsworth, P. A., 18
Wagner, C., 113
Wagner, C. D., 59, 62, 243, 244, 245,
      257
Wagner, E. C., 176
Walker, D. C., 226, 233
Walker, J. Q., 23, 28
Walker, M. T., 299
Walley, G., 170, 173
Wanags, G., 266, 276
Wankat, C., 267, 276
Ward, C. C., 267, 276, 298, 300, 411,
      416
Ward, G. A., 234
Warshowsky, B., 163
Wartburg, A. F., Jr., 114

Warth, H., 315
Washall, T. A., 365
Waterman, H. I., 34
Watson, J. T., 405, 415
Watson, W. F., 55
Weast, R. C., 64
Webb, I. D., 56
Weber, W. J., 353, 354
Webster, P. V., 376, 412
Weiss, F. T., 53, 56, 62, 83, 95, 96,
    97, 98, 113, 146, 163, 216,
    238, 239, 256, 267, 268, 276,
    280, 281, 282, 293, 299, 323,
    352, 354, 358, 365, 418, 419,
    422
Weiss, M. D., 413, 414
Weissberger, A., 199
Weitzman, P. D. J., 299
Wells, W. W., 150, 163, 415
Wender, I., 163
Wenner, G., 55
Wentworth, J. T., 331
West, P. W., 114
Westaway, M. T., 422
Westbrook, J. J., III, 83
Wetterau, F. P., 186
Wexler, A. S., 186
Wheaton, R. M., 374, 412
Wheeler, R. J., 300
White, R. F. M., 234
White, T. T., 238, 239, 256
Whitehurst, D. H., 265, 276
Whitham, B., 10, 18
Wier, T. P., Jr., 8, 17
Wiggins, L. F., 212, 217
Wijs, J. J. A., 34, 55
Wilhelm, G., 121, 123

Williams, D. H., 415
Williams, R. E., 415
Williams, W. A., 113
Willis, A. A., 306, 316
Willits, C. O., 231, 234
Willmot, F. W., 311, 316
Wilson, J. N., 376, 412
Wimer, D. C., 242, 248, 257
Winsor, P. A., 340, 354
Winstein, S., 217
Winterscheidt, H., 347, 354
Witnauer, L. P., 231, 232, 234
Wolfgang, R., 406, 415
Wood, D. J. C., 212, 217
Woodbrey, J. C., 307, 316
Woods, F. J., 414
Wopat, F., 113
Wragg, A. L., 310, 316
Wright, C. M., 120, 121, 123
Wyld, G. E. A., 68, 69, 71, 83, 429,
    440

Yasuda, S. K., 311, 312, 316
Yoe, J. H., 113
Young, W. G., 56

Zahn, C., 28
Zahn, V., 180, 186
Zechmeister, L., 411
Zelinsky, N. D., 18
Zinkel, D. F., 122, 123
Zlatewa, M., 114
Zlatkis, A., 23, 25, 28, 83, 316, 412,
    413, 414
Zuman, P., 113, 114, 115, 234, 276
Zweig, A., 299
Zweig, G., 379, 412

SUBJECT INDEX

Acetals, 109, 112
  behaviour in aldehyde
    determination, 96
  behaviour in carbonyl methods, 87
  behaviour in hydroxyl
    methods, 130
  determination of, 111
  hydrolysis rates, 110
Acetic anhydride, titration
    solvent, 242
Acetic Anhydride Method, for
    hydroxyl, 135
Acetylation-Perchloric Acid Method,
    for tertiary amines, 246
Acetyl Chloride Method, for
    hydroxyl, 134
Acetylenes, 57-62
  determination of, 58
  gas chromatography, 59
  gas-forming reactions, 60
  hydration, 59
  proton magnetic resonance, 61
  Silver Nitrate Method, 58
Acid anhydrides, determination
    of, 81-82
Acid hydrolysis, for amides and
    nitriles, 261
Acid Hydrolysis Method, for alkyl
    sulfates, 351
Acids, 63-81
  acid groups in polymers, 306-307
  behaviour in aldehyde deter-
    mination, 96
  behaviour in carbonyl methods, 87
  behaviour in hydroxyl methods,
    129, 130
  behaviour in unsaturation
    methods, 36
  Colorimetric Pinacyanol
    Method, 80

Acids (Continued)
  determination of, 66
  differential acidity, 66
  dissociation constants, 64
  features of methods, 65
  free sulfuric acid, 67
  gas chromatography, 74
  hydrogenation, 410
  ion exchange, 78
  Methylation-GLC Method, 75
  Pinacyanol Method, 80
  Tetrabutylammonium Hydroxide
    Method, 73
  total acidity, 64
  trace analysis, 79, 323
  ultraviolet, 74
  water determination, 421
Active Hydrogen, 125
  Grignard reagent, 125
  lithium aluminum hydride
    reagent, 125
  phenol determination, 175
Adsorbents, 370-372
Adsorption chromatography, 370
Air analysis, 329
Air contamination, 445
Alcohols (see also Hydroxyl
    group), 124-164
  behaviour in aldehyde
    determination, 98
  behaviour in unsaturation
    methods, 33, 36
  determination of, 134-162
  hydrogenation, 410
  polyhydroxy, 165
  polyhydroxy by periodate
    oxidation, 167
Alcohol sulfates, 335
Aldehydes, (see also Carbonyl
    compounds), 84-107

461

Aldehydes *(Continued)*
  acrolein, 106
  Argentimetric Method, 97
  behaviour in epoxy methods, 214
  behaviour in ester determina-
      tion, 117
  behaviour in hydroxyl
      methods, 129, 130
  bisulfite procedure, 94
  colorimetric procedure, 100
  determination in presence of
      ketones, 95
  formaldehyde determination, 102
  hydrogenation, 410
  hydroxylamine procedures, 84-89
  infrared, 107-109
  Methyl Benzothiazolone Hydrazone
      Method, 100
  oxidation with silver ion, 95
  reaction with bisulfite, 93
  Sodium Bisulfite Method, 94
  trace analysis, 99
  ultraviolet
Alkoxyl groups, 187
Alkylarylsulfonates, 335
Alkylbenzene sulfonates, 352
Alkyl nitrates, 260
  electron-capture detector, 274
  gas chromatography, 274
Alkyl phenols, ion exchange, 376
Alkyl sulfates, 336, 351
Alumina Decomposition Method for
      nonthiophenic sulfur, 292
Amides, 259
  acid hydrolysis method, 261
  behaviour in hydroxyl methods,
      129, 131
  determination of, 261
Amine oxides, 247
  behaviour in sulfonate analysis, 341
  reduction by titanous chloride,
      248, 274
  Titanous Reduction Procedure, 249
  titration, 248
Amines, 235-247
  Acetylation-Perchloric Acid

Amines *(Continued)*
      Method, 245, 246
  Azomethine Titration Method,
      243, 246
  behaviour in epoxy methods, 214
  behaviour in hydroxyl methods,
      129, 131
  chromatography, 253
  Colorimetric Bromophenol Blue
      Method, 251
  conversion to ammonia for coulo-
      metric titration, 255
  features of methods, 238
  gas chromatography, 254
  Methyl Red Indicator Method, 237
  Perchloric Acid-Glacial Acetic Acid
      Method, 241
  primary, 243, 251, 252
  secondary, 243, 251, 252
  tertiary, 243, 251
  trace analysis, 250
  trifluoroacetyl derivatives, 255
  ultraviolet, 251
  Van Slyke Method, 243
  weak bases, 237
Aminoantipyrine Method for
      phenols, 179
Ammonium thiocyanate solution, 436
Analytical equipment, 439
  buret assembly, 440
  ion exchange apparatus, 441,
      442, 443
  purging adaptor, 441
  titration cell, 440
Aniline Precipitation Method for free
      sulfuric acid, 67
Anionic surfactants, 335-354
Aqueous Hydroxylamine Method for
      carbonyl compounds, 88
Aqueous Magnesium Chloride-HCl
      Method for epoxides, 203
Argentimetric Method for alde-
      hydes, 97
Argentimetric titrations, reagents, 436
Aromatic hydrocarbons, 19-28
  adsorption chromatography, 22

Aromatic hydrocarbons *(Continued)*
  behaviour in unsaturation
    methods, 32
  crude oil, 355
  fluorescence, 21
  gas chromatography, 22
  liquid chromatography, 25
  nuclear magnetic resonance, 21
  petroleum products, 355
  polynuclear in air, 333
  ultraviolet, 19
Atmospheric analysis, 329
Azo compounds, 272
Azomethine Titration Method, for
    secondary plus tertiary
    amines, 246
Azoxy compounds, 272

Bases (*see also* Organic Bases), 235-258
  determination of, 237, 241
  dissocation constants, 236
  features of methods, 238
  Methyl Red Indicator Method, 237
  Perchloric Acid-Glacial Acetic Acid
    Method, 241
  very weak bases, 242
  weak bases, 237
Basic Nitrogen Compounds (*see also*
    Amines), 235-247
  chromatography, 253
  crude oil, 355
  gas chromatography, 254
  ion exchange, 376
  Nitrogen bases, 235-245
Benzidine Hydrochloride Method for
    sulfonates, 337
BF₃-Fischer Reagent Method for
    hydroxyl, 137
Bioassay for trace analysis, 317, 327
Borate complexes, 374
Bromide-Bromate Method for
    unsaturation, 39
Bromide-bromate solution, 435
Bromine in Carbon Tetrachloride
    Method for unsaturation, 37
Bromine in carbon tetrachloride

reagent, 434
Bromine in potassium bromide
    solution, 434
Bromine number, 34
Bromocresol Green Titration Method
    for sulfonates, 346
Bromophenol Blue Method for cation-
    active materials, 251
Buret assembly, 440

Capillary columns, characteristics,
    381, 384
Carbazoles, 260
  in petroleum, 266
  ion exchange behavior, 376
Carbonyl Group, 84-115
  addition reactions of, 84
  aldehyde reaction with bisulfite, 93
  Aqueous Hydroxylamine Method,
    86, 88
  Argentimetric Method, 95, 97
  behaviour in unsaturation methods,
    33, 36
  colorimetic, 91
  determination in polyacrolein, 107
  Dinitrophenylhydrazine Colorimet-
    ric Method, 91
  features of methods, 85
  Fischer Reagent Method, 86, 89
  hydroxylamine reaction, 84
  infrared, 107
  polarography, 112
  polymers, 305
  Sodium Bisulfite Method, 94
  trace analysis, 90, 323
  ultraviolet, 106
Carboxylic acids (*see* Acids), 63-81
Catalyst poisoning, 35
Catalytic Desulfurization, 293
Cationic surfactants, 250
  Colorimetric Bromophenol Blue
    Method, 251
  in water, 250
  ion exchange, 347
Cetyl pyridinium bromide, 339
Charge-transfer reactions, 19, 23

Cholinesterase, 328
Chromatography, 369-416
Chromotropic Acid Method for formaldehyde, 104
Coating procedure for gas liquid columns, 382
Cobalt thiocyanate, reaction with polyalkylene oxides, 196
Cobalt Thiocyanate Method for poly-alkylene oxide surfactants, 197
Colorimetric Aminoantipyrine Method for phenols, 179
Colorimetric Analyses, 152
    acids, 80
    amines, 251
    cation-active materials, 251
    determination of carbazole, 266
    features of methods, 323
    formaldehyde, 104
    methylene blue method, 338, 343
    peroxides, 224
    phenol determination, 175, 177
    polyalkylene oxide surfactants, 197
    pyrroles, 269
    trace analysis, 317, 321
Colorimetric Bromphenol Blue Method for cation-active materials, 251
Colorimetric Chromotropic Acid Method for formaldehyde, 104
Colorimetric Cobalt Thiocyanate Method for polyalkylene oxide surfactants, 197
Colorimetric Dimethyl-aminobenzal-dehyde Method for pyrroles, 269
Colorimetric Methylene Blue Method for sulfonates, 343
Colorimetric Pinacyanol Method for trace acids, 80
Colorimetric Thiocyanate Method for peroxides, 224
Coulometric titration apparatus, 402
    detector, 401
    determination of amines, 256
    determination of sulfur

Coulometric titration apparatus
(Continued)
    compounds, 295
    for trace analysis, 317
Crude oils, 4, 7, 15
    basic nitrogen, 238
    composition, 355
    isoparaffins, 15
Curie point in pyrolysis, 311

Dehydrogenation, 16
Detectors for chromatographic separations, 391-407
    differential refractometer, 377
    electron capture, 25, 398
    flame ionization, 396
    flame, photometer, 403
    ionization chamber, 406
    mass spectrometer, 403
    microcoulometer, 255, 295, 401
    principal characteristics, 393
    proportional flow counter, 405
    pyrolysis, 377
    radioactivity, 405
    refractive index, 377
    thermal conductivity, 392
    thermionic emission, 403
    ultraviolet, 27, 377
Detergents (*see* Surface-active materials), 335-354
Deuterium Exchange Method for hydroxyl, 157
Dialkyl peroxides, determination of, 223
Diazomethane for methylation of acids, 75
Diesel exhaust, hydrocarbons in, 333
Dimethylaminobenzaldehyde Method for pyrroles, 269
Dinitrophenylhydrazine Colorimetric Method for trace carbonyl, 91
Disulfides, comparison of reduction methods, 286
    determination of, 289
    polarography, 284, 286
    reaction over alumina, 281

Disulfides, comparison of reduction
methods *(Continued)*
reduction techniques, 280, 286
Zinc Reduction Method, 289
Drying Oils, unsaturation, 34
Dye partition techniques, cationic
surfactants, 250
end groups in polymers, 309
sulfonates, 338

Electron-capture detector, 25, 398
Elemental sulfur, determination by
reaction with cyanide,
285, 288
Spectrophotometric Thiocyanate
Method, 290
End groups in polymers, 308
Engine exhaust, hydrocarbons,
330, 331
α -Epoxides, 200-217
Aqueous Magnesium Chloride-HCl
Method, 203
behaviour in aldehyde determination, 96
behaviour in carbonyl methods, 87
behaviour in ester determination, 117
behaviour in hydroxyl methods,
129, 130
behaviour in periodate method, 167
comparison of methods, 211
features of methods, 202
HBr-Acetic Acid Method, 209
HCl-Dioxane Method, 207
HCl-Dioxane-Argentimetric
Method, 210
infrared, 214
near-infrared, 216
polymers, 305
Pyridinium Chloride Method, 205
recovery of epoxides, 212
reactions, 201
resin analysis, 213, 215
water determination, 420
Epoxy resins, epoxide content,
213, 305

Epoxy resins
(Continued)
hydroxyl, 125
infrared, 215, 307
Esterification rates of acids of increasing chain length, 304
Esters, 116-123
behaviour in adlehyde determination, 96
behaviour in carbonyl methods, 87
behaviour in epoxy methods, 214
behaviour in hydroxyl methods,
129, 131
behaviour in unsaturation methods,
30, 33
colorimetric, 120
gas chromatography, 122
hydroxamic acid reaction, 120
polymers, 305
Saponification Method, 118
saponification rates, 119
Ethanolamines, behaviour in
periodate method, 166
Ethers, 187-199
alkyl group determination, 191
behaviour in hydroxyl methods,
129, 130
behaviour in unsaturation methods,
33, 36
determination of oxyethylene
content, 187-191
determination of traces of polyalkylene oxides, 195-198
determination of vinyl, 193
halogenation techniques, 192
nuclear magnetic resonance, 192
oxyethylene distribution, 188
Ethers, cyclic (*see* Epoxides), 200-217
Ethylene Glycol-Pyridine reagent, 423

Fatty Oils, unsaturation in, 30, 34
Fischer Reagent Methods, acid
anhydrides, 81
carbonyl compounds, 89
hydroxyl, 137
methylol groups, 148

Fischer Reagent Methods *(Continued)*
  reagent preparation, 423
  water determination, 419
Flame Ionization detector, 396
  hydrocarbons in atmosphere, 329
Flame-Photometric Detector, 403
Fluorescence spectroscopy, 21
  aromatic hydrocarbons, 21
  polynuclear aromatics, 333
Fluorescent Indicator Adsorption
      Method for hydrocarbon types,
      359, 369, 370
Formaldehyde, Colorimetric Chromo-
      tropic Acid Method, 104

Gas chromatography, 380-416
  acetylenes, 59
  acids, 74
  alcohols, 149
  amines, 254
  aromatic hydrocarbons, 22
  capillary columns, 381, 384
  chemical reactions, 407
  elution of hydrocarbons, 5
  esters, 122
  formaldehyde, 102
  glycols, 172
  hydroxyl compounds, 149
  isoparaffins, 15
  Methylation-GLC Method for
      acids, 75
  Molecular Sieve-Gas Chromato-
      graphic Method, 11
  naphthenes, 16
  normal paraffins, 10
  olefins, 30, 51
  packed columns, 381, 384
  phenols, 151, 175
  polyalkylene oxides, 191
  polynuclear aromatics, 24
  Ponca City crude, 7
  process unit, 26
  resolution, 390
  saturates, 3
  S. C. O. T. columns, 382
  selectivity, 385

Gas chromatography *(Continued)*
  stationary phases, 385-389
  trace analysis, 317
  Trimethylsilyl Ether-Gas Chroma-
      tographic Method, 151
  Urea Adduction-Gas Chromato-
      graphic Method, 14
Gas-liquid chromatography, 369
Gas-Liquid Radiochromato-
      graphy, 407
Gas-solid chromatography, 369
Gasolines, alkyl phenols, 177
  composition, 358
  dehydrogenation, 16
  hydroperoxides, 226
  pyrrolic nitrogen, 269
  saturates, 3
  sulfur compounds, 298
  unsaturation, 30
Glycerol, Sodium Periodate-Acidi-
      metric Method, 171
  specific determination, 169
Glycols, 165
  gas chromatography, 172
  thin-layer chromatography, 172
Group sulfur, 278
  analysis of petroleum fractions, 282

HBr-Acetic Acid Method for
      α-epoxides, 209
HCl-Dioxane-Argentimetric Method
      for α-epoxides, 210
HCl-Dioxane Method for
      α-epoxides, 207
Heterocyclic compounds, basic
      nitrogen compounds in
      petroleum, 239
  chromatographic separation, 253
  crude oil composition, 355
  nonbasic nitrogen compounds
      in petroleum, 266
  pyrroles, 267
  thiophenes, 278
Heterotactic configuration, 307
Hydrazones, absorptivity of
      carbonyl derivatives, 91

Hydrocarbons, in atmosphere, 329
  in engine exhaust, 331
  in ocean water, 331, 332
  in Los Angeles atmosphere,
    331, 332
  trace, 329, 331
  water determination, 421
Hydrocarbons, acetylenic (*see*
    Acetylenes), 57-62
Hydrocarbons, aromatic (*see*
    Aromatic hydrocarbons), 19-28
Hydrocarbons, saturated (*see*
    Saturated Hydrocarbons), 3-18
Hydrocarbons, unsaturated (*see*
    Olefins), 29-62
Hydrocarbon type analysis, 357
  Fluorescent Indicator Adsorption
    Method (FIA), 359
  from mixtures, 362
Hydrogenation, catalyst poisoning, 35
  determination of unsaturation,
    32, 34
  nitriles, 264
  nitro compounds, 264
  olefins, 36
  petroleum fractions, 37
  products obtained, 298, 409
  pyrroles, 264
  simplification of analysis, 299, 409
Hydrogen Iodide Method, dialkyl
    peroxides, 223
  polyethylene oxides, 189
Hydrogen sulfide, extraction with
    cadmium chloride, 278
  titration with silver nitrate, 283
Hydrolysis Method for acetals, 111
Hydroperoxides, Sodium Iodide
    Method, 222
Hydroxamic Acid, alcohol determin-
    ation, 153
  ester determination, 121
Hydroxylamines, 272
Hydroxyl Group, 124-164
  Acetic Anhydride Method, 135
  Acetyl Chloride Method, 134
  alternate esterification

Hydroxyl Group (*Continued*)
    methods, 133
  behaviour of types, 126, 128
  colorimetric analysis, 152
  determination in polymers, 305
  deuterium exchange method, 157
  differentiation primary, secondary
    and tertiary, 162
  features of methods, 132
  gas chromatography, 149
  infrared, 153
  Lithium Aluminum Hydride
    Method, 139
  methylol group, 145, 148
  nuclear magnetic resonance,
    151, 161
  phenolic, 174
  Phthalic Anhydride Method, 136
  reactions, 125
  Trimethylsilyl Ether-Gas Chromato-
    graphic Method, 151

Impingers for air sampling, 329
Indoles, 260
  hydrogenation, 409
  in petroleum, 266
Infrared Absorption Spectroscopy,
    alcohols, 126, 132, 153
  carbonyl compounds, 85, 107
  deuterium oxide, 156
  α-epoxy compounds, 214
  hydrocarbons in atmosphere, 329
  hydroxyl group, 126, 132, 153
  olefin types, 30, 44, 45
  peroxyacyl nitrates, 275
  phenols, 174, 175
  polyisoprenes, 49
  polymers, 306
  saturated hydrocarbons, 4, 8
  trace analysis, 317, 321
  water, 154
Insecticides, 328
Iodine Monochloride Method for
    unsaturation, 43
Iodine number, 34
Ion Exchange, 374-376

Ion Exchange *(Continued)*
    acids, 78
    equipment, 441, 442, 443
    separation nitrogen bases from
        petroleum, 253
    separation phenols from
        gasoline, 177
    surfactants, 347
Ion-Exchange Acidimetric Method
    for detergents, 348
Ion-Exchange Gravimetric Procedure
    for nonionics, 349
Ion Exclusion for acid separation,
    78, 374
Ionization chamber, 406
Isoprenoid hydrocarbons, 15
Isotactic configuration, 307

Kerosine, n-paraffins, 10
    unsaturation, 30
Ketones *(see also* Carbonyl group),
    84-115
    behaviour in ester determina-
        tion, 117
    behaviour in hydroxyl methods,
        129, 130
    determination of, 88-93
    water determination, 420

Laboratory safety, 444
Liquid-liquid chromatography,
    369, 376
Liquid-solid chromatography,
    369, 370
Lithium Aluminum Hydride method
    for hydroxyl, 139
    behaviour of other functional
        groups, 130, 131

Magnesium Chloride-HCl Method for
    α -epoxides, 203
Malaprade oxidation, 166
Mass spectrometer, napthenes, 16, 17
    saturates, 4, 8
    trace analysis,
        317, 321

Mass Spectrometer-gas chroma-
    tography, 403
Mercaptans, 278
    "aromatic mercaptan
        precursors", 279
    behaviour in bromination
        methods, 34
    coulometric determination, 297
    determination of, 285-289
    Electrometric Titration, 285
    hydrogenation, 410
    in petroleum products, 282, 298
    microcoulometric detector, 296
    reaction in microcoulometer, 295
    reaction over alumina, 281
    reaction with α , β unsaturated
        nitriles, 265
    titration with silver nitrate,
        283, 285
Methane, in atmosphere, 330
Methylation-GLC Method for
    acids, 75
Methyl Benzothiazolone Hydrazone
    Method for aldehydes, 100
Methylene Blue Titraton Method
    for sulfonates, 345
Methylol Determination, 145
Methyl Red Indicator Method for
    amines, 237
Microanalysis, 319
Microcoulometer, 401
    detection of ammonia from reduc-
        tion of nitrogen com-
        pounds, 255
    detection sulfur compounds, 295
Molecular sieves, application to
    petroleum fractions, 11
    behaviour of materials, 373
    composition, 372
    isolation normal paraffins, 10
    separation isoparaffins, 15
Molecular-Sieve Gas Chromatographic
    Method for normal para-
        ffins, 11

Naphthenes, catalytic
  dehydrogenation, 16
in crude oil, 355
in petroleum products, 357
mass spectrometry, 9, 17
Nitriles, 260, 263
  acid hydrolysis method, 261
  determination of, 261
  hydrogenation, 263
  reaction with hydrogen perox-
    ide, 265
  reaction with mercaptan, 265
Nitro compounds, 260
  hydrogenation, 264
  reduction with tin, 272
  reduction with titanous
    reagents, 272
Nitrogen bases (see also Bases),
    235-245
  behaviour on titration, 236
  chromatography, 253
  crude oil, 355
  determination of, 241
  features of method, 238
  ion exchange, 376
  petroleum, 238
  water determination, 421
Nitroso compounds, 260
  reduction with hydrogen
    iodide, 273
  reduction with titanous
    chloride, 273
Nonaqueous titrations, 68
Non-aqueous Potassium Hydroxide
    Method for acid, 71
Nonbasic Nitrogen, 259, 277
  alkyl nitrates, 260
  amides, 259
  carbazoles, 260
  crude oil, 355
  features of methods, 260
  indoles, 260
  nitro compounds, 260
  nitroso compounds, 260
  pyrroles, 260
Nonionic surfactants, 195, 335

Nonionic surfactants (Continued)
  Colorimetric Cobalt Thiocyanate
    Method, 197
  in water, 196
  Ion-Exchange Gravimetric
    Procedure, 349
Nonthiophenic Sulfur, Alumina
    Decomposition Method, 292
Nuclear magnetic resonance spec-
    troscopy, acetylenes, 61
  alcohols, 132, 158
  aromatic hydrocarbons, 21
  hydroxyl group, 132, 158
  olefins, 44, 45, 46
  peroxides, 233
  phenols, 175
  polyalkylene oxides, 192
  polyisoprenes, 49, 307
  polymers, 306
  primary hydroxyl group, 162
  saturates, 4
  secondary hydroxyl group, 162
  tertiary hydroxyl group, 162
  trace analysis, 317, 321

Olefins (see also Unsaturation,
    olefinic), 29-62
  cleavage reactions, 50
  crude oil, 355
  determination of, 37-44
  gas chromatography, 51-55
  infrared, 45
  nuclear magnetic resonance, 45
  ozonolysis, 50
  petroleum products, 357
  polymeric, 47
  silver nitrate complexes, 53
  types, 44
  ultraviolet, 47
Organic Bases, determination of,
    235-258
  dissociation constants, 236
  features of methods, 238
  Methyl Red Indicator Method, 237
  Perchloric Acid-Glacial Acetic
    Acid Method, 241

Organic Bases *(Continued)*
  very weak bases, 242
  weak bases, 237
Organic Disulfides, 278
  polarographic, 284, 286
  reaction over alumina, 211
  reduction techniques, 280, 286
  Zinc Reduction Method, 289
Organic peroxides (*see* Peroxides),
    218-234
Organophosphorus insecticides, 328
Osmium tetroxide oxidant, 50
Oxyethylenes, Hydrogen Iodide
    Method, 189
Ozonolysis, 50

Packed columns, characteristics,
    381-384
Paper chromatography, 379
  phenol determination, 175, 177
  polynuclear aromatics, 333
  trace analysis, 317
Paraffinic hydrocarbons, determina-
    tion of, 3-16
  in crude oil, 355
  in petroleum products, 357
Paraffins, iso, 15
Paraffins, normal, determination of,
    3-15
  Molecular Sieve-Gas Chromato-
    graphic Method, 11
  Urea adduction-Gas Chromato-
    graphic Method, 14
Perchloric Acid-Glacial Acetic Acid
    Method, for weak bases, 241
Periodic Acid Method for
    glycols, 167
Periodic acid oxidation, 165-172
Peroxides, 218-234
  arsine reaction, 226
  behaviour in carbonyl methods, 87
  behaviour in ester determina-
    tion, 117
  behaviour in hydroxyl
    methods, 131
  Colorimetric Thiocyanate

Peroxides *(Continued)*
  Method, 224
  determination by chemical tech-
    niques, 219-230
  dialkyl peroxides, 223
  extent of reaction, 227
  features of methods, 220
  ferrous ion methods, 221
  hydroperoxides, 222
  iodide ion methods, 219
  nuclear magnetic resonance, 233
  peroxyacyl nitrates, 275
  phosphine reduction, 226
  polarographic reduction, 231
  polymeric, 227
  sodium arsenite reaction, 226
  Sodium Arsenite Method, 227
  Sodium Iodide Method, 222
  types of peroxides, 219
Peroxyacyl nitrates, 275
Petroleum Fractions, 355
  alkyl phenols, 177
  basic nitrogen, 238
  carbazoles, 266
  crude oil composition, 7
  group sulfur results, 282
  heterocyclic compounds, 253
  hydroperoxides, 226
  indoles, 266
  isoparaffins, 15
  mass spectrometer, 9
  naphthenes, 17
  nitrogen compounds, 177
  normal paraffins, 10
  oxygen compounds, 177
  phenols, 177
  pyrroles, 266
  pyrrolic nitrogen in fractions, 269
  saturates, 3
  separation, 363
  sulfur compounds, 278
  unsaturation in products, 10
Petroleum sulfonates, 340
Phenolic resins, 145, 148
Phenolphthalein Indicator Method
    for acids, 66

Phenols, determination of, 174-186
  behaviour in hydroxyl
    methods, 128
  colorimetric determination, 177
  Colorimetric Aminoantipyrine
    Method, 179
  determination by hydroxyl
    methods, 132
  dissociation constants, 64
  features of methods, 175
  gas chromatography, 177
  hydrogenation, 410
  in crude oil, 355
  in rubber, 181
  in water, 181
  ion exchange, 376
  molar absorptivity of adducts, 323
  Nitrosophenol Method, 180
  paper chromatography, 177
  photometric titration, 74
  reaction with Br$_2$, 30, 33
  reagent in methylol determina-
    tion, 146
  reduction of nitrophenol, 274
  tetrabutyl ammonium hydroxide
    titrant, 71
  thin-layer chromatography, 177
  titration in nonaqueous sol-
    vents, 68
  trace determination, 181, 319, 324
  Trimethylsilyl Ether-Gas
    Chromatographic Method, 151
  ultraviolet, 181
  Ultraviolet Absorption
    Method, 184
Phenyl ethers, behavior in unsatura-
    tion methods, 30
Phthalic Anhydride Method for
    hydroxyl, 136
Pinacyanol Method for trace
    acids, 80, 323
Polarography, for carbonyl com-
    pounds, 112
  for disulfides, 284
  for peroxides, 231
  for trace analysis, 317

Polyacroleins, 107, 305, 308
Polyalkylene oxides, 191
  alkyl groups, 191
  Colorimetric Cobalt
    Thiocyanate Method, 197
  low concentrations, 195
  nuclear magnetic resonance, 192
Polyethylene, 312, 313
Polyethylene Oxides, 187
  Hydrogen Iodide Method, 189
  oxyethylene content, 187, 188
Polyglycerols, 172
Polyhydroxy alcohols, 165-173
  ion exchange as borate com-
    plexes, 374
  Quaternary Ammonium Periodate
    Method, 168
  Periodic Acid Method, 167
Polyisoprene, analysis, 49
  nuclear magnetic resonance, 307
  pyrolysis, 312
  structural forms 48
Polymeric peroxides, 227
Polymers, 303-316
  acid content, 306
  carbonyl content, 305
  end groups, 308
  α-epoxy content, 305
  ester content, 305
  hydroxyl content, 305
  infrared, 306
  interconversion for analysis, 306
  nuclear magnetic resonance, 306
  pyrolysis, 309
  radiochemical, 309
  unsaturation, 30, 34
Polymethacrylates, 305, 306
Polymethacrylonitrile, 306
Polynuclear aromatic hydrocarbons,
    air analysis, 333
  airborne particulates, 22
  behaviour in unsaturation
    methods, 30
  electron-capure detector, 23, 24
  gas chromatography, 24
  molar absorptivity, 322

Polynuclear aromatic hydrocarbons
(Continued)
   separation by fluid-solid
      chromatography, 379
   ultraviolet spectra, 21
Polypropylene, 312, 314
Polysulfides, 278
Polyvinyl acetate, 306
Potassium hydroxide in isopropyl
   alcohol reagent, 427
Potassium Tribromide Method for
   unsaturation, 41
Process gas chromatograph, 25
Proportional flow counter, 405
Pyrolysis, in analysis of
      polymers, 309
   apparatus, 311
   Curie point, 311
   polyethylene, 313
   polyisoprenes, 312
   polypropylene, 314
Pyridines, basic strength, 236
   chromatography, 253
   ion exchange behavior, 376
Pyridinium Chloride Method for
   α-epoxides, 205
Pyrroles, 260
   Colorimetric Dimethylamino-
      benzaldehyde Method, 269
   hydrogenation, 264, 409
   in petroleum, 266
   reaction with Dimethylamino-
      benzaldehyde, 268

Quaternary Ammonium Periodate
   Method for glycols, 168

Readiochemical analysis, end groups
      in polymers, 309
   gas chromatography, 405
   ionization chamber, 406
   proportional flow counter, 405
   purity, 325
   trace analysis, 317
Reaction Gas chromatography, 407
Reagent preparation, 423-438

Reagent preparation (Continued)
   ammonium thiocyanate, 436
   ethylene glycol-pyridine
      mixture, 423
   ferric ammonium sulfate, 437
   Fischer reagents, 423
   halogenation, 434
   silver nitrate, 437
   sodium thiosulfate, 432
   standard acids, 429
   standard bases, 425
   starch solution, 433
   sulfur dioxide and pyridine, 424
Refractometer, as detector, 377
Resins, epoxy, 213, 214, 216
   phenolic, 145
Resolution in gas chroma-
      tography, 390
Rubber, 48, 49
Ruthenium tetroxide oxidant, 51

Safety, 444-446
Saponification Method for ester, 118
Saponification Rates of esters,
      119, 304
Saturated hydrocarbons, behaviour in
      unsaturation methods, 32
   determination, 3-18
   gas chromatography, 3
   infrared, 4
   isolation from petroleum dis-
      tillates, 363
   isoparaffins, 15
   mass spectrometry, 8, 9
   naphthenes, 16
   normal paraffins, 10
   nuclear magnetic resonance, 4
Saturated sodium hydroxide, 426
Selectivity in gas chroma-
      tography, 385
Sewage effluent, surfactants, 340
S. C. O. T. columns, 382
Shale oil, nitrogen compounds, 256
Silver acetylides, 57
Silver Nitrate Method for
      acetylenes, 58

Silver nitrate-olefin complexes, 53
Silver nitrate solution, 437
Silver oxide, for aldehyde
    determination, 95-99
Sodium Aresenite Method for
    peroxides, 227
Sodium borohydride, 35
Sodium carbonate, primary
    standard, 431
Sodium carboxylates, behavior in
    sulfonate methods, 341
Sodium Hydroxide in methanol
    reagent, 428
Sodium Iodide Method for hydro-
    peroxides, 222
Sodium Periodate-Acidimetric Method
    for glycerol, 171
Sodium thiosulfate solution, 432
Spectrophotometric Thiocyanate
    Method for elemental
    sulfur, 290
Spectroscopic, definition of
    terms, 321
Standard Bases, 425
Starch solution, 433
Stationary phases for gas
    chromatography, 385
Sulfides, bromination, 34
    determination of free sulfur in
        presence of, 288
    in petroleum products, 278
    mercuric nitrate reaction, 278
    reaction over alumina, 281
    reaction with silver nitrate, 283
Sulfur, Elemental, Spectrophoto-
        metric Thiocyanate
        Method, 290
    determination by reaction with
        cyanide, 285
Sulfur compounds, 278-300
    adsorption chromatography, 295
    Alumina Decomposition
        Method, 292
    behaviour in unsaturation
        methods, 36
    catalyst poisoning, 35

Sulfur Compounds *(Continued)*
    chromatography, 295
    crude oil, 355
    disulfides, 278, 280
    gas chromatography, 295
    group sulfur analysis, 278
    hydrogenation, 298
    hydrogen sulfide, 278
    in petroleum products, 282
    mass spectroscopic analysis, 9
    mercaptans, 278
    polarography, 284
    reaction over alumina, 280, 281
    results on hydrogenation, 298
    thiophenes, 278
Sulfuric acid: Aniline Precipitation
        Method, 67
Supercritical fluid chroma-
        tography, 27, 378
Surface-active materials, 335, 354
    alkyl sulfates, 336, 351
    anionic, 335
    Benzidine Hydrochloride
        Method, 337
    Bromocresol Green Titration
        Method, 346
    carboxylic acid salts, 80
    cationic, 250
    Colorimetric Methylene Blue
        Method, 343
    features of methods, 341
    ion exchange, 347
    Methylene Blue Methods,
        343, 345
    nonionics, 195, 349
    sulfonates, 336
    p-Toluidine Hydrochloride
        Method, 338, 342
    types of materials, 336
Syndiotactic configuration, 307

Tetrabutylammonium hydroxide
    reagent, 428
Tetrabutylammonium Hydroxide
    Method for acids, 73
Thermal conductivity detector, 392

Thin-Layer Chromatography,
369, 379
oxyethylene distribution, 188
phenol determination, 175, 177
polynuclear aromatics in air, 333
trace analysis, 317
Thiophenes, behavior in unsaturation
methods, 34
hydrogenation, 410
mass spectrometry, 9
reaction over alumina, 281
Threshold limits, 446
Titanous chloride reduction for
amine oxides, 247
nitro compounds, 272
nitroso compounds, 273
Titanous Reduction Procedure for
amine oxides, 249
Titration cell, 440
Toluene sulfonates, 341
p-Toluidine Hydrochloride Method
for sulfonates, 338, 342
Toxicity, 444
Trace analysis, 317-334
acids, 79
acrolein, 106
aliphatic aldehydes, 99
alkyl polynitrates in air, 275
amines, 250
carbonyl compounds, 90
Colorimetric Methylene Blue
Method, 343
features of methods, 317
formaldehyde, 102
peroxyacyl nitrates in air, 275
polyalkylene oxides, 195
Trimethylsilyl Ether-Gas Chromatographic Method for alcohols
and phenols, 151

Ultraviolet Absoprtion Method for
phenols, 184
Ultraviolet absorption spectroscopy,
acids, 74
alkylbenzene sulfonates, 352
amines, 251

Ultraviolet absorption spectroscopy
(Continued)
aromatics, 19, 25
basic nitrogen in petroleum 253
carbonyl compounds, 106
detectors, 27
olefins, 47
phenol, 175, 181
polynuclear aromatics, 21
trace analysis, 317, 321
Unsaturation, olefinic, 29-62
Bromide-Bromate Method, 31, 39
Bromine in Carbon Tetra-
chloride Method, 31, 37
electronic absorption spectroscopy, 47
features of methods, 30, 32, 35
gas chromatography, 51
hydrogenation, 34
infrared, 49
Iodine Monochloride Method,
34, 43, 48
nuclear magnetic resonance, 44
olefin types, 44
ozonolysis, 50
polymeric olefins, 47
Potassium Tribromide Method,
34, 41
ultraviolet, 47
Urea adduction, for hydrocarbon
determination, 11, 14
Urea Adduction-Gas Chromatographic
Method for normal paraf-
fins, 14

Van Slyke Method for primary
amine, 243
Vinyl ethers, 193

Water, determination of, 417-422
determination by gas chromatography, 392, 419
determination by reaction with
calcium carbide, 419
Fischer Reagent Method for, 419
infrared spectrum of, 154

Water, determination of impurities,
    acid determination, 79
  anionic surfactants in,
    340, 343
  cationic surfactants in, 250
  phenol determination in, 178, 182
  polyalkylene oxide, determination
    in, 195
  separation of organics in, 392
Water, reaction with epoxy
    group, 201
  retention by molecular

Water *(Continued)*
  sieves, 373
  sewage analysis, 340
  Wijs Method, for unsaturation,
    34, 43

Xylene sulfonates, 341

Zeisel alkoxyl, 187
Zeolites, 10, 373
Zinc Reduction Method for
    disulfides, 289